The Society of Arcueil

By the Same Author

HISTORICAL STUDIES IN THE LANGUAGE
OF CHEMISTRY

The Society of Arcueil

A VIEW OF
FRENCH SCIENCE
AT THE TIME OF
NAPOLEON I

by

Maurice Crosland

HARVARD UNIVERSITY PRESS

CAMBRIDGE, MASSACHUSETTS

1967

Printed in Great Britain

Contents

Preface

ONE OF the purposes of this book is to make amends for the general neglect of the Society of Arcueil, which published its final volume of memoirs exactly 150 years ago.[1] At the beginning of the nineteenth century, the Society was as important in its own way as the *Académie des Sciences* in France or the Royal Society in Britain. It is possible that the lessons to be learned by looking at the scientists who met at Arcueil, near Paris, may cast some light on the permanent problems of scientific organization. It was in France around 1800 that there emerged for the first time in modern history the *profession* of science, usually related to the tenure of a post in one of the many institutions for higher education which had been developed in Paris after the French Revolution.

The period of Napoleon Bonaparte's rise to power is one of exceptional interest, and although the familiar political and military history must be put to one side, the effect of the political scene on the men of science, and their contribution to the national economy of France, may be not the least interesting aspect to emerge. One conclusion which the reader may draw from this study is that men of science tend to be less sensitive to political changes than scholars in other fields. Yet it was no mere coincidence that the Society of Arcueil came into being with the Empire of Napoleon and declined after his fall from power in 1814. Although the book is concerned chiefly with the lives of the Arcueil scientists, I have also examined briefly Bonaparte's attitude to science throughout the career of that extraordinary military dictator.

As far as the history of science is concerned, this book attempts to do something to describe the state of French science in the two decades after the death of Lavoisier. The programme of research enunciated by Lavoisier was cut short by the guillotine in 1794 but a broadly similar programme was continued by his former colleagues, Berthollet and Laplace

[1] A facsimile edition of the three volumes of *Mémoires* of the Society of Arcueil is shortly to be published by the Johnson Reprint Corporation.

ix

and their protégés in the Arcueil group. In this way the book
fills a gap in the general knowledge of science on the continent
of Europe between the time of Lavoisier and that of Liebig.
It also traces a connection between the brilliant French school
at the end of the eighteenth century and the dominant German
research schools which had developed by the mid-nineteenth
century.

We are concerned both with the *lives* and the *work* of the
members of the Society of Arcueil, who included a number of
important figures such as the naturalist, explorer and universal
man of science Humboldt, the chemists Berthollet and Chaptal
and the mathematician Laplace. Humboldt has been the subject of numerous studies although none have devoted their
attention exclusively to his association with the men of science
in Paris, his adopted home. Chaptal was a most successful
Minister of the Interior under Bonaparte, and Berthollet and
Laplace served the same master in the Senate. By 1800 Berthollet had acquired international fame from his method of
bleaching based on the use of chlorine ('oxymuriatic acid').
Laplace had published a system of cosmology and was becoming recognized as the Newton of his age.

A recent article on 'Laplace and the Speed of Sound'[1]
mentions successively the names of Newton, Laplace, Biot,
Poisson, Delaroche, Bérard, Gay-Lussac, Welter, Berthollet
and Dulong. It is not pointed out that nine of these men were
compatriots and contemporaries. I hope to show that these are
not merely names associated with a particular theory or
experimental determination which each happened to produce.
In this list the name of Newton stands apart. The other names
are those of men who knew and respected each other—men
who carried out an experiment in order to throw light on a
particular problem suggested by a colleague. In the last analysis
the history of science is not about data but about men who
are stimulated to investigate certain problems rather than
others by the total social and cultural situation in which they
find themselves. A major factor in this environment is the
nature of the scientific institutions which may promote work
of a particular kind. Some understanding of the organization

---

[1] *Isis*, lv (1964), 7–19. This paper makes a valuable technical contribution to the history of physics.

of science in early nineteenth-century France is therefore necessary and one chapter is devoted to a discussion of the subject.

Although Chapter Two is largely biographical, it does not give an exhaustive account of the individual lives of the fifteen full members of the Society of Arcueil. If this is desirable, it can be done later in separate biographies. In this book I have tried to emphasize common features in the education and professional lives of the Arcueil group in the hope that a reasonably representative picture may emerge of the social background of science at a particular time and place. Throughout the book the influence of one man on another has been stressed. Co-operation can come about in many ways and with far-reaching consequences for the progress of science. In this sense, the history of the whole of the Arcueil group adds up to very much more than the sum of the contributions of its individual members. A second factor affecting scientific achievement is competition. This is seen most interestingly in the rivalry between Humphry Davy in England and Gay-Lussac and Thenard in France. Finally, science can be encouraged and directed by the exertion of patronage by those with power and money. The story of the group which assembled at Arcueil provides a case history of such patronage.

One of the difficulties about describing the activities of the Society of Arcueil is that we cannot expect to find a minute-book with a record of proceedings. Whereas we may know in detail about the activities of some very minor French societies of the period, the essential informality of the Arcueil group is a stumbling block for the historian. Men who saw each other perhaps several times a week in Paris had no need to write letters. Foreign correspondence, however, is a help and it is fortunate that Berthollet had several regular correspondents outside France, his letters to Blagden (one time Secretary of the Royal Society) being particularly valuable. The fact that nearly every distinguished foreign scientist who went to Paris in the early nineteenth century made a point of visiting Berthollet provides a further source of documentation.

Although it is hoped that the book will be of some general interest, it is impossible to discuss the history of science without at least a few technicalities. These have been concentrated as

far as possible in the first part of Chapter Seven. This book is
not concerned exclusively with any one science. If chemistry
is mentioned most frequently it is because this science had
become prominent both on account of its recent theoretical
advances and its practical applications. On the predominant
place of chemistry among the experimental sciences at the
beginning of the nineteenth century, the remark made by
Delambre in 1808 might be quoted:

> That the revolution recently brought about in chemistry could
> not happen without turning many experimentalists a little out of
> their ordinary course, when they saw in a neighbouring science
> a road opened that promised more numerous discoveries.[1]

Only a matter of months after these words had been spoken,
Malus, an associate of the Arcueil group, discovered the polarization of light by reflection. This discovery opened up a new
field of research which was to have important consequences for
science for the remainder of the nineteenth century.

As attention is directed in the course of this book to the
financial support of the early nineteenth-century scientists in
France, a word must be said about monetary values. It is
hardly sufficient to know that the rate of exchange was approximately 25 francs for £1 sterling. Probably a more helpful
comparison can be based on the average wages of lower paid
workers in Paris in 1807, which was 2 fr. 50. a day. At the other
end of the social scale one estimate[2] of the cost of living at the
end of the Empire was that a comfortable annual income for
a bachelor in Paris would have been 15,000 francs, the 'support
of a plain family establishment' would have cost 40,000
francs, and 'the maintenance of a family in a style of elegance'
would have required an income of about 100,000 francs. These
estimates, which make allowance for a rise in prices in the later
years of the Empire, do something to provide a modern sterling
or dollar equivalent.

In the period 1793–1805 a revolutionary calendar was in use
in France. In nearly all cases in this book dates have been given
simply according to the Gregorian calendar without con-

---

[1] Report on the progress of science in the period 1789 to 1808 (read
3 February 1808) quoted by John Playfair, *Edinburgh Review*, xv (1810), 12.
[2] [April 1816] Las Cases, *Journal of . . . Napoleon at Saint Helena*, trans.,
1824, vol. ii, part 3, p. 76.

tinually distracting the attention of the reader with two sets of dates. Similarly I have considered it pedantic to refer to every chemical substance by its contemporary name rather than its modern name. Dulong, for example, is said to have discovered the explosive nitrogen trichloride; although Dulong did not give it this name at the time, it serves the purpose of compact description. In the case of chlorine, however, Berthollet and the Arcueil chemists were at first so convinced of its compound nature that to use the modern name would be misleading.

A deliberate attempt has been made to keep the bibliography as short as is consistent with the intention of providing a useful guide to the sources. The bibliography has accordingly been restricted to items of *general* relevance; works used only to establish isolated points are given in footnotes. In some respects the footnotes and the select bibliography are therefore complementary.

This may be the beginning of a period of reappraisal of French science in the nineteenth century. I hope that subsequent works may be able to derive some benefit from this study and I trust that they will correct any errors of fact or interpretation.

Manuscript Sources

As THE bibliography at the end of the book only provides a selection of *published* sources used in this study, it may be of value to mention the libraries which provided manuscript material. In appending this list I should like to thank the various custodians of these documents for their kind co-operation. If this study provides any insight into the personal lives of French men of science at the beginning of the nineteenth century, it is largely thanks to the letters, diaries, registers and other precious sources which they have allowed me to consult.

ANNECY Archives de la Haute Savoie
GENEVA Bibliothèque Publique et Universitaire
LONDON British Museum (Department of Manuscripts)
 Royal Astronomical Society
 Royal Society
 Natural History Museum (Department of Botany)
 Wellcome Historical Medical Library
PARIS Académie des Sciences
 Archives Nationales
 Archives de la Seine
 Bibliothèque Nationale (Manuscrits)
 École Polytechnique
 Institut National
 Observatoire
 Sénat
 Service historique de l'Armée, Vincennes.

There also exists in private hands a number of documents which would help to throw light on particular aspects of the story of the Arcueil scientists. As further documents become available it will be possible to modify in some ways the conclusions presented here. Fortunately a considerable amount of source material has already been published including, for example, Candolle's autobiography and many of Humboldt's letters.

Acknowledgements

WHEN one has received help from so many quarters, it is possibly invidious to single out any institution for particular mention. I feel obliged, however, to emphasize my indebtedness to the *Archives Nationales* in Paris and the Royal Society of London. In granting permission for the inclusion of extracts from the diary and personal letters of Sir Charles Blagden, the librarian of the Royal Society wishes me to state that the copyright of these extracts remain with the Royal Society. I have also received assistance over a long period from members of the staff of the Brotherton Library, University of Leeds.

I make separate acknowledgement on page xiv to those libraries which have allowed me to draw on their manuscript collections. I am also grateful for facilities for research in the following libraries: *Bibliothèque Nationale* (imprimés, periodiques), British Museum (printed books), *Conservatoire des Arts et Métiers*, Institute of Historical Research, London, University College, London, University of London, Wellcome Historical Medical Library.

For assistance towards expenses involved in making several visits to libraries in Paris, I am glad to acknowledge help from funds of the Department of Philosophy, University of Leeds.

In my search for suitable illustrations, I have been helped by the courtesy of several institutions and the kindness of many private individuals in France. The photograph for Plate 1 was generously given to me by Baron Paul de Chaubry. I should like to thank Chanoine R. Chaptal for a portrait of his famous ancestor (Plate 8a). In seeking an illustration of Gay-Lussac as a young man, I received the kind co-operation of Madame Roger Gay-Lussac. Baron O. Thenard and Monsieur Arnould Thenard were kind enough to present me with the photographs for Plates 11b and 20a. I owe the photograph of the rare print of Descotils (Plate 12b) to the generosity of Monsieur R. Fischesser, Director of the *École Supérieur des Mines*. Plates 2, 6 and 20b are reproduced through the kind co-operation of the Secretaires perpetuels of the *Académie des Sciences* and of Madame

Gauja. The originals of Plates 10a and 10b are in the Musée Carnavalet, Paris, which kindly allowed their reproduction. Plates 13 and 14 are from the Archives Nationales. Plate 19 is reproduced through the kind co-operation of Mr Kaye, Librarian of the Royal Society. Plates 4, 5a, 5b, 7, 8b, 9a, 9b, 12a, 15b, 16a, 16b, 17, 18a, 18b are taken from the Departments of Printed Books, Prints, and Maps of the British Museum and are reproduced by permission of the Trustees.

I must express my warm thanks to Dr W. A. Smeaton of University College, London, for his detailed work in improving the typescript of this book both in content and style. I owe him much for his frank comments and criticisms. Dr Roger Hahn of the Department of History, University of California, Berkeley, has also been kind enough to read through my draft typescript and make suggestions for improvements, particularly in relation to Chapter One. I also owe him thanks for some details about Laplace's family. For various other points, I have profited from conversations with or communications from: M. A. Desguine, Dr F. L. Holmes, Dr Frank Healey, Mr Gerald Flynn, M. George Poisson, Mme Sadoun-Goupil, Professor L. Pearce Williams, and Mlle. Y. Vidal. I have also been guided by suggestions made by a referee appointed by the publishers. There are many others to whom I am grateful for courteous replies to my letters. While thanking all concerned for their kind help, I must take personal responsibility for errors and omissions. Contemporary translations have been used in the book wherever possible, but in many cases where none exist, I have undertaken the translation myself. I should like to acknowledge the valuable assistance of my wife in translation from German sources.

List of Plates

(between pages 284 and 285)

17. Map of the Paris region, showing Arcueil and Jouy
18. Gay-Lussac's apparatus for investigating the thermal expansion of gases
19. The Royal Society copy of the first volume of Arcueil *Mémoires*
20a. Thenard in his full academic robes
 b. Biot photographed in his laboratory at the *Collège de France*

Abbreviations

A.C.R.	Alembic Club Reprint, Edinburgh.
Ann. chim.	*Annales de chimie,* Paris.
Ann. chim. phys.	*Annales de chimie et de physique,* Paris.
Comptes Rendus	*Comptes Rendus Hebdomadaires des Séances de l'Académie des Sciences,* Paris, 1835–.
Mém. Acad. Sc.	*Mémoires de l'Académie Royale des Sciences,* Paris.
Mém. Acad. Sc. Inst.	*Mémoires de l'Académie Royale des Sciences de l'Institut de France,* Paris, 1816–.
Mém. Inst.	*Mémoires de l'Institut National des Sciences et Arts. Sciences Mathématiques et Physiques,* Paris, 1798–1815 (1818).
Mém. Sav. Étr.	*Mémoires présentées à l'Institut des Sciences, Lettres et Arts par Divers Savans et lus dans ses Assemblées. Sciences Mathématiques et Physiques,* 2 vols., 1805, 1811.
M.S.A.	*Mémoires de physique et de chimie de la Société d'Arcueil.*
P.V. Inst.	*Procès-verbaux des Séances de l'Académie des Sciences tenues depuis la fondation de l'Institut jusqu'au mois d'août 1835,* 10 vols., Hendaye, 1910–22.

The Society of Arcueil

The members of the Society of Arcueil were:

		Age in 1807
1. Claude Louis BERTHOLLET	(1748–1822)	59
2. Pierre Simon LAPLACE	(1749–1827)	58
3. Friedrich Heinrich Alexander Baron von HUMBOLDT	(1769–1859)	38
4. Jean-Baptiste BIOT	(1774–1862)	33
5. Louis Jacques THENARD	(1777–1857)	30
6. Joseph Louis GAY-LUSSAC	(1778–1850)	29
7. Augustin Pyramus De CANDOLLE*	(1778–1841)	29
8. Hippolyte Victor Collet-DESCOTILS	(1773–1815)	34
9. Amédée Barthélemy BERTHOLLET	(1780–1810)	27

The following joined the Society after July 1807:

10. Étienne Louis MALUS	(1775–1812)	32
11. Dominique François Jean ARAGO	(1786–1853)	21
12. Jacques Étienne BÉRARD	(1789–1869)	18
13. Jean Antoine CHAPTAL	(1756–1832)	51
14. Pierre Louis DULONG	(1785–1838)	22
15. Siméon Denis POISSON	(1781–1840)	26

* Following the practice of the *Académie des Sciences*, the botanist A. P. De Candolle is referred to hereafter as Candolle. Similarly Collet-Descotils is referred to more simply as Descotils.

Introduction

THIS IS a book about patronage. The pursuit of science no less than that of the arts has always required patrons. Sometimes a patron has provided friendship or hospitality or equipment or money or facilities for publication. Berthollet and Laplace, two of the greatest men of science of the Napoleonic age, were able to provide all these as well as their own valuable experience and advice.

Shortly after his return with Bonaparte from Egypt in 1799, Berthollet bought a country house at Arcueil, then a village three miles to the south of Paris. When in 1806 Laplace bought the neighbouring property at Arcueil the scene was set for the curtain to go up on the most important private scientific society of the age, the Society of Arcueil.

Yet it was only because of their well-paid positions as Senators and because they had other income from the state that Berthollet and Laplace were each able to buy and maintain a spacious country house. As personal friends of Napoleon Bonaparte, they received particularly favourable treatment under the Consulate and Empire. Berthollet decided to devote a substantial part of his wealth to equipping a room with physical instruments and another room at Arcueil was transformed into a chemistry laboratory. Here Berthollet invited a few chosen young men at the beginning of their scientific careers to carry out research. The patronage of Berthollet and Laplace was not, however, confined to a kind of narrowly-channelled hospitality. It was more than a coincidence that a nominee of Arcueil usually had the best chance of any salaried vacancy, whether in the official body of French science, the 'First Class' of the Institute, or at the *École Polytechnique*, at the *Bureau des Longitudes*, or elsewhere.

There was almost a hierarchy of patronage in the dedication of books by members of the Arcueil circle. Whereas Laplace chose to dedicate one of the volumes of his monumental *Mécanique céleste* to Bonaparte, Biot dedicated his books to Laplace and Berthollet. A logical order in which to consider the patronage relevant to this book is therefore to begin with

Bonaparte, to pass on to Berthollet and Laplace and then to look at their protégés, Gay-Lussac, Biot, Dulong, Arago and the rest. In the final chapter we shall find that the younger men of Arcueil had in their mature years attained positions of power and influence so that they were able to repay the debt of patronage on which their own successful careers had been based.

Napoleon had written:

> Our society is constituted in such a way that consideration and esteem are accorded to visible distinctions and to large fortunes. We should like those of our subjects to enjoy such esteem who are great in respect of their *talents*, their *service* and their *character*.[1]

Berthollet, a distinguished scientist, a friend of Napoleon and a man of upright character, qualified in all three of these respects. He was made a Count of the Empire[2] and we shall see how his fortune also depended directly on the favour of the Emperor.

The Society of Arcueil was a small society, but it made up in quality what it lacked in quantity. The Society revolved around Berthollet and Laplace but other senior members were Chaptal, the chemist and ex-minister of Napoleon, and that universal man of science, Humboldt. Younger members of the Society included Gay-Lussac, Thenard, Biot, Arago, De Candolle, Dulong, Malus and Poisson. All these men were scientists of the first rank, whose interests ranged from mathematics to botany. The society, however, did not make the mistake of attempting to study the whole field of science. Rather it concentrated on problems in the fields of physics and chemistry, its contributions to optics and physical chemistry being particularly noteworthy.

The development of such a group as the Society of Arcueil in the early nineteenth century may seem something of an anachronism to anyone who remembers the groups which studied natural philosophy in early seventeenth-century Italy, France and England and which later developed into formal scientific societies. It would be easy to assume that such societies, once established, rendered superfluous smaller informal associations. The very existence of the Society of Arcueil demonstrates that this was not so.

Meetings were held fairly regularly at Arcueil at the week-

[1] Napoléon, *Correspondance*, vol. xv, no. 12666 (my italics).
[2] Decree of 1 March 1808.

end in the period 1807–13 and although memoirs were read on many occasions, as at the official body of French science, the First Class of the Institute (renamed the *Académie des Sciences* in 1816), the main function of the Society was not as a parallel society to the First Class but rather as a complement to it. In so far as the members of the Society of Arcueil were also members of the First Class, the Society constituted an academy within an academy. But there were opportunities at Arcueil which were lacking at the Institute, particularly the provision of laboratory facilities, the training of young men in methods of research and the full and frank discussion of work among friends. From 1802 onwards important experimental work was carried out at Arcueil. Berthollet's country house also became a centre of scientific intelligence both through his international correspondence and through the many visitors both French and foreign who went there.

CHAPTER ONE

Napoleon Bonaparte and Science

Introduction

IN A survey of French science at the time of Napoleon Bonaparte it is of some interest to examine the attitude to science of the man who was to become head of state. The attitudes and prejudices of one man have seldom been of such great influence. The period of Bonaparte's power (1799–1814) is not usually considered one of great achievement in French literature or art, yet the same period constitutes one of the peaks of French science. There is evidence enough that Bonaparte's censorship of free expression and his efforts to direct thought did much to prevent the flourishing of the arts. The question to be discussed here is to what extent Bonaparte supported the development of pure and applied science, whether directly or indirectly, and with what degree of success. Can the flourishing of French science and the emergence of a powerful technology on French soil under the Consulate and Empire be in any way attributed to the sympathies, ideas or influence of Napoleon Bonaparte?

It would be appropriate to begin by briefly examining Bonaparte's education and his attitude to science as a young man, influenced as it was by the later phases of the French Enlightenment. Special attention might be paid to Bonaparte's opinion of various branches of science and also his private contacts with scientists before he came to power in November 1799. His relations with the 'First Class' (i.e. the scientific section) of the Institute provide an indication of his public attitude to science. Bonaparte's brief career as a participating member of the First Class was followed by a longer period of patronage. The simple view of Napoleon as the great patron of science and industry cannot, however, be held without certain reservations.

There can be no doubt that Bonaparte wished to appear as a patron of science. It remains to be discussed whether this was no more than a façade. In the founding of the Royal Society of

London it had been possible to obtain royal approval in the form of a charter but one ought not to distort the slight interest of Charles II in the affairs of his gentlemen of the Royal Society. He may have been curious enough to have looked through Newton's model telescope, but his understanding of the 'mechanical philosophy' was no greater than that of most of his subjects and he is reported to have laughed at the attempts of the virtuosi to weigh air. Across the Channel Louis XIV had been persuaded by Colbert to extend his patronage to the *Académie des Sciences*. Charles II had been content to present the Royal Society with a mace. Louis XIV went further and provided pensions for the members of the *Académie*. Yet, as the president of the Institute was careful to point out when that body went in February 1809 to congratulate Napoleon on his return from Spain, although Louis XIV had been the *protector* of the *Académie Française* and the *Académie des Sciences*, he had never been a *member*. Napoleon, on the other hand, had once as General Bonaparte been elected to ordinary membership of the Class of Mathematical and Physical Sciences of the Institute. He had taken his seat among the leading French *savants* but now as Emperor he still looked with favour on the pursuit of science and was in the position of a powerful patron.

The case could hardly be argued that French science, having languished in the eighteenth century, suddenly blossomed out in the first years of the nineteenth century under Bonaparte. Quite the contrary. We need only think of Lavoisier's monumental work in the 1770's and 1780's which virtually laid the foundations of the modern science of chemistry. Lavoisier became quite a wealthy man through his work in the administration of taxes and consequently he was able to carry out his scientific research independently. Only in a marginal sense did he depend on royal patronage. Lavoisier played a prominent part in the *Académie Royale des Sciences* but the patronage of Louis XVI was somewhat remote. State patronage depended rather on energetic ministers like Turgot.

The revolutionary ideals were generally sympathetic to science and the brief period of iconoclasm was soon replaced by a constructive spirit which led to the foundation of several new scientific institutions. When Bonaparte came to power at the end of 1799 science was flourishing. We shall see how the

Enlightenment philosophy of the young general Bonaparte was entirely favourable to the pursuit of science. Later when he became Emperor, rather different considerations may have become increasingly important. If the Bourbons had played the role of patrons of science, the new Napoleonic dynasty must do at least as well. Not the least of Napoleon's reasons for his support of science was his deep concern for international prestige. The previous decade had also proved the utility of science to the French state especially in the art of war.

Bonaparte as a Child of the Enlightenment

The intellectual development and presuppositions of Bonaparte in relation to the Enlightenment would merit detailed study. Here it may be sufficient to quote the opinion of science and the value of scientific study expressed by Condorcet in a report he presented to the National Assembly in 1792. This passage has a certain intrinsic interest but it also contains several ideas which later found expression—and influence—in Bonaparte:

> Many motives have brought about the kind of preference which is accorded to the mathematical and physical sciences. Firstly, for men who do not devote themselves to long meditations, who do not fathom any kind of knowledge—even the elementary study of these sciences is the surest means of developing their intellectual faculties, of teaching them to reason rightly and to analyse their ideas . . . The natural sciences . . . offer a remedy for prejudice, for smallness of mind . . . Those who follow their course see the coming of an epoch when the practical usefulness of their application will reach greater dimensions than were ever hoped for, when the progress of the physical sciences must produce a fortunate revolution in the arts. And lastly, we have yielded to the general tendency of men's minds, which in Europe seem to incline towards these sciences with an ever increasing ardour . . . Literature has its limits, the sciences of observation and calculation have none. Below a certain degree of talent, the taste for literary occupations produces either ridiculous pride or a mean jealousy towards such talents as one cannot attain. In the sciences, on the contrary, it is not with the opinion of men but with nature that we have to engage in a contest, the triumph of which is nearly always certain, where every victory predicts a new one.[1]

---

[1] C. Hippeau, *L'Instruction Publique en France pendant la Révolution*, 1st series,

As will be seen later, Bonaparte had the same ideas on the value of science to free the mind from prejudice, the idea of science as, unlike literature, capable of indefinite progress and having applications useful to society; even the metaphor of winning victories over nature is one which had an obvious appeal to the soldier.

Bonaparte's Early Education: His Interests and Abilities

It may be convenient to divide Bonaparte's education into three main periods, on the assumption that education does not cease on leaving school. There was first his formal education as a child at the Collège of Autun and at the military schools of Brienne and Paris. After graduating as a young artillery officer Bonaparte, who had often isolated himself in his books as a child, continued a programme of self-imposed education by fairly wide reading. The third phase of Bonaparte's education came when, in a position of power, he made use of other men's knowledge. They became his educators, not only in affairs of state, law and finance but in matters of science too.

Bonaparte spent only three months at the Collège of Autun. There the little Corsican boy learnt enough French to speak it reasonably well and to begin to write in French. He spent all the remaining years of his formal education in military schools and one consequence of this was that he did not undergo the exclusively classical education of many of his contemporaries. This is not to say that the boys at Brienne and Paris were given a purely military education but rather they were given a grounding in what was hoped would be useful later and in this grounding mathematics figured fairly prominently. With little interest in languages, young Bonaparte turned with more enthusiasm to history and geography and he excelled in arithmetic and geometry.[1] In 1785 he went to the *École Militaire* in Paris, where his studies were more advanced. In mathematics, for example, he had lessons in algebra, analytical geometry, mechanics and hydrostatics and elementary calculus. His progress was good enough for him to pass out in one year instead of two; his

pp. 203–4, 258. Trans. J. T. Merz, *A History of European Thought in the Nineteenth Century*, 2nd ed., 1904, vol. i, pp. 110–11.
[1] J. B. Marcaggi, *La genèse de Napoléon*, 1902, p. 79.

mathematical ability directed him to a post in the artillery. He thus entered a branch of the army where advance was related to merit and mathematical skill much more than in the infantry. It is not without significance for the subject of this book that Bonaparte's examiner when he passed out in September 1785 was Laplace. Bonaparte's mathematical teacher had been Louis Monge, whose brother Gaspard also played a part in Napoleonic science.

When Bonaparte was posted as a second lieutenant in an artillery regiment at Valence his education was not finished. Apart from the course on artillery which he followed assiduously at Auxonne in 1788, he had mapped out a programme of reading in which history had a prominent place but which also included natural history.[1] It was the *Histoire naturelle* of Buffon, one of the idols of his age, that Bonaparte read and he made notes on theories of the formation of the earth and the solar system and the generation of man and animals. He also, following Buffon, drew up a table of probabilities of life.

Bonaparte never made the mistake of confusing education with the years of formal schooling. His programme of self-education was combined with a willingness, indeed a design, to learn from others. Egoist though he was, as a young man Bonaparte was always eager to listen to new ideas and to acquire new information. In government he brought this technique to the greatest use in his Council of State, but from the very beginning as Consul, Bonaparte had made the greatest use of his ministers, asking them questions as a student might ask his tutor.

In his relations with men of science there is a parallel. In mathematics his knowledge would at least put him in the position of knowing what questions to ask. We have seen how he acquired some knowledge of natural history by his reading. But what of chemistry, that study which had been firmly placed among the sciences by the work of Lavoisier and his contemporaries? Chemistry came to the fore in the last quarter of the eighteenth century as the latest example of a science which not only provided an understanding of a part of nature but which in the Revolutionary Wars proved of the greatest utility to France. Chemistry does not appear to have figured either in Bonaparte's formal education or in his early private reading, yet

[1] J. P. Marcaggi, *La genèse de Napoléon*, 1902, pp. 151ff.

when in power he was well aware of its utility and, not least, the contribution it could make to French industry. There remains the third method of learning—*viva voce* exposition by the expert. It is one of the lesser claims to fame of the chemist Berthollet to have filled this role.

Bonaparte made Berthollet's acquaintance in Italy in the summer of 1796. Berthollet had been sent by the Directorate as one of the Commissioners to the Army in Italy with respon-sibility for the selection and despatch to Paris of art treasures, manuscripts and objects of scientific value. On 21 June 1796 Bonaparte as commander-in-chief of the army in Italy in-formed the Directorate that while Barthélemy was busy in Bologna, choosing fifty of the most valuable paintings in the city to despatch to France, the mathematician Monge, the chemist Berthollet and the biologist Thouin were in Pavia selecting specimens to enrich the *Muséum d'Histoire Naturelle* in Paris.[1]

Bonaparte's Candidature for the Institute

A part of Bonaparte's claim to have been genuinely interested in science is based on his membership of the Institute. This was not a formality undergone when he was in the possession of absolute power in France but a part of his earlier career. For this reason it is worth examining for its effect in bringing Bona-parte into closer contact with the scientists of the period. It might also be examined for its sincerity, although it is not diffi-cult to interpret Bonaparte's relations with the *savants* as a means of winning their approval and thus obtaining their support in his rise to power.

Bonaparte was not without influential friends among the scientists in the Institute. In the first place there was Monge, the senior member of the section of mechanical arts, who on his return to Paris from Italy at the end of October 1797 was able to tell his colleagues of the scientific aspirations of the young general and thus prepare the way for his election. Then there was his old examiner, Laplace, and Berthollet, who had become a personal friend. When Bonaparte finally took his seat as a member of the Institute he was accompanied by Laplace and Berthollet and they signed the register of attendance immediately

[1] Napoléon, *Correspondance*, vol. i, no. 663.

after him.[1] A fourth prominent member of the Institute who might have been expected to have favoured Bonaparte was the astronomer Lalande who had been in correspondence with him during the Italian campaign. Bonaparte had expressed his satisfaction in being able to be of service to him and astronomy.[2]

Considering Bonaparte's friendship with Monge, it comes as less of a surprise that Bonaparte chose him to accompany General Berthier back to Paris to present the treaty signed at Campo-Formio on 18 October 1797. The messengers also carried a letter to the Directorate, a letter which is of some interest for its generous tribute to science. The relevant part runs as follows:

> Citizen Monge, one of the members of the commission of sciences and arts, is well known for his learning and his patriotism. He has made the French respected by his conduct in Italy; he has gained an important place in my friendship. The sciences, which have revealed so many secrets to us and destroy so many prejudices, are called to render still greater services for us. New truths and new discoveries will reveal secrets even more essential to human happiness; but we must show our love for scientists and protect the sciences.[3]
>
> I beg you to receive with equal distinction the distinguished general and the learned physicist. Both contribute to make their country illustrious and they bring fame to the French name.

The most surprising thing about this letter is that, although it was addressed to the Directorate, it was read out by Fourcroy at a meeting of the Institute on 1 November 1797. The motive may have been simply to honour one of their number but it is more probable that this was the first shot in an election campaign. The election at the Institute arose from the government decree proscribing five members for political reasons. Of these five vacancies only one was in the First Class (i.e. the scientific section) of the Institute and this was the place which had been held by Lazare Carnot. The Minister of the Interior in a letter of 26 September had reminded the Institute of its duty to re-elect and on 17 October the Institute had agreed to look for a

---

[1] See Plate 2.

[2] Napoléon, *Correspondance*, vol. ii, no. 1231.

[3] 'Il faut que nous aimions les savants et que nous protégions les sciences.' *Ibid.*, vol. iii, no. 2306.

suitable candidate in the appropriate section of 'mechanical arts'.

Mechanics was probably the most appropriate section to which an artillery officer might be elected. Had the vacancy been in, say, astronomy, natural history or anatomy, the system of elections of the Institute, although sometimes noted for its pliancy, might have been strained beyond its elastic limit. Yet what had Bonaparte published to support his election?—a few minor works on Corsican history and moral philosophy and his *Souper de Beaucaire*, contributions, one might think, more suitable for an aspiring member of the Second Class (Moral and Political Sciences) or even the Third Class (Literature and Fine Art). Whatever may be the judgement of history on Bonaparte's application of moral science, no-one in the light of subsequent events could dispute his right to become a humble member of a group devoted to the study of political science. Yet membership of the Second or Third Classes held no attraction for Bonaparte. His training in military mathematics led him to aspire to join the great physical scientists of the day, to belong to a group which included his friends Monge and Berthollet as well as Laplace and others whom he held in great esteem.

Bonaparte had serious rivals for the vacancy. On the preliminary list there were twelve candidates. Apart from several skilled practical mechanics there was Dillon, who had published several important memoirs on hydraulics and had been appointed inspector general of the new system of weights and measures. Montalembert was a distinguished engineer who had been a member of the old *Académie des Sciences* and was the author of several works on military engineering. There was also Lamblardie who was director of the *École des Ponts et Chaussées*. Against such candidates what chance had Bonaparte, a young man of twenty-eight whose scientific knowledge hardly went beyond the four volumes of the classic text-book of Bézout: *Cours de mathématiques à l'usage du corps royal de l'artillérie*, which he had studied as a student at the École Militaire in Paris. Bonaparte had had no time subsequently to do original scientific work; he had been too busy carrying out his military duties with great distinction. When Monge returned to Paris with the treaty which gave France undisputed rights to the left bank of the Rhine, the Directorate showed its pleasure by appointing

Bonaparte commander-in-chief of the army to invade England. Bonaparte was a national hero and it was for this reason that he was elected to the vacant place in the Institute in preference to several senior men of greater technical competence and with more relevant qualifications.

On 11 November the First Class under the presidency of Lacépède reduced the twelve names to three to be submitted to a meeting of all Classes. Of 40 valid ballot papers, 26 showed Bonaparte as their first choice and a further 7 placed him either second or third. At the final election of 25 December he headed the list. At the time of the preliminary ballot Bonaparte had been in Milan but he returned to Paris early in December. On 11 December a dinner was given in his honour and this was attended by a large number of influential members of the Institute. Bonaparte made a great impression, his conversation ranging from metaphysics to politics, from poetry to mathematics according to his audience of the moment. Laplace and Lagrange were taken aback by a rapid exposition he gave of a geometrical construction taken from a book on mathematics which had just been published in Italy.[1] By such tactics Bonaparte increased his slight majority over his two rivals, Dillon and Montalembert, into an absolute majority. One of Bonaparte's first political triumphs therefore took place within the Institute.

Bonaparte's Early Relations with the Institute

In fact the Institute had used the election to honour a young general favoured by the government of the day and thus to bring favour on themselves. It was an honour for the Institute but it was also an honour for Bonaparte. When he had been asked in Italy what he would do when peace came, he replied that he would work so that one day he would deserve a place in the Institute.[2] It has frequently been pointed out that after his election Bonaparte often signed his proclamations to the army under his command with the title of member of the Institute. The day after his election Bonaparte dictated to his secretary the following letter of thanks. It was given publicity in the

---

[1] Mascheroni, *La Geometria del Compasso*, Pavia, Anno V. Maurice, Art: 'Lagrange', *Biographie universelle*, vol. xxiii (1819), p. 166n.

[2] *Moniteur*, 9 January 1798.

Moniteur and deserves to be reproduced here as a public statement of his attitude to science. It also contains an idea which
was to remain constant in Bonaparte's mind—that France
should dominate the world not only politically but by the
quality and achievements of her men of science:

> The approbation of the distinguished men who make up the
> Institute does me honour. I realize that before becoming their
> equal I shall long be their pupil. If there was a more expressive
> way of conveying to them the esteem in which I hold them I
> would use it.
>
> True victories, the only ones which leave no regret, are those
> made over ignorance. The most honourable occupation and the
> most useful to nations is to contribute to the extension of human
> ideas. The true power of the French republic must henceforth
> consist in not allowing there to be new ideas which do not belong
> to it.[1]

This last sentence may be compared with a statement made by
Bonaparte in a letter written in May 1796 to the Italian astronomer Oriani in Milan, in which he says that all men of arts and
science 'are French, whatever the country of their birth'.[2] This
curious remark can only be interpreted as a desire to have
within the French empire all that was best of human culture.
The utilitarian motive was disregarded; this was a matter of
national prestige.

It is, of course, one thing to belong to an organization and
quite another to take an active part in it. Bonaparte's military
duties involved a tour of inspection of the north of France in
February 1798 and preparations for the expedition to Egypt in
March and April. By the beginning of May when the Corsican
general left Paris he had in the course of four months attended a
total of sixteen meetings of the First Class of the Institute, about
two-thirds of the total possible. At the first meeting he attended
the day after his election Bonaparte was appointed in conjunction with Monge and Prony to examine a printing device.
When the report on this invention was read at the next meeting
of 5 January, Bonaparte together with Laplace, Coulomb and
Borda was asked to report on a trivial military invention. On 30
January he was again a member of a commission, this time to

---

[1] Napoléon, *Correspondance*, vol. iii, no. 2392.
[2] *Ibid.*, vol. i, no. 491.

c

judge the merits of a steam carriage. His selection is explained by the fact that it was he who brought the matter to the attention of the Institute as he had done previously in the case of the typographical invention. Bonaparte therefore contributed to the work of the Institute by acting as an intermediary for the work of people outside. He also made occasional gifts to the Institute.

The Institute of Egypt

Bonaparte's next concern for science is shown in his plan for the Institute of Egypt. The difficulties of invading England having become increasingly apparent, the Directorate saw a political advantage in seizing Egypt and threatening India. Bonaparte himself, the hero of the Italian campaign, was attracted by the prospect of another campaign and all the more as Egypt conjured up in the mind the romance of the East. Already in September 1797 he had spoken in confidence to Monge about the possibility of an expedition to Egypt and Monge had begun to collect appropriate maps and information.

This was to be an expedition not only of conquest but of possible colonization and enlightenment of the native population. Bonaparte took with him a Commission on Science and the Arts. To be sure, the substantial number of engineers, surveyors and cartographers as well as interpreters had an obvious practical purpose. Yet Bonaparte also tried to secure the services of eminent musicians, poets and artists. The greatest names in the expedition, however, are those of scientists—the chemist Berthollet who was in charge of recruitment, the mathematicians Monge and Fourier, the zoologist Geoffroy Saint-Hilaire and the inventor Conté. Dolomieu too sailed with Bonaparte as did Malus. These were the men who were to constitute the backbone of the new Institute to be founded in Cairo. Here among the 'barbarians' scientific work was to be carried out not only for practical purposes but as evidence of the superiority of the Frankish civilization. Bonaparte in a letter to the Directorate summed up the people of Egypt as 'wretched, ignorant and brutish'.[1] The wretchedness of the people could be lessened by his government. Ignorance and brutality were to be

---

[1] Napoléon, *Correspondance*, vol. iv, no. 2834 (p. 356, 24 July 1798).

countered by the educating and civilizing influence of his *savants*. When the sheiks were invited to the Institute, they were expected to react with childish amazement at a demonstration by Berthollet of chemical and electrical experiments.

When Bonaparte left Toulon on 19 May 1798, he bade a prolonged farewell to the comforts of Parisian life but he took with him a microcosm of his concept of civilization. On board the *Orient* Bonaparte would summon his staff officers and the available *savants* and hold what he termed his 'Institutes'. These consisted of discussions on a variety of topics—politics, religion and science being particularly prominent.[1] If Bonaparte was to combine in Egypt the exercise of military and political power, if he was at once commander-in-chief, governor-general, administrator and explorer, he also seemed at times to have a missionary zeal based not only on the power of French arms but also on his faith in French culture in general and in French science in particular.

The Institute of Egypt, therefore, was not something which arose spontaneously in North Africa as a means of occupying the leisure hours of army officers. When the organization was formally created on 22 August 1798, it was according to a preconceived plan. On 24 July Bonaparte after the battle of the Pyramids made his entry into Cairo. Ten days later he wrote a letter addressed to Berthollet, Monge and Caffarelli (a general in the engineering corps) in which he asked them to select a suitable building for the establishment of a printing press for both French and Arabic, a chemistry laboratory, a physics laboratory, a library and if possible an observatory.[2] There was also to be a suitable room for meetings of the Institute. The place chosen was a spacious palace on the outskirts of Cairo. If Bonaparte's esteem for the Institute was in any way reflected in the accommodation chosen for it, he must have thought highly of the work of his *savants*.

Bonaparte had decided very definitely that science should have an important place in the new colony in North Africa. He also wished to associate himself with an enterprise which might

[1] 'On board the *Orient* he [Bonaparte] took pleasure in frequent conversations with Monge and Berthollet; these discussions were usually concerned with chemistry, mathematics and religion'—Fauvelet de Bourrienne, *Mémoires*, 1831, vol. i, p. 242.
[2] Napoléon, *Correspondance*, vol. iv, no. 2938.

be considered one of the milestones of civilization. He was not content to be a victorious general. Looking to the judgement of history he wanted a lasting memorial. Only a monument of legislation or of scientific progress would achieve this. When he read history he saw not only Alexander the Great and Charlemagne but also Galileo and Newton. Bonaparte's participation in the activities of the Paris Institute were cut short by his expedition to Egypt but he thought that he might carry the torch with him. In stressing the continuity of Bonaparte's participation in the 'Institutes', we must not take too seriously the discussions which helped to pass the time on the Mediterranean crossing. But we can hardly exaggerate the role of the Institute of Egypt in the expedition. This was part of the grand plan of Bonaparte and he was able to put it into execution with the help of two men of science who were his personal friends, Monge and Berthollet.

When Bonaparte returned suddenly to France, he abandoned the army and most of the members of the Commission of Arts and Sciences but he took with him Monge and Berthollet. On their last evening on Egyptian soil on 18 August 1799 Bonaparte was in an expansive mood and he elaborated on his attitude to science:

> I have used the imposing phrase 'dignity of science'. It is the only one which conveys my thought exactly. I know of no better way for a man to spend his life than to work to know nature and all things of use accessible to reason in the material world.[1]

On another occasion Bonaparte claimed that if he had not become a general with the destiny of leading the French nation, he would have devoted his life to science:

> I would have thrown myself into the study of the exact sciences. I would have traced a path following the route of Galileo and Newton. And because I have always succeeded in my great enterprises, I should also have won great distinction for myself by scientific work. I would have left behind me the memory of great discoveries.[2]

There are many things that one could say of such a claim. Here it may serve as evidence not of Napoleon's vanity but of his

[1] Geoffroy Saint-Hilaire, *Lettres écrites d'Égypte*, ed. E. T. Hamy, 1901, pp. 238 ff.   [2] Arago, *Notices Biographiques*, vol. i, p. 250.

view that a career in science was worthy of esteem and that scientists no less than generals left their mark in history.

Bonaparte's Continued Association with the First Class of the Institute

Bonaparte arrived back in Paris on 16 October 1799. According to the *Moniteur* the first carriage to arrive (several hours before the others) contained the two generals Bonaparte and Berthier and the two scientists Monge and Berthollet. Bonaparte's first duty was to report to the Directorate but by 23 October he was not too busy to attend a meeting of the First Class of the Institute. The latter resolved to record in the minutes 'its satisfaction in seeing our colleague Bonaparte in its midst'. Bonaparte made no contribution to the meeting but he was chosen in association with Laplace and Lacroix to present a report on a mathematical memoir by Biot. At the same meeting Berthollet began to read his important memoir, inspired by his observations in Egypt, on a new concept of chemical affinity.

Four days later, however, Bonaparte had a further chance to associate himself with the activities of the Institute since on 27 October a General Meeting of the entire Institute was to be held. Bonaparte took the opportunity to give his colleagues news of the Egyptian expedition that would interest them. He spoke first of the Rosetta stone with its inscriptions in Greek, Coptic and Hieroglyphics which was to provide the long-awaited key to the written language of ancient Egypt. He described the Egyptian expedition as one of research and discovery particularly with respect to a canal at Suez and gave details of the supposed different water levels at each end. It was at this meeting that a medal in platinum was presented to Bonaparte on behalf of the Institute. The medal was to commemorate the peace following the Italian campaign and on one side Bonaparte was portrayed on horseback; an inscription testified to the homage of 'grateful science and the arts'.

Bonaparte continued to attend meetings of the Institute in the fateful month of *brumaire* when he used the force of his military command to expel the Council of Five Hundred and establish himself together with Sieyès and Roger-Ducos in a position of political power under the name of the Consulate. At a meeting of the First Class of the Institute on 12 November,

two days after the *coup d'état*, he was present to hear the report
which he had signed on Biot's differential equations.

Bonaparte attended a further three meetings of the Institute
in the winter of 1799–1800, thus keeping in touch without
exaggerating his interest in its affairs. Nevertheless, at a meeting
of the First Class on 22 March 1800 when the place of president
for the next six months fell vacant, he was elected. The full
details of this election are not known. The minutes of the Institute do tell us, however, that Bonaparte obtained an absolute
majority at the first ballot. He was not present at this meeting
but he attended the next meeting five days later when he
suggested that the method of balloting should be reformed.
The Class obediently nominated two of Bonaparte's known
friends, Laplace and Monge, together with the secretary,
Delambre, to consider this reform.

Commenting on Bonaparte's presidency at one of the four
annual public meetings of the Institute on 5 April 1800 the
Moniteur was able to remark that the First Consul now filled the
double role of 'president of the French republic and president
of the republic of letters'. At this meeting Bonaparte was very
conscious that he was in the public eye and he took care not to
assume a superior attitude at variance with republican principles. Bonaparte took some pride in his double role of head of
state and president of the official body of science. He is reported[1]
to have sent various sumptuously bound volumes to the Royal
Society on behalf of the Institute, accompanied by a letter
signed: 'Bonaparte, président de l'Institut national et premier
Consul'.

Bonaparte did not take his duties as president of the First
Class of the Institute too seriously, although we should take
into account the fact of his considerable period of absence from
France during the term of his presidency. In fact he presided at
only four meetings of the First Class and at the next election at
the end of September 1800 Berthollet was elected to succeed
him; there could be no official disapproval of such a choice.
Bonaparte had been absent in Switzerland and northern Italy
during the months of May and June 1800. One letter he wrote
to his fellow consuls when he was in Milan is of particular
interest. His brother Lucien, Minister of the Interior, had

[1] Aulard, *Paris sous le Consulat*, vol. ii, p. 149.

stopped publication of the paper *Ami des lois* on the grounds that it had criticized the Institute. The First Consul remarked that the Institute had a reputation throughout Europe and was above such attacks. Besides, too stern measures would result in the Institute becoming unpopular.

> I assure you that, as president of the Institute, I would protest on the least pretext. Yet let them say if they wish that the Sun moves,[1] that it is the melting of ice which causes the tides[2] and that we [i.e. members of the Institute] are charlatans; the greatest liberty must prevail.[3]

Bonaparte's support of freedom of the press was noticeably absent when it was he who was under fire.

At a meeting of the Institute on 22 December 1800 Bonaparte was able to give his colleagues news from Egypt and on 15 February 1801 he presented the Institute with two papyri. There can be no doubt that Bonaparte attached importance to the publication of the *Mémoires sur l'Égypte*, the transactions of the Institute of Egypt, and he saw that the Paris Institute received a copy. Cuvier as secretary wrote to thank Bonaparte:

> The National Institute has asked me to thank you for the copy of the Memoirs on Egypt . . . The love of science and measures to support it have always occupied your attention even in the midst of the most brilliant victories and all Europe was waiting for the fruits which this love of science would produce in this cradle of civilization which you have added to your conquests.

In the field of science, as in the field of pure politics, there was never a lack of flatterers. Perhaps more impressive was the action taken by the Institute when, two days after the unsuccessful assassination attempt of 24 December 1800, they went in a body to congratulate the First Consul on his escape and convey their sense of outrage at the event. Again, when the preliminaries of peace were signed with Great Britain in October 1801 the pleasure of the Institute was conveyed to Bonaparte.

---

[1] This idea was being discussed publicly by Louis Sebastien Mercier.
[2] I.e., the theory of Bernardin de Saint Pierre.
[3] Napoléon, *Correspondance*, vol. vi, no. 4890.

The Prize for Research on Voltaic Electricity

After the Peace of Amiens Bonaparte could turn his attention to the internal affairs of France. An event of much greater importance than it might at first appear was the visit in the winter of 1801–2 of the great Italian physicist Volta to Paris. Volta was not summoned to Paris by the First Consul. It was at his own request and after obtaining assurances of a safe passage from the commander of the French forces in Italy that Volta set out. Nevertheless, his visit may be conveniently taken to mark the beginning of a new chapter in Bonaparte's patronage of science. This period of peace in 1801–2 sees the beginning of a new relationship between Bonaparte and the world of science and after 1802 he never attended the meetings of the Institute. In the Institute of Egypt when he had made a rather stupid comment on a scientific question, he had had to allow the correction of a colleague. In 1800 he had still been prepared to sit among the scientists of the Institute. By August 1802, however, he had secured the consulate for life. His power was increasing and also his pride.

In 1801 Bonaparte made a point of attending all the three meetings of 7, 12 and 22 November at which Volta read a memoir on his theory of electricity and performed experiments. At the first meeting Bonaparte made a speech showing that he considered this to be an occasion of great consequence. The minutes of the meeting read as follows:

> Citizen Bonaparte proposed that, from the beginning of the general peace, the Class should demonstrate its desire to gather together the wisdom of all those who cultivate the sciences, and should present a gold medal to citizen Volta, the first foreign man of science or letters who has personally read a memoir to the Class since the peace, as a mark of its special esteem for this professor and of its eagerness to welcome the work of all foreign scientists. He also proposed that a commission should be given the task by the Class of carrying out on a large scale all experiments which might throw a new light on the important branch of physics, which Citizen Volta has just expounded to the Class.

Bonaparte's remarks are important not only because they reiterate his wish to associate the best scientific work with France and because of his readiness to patronize foreign scientists but also because this marks the beginning of his policy of offering substantial monetary rewards for first class scientific work. This is made clear in a letter written by Bonaparte to Chaptal as Minister of the Interior on 15 June 1802. He began by stating his intention of awarding an annual prize of a medal worth 3,000 francs for the best original experimental work on voltaic electricity. In addition, he said,

> I wish to give by way of encouragement a sum of 60,000 francs to the person who, by his experiments and his discoveries, advances electricity and galvanism to a degree comparable to the advances made in these sciences by Franklin and Volta; and this to be judged by the Class.
>
> Foreigners of all nations are to be admitted to the competition on equal terms.[1]

Bonaparte said that his object was to encourage physicists to concentrate on this branch of their science since he foresaw that it would be along this path that great discoveries would be made.

A copy of this letter was sent to the First Class of the Institute and a commission of five members including Laplace and Biot was appointed to consider the means of carrying out Bonaparte's wishes. The prize for galvanism was given great and immediate publicity. The details were announced at a public meeting of the Institute on 6 July 1802 and the speech made by Biot on behalf of the commission appeared in many journals including Tilloch's *Philosophical Magazine* for July 1802:

> The First Consul, who even amidst the cares of war has caused the sciences to flourish, being desirous that peace should carry them to the highest degree to which they can attain, has given to the National Institute the means of accelerating their progress.

There followed the text of Bonaparte's letter and a sketch of the history of electricity. The commission stated that the Institute had not previously offered a prize because the vast extent of the subject seemed to demand more than one competition. They were glad, however, that the initiative for stimulating research in this direction had now been taken:

> To fulfill the intentions of the First Consul, and to give the competition all the solemnity which the importance of the object,

---

[1] Napoléon, *Correspondance*, vol. vii, no. 6132.

the nature of the prize and the character of the founder require, the commission unanimously propose as follows:

The Class of the Mathematical and Physical Sciences of the National Institute opens the general competition required by the First Consul.

All the learned of Europe, including the members and associates of the Institute are admitted to the competition.

The Class does not require that the memoirs should be immediately addressed to it. Every year it will crown the author of the best experiments which come to its knowledge and which have advanced the progress of the science.

The grand prize will be given to the person whose discoveries form a memorable epoch in the history of electricity and galvanism.

The present report, containing the letter of the First Consul, shall be printed and serve as a programme.

Enacted at the National Institute, Messidor 11, year 10.

(Signed) LAPLACE, HALLÉ, COULOMB, HAÜY, and
BIOT, reporter.

The prizes to be awarded for research on electricity was thus launched with a fanfare of trumpets. The subsequent history of the prize was not to live up to early expectations. The offer of 60,000 francs (equivalent to about 2,400 pounds sterling in England at that time) must have offered a very considerable inducement to experimental scientists to turn their attention to electricity. Yet this prize was only to be awarded for discoveries equalling in importance those of Franklin and Volta—no mean achievement. Probably only Davy's decomposition of the alkalis by means of electricity merited this prize, yet it was not this but the comparatively modest annual prize that was awarded to Davy and, ironically enough, not for his isolation of potassium and sodium announced in the Bakerian lecture to the Royal Society in November 1807, but for his general comments on electricity contained in the Bakerian lecture of the previous year.

The fate of the 'annual' prize is not a very encouraging story. At the end of the first year the commission of five met to compile a report on the year's work in electricity. Their long and impartial report set out the contributions of all serious workers in the field and was presented at a private meeting of the First Class of the Institute on 17 October 1803. It was decided not to award the prize that year and it was not until 1806 that an award was made. In the public meeting of January 1807 the prize was given to Paul Erman of Berlin for his work on the conducting properties of flames. Erman's work was published in the *Journal de physique* in the following month.

On 7 December 1807 the commission on galvanism announced to the First Class that it had unanimously decided to award the annual prize of 3,000 francs to Davy for his Bakerian lecture 'On some chemical agencies of electricity' read to the Royal Society in London on 20 November 1806. It had been published in Part 1 of the *Philosophical Transactions* for 1807, which appeared in the spring of that year. Yet on 19 November 1807 Davy announced the decomposition of the alkalis. News of Davy's achievement arrived in Paris in mid-December, just after the decision to award Davy the prize for his previous work. These were the circumstances that enabled Gay-Lussac when addressing the public meeting of the Institute in January 1808 to announce the award of the prize to Davy for the Bakerian lecture of 1806 and at the same time to mention his more recent work.

Davy had started his experiments on the decomposition of the alkalis on the principle that 'the powers of electrical decomposition were proportional to the strength of the opposite electricities in the circuit' and had accordingly used 'the highest electrical power [he] could command, which was produced by a combination of voltaic batteries belonging to the Royal Institution'. This contained about 250 plates and it was with such a battery that Davy isolated potassium in October 1807. He then suggested to the managers of the Royal Institution that a subscription should be opened for the purchase of a large voltaic battery to replace the one he had used and which was now badly corroded. The new battery, constructed under Davy's supervision in July 1808, consisted of 2,000 double plates of zinc and copper and it was the most powerful battery then in existence. Yet this extra power was not really necessary to decompose the alkalis although it was useful for preparing larger quantities of the alkali metals. In 1809–10 Davy was able by means of the new battery to give the first display of the continuous electric arc.

Meanwhile the news in the winter of 1807–8 of Davy's isolation of potassium and sodium had stirred the imagination of the French men of science and to Napoleon it seemed to confirm his earlier idea of the importance of research on electricity. In the words of Cuvier, reporting as secretary of the First Class of the Institute:

> His Imperial Majesty in the middle of his concern for affairs of state does not ignore any important progress in science and does not refuse to the sciences anything that might contribute to further success. He ordered that there should be constructed at the *École Polytechnique* voltaic piles of different sizes including one which should be bigger than any used hitherto.[1]

Such an enterprise obviously required money and on 13 February 1808 Lacuée, governor of the *École Polytechnique*, wrote a letter to Monge as president of the commission appointed to organize the construction of the voltaic pile, telling him that Napoleon had provided 20,000 francs for the purpose.[2] The commission could now go ahead with their plans and on 29 July of that year the giant pile was finally ready. It consisted of 600 pairs of square plates of copper and zinc each of side 30 cm. The plates were soldered together and arranged horizontally in a trough which was filled with a dilute acid, The working of the pile was entrusted to Gay-Lussac and Thenard, who began by repeating Davy's experiments and decomposed not only potash and caustic soda but also the earths corresponding to the metals barium, strontium and calcium. They went on to compare the effects of this pile with those of other batteries but their results were rather disappointing. To quote Berthollet:

> This type of research did not hold out for them results important in themselves because M. Davy and other physicists had almost exhausted this field of research.[3]

Nevertheless, in the course of their research Gay-Lussac and Thenard rightly suspected that the rate of decomposition of an electrolyte depends only on the strength of the current (and not, e.g., on the size of the electrodes) and they used chemical de-

[1] *Mém. Inst.*, 1810, Part 2, pp. liv–lv.
[2] Hachette, *Correspondance sur l'École Polytechnique*, 2nd edn., 1813, vol. i, p. 450; vol. ii, p. 28.
[3] *Journal de physique*, lxxii (1811), 230.

composition as a measure of electric current thirty years before Faraday.[1]

In the autumn of 1808 the commission on galvanism met again but they could find no outstanding work for that year. There was, however, an alternative suggestion for the use of the prize and at the meeting of the First Class on 13 February 1809 there appears the following minute:

> The commission on galvanism proposed to ask his Imperial Majesty that the 3,000 francs which we have not been able to award this year for a discovery in electricity should be used for a work on the mathematical analysis of the experiments of M. Chladni on the vibration of sounding plates.

This request was made in the light of Napoleon's interest in Chladni's work. When Chladni visited Paris in 1808 he was presented to the Emperor by Laplace.[2] Napoleon spent two hours questioning Chladni on his theory of acoustics and the next day awarded him a sum of 6,000 francs to cover his expenses in Paris. Berthollet, Laplace and other members of the Institute urged Chladni to translate his work on acoustics into French and in 1809 there appeared the *Traité d'Acoustique* with a dedication to Napoleon:

> Napoleon the Great has deigned to accept the dedication of this work after having seen the basic experiments.

Although there now seemed to be a precedent for the wider application of the money associated with the prize for electricity, its next award reverted to its original purpose. At the meeting of the Institute of 26 December 1809 Laplace, Berthollet, Haüy, Charles and Biot were elected to form a commission to judge the award and they immediately decided to recommend that the prize be awarded jointly to Gay-Lussac and Thenard for their work on electricity. After this the prize fell into abeyance, until it was revived by Napoleon III.

Precedents for the Award of Prizes for Scientific Work

The award of prizes by Napoleon Bonaparte for scientific research and industrial development and invention is an important

[1] *Recherches physico-chimiques*, 1811, p. 12. Faraday, *Experimental Researches*, 1839, vol. i, p. 217n.
[2] Parisot, *Biographie Universelle, Supplément*, vol. lxi, p. 27.

aspect of his relations with the world of science and it would be misleading to go on to describe some of the other prizes sponsored by Napoleon without filling in a little perspective, mentioning in particular the prizes offered in England and France in the eighteenth century. We shall find, for example, that the 3,000 francs offered annually by Bonaparte for work on electricity was of equal value to another prize for physical science offered by the Institute. Also, under the Consulate and Empire, money offered for prizes was usually paid, something which had by no means been a necessary consequence in England or in revolutionary France.

Probably the most famous prize offered in England in the eighteenth century was won by John Harrison's chronometer. The financial inducement offered was very considerable, but, despite the merits of Harrison's work, he had the greatest difficulty in obtaining his just reward.

A more constant source of encouragement in Britain to inventors, where the prizes, though more modest, were at least forthcoming, was the Royal Society of Arts. This was founded in 1754 solely to encourage industries and arts and crafts by the offer of prizes. It was typical of the English way of doing things that this was financed entirely by private subscription, the society being known as 'The Society for the Encouragement of Arts, Manufactures and Commerce'; the society had been in existence for 150 years before royal patronage was extended, giving the society its present title.

Following the example of the Society of Arts, a society for the encouragement of applied science and industry was founded in France in 1776. France was after all the country of Diderot's *Encyclopédie* with its emphasis on technology. The full title of the society was: 'Société libre d'émulation pour l'encouragement des inventions qui tendent à perfectionner la pratique des arts et métiers a l'imitation de celle de Londres'. Although it awarded several prizes for developments in industry, agriculture, chemistry, etc, nearly all its members were aristocrats who had little contact with the world of industry and after five years the society was dissolved due to the lack of interest of its members. Nevertheless, the idea of a 'Société d'encouragement' was taken up later by Chaptal with important consequences for the development of applied science and industry in France.

In eighteenth-century France many prizes were awarded by the *Académie des Sciences* and once the *Académie* had established the tradition of offering prizes, the French government was able to use it for matters of immediate national concern. About 1775 the supply of saltpetre in France was diminishing and the government was worried about the effect this would have on the supply of gunpowder. Turgot asked the *Académie des Sciences* to offer a prize for the exploitation of saltpetre. Lavoisier was appointed to a commission on France's natural resources of saltpetre, a subject which was to continue to be a major concern during the period of the revolutionary wars and on which other distinguished chemists such as Berthollet and Chaptal worked. Well known is the prize offered by Louis XVI of 2,400 livres for a method of converting salt to soda. The *Académie* published this as a prize for the year 1783 and the offer was renewed for the next five years, but despite the submissions of Leblanc and others, the Académie did not consider that any of the processes submitted deserved the prize and this was never awarded.

The *Bureau de Consultation des Arts et Métiers*, established in September 1791, expanded the traditional programme of prizes of the *Académie des Sciences* and gave advice on financial rewards to be made for contributions to industry. It was composed of thirty members, none of whom received payment, fifteen from the *Académie des Sciences* (including Lavoisier, Berthollet, Laplace and Lagrange) and fifteen other members representing the artisans and industry. The original number of members soon dwindled, either by retirement, arrest or execution. Nearly half the remainder, including Berthollet, were busy on other government commissions. It was not only the drastic reduction of membership that prevented the Bureau doing its work properly. Equally important was the availability of funds. In theory 300,000 livres was set aside annually for this purpose, but the *Bureau* found it almost impossible to obtain this money, particularly when Roland was appointed Minister of the Interior. Nicolas Leblanc, for example, was awarded a sum of 3,000 francs in September 1794 to cover a part of his expenses in the manufacture of soda, but this money was never paid. Nevertheless, the *Bureau* continued to function and do useful work for the rest of the period of the Convention. Under the Directory its functions were transferred to the Institute on 28 May 1796.

The First Class of the Institute by the law of 5 March 1796 was given the task of awarding two prizes each year, one subject to be proposed by the mathematical sciences group and the other by the group of physical and biological sciences. The value of the prize was fixed at 1 kgm. of gold. Entries were to be submitted anonymously but accompanied by a sealed note containing the author's identity. In 1803 the value of the prizes was fixed at 3,000 francs. These prizes not only encouraged development in particular fields; there was also the hope that they might foster international goodwill, since they were theoretically open to men of every nationality. This was an aspect which appealed to Bonaparte and he took advantage of his tenure of the office of president of the First Class of the Institute to send the following circular to foreign Academies. Bonaparte's motives are not unambiguous but the text of the letter of 5 April 1800 is worth reproducing:

> We are sending you the programme of questions on the physical sciences which the National Institute proposes to scientists of every country. The prizes which it intends to award for the solution which it judges best will no doubt be, for persons working on these subjects, much less powerful motives than the honour of having contributed to the progress of human knowledge. Convinced that all that can hasten this progress is regarded as a sacred duty by enlightened men of all countries, the National Institute hopes that you will give to this programme all possible publicity . . .[1]

Other Prizes Sponsored by Napoleon

Bonaparte's prize for electricity was only the first of a series of prizes he proposed to encourage scientific work. The most famous of his prizes are probably the *Prix décennaux*, instituted not long after he had become Emperor. By a decree signed at Aix-la-Chapelle on 11 September 1804 Napoleon founded a series of prizes which he intended to present every ten years on the anniversary of the *coup d'état* of 18 brumaire. There were to be nine grand prizes of 10,000 francs each, of which two were to be awarded for the best published work in science, one for the best machine, another for the best factory or farm. The remain-

---

[1] Quoted by Maindron, *Les prix de l'Académie des Sciences*, 1881, pp. 55–6.

Baron de Chaubry

1. Bonaparte and Berthollet on board the *Orient*, sailing to Egypt (1798). Berthollet, standing on the left, faces Bonaparte. Seated in the centre is Monge.

2. Attendance sheet of the First Class of the Institute on 26 December 1797. The signature of Bonaparte is followed by those of Laplace and Berthollet.

LE MINISTRE DE L'INTÉRIEUR.
Présente à l'Empereur du Sucre de Betterave.

3. Napoleon is presented with samples of beet-sugar.

4. Napoleon's visit to Oberkampf's factory at Jouy on 20 June 1806.

ing five prizes were for history, drama, painting, sculpture and opera. There were also to be a number of smaller prizes. The competition was to be judged by a jury consisting of the permanent secretaries and presidents of the four Classes of the Institute. On 7 March 1807 Napoleon wrote to the Minister of the Interior, reminding him that the time for the award of these prizes was approaching. Further publicity should be given in the *Moniteur* and perhaps a letter sent to the Institute to reassure its members that these prizes would not be allowed to lapse. By a second decree of 28 November 1809, very much at the eleventh hour, Napoleon extended the number of prizes to thirty-five, nineteen of these to be grand prizes.

In 1810 all four Classes of the Institute made preparations to judge for the prizes, but political events prevented the actual award of these except for those of the favoured First Class. Nine of the prizes were awarded in the field of pure and applied science and the recipients bore such famous names as Lagrange, Laplace, Berthollet, Cuvier, Montgolfier and Oberkampf. The jury which recommended the award of a prize to Laplace said that they had no hesitation in making this choice. There was no other contemporary work which could compete with the *Mécanique céleste*, not only for its contributions to mathematical astronomy but also for its contribution to physics made in the supplements on capillary action. The next prize covered the field of physics, chemistry and mineralogy. Berthollet was recommended for this prize for his *Statique chimique*, for which the jury congratulated the author on his original approach to a general theory of chemistry but also commented on some of the obscurities it contained. Haüy's *Traité de Minéralogie* was commended for its originality. Two books received an honourable mention: Fourcroy's *Système des connoissances chimiques* and Lacépède's *Histoire des poissons*. The authors were both men who had rendered sterling service to the Napoleonic state but it was their original contributions to science rather than their personalities which were on trial and the jury was not prepared to make an award merely to compensate the industry involved in the compilation of these long and painstaking works. Cuvier obtained another prize and the award for the most important machine went to Joseph Montgolfier (1740–1810) for his hydraulic ram. A further prize went to Oberkampf for having founded an

D

outstanding factory. In all these cases impartial judgement was not easy since in most cases the members of the Institute were judging their colleagues and friends. The jury which recommended Oberkampf, for example, contained a majority of his friends, Berthollet, Chaptal and Gay-Lussac. Of the minor prizes only one was for science and this was awarded to Delambre for his measurement of the arc of the meridian between Dunkirk and Barcelona.

A further prize instituted by Napoleon was on a more personal note. On 5 March 1807 Napoléon-Charles, the eldest son of his brother Louis, died of croup. Napoleon, always conscious of the problem of his succession, was more concerned by this than the death of a thousand of his troops. Writing on 4 June 1807 (ten days before the battle of Friedland) to Champagny, then Minister of the Interior, he proposed that the Institute should award a prize of 12,000 francs for work on the study and treatment of croup. Doctors from all countries were invited to compete. When the prize was awarded on 15 May 1811, after the original period for the competition had been extended, the decision was fairly international. The prize was divided between two doctors from Geneva, one from Bremen and two from Bordeaux.

Finally mention must be made of the largest prize of all. As opposed to many prizes and awards given for contributions to industry by the *Société d'Encouragement*, this involved the Emperor himself. A decree by Napoleon, published in the *Moniteur* of 12 May 1810 (a year when he was showing particular concern about the state of French industry) offered a million francs to the inventor of any nation who could produce the best machine to spin flax. Already in 1800 Berthollet[1] and others had been trying to treat flax in such a way as to give it some of the properties of cotton. The spinning of cotton had already been successfully mechanised and Arkwright's machine had been adopted in France in the first years of the nineteenth century. Napoleon was hoping to stimulate the invention of a similar machine suitable for dealing with the special problems of linen. At a time when little cotton was being imported due to the blockade, fine linen seemed to offer an obvious alternative if only certain technical difficulties could be overcome.

[1] *P.V. Inst.*, vol. ii, pp. 170–2; *Journal de l'École Polytechnique*, iv (cahier 11, 1802), 319–21.

This problem was solved by Philippe de Girard (1775–1845) who already had several minor inventions to his credit. Within a few days of the appearance of the announcement in the *Moniteur*, Girard had solved the problem in principle. He spent two months devising appropriate machinery and on 18 July 1810 he took out a patent for a process in which dry combing of the filaments was followed by treatment with water and spinning. If ever there was a clear case of the incentive to invention provided by the offer of a large cash prize, it is that of Girard; yet the sequel to the story is less encouraging. Six months after the imperial decree had been published throughout the French Empire and four months after Girard had registered his process, the government had second thoughts. It had no intention of awarding a large sum of money for a process which was so simple. It therefore announced a revised and restricted programme for the prize, in which one of the conditions was that the prize-winning machine should be capable of producing a thread of 400,000 metres per kilogram. The excessive fineness of the thread demanded posed a formidable problem but Girard eventually succeeded in 1813 in overcoming it. Unfortunately for Girard, the Empire was collapsing, and he could hope for no prize from Napoleon. Nor was the government of Louis XVIII more helpful and Girard having found no proper appreciation of his talents in his own country, went to Warsaw to set up a mill.

Bonaparte has been criticized for his failure to support the inventor Robert Fulton. Fulton's 'submarine', the *Nautilus*, was tried out at his own expense on the Seine in Paris in June 1800. The inventor was confident that this would prove a crucial weapon against the British navy but he demanded a letter of protection from the First Consul to cover the possibility of his being caught and treated as a pirate. Laplace and Monge were appointed by Bonaparte to examine the submarine. In November 1800 they reported personally to him and on their recommendation Fulton was given a government grant. At the end of a series of trials at Brest, his expenses had amounted to nearly 7,000 francs. Support was withdrawn when it was clear that Fulton's invention would not be of immediate use. Submarines could never be more than interesting toys until the problem of self-propulsion under the sea could be solved by a suitable motor.

Fulton's other great idea was his steam boat. When Bonaparte heard of the American inventor's trials in Paris in July 1803, he immediately asked for a report from the Institute, saying that this was an invention which 'may change the face of the world'. Yet Fulton failed to impress the French scientists and he left France for England and thence returned to his native United States. If Bonaparte did not give Fulton all the support he might have done, we may reflect that the inventor received even less help from the governments of King George III and President Jefferson.

The Exploitation of Beet Sugar in the Napoleonic State

After 1807 Napoleon sought to close the continent of Europe to British commerce, the so-called 'Continental system'. Whatever grave faults were possessed by the Continental system and whether or not the system was successful in crippling British trade, there can be no doubt, if we look at the other side of the coin, that French industry and agriculture were given a powerful stimulus. A serious effort was made to make France independent of foreign imports by suitable cultivation and processing on French soil. This was tried with tobacco, dyestuffs such as indigo, cotton and sugar. Tobacco had already been grown in France on a limited scale before the French Revolution. In 1810 it was made a state monopoly (as it still is in France today) and the planting of tobacco was therefore carried out on a much larger scale as determined by the government. The cultivation of indigo and cotton had been studied in Egypt by Bonaparte's *savants*. The cultivation of cotton in France was a complete failure, but the growing of woad was successful in the south of France and in northern Italy and in 1813 Napoleon established three factories to produce indigo from it at Toulouse, Turin and Florence. Several attempts were made to grow sugar cane. Yet, although the cane grew to the normal height, it did not ripen sufficiently. Attempts to find other sources of sugar were made and some of these will be described here briefly since they provide a case history of the relations between science, commerce and the state under Napoleon.

In 1747 the Prussian chemist Marggraf showed that many plants contained sugar apparently identical with cane sugar and, by treating the dried roots with alcohol, he was able to extract a significant amount of sugar from beet. Marggraf's successor as professor in the Berlin Academy, Achard, carried Marggraf's work further to the stage of large-scale production of sugar from beet. In 1799 he was able to present King Frederick William III with a sugar-loaf made from his beet sugar. The king of Prussia appointed a committee to supervise further trials and when these were successful, Achard was given financial support to open a sugar beet factory in Silesia in 1801. Meanwhile, Achard had written to his friend Van Mons, one of the editors of the *Annales de chimie* and this letter was published in the number for the historic month of November 1799.[1] Achard described his product as 'European sugar' and his aim was to free Europeans from dependence on imports from the West Indies. Achard's method of treating the sliced beet with hot water was more economical than Marggraf's use of alcohol but the proportion of sugar extracted was comparatively low.

A commission, which included Chaptal, Fourcroy, Guyton and Deyeux, was appointed by the French Institute to examine Achard's process.[2] They reported that their tests had vindicated Achard's claims, although they found that the yield of sugar was even lower than Achard's. According to their calculations, sugar extracted from the beet grown near Paris would cost about 1 franc 80 centimes a kilo, whereas, according to Achard's yield, the price would be less than half this. The price was, of course, the crucial factor. Since the Revolution the price of cane sugar had increased continuously due to the difficulty of shipment when France was at war with England. The peak price was to come in 1811 and 1812 during the blockade of French ports by the British navy, when the price of cane sugar rose to 12 francs a kilo as compared with 1 franc before the Revolution.

There were obviously strong economic as well as political reasons for investigating alternative sources of sugar. The French chemist Proust (1754–1826), who had accepted a teaching post at an artillery school in Spain with a high salary and for whom the Spanish king, Charles IV, had built a splendid

---

[1] *Ann. chim.*, xxxii (1799), 163–8.

[2] *Ann. chim.*, xxxv (1800), 134–52. The notable absence of Berthollet from this commission is explained by the fact that it was appointed on 20 May 1799 when he was in Egypt.

laboratory in Madrid, had also turned his attention to sugar. In 1799 he succeeded in extracting sugar from grapes. He continued to work on this problem and in 1805 he sent a memoir on the subject to the Institute in Paris, of which he was a corresponding member. In 1806 he obtained an extended leave to go to Paris and his 'Memoir on Grape Sugar' was published in the *Journal de physique* that autumn. Grape sugar is not the same as cane sugar and Proust admitted that it was not the perfect substitute. Yet with the price of cane sugar continually rising, grape sugar might prove an acceptable alternative, at least for culinary purposes. He hoped that the abundance of grapes in Spain would make Europe independent of supplies from the colonies. Chemists should now exploit this hitherto neglected source of sugar. Proust suggested the setting up of an organization to extract and refine grape sugar. Proust concluded his memoir with an eloquent plea for Spain to give the lead to the rest of Europe.

Proust's feelings for his adopted country suffered a blow in 1808 when Spain was overrun by French troops and his patron Charles IV was deposed and replaced by Joseph Bonaparte. Proust was left without resources and, having returned to France, retired to the country. In 1810 he was rewarded with a sum of 100,000 francs by Napoleon for his discovery of grape sugar and he was also awarded the Legion of Honour.[1] Although Proust was unable to make any further contribution to relieve the shortage of sugar in France, in the period from April 1810 to March 1814 he published a succession of nine memoirs on gunpowder which may have made a belated contribution towards the effectiveness of Napoleon's artillery.

During the first decade of the nineteenth century there was a continual interest in France in the problem of obtaining sugar from sources other than sugar cane and this is particularly noticeable towards the end of the decade. On 7 June 1808 an article on a substitute for cane sugar to be used in cooking and medicine was published in the official *Moniteur* by Parmentier, whose name is remembered today by chefs in connection with the potato. On 9 October 1809 the First Class of the Institute, at the suggestion of Deyeux, agreed to re-examine Achard's process for extracting sugar from beet and on 18 March 1811

[1] Chaptal, *Mes Souvenirs sur Napoléon*, 1893, p. 118.

a booklet on the subject was distributed at a meeting of the First Class. Outside the Institute Chaptal had for several years devoted a substantial acreage on his estate at Chanteloup to the experimental cultivation of sugar beet. Berthollet too investigated other possible sources of sugar and was approached directly by the Emperor on the subject.[1] Both Chaptal and Berthollet had collaborated in the production of a report on the extraction of grape sugar. This was published as a booklet in 1810 by the imperial press; it was translated into German, Italian and Spanish and was obviously intended for use throughout the Empire.

By 1811 the problem of an alternative source of sugar had become more urgent and in March Napoleon proposed that each department of France should be required to set aside a certain acreage for the cultivation of sugar beet.[2] At the end of the year the Emperor reproached the then Minister of the Interior, Montalivet, for not spending enough to meet this emergency. At a meeting of his newly-founded council of industry and commerce held on 30 December 1811 Napoleon made plans for what amounted to a crash programme for the production of beet sugar.[3] He argued that it was not sufficient to rely on existing factories to deal with the beet produced by farmers. New factories must be built in anticipation of a larger crop and their very existence would encourage increased sowing. The producers of sugar beet should have an assurance from the government that all their crop would be bought for several years ahead. Chaptal was given the task of preparing a detailed memoir for the next meeting of the council. The memoir was to describe the details of a sugar beet factory and Chaptal was to calculate how many such factories would be necessary. Napoleon was prepared to spend large sums of money on the basis of such expert technical advice.

Although the extraction of sugar from beet had been possible since the very beginning of the century, the constant aim of the French workers was to bring down the price of beet sugar below that of cane sugar. In the later years of the Empire this was not so difficult if we remember the high price of sugar from the West Indies but the real advance came at the beginning of 1812 when

[1] Napoléon, *Correspondance*, vol. xvi, no. 13580.
[2] *Ibid.*, vol. xxi, no. 17485.   [3] *Ibid.*, vol. xxiii, no. 18396.

the production of beet sugar became economic for the first time. This was the achievement of Benjamin Delessert, a banker and a philanthropist with interests in botany and chemistry. He had started investigating the extraction of sugar from beet in 1801 in a small factory at Passy on the outskirts of Paris. In 1811 the renewed interest in the problem in France was reflected in his own activities and by 1 January 1812 he had solved the problem of obtaining well-crystallized beet sugar on a large scale. He immediately informed Chaptal, who in turn informed the Emperor. Napoleon decided to visit Delessert's factory in person. This he did on 2 January and, according to the *Moniteur*,[1] he inspected the factory in great detail. At the end of the visit the Emperor decorated Delessert with the Legion of Honour and gave the equivalent of a week's extra pay to the employees.

Napoleon's plan was to make France self-sufficient in sugar obtained from beet so that by 1813 cane sugar could be prohibited completely as 'English produce'. There was not only the building programme for factories but also the problem of technical education that had to be solved. Five of the factories were to be designated 'Special schools of chemistry for the manufacture of beet sugar'. Napoleon suggested that 'Good chemists should be put in charge of these establishments'[2] and in this enterprise of national importance there were to be a hundred students drawn from the ranks of young men who were studying medicine, pharmacy or chemistry. This was a magnificent national programme but it never had a chance to prove its merits, since with the collapse of the continental system and the dissolution of the Empire cane sugar was again imported.

Napoleon's Encouragement of French Industry

In a broad survey of the patronage extended by Bonaparte to pure and applied science, we cannot ignore some other aspects of French industry. Chaptal's influence was of considerable importance here. It was he, for example, who took up an earlier idea for an exhibition of French industry. On the basis of Chaptal's advice, a Consular decree of 4 March 1801 established an annual exhibition in Paris to be held in September at the end of

---

[1] *Le Moniteur*, 3 January 1812.
[2] Napoléon, *Correspondance*, vol. xxiii, no. 18417.

the Republican year. Chaptal, as Minister of the Interior, sent a circular letter to prefects, urging them to obtain contributions from their departments. The exhibition of the year IX opened in the courtyard of the Louvre with 220 exhibits. The jury of fifteen appointed to award prizes included the chemists Berthollet and Guyton de Morveau and five other members of the Institute, among them the engineer Prony. On 22 September 1801 Bonaparte, accompanied by Chaptal, visited the exhibition and made a thorough tour of inspection, questioning all the exhibitors in turn. Nineteen gold medals were awarded for developments in a wide field from textiles to mathematical instruments.

In such exhibitions there was always the tendency to produce something special which was unrepresentative of normal production. For the exhibition held in September 1802 Chaptal insisted that exhibits should be representative of French industry. Although there were twice as many exhibits as in 1801, it was felt that an interval of a year between exhibitions gave insufficient time to bring new ideas to a satisfactory state of development. The next exhibition did not take place till 1806. This time there were over 1,400 exhibitors and the jury presided over by Monge split up into four sections to examine the products: mechanical arts, chemical arts, fine arts, and textiles. In the chemical section the jury praised the improvement in the quality of alum but expressed concern that in the production of soda France was still not independent of Spain. In the textiles section Oberkampf, exhibiting for the first time, was awarded a gold medal.

Oberkampf was a close friend of Berthollet and some of the members of the Arcueil group and he was also singled out by Napoleon as a man of particular merit. We may therefore be pardoned for an apparent diversion to give a brief account of Oberkampf's career. Christophe Oberkampf, born in the kingdom of Wurtemberg, had come to Paris in 1758 at the age of twenty. He had been apprenticed to his father in the dyeing and printing of cloth and it was in this trade that he was employed for a short time in Paris before he decided to set up his own business at Jouy on the banks of a stream called the Bièvre and not far from Versailles. Here he produced cotton prints, an industry new to Europe, and he had an immediate success. The original modest factory was expanded, more workers were brought in and the profits increased. In 1769 these already amounted to half a million *livres*. In 1783 the factory at Jouy was recognized by Louis XVI with the title of 'manufacture royale'. The business survived through the period of instability of the Revolution. Oberkampf was joined by his nephew Samuel Widmer, who took the opportunity while in Paris of studying physics and chemistry privately with Charles and Berthollet respectively. In 1797 Widmer developed the idea of printing by roller, thus increasing the output over the old system of block printing. Mechanics and chemistry were the two sciences on which the technical improvements of production were based. Mechanization was accompanied by research into dyeing and it was at Jouy that one of the first large-scale applications of Berthollet's method of bleaching by chlorine took place. Chaptal, even during his period of office as Minister of the Interior, is reported to have visited Jouy frequently with samples of his own dyeing to ask Widmer to repeat the process on a large scale.

Napoleon's visit to Oberkampf's factory on 20 June 1806 is mentioned in many of the standard histories of the period. The Emperor was shown the latest machine, which was capable of printing fabrics at the rate of $7\frac{1}{2}$ metres a minute. In a matter of seconds the cylinder was changed and another pattern was printed. Napoleon was suitably impressed by the speed of the process and asked many questions. At the end of the visit in the presence of nearly four hundred workers Napoleon unpinned his own decoration of the Legion of Honour and presented it to Oberkampf.[1] The gold medal awarded to Oberkampf at the industrial exhibition of September 1806 has already been referred to. The highest honour, however, was the selection of Oberkampf for one of the *prix décennaux* as the founder of the most useful industry. The report read to the First Class of the Institute on 20 April 1810 mentioned in particular his printing machine, the machine used to engrave the cylinders and the discovery by Samuel Widmer of a solid green which dyed with

[1] Berthollet wrote to Oberhampf later that day to congratulate him and say that Napoleon had remarked to him (i.e. Berthollet) on the great achievement of the factory (H. Clouzot, *Histoire de la manufacture de Jouy*, 1928, p. 25).

one application—a great improvement on the previous system in which the cloth was dyed successively yellow and blue.

Napoleon paid a second visit to Jouy in 1810. He also invited Oberkampf to his palace at Saint Cloud. Widmer took advantage of this audience to ask for a passport to visit factories in England, mentioning that this project was supported by Chaptal and Berthollet. After granting Widmer this unusual privilege, Napoleon spent more than an hour in private conversation with Oberkampf. The Emperor appears to have been most impressed with Oberkampf's fortune, although his later claim to have consulted the proprietor of Jouy about the tariffs on imported goods is without foundation. Napoleon is, however, reported to have said familiarly to Oberkampf, 'You and I are waging a tough war against the English—you by your industry and I by force of arms.'

Oberkampf was perhaps typical of the best of industrial enterprise in France under Napoleon and his activities were not confined to dyeing. In 1796 he had opened a large bleaching establishment. He had long had the ambition of producing prints, starting from bales of raw cotton and carrying out the spinning and weaving himself. He eventually achieved this and it would be fair to say that Oberkampf and his family were responsible for an appreciable part of the running and improvement of the French textile industry under the Empire. In 1813 Jouy saw for the first time a machine capable of printing two different colours simultaneously. This was a development which Oberkampf's nephews, Samuel and Gottlieb Widmer, had observed in Manchester during their visit to England. Oberkampf himself died in October 1815 at the age of seventy-seven. The factory at Jouy soon declined, hastened by competition from other parts of France, notably Mulhouse and Rouen.

If Oberkampf's work reached its peak under Napoleon, it was not because the latter made any direct provision of money or technical aid. These Oberkampf had always obtained independently through his business associates or friends. It cannot be claimed that Napoleon subsidized the manufacturer financially, although despite his usual suspicions of business men with large fortunes, he never made the mistake of penalizing Oberkampf for his wealth. The Emperor let it be widely known that he had a high regard for the man and his work. According to Napoleon's view of human psychology, men could be driven by the goal of honour rather than wealth. On this principle he founded the Legion of Honour and this decoration was one of several means used by the Emperor to give support to Ober-kampf's work.

Napoleon's concern for French industry was not limited to the awards of honours, nor was it confined to the Paris region. Chaptal in his memoirs describes some of the tours of inspection in the provinces when he accompanied the First Consul. When at Sedan in the Ardennes in August 1803 he heard of the ruin of a factory at the time of the Revolution and awarded the pro-prietor's widow a sum of 60,000 francs to get the factory going again.[1] Two years later he was concerned with the textile in-dustry of Rouen[2] but it was probably the silk industry of Lyons which had most reason to be grateful to Napoleon. Since 1792 the wave of the Revolution had brought about a serious decline in the silk industry, but between 1800 and 1810 the number of works increased threefold, thanks to government encourage-ment and subsidy. In 1807 Napoleon placed an order for one and a half million francs with the Lyons industry and in 1810 he gave orders for several million francs worth of materials to be used for furnishing his palaces.[3] Napoleon's frequent subsidies were not intended to save business men from bankruptcy but to prevent factories closing and creating unemployment.[4] On the positive side he suggested expansion, for example, at the Gobelins.[5] Government subsidy was increased during the econo-mic crisis of 1810–11 and in March 1811 the factories of Amiens received an advance of a million francs.[6] So much was lent that, at the end of the Empire, only a fraction had been repaid.

The Place of the Institute under the Consulate and Empire

In speaking of the Institute, attention has so far been concen-trated on the First Class and it may now be worth while to look at Bonaparte's relations with the Institute as a whole. By so doing we may clarify the distinction between Bonaparte as a

[1] Napoléon, *Correspondance*, vol. viii, no. 6996.
[2] *Ibid.*, vol. xi, no. 9035.
[3] *Ibid.*, vol. xiv, no. 12187; vol. xxi, no. 17227.
[4] *Ibid.*, vol. xiv, no. 12187.   [5] *Ibid.*, vol. xxi, no. 16779.
[6] *Ibid.*, vol. xxi, no. 17416.

patron of science and Bonaparte as a patron of other branches of learning with more immediate political implications.

The most famous example of Bonaparte's interference with the affairs of the Institute was the reorganization which was effected by the law of 23 January 1803. This involved the suppression of the Class of moral and political science. At the same time an extra Class was made by dividing the Class of literature and fine arts. The Institute was thus constituted as follows:

First Class	Science
Second Class	French literature
Third Class	History and ancient literature
Fourth Class	Fine Art

To be more precise the subject of study of the Third Class was: 'Ancient languages, antiquities and monuments, history and all moral and political sciences in their relationship with history'. Politics was thus rendered harmless by being submerged in history. This was Bonaparte's method of dealing with the *Idéalogues*. It was one stage in Napoleon's life-long struggle to power by silencing the opposition without needless recourse to brutal methods.

Later there was the case of Chateaubriand's proposed speech to the Institute in 1811, a speech which discussed the possible return of the Bourbons with a frankness intolerable to Napoleon. He is reported by Las Cases to have said to one of his household who had supported Chateaubriand:

> How long is it, sir, since the Institute has presumed to assume the character of a political assembly? The province of the Second Class of the Institute is to produce poetry and to censure faults of language; let it beware how it forsakes the domain of literature, or I shall take measures to bring it back within its limits.[1]

Various other changes were made to the Institute in 1803 which have more bearing on the position of science in Napoleonic France. The tradition of holding annual competitions and awarding prizes was continued, but it is surely significant that the value of the prize awarded by the First Class was to be 3,000

---

[1] Las Cases, *Journal of . . . Napoleon at Saint Helena*, trans., 1824, vol. ii, part 4, pp. 98–9.

francs, whereas a prize for literature, for example, was worth only 500 francs. In the matter of pensions too, scientists seem to have been accorded particularly favourable treatment by Napoleon.[1]

After the period of his personal participation at the meetings of the Institute, Napoleon did not fail to keep informed about its activities and the activities of its members. We find him, for example, on 13 December 1805 writing from Schönbrunn to complain about the way in which the aged astronomer Lalande, a member of the Institute, had allowed his name to be linked with an atheist publication.[2] In fact Lalande had written and had had printed privately a supplement to the *Dictionnaire des athées*, which he had distributed to owners of the Dictionary. Napoleon asked Champagny, Minister of the Interior, to summon the presidents and secretaries of the different Classes of the Institute to tell them to take steps to prevent one of their members supporting a creed harmful to public morals. (Napoleon had by now decided that religion was a powerful force which could be enrolled to consolidate his own power.) Accordingly an extraordinary general meeting of the Institute was called immediately for 26 December and the president read the Emperor's letter to Lalande to the assembled members of the Institute. Lalande obediently agreed to conform to the Emperor's wishes and the meeting was adjourned. Napoleon, however, was not satisfied. It seemed to him that the Institute had merely passed on the message without associating itself with it. Delambre, a ssecretary of the First Class, had to assure the Minister of the Interior that the formula used had been a 'fraternal invitation . . . in the name of the Institute'. Napoleon accepted this explanation. For him the Institute as a state institution owed an obvious duty to the state. Napoleon pointed this out again in 1807—the Institute existed to carry out the wishes of the government and was not entitled to oppose suggestions made to it.[3]

The Institute did not always serve Napoleon's political ambitions with unswerving loyalty. When Napoleon was declared Emperor, there were many who, like Beethoven, felt that their

---

[1] See, e.g., Napoléon, *Correspondance*, vol. xx, no. 16105.
[2] *Ibid.*, vol. xi, no. 9562.
[3] *Ibid.*, vol. xv, no. 12415, p. 127.

trust had been betrayed. Napoleon's supporters among the Class of French language and literature demanded an extraordinary general meeting of the Institute on 18 May 1804 to discuss passing a motion of support for the political change which the Senate approved that same day. Several members, including Biot, spoke out strongly against any incursions of the Institute into politics, and the non-political nature of the Academies of Berlin and St. Petersburg was cited. There was a strong feeling that no action should be taken and the meeting adjourned. When this was put to the vote the motion for the adjournment was carried by a vote of 38 to 25. As if frightened by its own audacity, the Institute met again the next day and it was agreed to go in a body to the Emperor to pay their respects and offer their congratulations.

Apart from the several formal occasions when the Institute paid homage to Napoleon, it generally had little contact with the Emperor. The Institute was, however, called upon by Napoleon to present reports on the progress of science, literature and the arts and its services were also used to judge the *prix décennaux*.

The original constitution of the Institute made it clear that members would not be allowed to carry on their work in private isolation. They were required to publish their work, to hold four public meetings each year and, not least important, they were to give a yearly report on the progress of science and the work of each of the Classes to the Legislative Body. Under the Directory and at first under the Consulate this clause was forgotten but by a Consular Decree of 4 March 1802 Bonaparte reminded the Institute of its obligations. A report was to be drawn up by each class of the Institute to describe progress since 1789. At the same time the Institute was to have the opportunity of expressing its views about the practical applications of its work. It would also provide an occasion to ask for any specific help from the government. In fact five years were allowed to elapse before the Institute was required to act. A general meeting of the Institute in October 1807 arranged for the drawing up of a series of five reports—two for the First Class and one each for the other classes of the Institute. Napoleon is reported to have told Cuvier to exercise extreme care in drawing up his report since it would be read by educated men throughout Europe.[1] The Emperor was most anxious that the rest of Europe should see how experimental science had flourished under his regime.

Accordingly with all due solemnity at a meeting of the *Conseil d'État* on Saturday 6 February 1808 a deputation of the First Class of the Institute headed by the elderly Bougainville (who happened to be president for that year) and the two permanent secretaries, Delambre and Cuvier, and also including Lagrange, Monge, Berthollet, Haüy, Lacépède and others was formally received by Napoleon. Bougainville made a short speech in which he claimed that the period under review (1789–1808) was not only a memorable epoch in political and military history but also one of the most brilliant for the history of science; the French men of science had been responsible for much of this progress.

Delambre then gave an account of the 'mathematical sciences' according to the division of science accepted by the Institute. In a speech which in the printed memoirs of the Institute occupies thirty pages, Delambre singled out the work of Lagrange and, above all, Laplace for special mention. Looking to the future, there was little doubt about the progress of French science because of the efficient organization of scientific education. Delambre mentioned in particular the *École Polytechnique*:

> Already we have seen graduating from this school more than one young man of science who, like MM. Biot, Poisson, Malus, following in the footsteps of the greatest mathematicians, promise to be their worthy successors . . .[2]

Delambre concluded with the rather hackneyed reminder to Napoleon that he would have made some direct contribution to the mathematical sciences himself[3] if he had not been placed in a position where he was rather a patron of science.

Cuvier, when his turn came, spoke of the difficulty of covering every part of the non-mathematical sciences but as a common thread he selected the concept of attraction. This applied particularly to the new science of crystallography established by

[1] Thibeaudeau, *Le Consulat et l'Empire*, 1835–7, vol. ii, p. 496, quoted by Merz, *op. cit.*, vol. i, p. 150n.

[2] *Mém. Inst.*, 1808, 161–229; see especially p. 201.

[3] At least one contemporary British man of science, John Playfair, considered this to be a fair claim—*Edinburgh Review*, xv (1810), 16.

Haüy and to Berthollet's work on chemical affinity. Lavoisier had put chemistry on a new footing and the combined efforts of his colleagues, particularly Fourcroy, Berthollet and Guyton, had made this new theory known throughout Europe as 'French chemistry'. Cuvier found it difficult to avoid allowing his summary to degenerate into a list of the names of scientists and their works. As regards institutions, he did not neglect to mention the *Muséum d'Histoire Naturelle* which had benefited by Napoleon's patronage.

Cuvier, who outshone Delambre in his flattery of Napoleon, suggested that an 'ordinary prince' would have insisted on immediate utility as a guide to research but he hoped Napoleon would agree that everything in science was of some use. Yet the greatest contribution of science to the advancement of civilization was its appeal to reason, which should guide public opinion rather than prejudice and passions. On a more practical note Cuvier suggested that the Emperor should sponsor a fundamental study of natural history by French scientists, holding out the inducement that the frontispiece of any such fundamental work that appeared would bear the name of Napoleon and would provide a further claim to immortality.

After listening to these two long discourses, Napoleon made a short reply in which he said that he wanted these reports on the progress of science to be heard by all nations. This would surely 'shut the mouths of the detractors of our century who, seeking to turn back man's mind, seem bent on extinguishing it'. This was surely a reference to Chateaubriand and other Romantics who had never accepted the legitimacy of the new order nor approved of its sense of values. Napoleon concluded,

> The well-being of my peoples and the glory of my throne are equally concerned with the prosperity of the sciences.
>
> My Minister of the Interior will make a report on all your requests; you can rely constantly on my support.

At the meeting of the First Class the following Monday these speeches were repeated and the Class agreed that the Emperor's reply should be transcribed in its registers as 'a testimony of the interest of Napoleon in the sciences and his patronage to those who study them'.

Napoleon's Scientific Reading

As an indication of how genuine was Napoleon's interest in science it might be useful to consider the time he devoted to reading the works of the eminent scientists who were his contemporaries, his compatriots and, finally, his subjects. Two factors in particular would minimize his serious reading: the technical difficulties of specialized works in various branches of science and, more important, the little spare time available to a man with constant major military, political and administrative duties. Both these difficulties seem to be reflected in a note which Bonaparte sent to Laplace in answer to the latter's gift of the first two volumes of his *Mécanique céleste*. Bonaparte wrote, 'The first six months which I can spare will be employed in reading it'.[1] The heavy irony of this comment was tempered by an invitation to dinner!

Encouraged by Bonaparte's mild praise, Laplace dedicated the next volume of his *Mécanique céleste* (volume three, 1802) to the First Consul, whom he called,

> the enlightened protector of science, who has been educated in the sciences and who sees in their study the source of the most noble delight and in their progress the perfection of all the useful arts and of social institutions.

Bonaparte replied with great courtesy and only some slight hypocrisy:

> Citizen Laplace, Senator.
>
> All that I have read of your work has seemed so perfectly clear to me, that I would like to be able to devote a few weeks to finish reading it. I very much regret not being able to spend the time on it and to give it the attention it deserves. For me it is another occasion to grieve about the force of circumstances which has directed me to another career where I am so far from science. I thank you for your dedication, which I accept with pleasure, and I should like future generations when reading your *Mécanique céleste* not to forget the esteem and friendship which I have borne for its author.[2]

As the Consulate was succeeded by the Empire, Napoleon

---

[1] Napoléon, *Correspondance*, vol. vi, no. 4384.
[2] *Ibid.*, vol. viii, no. 6454.

gave up more and more any claim he might have thought he had as a man of science and established his position unequivocally with relation to French science as its arch patron. Thus when Laplace sent him his *Traité analytique des probabilités* published in 1812, Napoleon replied that at one time he would have read it with interest.

> Today I must confine myself to expressing to you the satisfaction I experience every time I see you publishing new works which perfect and extend this first of all sciences. Your works contribute to the glory of the nation. The progress and perfection of mathematics are linked closely with the prosperity of the State.[1]

Whether Consul or Emperor, Napoleon Bonaparte clearly had little time to devote to the serious study of technical works. There were, however, two particular occasions between 1798 and 1815 when enforced idleness allowed Napoleon to undertake a programme of reading. The first occasion was the journey by sea from Toulon to Alexandria in 1798 which took about six weeks. The return in 1799 from Alexandria to Marseilles took about the same time. Bonaparte had planned a travelling library to occupy his leisure at sea. The library was divided into six sections: (i) science and technology, (ii) geography and travels, (iii) history, (iv) poetry, (v) novels, (vi) political and moral philosophy. The section concerned with science contained fourteen volumes, including Fontenelle, Euler's *Letters to a German Princess*, works on military technology and the six volumes of the lessons at the *École Normale*. This collection contained contributions by Lagrange and Laplace on mathematics, Haüy on physics and Berthollet on chemistry and being of an intermediate standard was certainly not beyond the capacity of the future master of Europe.

The second period when Napoleon had abundant leisure was, of course, on the island of Elba where he had been sent in 1814. On his return to power during the Hundred Days, he visited the *Muséum d'Histoire Naturelle* in Paris (12 April 1815) and told the abbé Haüy, professor of mineralogy, that he had taken his text-book of physics with him in his banishment and he had 'read it again with the greatest interest'.[2] This book had in

---

[1] *Ibid.*, vol. xxiv, no. 19028.
[2] A. Lacroix, 'La vie et l'œuvre de l'abbé René-Just Haüy', *Bulletin de la Société Française de Minéralogie*, lxvii (1944), 54.

fact been commissioned by Bonaparte. Writing to Haüy on 8 February 1803, Bonaparte instructed him to abandon his important research on crystallography for six months so that he could devote himself entirely to writing a text-book of physics for the lycées.[1] Bonaparte urged Haüy to regard education ('la propagation des lumières') as a matter of great importance. Haüy took advice from another priest who pointed out that the author of such a book in speaking of the physical world would have an opportunity to mention its Creator. This Haüy did, but it is as a text-book of physics that the resulting book should be judged. Haüy mentioned the help of several contemporaries and acknowledged particularly the assistance of Laplace and Biot. The book proved a great success and ran through three French editions and was translated into English and German. Haüy was rewarded by Napoleon with a pension of 6,000 francs per annum.[2]

Finally for Napoleon there was the period of enforced leisure on the island of Saint Helena from 1815 till his death in 1821. The library he took with him is not without interest. The catalogue of the library as sold at Sotheby's after Napoleon's death includes about a dozen titles related to science. By far the bulkiest of these works was Buffon's *Histoire Naturelle* in 127 volumes. Also present were works on mathematics, agriculture and industry. Delambre's astronomy, Fourcroy's chemistry and Haüy's mineralogy represented the work of former members of the First Class of the Institute under the Empire.

Napoleon's much-recorded conversations at Saint Helena should not be overlooked, however suspect they may be as examples of self-justification consciously directed to a European audience. There was, for example, his conversation with Mark Wilks, governor of Saint Helena for the first year of his captivity, and a Fellow of the Royal Society. Hearing that Wilks was interested in chemistry, Napoleon began a conversation by saying that it was not for him to state on which side of the English Channel the best chemists were to be found, but as regards the general dissemination of chemical knowledge among the population, there was much more in France because of its wide industrial applications. He went so far as to claim that this

---

[1] Napoléon, *Correspondance*, vol. viii, no. 6573.
[2] *Ibid.*, vol. xx, no. 16105.

was one of the characteristics of 'his school'.[1] Had he been longer in power, the old trades would have been replaced by a new technology. He mentioned the search for new sources of sugar and dyestuffs and suggested that chemistry had brought about a revolution comparable to the effect of the invention of the compass on commerce. If we wanted to select names to characterize the French school, we should be unlikely to choose Napoleon. The names Lavoisier, Chaptal and Berthollet fit the pattern of the development of pure and applied chemistry in France during the lifetime of Napoleon. Yet, as in other places, Napoleon's vanity here reveals something of his sense of values.

Summary and Conclusion

One could, like Chateaubriand, smile at Bonaparte's pleasure in being made a member of the Institute. But in so far as it is indicative of the scale of values of the future Emperor, it is highly relevant in any discussion of his attitude to science. When Napoleon divorced Josephine to marry Marie Louise, he was proud to be the husband of an arch-duchess and this pride was reflected in his pleasure in recruiting his staff from among the old nobility. In a similar way Bonaparte, member of the First Class of the Institute, was permanently prejudiced in favour of men of science in a way in which no subsequent ruler of comparable power has been. An example of this can be seen in the recruitment of his government and administration. For ministers he chose Laplace and Chaptal. In reorganizing education the chemist Fourcroy was invaluable and he was helped by the zoologist Cuvier. The naturalist Lacépède proved a capable administrator of the Legion of Honour, of which he was put at the head. On the other hand the republican general and mathematician Lazare Carnot was excluded from any part in the government except for two short periods in 1800 and 1815. Whether by appointing the mathematician Fourier[2] as prefect of Isère, Bonaparte was contributing to the progress of science is a debatable point. Yet by their positions in the Senate others

[1] 'mon école'. Las Cases, *Journal*, Napoléon, *Correspondance*, vol. xxxii, p. 327. *Journal*, trans., 1824, vol. i, Part 2, pp. 127-8.
[2] Bonaparte arranged for Berthollet to discuss this appointment tactfully with Fourier before it was made official on 2 January 1802 (J. J. Champollion-Figeac, *Napoléon et Fourier*, 1844, p. 22).

such as Berthollet and Monge were able to make some contri‐
bution to government and still have leisure for the pursuit of
scientific research.

Bonaparte went out of his way to encourage foreign men of
science to reside in France. When Rumford arrived in Paris at
the end of October 1801 he had spoken of his very flattering
reception by the scientists of the capital. In November he wrote:

> I have had the opportunity of making the acquaintance of several
> of the most distinguished characters now in power in this country.
> I am very intimate with Chaptal, the Minister of the Interior, and
> frequently see Talleyrand, the Minister for foreign affairs; I have
> dined with both of them and visit them often. Laplace and
> Berthollet are very civil and attentive to me and have each of
> them given me a dinner, where I have met most of the men of
> science of distinction in Paris.[1]

In short, Rumford was genuinely impressed by the new men
who had come to the fore under the Consulate. On the re‐
organization of the Institute in January 1803 Rumford was
nominated one of the seven foreign associates of the First Class.
When he visited France again later that year, he sent one of his
memoirs on heat to Bonaparte. Bonaparte took the trouble to
read this memoir and compose a letter in which he attempted
to discuss it intelligently.[2] The First Consul clearly wished to
create the impression that France's new government was par‐
ticularly favourable to science.

Some of Bonaparte's statements and actions suggest that he
believed that science transcends national frontiers. If the record
is examined more critically, however, it shows that he was
really concerned with enhancing the reputation of his govern‐
ment. In a few cases, notably those of Blagden and Humboldt,
Bonaparte's customary welcome of foreign scientists was tem‐
pered by suspicions of spying. He was not prepared to allow his
self-appointed role as an international patron of science to be
used as a means of threatening state security. Yet there can be
no doubt that he did care about the international prestige of
French science.

During the Consulate and Empire there was no one year

---

[1] British Museum, Add. MS. 8099, f. 108v.
[2] Napoléon, *Correspondance*, vol. ix, no. 7141.

comparable to the republican year II (1793–4), in which a national emergency brought about a great mobilization of talent and the successful application of science to a fairly wide range of industry. Yet, although the concentration of effort was less remarkable, its steady application for more than a decade built up the strength of French industry. Bonaparte had a genuine concern for the state of agriculture and industry which he was prepared to support by subventions and other awards. Furthermore France under Bonaparte enjoyed a period of political stability which to many was a welcome alternative to the anarchy which had followed the Revolution. The Continental system was a further stimulus to industrial development and the exploitation of France's natural resources. Freedom from competition allowed the cotton industry to rise from nothing to be almost the equal of that of England and in the chemical industry the Leblanc process could only come into operation sheltered by the prohibition of foreign soda.

Napoleon encouraged industry not only by subsidies and loans but also by the much cheaper reward of honour. Placing a high value on honour as a motivating power in society, he had inaugurated the Legion of Honour in the face of opposition from many of his advisers. If the majority of the awards went to men who had distinguished themselves by their bravery on the field of battle or by their competence in the civil service, Napoleon did not neglect men who had made important contributions to industry or technology, such as Oberkampf and Delessert. Yet when money was required, Napoleon was usually prepared to advance it. He was particularly generous to the textile manufacturer Richard (of the famous company Richard-Lenoir), to whom he lent a total of one and a half million francs. Although there are a few outstanding cases where the offer of a prize led to a new discovery or significant development, much more important was the provision of sums of money over a sufficiently long period to give the freedom to concentrate on particular problems. Financial backing was important in technology and in the field of pure science the value of a steady income is illustrated by Berthollet's ability to finance the work of the Society of Arcueil.

Napoleon's attitude to science may be contrasted with his attitude to literature. Evidence comes from various sources including Bourrienne,[1] Bonaparte's secretary up to the autumn of 1802. Himself a man of literary interest and accomplishment, Bourrienne complained of the slight esteem in which Bonaparte held men of letters. His attitude was roughly that such men could make up fine phrases or could arrange words to give a striking effect to the ear and yet be empty of meaning. Bonaparte had once thrown away a book he had started to read and complained to his secretary of the emptiness of much literary production:

> . . . These men are good for nothing under any government. Yet I will grant them pensions as is my duty as head of state; they provide an occupation for the idle and amuse them; but I will make Lagrange a senator—there's a brilliant man.

This antithesis of Bonaparte's toleration of literature and admiration of science is brought out in a document sent by the Emperor in 1807 in reply to the request of Champagny, then Minister of the Interior, who had asked for the authorization of a special school of literature and history at the *Collège de France*.[2] Napoleon contrasted the progress of science with the apparent lack of advance in literary studies. For this reason higher education was desirable in the former but of little use in the latter:

> Mathematics, physical and natural science, medicine, and jurisprudence are sciences because they are built on facts, observations, comparisons; because discoveries that they make successively accumulate from century to century and come to increase daily the domain of science . . . [yet] we have not surpassed the Greeks either in tragedy, comedy or in epic poetry.

Under the Consulate and Empire literary works and theatrical presentations were subjected to such an intolerant system of censorship that Napoleon should not have been surprised that no outstanding work was done in these fields when France was under his control. The two most distinguished French writers of the Napoleonic era, Chateaubriand and Madame de Staël, were strongly opposed to Napoleon and lived in virtual exile.

This situation may be contrasted with the state of affairs in science. It is not only that distinguished French scientists were not driven out of France; on the contrary they were loaded with

---

[1] Bourrienne, *Mémoires*, vol. v, pp. 126–7.
[2] Napoléon, *Correspondance*, vol. xv, no. 12416.

honours and given pensions. Bonaparte went out of his way to attract scientists from other countries. Rumford was encouraged to stay in France, Volta was given a medal, Chladni was given money. When in 1802 the *Bureau des Longitudes* awarded a prize of 6,000 francs to the Austrian astronomer Bury for his lunar tables, Bonaparte doubled the prize and Chaptal wrote Bury a letter telling him of the favourable treatment he would receive if he came to France.[1] The most famous example of the special place of science in the Napoleonic regime is the visit of the English scientist Sir Humphry Davy to France in 1813, a time when the French armies were particularly hard-pressed.

If Napoleon's attitude to science contrasts with his appreciation of literature, his appreciation of the graphic arts was even more limited.[2] He would judge a painting or a statue as a replica of nature and he saw little merit in the process of copying nature. Artists, nevertheless, were useful to Napoleon to the extent that they were able to portray his military victories and produce monuments to his glory. To a limited extent he may have valued the arts as a facet of national achievement but this was not something which he personally could understand. He had often said that the two things that had impressed him most were the pyramids of Egypt and the size of a circus giant. In other words, a feat of engineering and a question of magnitude were closer to Napoleon's sympathies and understanding than the greatest achievements of the arts.

There is substantial evidence that Napoleon favoured the pursuit of science. Sometimes his contact and influence was direct, often it was more remote. Yet French science, which came to the fore towards the end of the eighteenth century, continued to flourish under the Consulate and Empire and Napoleon claimed some of the credit for this. In retrospect one of the major weaknesses of the thesis that Napoleon supported the cause of science was the failure of the French educational system to provide adequate secondary education in science.[3] In the *lycées*, founded by Bonaparte in 1802, the emphasis was on

[1] Aulard, *Paris sous le Consulat*, vol. iii, p. 136.

[2] Chaptal, *Mes souvenirs sur Napoléon*, 1893, pp. 269–70.

[3] See especially the indictment by L. Pearce Williams: 'Science, Education and Napoleon I', *Isis*, xlvii (1956), 369–82, particularly pp. 371–2, 379–380. The record of the Consulate and Empire on *technical* education is rather better.

humanities, although mathematics also figured quite prominently. By 1808 forty-four *lycées* were in existence but only eight of these offered instruction in physics, chemistry or natural history and these courses were not well-attended. Even in Paris where the standard of science teaching was probably better than in any other part of France, a study of prizes awarded to senior pupils in the years 1809–12 shows that science played only a minor role. Pearce Williams has argued that 'when viewed against the provisions for the teaching of science in the Napoleonic schools' Napoleon's attempts to play the part of a patron of science can hardly be regarded as sincere. While there may be some justice in attributing to the head of state the imperfections of one aspect of one of his ministries, one can also see that the question of education only becomes of crucial importance from the long-term point of view.

The problem is probably most easily resolved by distinguishing education at different levels. Under the Directory, the Consulate and the Empire a boy of genius with mathematical ability had a fair chance of learning enough elementary mathematics to be in a position to receive the finest scientific education available anywhere in the world at the *École Polytechnique*. We shall see later how this happened to young men like Gay-Lussac and Arago. On the other hand at a lower level there was no crusade for science in the *lycées*. In any case parents may have been reluctant to direct their sons towards mathematics which was so often linked with a career in the artillery or the engineering corps,[1] when there were alternative careers open in civil administration. The final Napoleonic educational system was embodied in the so-called *Université Impériale*, which included education at all levels. Napoleon imagined that in entrusting this to Fontanes,[2] he would have a reliable servant. In fact many of the features of the educational system that emerged, including the minor role of science in secondary education, may be attributed directly to the influence of the Grand Master of the University, Fontanes.

[1] See, however, Chapter Two, where we find that in many cases, such as those of Biot and Arago, mathematics and science provided an *alternative* to (or even an escape from) a military career.

[2] The chemist Fourcroy probably expected to be appointed Grand Master of the 'University' but his former Jacobin sympathies made him suspect in the eyes of Napoleon.

Under Napoleon, especially in the years 1800–10, there was considerable mobility of society in France. A new nobility replaced and complemented the old nobility. Titles were conferred for sterling service to the state either in the army or at home. A subject of Napoleon might make his name in a variety of ways ranging from pure science to public administration. If he succeeded, he was rewarded not only financially but also with an honourable position in society. Stendhal, who witnessed Napoleon's government when in attendance at the Council of State, remarked on the spirit of emulation which the Emperor inspired in all sections of society. Merit was rewarded:

> The least pharmacist's boy, working in the back shop of his master, was inspired with the idea that if he made a great discovery, he would have the Cross [of the Legion of Honour] and would be made a Count.[1]

This book is about the chemist Berthollet and his circle at Arcueil. Berthollet lived on the income he received directly and indirectly from Napoleon. Berthollet was made a Count.

Bonaparte's support of science was not always consistent. Yet, whatever ambiguities remain in Bonaparte's position as a patron of science, it is as the patron of Berthollet that he appears in this book and of this patronage there can be no doubt.

[1] Stendahl, *Vie de Napoléon*, ed. L. Royer, 1929, p. 193.

CHAPTER TWO

The Men of Arcueil

Napoleon and the Leaders of the Arcueil Group

IN THE previous chapter we were concerned with the contact of Napoleon with the science and technology of his day and his general relationships with scientists. It is now time to look more closely at the particular scientists who were associated with Arcueil. The leaders of the Arcueil group, Berthollet and Laplace, were especially favoured by Bonaparte and it would not be out of place to look at this patronage (both direct and indirect) before considering the general background of the other men who became members of the Society of Arcueil.

This favour continued throughout the period of the Consulate and the Empire. Not only were Berthollet, Laplace and Chaptal all given particularly remunerative positions in the Senate, but in 1813 when Napoleon decided to award the Grand Cross of the Imperial Order of the Reunion to a favoured few, three of the four scientists who were deemed worthy of this honour were members of the Society of Arcueil: Laplace, Berthollet and Chaptal.[1] Nor was the honorary membership of Academies of foreign countries then under French control unrelated to political favour. In 1802 Chaptal and Laplace were nominated foreign associates of the Italian Institute[2] and in 1809 the Emperor's brother Louis, as King of Holland, gave approval to the nomination of a number of foreign associates of the Institute in Amsterdam; the two French names were those of Berthollet and Laplace.[3]

[1] *Le Moniteur*, 8 April 1813; the fourth scientist was Lagrange.
[2] Aulard, *Paris sous le Consulat*, 1903–9, vol. ii, p. 827.
[3] *Le Moniteur*, 24 May 1809. An alternative explanation of this choice would be simply that these were France's two most distinguished men of science.

Bonaparte and Berthollet

Bonaparte had first met Berthollet during the Italian campaign. Although the one was in the army and the other was a civilian, they were both under the orders of the Directorate in Paris. Bonaparte was genuinely interested in the new profession which Berthollet and Monge represented. Another bond between Bonaparte and Berthollet was that neither was purely French. Coming from Corsica and Savoy respectively, they had each learned what amounted to a dialect of Italian before coming into contact with the French language. Bonaparte's bad French was the subject of numerous comments but his native speech strengthened his contact with his subjects on the far side of the Alps. Berthollet's facility in Italian was useful when he was sent to Italy in 1796. He was later asked by the First Class of the Institute to translate an Italian work.[1] In a letter of 13 September 1797 to the Directorate, Bonaparte mentioned the civilian commissioners he had met and singled out Berthollet for recommendation as the president of an Academy of Rome—if the Directorate wished to have such an institution.[2] We may assume that Bonaparte had in mind Berthollet's knowledge of Italian and his university education at Turin as well as his personal qualities.

The work of the commissioners who followed the French army in Italy and organized on a large scale the removal of works of art and other objects of value to France was not seen by the French as robbery. When Berthollet and Guyton, collaborating with two members of the Class of Fine Arts of the Institute, wrote a report in 1802 on the restoration of a painting by Raphael, they used the following words:

> If a protective power had not taken care of several monuments of ingenious Italy, the name of Raphael would not have been widely known even in his own country . . . The arts, therefore, owe a great debt to the genius of the victory, who has gathered these scattered and neglected monuments to bring them together at the centre of the Republic, entrust them to an enlightened and watchful administration and present them as in a vast sanctuary to the

---

[1] *P.V. Inst.*, vol. ii, p. 591.
[2] Napoléon, *Correspondance*, vol. iii, no. 2192.

admiration of Europe and the study of those who aspire to the best in art.[1]

It had been Berthollet whom Bonaparte had chosen to organize the scientific commission that was to accompany the expedition to Egypt and apart from his scientific work he had been given a succession of administrative tasks that demanded absolute integrity. Berthollet's reputation for scrupulous honesty resulted in Bonaparte entrusting him with various tasks such as the safeguarding of valuables and the confiscation of goods; he was also concerned with a monetary system in Egypt and with Monge he was appointed inspector of the Mint.[2] It appears that he carried out all these tasks to the complete satisfaction of the commander-in-chief of the expedition.

Cuvier tells us that during Bonaparte's stay in Paris between the Italian and Egyptian campaigns, he would use his leisure to receive chemistry lessons from Berthollet.[3] Bonaparte from that time referred to him as 'my chemist' and, rather to Berthollet's embarrassment, considered him as a living source of all knowledge connected in any way with chemistry. If such a question arose, Bonaparte would say, 'I must ask Berthollet'. Bonaparte even relied on Berthollet for medical advice sometimes. Geoffroy de Saint-Hilaire records a conversation between Bonaparte and Berthollet on their last evening in Egypt. Bonaparte confided to the man of science:

> Something that I have never yet told you, Berthollet, is that these ideas of my youth come back to me at odd moments. I wanted at least to know if I really had any aptitude for science to the degree necessary to carry out my plans, and this is why I have employed all my spare time in hearing you talk about chemistry. But it has been to no avail that I have compelled myself to follow regular lessons, since I have only acquired a vague impression from these efforts.[4]

To understand the special bond between the two men it is not enough to think of Berthollet as a *savant* whose technical knowledge was always at the service of the French Republic nor to

[1] *Le Moniteur*, 23 February 1802.
[2] Napoléon. *Correspondance*, vol. iv, nos. 2762, 2766, 2871; vol. v, no. 3214.
[3] *Éloges*, vol. iii, pp. 205–6.
[4] *Lettres écrites d'Égypte*, ed. E. T. Hamy, 1901, Appendix 2, p. 242.

remind ourselves that Bonaparte received instruction in chemistry from him. Many men of science served the state after the Revolution. Bonaparte's educators can be numbered in dozens. Berthollet and Monge, however, shared with Bonaparte a bond which is usually found only in soldiers—they had shared the same campaigns. With a few exceptions Bonaparte always kept his fellow soldiers at a distance. A general who was treated familiarly by Napoleon might remind himself that Bonaparte too had once been a general. With Bonaparte's friends among the men of science there was no such danger, yet the bond was as close as between brothers in arms. This was hardly true of the Italian campaign where Monge and Berthollet as civilians followed behind the army. In the Egyptian campaign the bond was sealed. Here Bonaparte, officially commander-in-chief of the army, became in effect governor-general of Egypt. It was here that he first experienced supreme authority and he enjoyed loyal support from his civilian friends Monge and Berthollet.

Yet this was a military expedition. Battles had first to be fought and won before the country came under the French flag. The rigours of the climate, the desert and disease had all to be faced. In the army's progress through Egypt there were times when Monge and Berthollet were supplied with a carriage whilst the army and the other *savants* had to travel on foot. But in battle all were exposed to danger. Bonaparte in a letter to the Directorate singled out the courage of Monge and Berthollet in a major battle[1] and General Berthier in a despatch to the Minister of War also mentioned their bravery.[2] Even on the crossing to Egypt there had been military exercises and in a list of generals, commanders of gun batteries, etc. we find the order to Berthollet to take up his post at the powder magazine.[3]

When Bonaparte became First Consul he did not forget those who had served with him in Egypt, and his partiality towards them was well-known.[4] His aide-de-camp, Duroc, was appointed governor-general of his chateaux and later became Duke of Frioul; his chief of staff, Berthier, became Minister of

---

[1] Napoléon, *Correspondance*, vol. iv, no. 2834.
[2] *Réimpression de l'ancien Moniteur*, vol. xxix, p. 445.
[3] Napoléon, *Correspondance*, vol. iv, no. 2605.
[4] Schlabrendorf, Gustaf von Graf, *Bonaparte and the French People under his Consulate*, 2nd end., London, 1804, pp. 153–5.

War and he was also later awarded a dukedom and the principality of Neuchâtel; the infantry general Menou became administrator-general of the Piedmont; Denon, who had described the wonders of the Egyptian expedition, was appointed over the heads of senior men to be in charge of the museums and galleries of Paris and, despite the preference of the Council of State and the other two Consuls for another candidate, the printer Marcel, who had set up a printing office in Cairo, was designated by Bonaparte to be director of the state printing house with an annual salary of 60,000 francs. Monge and Berthollet were made Senators and when a small number of lucrative *sénatoreries* were created, each was nominated by Napoleon.

The favours conferred upon those who had shared the perils and triumphs of the Egyptian expedition may be contrasted with the fate of those who had been asked to go but had refused. They had not been far-sighted enough to foresee that the general in command of the army in Egypt would in a few years become the head of state. Bonaparte was a man of great generosity to his friends but also a man who seldom overlooked any slights experienced in his earlier career.

The engineer Prony, who had been associated with Berthollet and Laplace in the planning of the metric system, had refused Bonaparte's invitation to accompany him to Egypt.[1] His ambition was centred on the directorship of the *École des Ponts et Chaussées*. The director died during Bonaparte's absence in Egypt and Prony was appointed to succeed him. Prony kept this post when Napoleon was in power. Napoleon made use of him whenever a bridge, a canal or a new road was called for. The Emperor was not stupid enough to ignore the talents of a brilliant engineer, but his favour and his friendship were never extended to Prony. Despite a close friendship between Prony's wife and Josephine, Prony rose no further under Napoleon nor was he considered for one of the well-paid positions in the Senate. When other members of the section of mechanics of the First Class, including Monge, were made counts of the Empire or barons, Prony remained without a title. He had missed his opportunity.

If the expedition to Egypt marks the period of closest personal contact between Bonaparte and Berthollet, the statesman

[1] Parisot, art.: Prony, *Biographie universelle, Supplément*, vol. lxxviii, 1846.

did not lose sight of the scientist afterwards. The *Journal des Débats* of 8 February 1801, for example, reported that on the previous day Laplace, Lagrange, Monge, Berthollet and Prony in their capacity as governors of the *École des Ponts et Chaussées* had been called to Malmaison by the First Consul, where they had a long meeting on the subject of the development of canals in France. The next day Bonaparte left Paris to examine on the spot the project for the Saint Quentin canal, taking with him Monge and Berthollet.[1] There is nothing strange about a head of state seeking technical advice. The only name that stands out here as that of a man who had little knowledge of engineering or mathematics, and whose presence is to be explained rather in terms of personal favour, is Berthollet. During the period of the Empire, when Napoleon arrived back in Paris after a campaign or when he left Paris for Saint Cloud, he would hold a small reception (*petite entrée*). Among those habitually invited and later reported in close conversation with the Emperor were Berthollet and Laplace—right up until 1813, the year which saw the beginning of the final collapse of the Empire.[2]

Most important of all, when Berthollet was in debt in 1807, Napoleon, though out of France at the time, sent him 150,000 francs to clear his debt.[3] Without this aid there may never have been a Society of Arcueil. Berthollet's advice on chemical matters was always valued by Bonaparte. In August 1803 Bonaparte had said publicly that he would ask the opinion of Berthollet on the advisability of obtaining sugar from sugar-beet. This was duly noted by a Bourbon spy, who considered it as evidence that Bonaparte had lost his sanity![4] There is a letter dated 18 February 1808 in which Napoleon wrote that he had heard that sugar could be extracted from the maple and also from turnips. He asked Berthollet to carry out research on this question[5] with particular reference to the quality of the sugar

[1] Aulard, *Paris sous le Consulat*, 1903–9, vol. ii, p. 164.
[2] E.g. Marquis de Noailles, *Le comte Molé, 1781–1855. Sa vie, ses mémoires*, 4th edn., 1922, vol. i, pp. 130, 134.
[3] Napoléon, *Correspondance*, vol. xv, no. 12502. See also Chapter Six, p. 278.
[4] Remacle, *Relations secrètes des agents de Louis XVIII à Paris sous le Consulat (1802–3)*, 1899, p. 386.
[5] Napoléon, *Correspondance*, vol. xvi, no. 13580. Similarly Monge, who had also been made a Senator, was consulted on the manufacture of cannon, *ibid.*, vol. xxi, no. 17168.

obtained. Less serious was an analysis of bezoards carried out by Berthollet for the Emperor. The King of Persia had sent various gifts to Napoleon and among these were three bezoards. Napoleon considered that the most useful thing he could do with these curious objects would be to have a study made of their chemical composition. He accordingly handed them over to Berthollet and in due course a short report on them was published in the Arcueil *Mémoires*.[1] Napoleon considered that chemistry could serve the state in a wide variety of ways and in October 1808 we find Berthollet, at the Emperor's request, trying to detect invisible writing on papers intercepted by Napoleon's agents.[2]

An interesting example of Berthollet's role under the Empire as a consultant for chemical industry had been discovered by L. Pearce Williams.[3] In April 1807 Champagny as Minister of the Interior sent out a circular in the *Chambres consultatifs* established in many provincial towns, urging them to use their influence to establish Berthollet's method of bleaching by chlorine. On 28 April the *Chambre consultatif* of Tarare in the Rhône department wrote to the Minister that when they had used 'oxygenated muriatic acid' in bleaching muslin containing gold thread, this had produced permanent marks in the fabric. Champagny immediately (8 May) wrote to Berthollet for advice. Berthollet consulted his friend Widmer at the Jouy factory and was able to reply to the Minister on 4 June. The obvious solution to the problem (which may have been due to some impurity in the reagents) was to add the gold thread *after* the bleaching.

Berthollet did carry out some experiments on sugars at Arcueil and he also encouraged Proust in his research on the subject.[4] Arcueil never became a centre for applied scientific research but we do find members of the Arcueil group engaged in work of national importance. In 1810 Thenard was on a committee appointed by the First Class to examine a possible source of sugar in maize.[5] A more positive contribution was the production in 1812 of a booklet of instructions on the extraction

[1] *M.S.A.*, ii (1809), 448–54.
[2] Letter from Berthollet to Napoleon, 26 October 1808. Wellcome Historical Medical Library, Berthollet dossier, No. 67103.
[3] Private communication—Archives Nationales, F^{12}, 507.
[4] *Journal de physique*, lxxi (1810), 467.
[5] *P.V. Inst.*, vol. iv, pp. 412–13.

of indigo from woad. This was drawn up by a committee of five, four of whom were associated with the Arcueil group: Chaptal, Gay-Lussac, Thenard and Roard. Already in 1811 Candolle in Montpellier had been cultivating woad, which he gave to Bérard's father for his experiments on the extraction of indigo.[1]

Bonaparte and Laplace

Laplace had been the passing-out examiner for Bonaparte at the *École militaire* in Paris in 1785. Laplace had come into contact with Bonaparte again some ten years later at the meetings of the First Class. Bonaparte, then at the beginning of his political career, thought that the great mathematician would make a suitable Minister of the Interior; the choice of Laplace would, moreover, be appreciated in scientific circles where he was anxious to have support for the new regime. Laplace was not a success at the Ministry of the Interior. His appointment on 12 November 1799 was terminated six weeks later when Bonaparte nominated his own brother Lucien for the post. Lucien Bonaparte in turn was replaced by Chaptal, who in the course of four years in the Ministry rendered many important services to France.

Among the official letters written by Laplace as Minister of the Interior is one dated *30 brumaire an 8* (i.e. 21 November 1799), in which he refers to the liberation from superstition which is symbolized by the use of the republican calendar. Laplace wrote to the departmental authorities:

> Do not neglect any occasion of proving to your fellow-citizens that superstition will have no more cause for rejoicing than royalism over the changes made by the 18 brumaire. It is by continually ensuring the most meticulous observation of the laws instituting the national and decadal festivals, the republican calendar, the new system of weights and measures, etc., that you will justify the confidence of the government.[2]

It might have caused Laplace some embarrassment to have had

---

[1] *Notices des Travaux de l'Académie du Gard*, 1811, Part 1, 22–52; see especially pp. 23, 38 for references to Candolle and Chaptal.

[2] *Recueil des Lettres, Circulaires, Instructions, Arrêtés et Discours Publics émanés des Cns. Quinette, Laplace, Lucien Bonaparte et Chaptal, Ministres de l'Intérieur . . .*, vol. iii, p. 103. A. Aulard, *The French Revolution*, trans., 1910, vol. iv, p. 192.

this letter quoted a few years later when Bonaparte's policy towards the Church made expedient the return to the traditional calendar, a move fully supported by Laplace.

The kind of man needed in the Ministry of the Interior in 1799 was not someone who would debate minor points of justice but a man who would act promptly and forcibly. We may note the reference in the quotation above by Laplace to "the most meticulous observation of the laws". Looking back to the months of November and December 1799 from his exile at Saint Helena, Napoleon described Laplace in the following terms:

> Mathematician of the highest rank, Laplace was not long in showing himself an extremely poor administrator. From his first actions I realised that I had deceived myself. He sought everywhere for subtleties, had only problematic ideas, and carried the spirit of the 'infinitely small' into administration.[1]

As we shall see, Laplace was able to serve Bonaparte more usefully as a member of the Senate. Laplace was also called upon as a technical expert, e.g. on coinage.[2]

Laplace had several opportunities to dedicate his books to Bonaparte and each time the latter with some sincerity complimented the author. By contrast the majority of French scientists including Berthollet did not dedicate their books to the head of state and therefore such a dedication represents rather more than a formal gesture. The literary exchanges began when Laplace presented General Bonaparte with a copy of the first two volumes of the *Mécanique céleste*. They had appeared just before Bonaparte's return from Egypt and the first letter he wrote on his arrival back in Paris was a note dated 19 October 1799 thanking Laplace for his book.[3]

The dedication of a book to Bonaparte implied either that the book had been specially written at his suggestion or, as in the case of Laplace's works, that the contents would be appreciated by him either personally or as head of state. For Laplace to dedicate the third (1802) volume of his *Mécanique céleste* to Bonaparte was indeed a compliment. The dedication draws atten-

---

[1] *Oeuvres de Napoléon Ier à Sainte Hélène*, 'Consuls Provisoires', para III, *Correspondance*, vol. xxx, p. 392.

[2] Napoléon, *Correspondance*, vol. viii, no. 6451, 24 November 1802.

[3] *Ibid.*, vol. vi, no. 4384.

tion to the fact that the First Consul was a member of the First Class of the Institute and that he had had a scientific education. It refers to the useful function of science in society and ascribes to Bonaparte the role of an 'enlightened protector of science'. Bonaparte in his reply from Saint-Cloud on 26 November 1802[1] claimed that he had understood the volume as far as he had read it but that he would require several weeks if he were to read it fully. Laplace did not insert dedications in any of the other volumes of his *Mécanique céleste* but when the fourth volume was published in 1805, he sent a copy for Napoleon's library, which the Emperor, then in Milan, duly acknowledged.[2]

When Laplace published his highly technical *Théorie analytique des Probabilités* in 1812 it was with the following dedication:

To Napoleon the Great.

Sire, the kindness with which your majesty has deigned to receive the homage of my treatise on celestial mechanics has inspired me with the wish to dedicate to you this treatise on the calculus of probabilities. This fine calculus extends to the most important questions of life, which indeed for the most part, are only problems of probability. In this respect it should interest your majesty whose genius appreciates so well and so worthily encourages all that can contribute to the progress of enlightenment and public prosperity. I would go further and present this new homage based on the deepest gratitude and profound sentiments of admiration and respect . . .

If the language of this dedication seems extravagant, we should remember that this was written late in the period of the Empire, when such a style was common in addressing Napoleon. We might note the word 'gratitude' in the last sentence above. The Chancellor of the Senate was saying thank you for the social position and financial reward that favour with the Emperor had obtained for him. Napoleon's reply came from the front during the Russian campaign.[3] It was polite and not lacking in sincerity. Napoleon particularly welcomed the book as an important contribution to mathematics, the pursuit of which, he said, was linked to the prosperity of the State.

Napoleon referred to mathematics as the first of the sciences[4] and his admiration for Laplace and Lagrange was unfeigned.

[1] *Ibid.*, vol. viii, no. 6454. [2] *Ibid.*, vol. x, no. 8842.
[3] *Ibid.*, vol. xxiv, no. 19028. [4] *Ibid.*, vol. xiv, no. 12058.

There were, after all, some grounds for the complaint later made by Lamartine[1] that under the Empire mathematicians alone had power and influence:

Figures alone were permitted, honoured, protected and rewarded.

Napoleon's favours to Laplace extended to his family. Laplace's wife was appointed lady-in-waiting to Napoleon's sister, Elisa, Princess of Piombino and Lucca and later Grand Duchess of Tuscany. This meant that Madame Laplace was obliged to leave the Paris region from time to time (usually in the spring) during the period of activity of the Society of Arcueil.[2] Her absence probably brought Laplace into closer contact with the Berthollet family, all the more so as Laplace's son had also left home. The son had a commission in the artillery and was honoured by being selected as an aide-de-camp to the Prince of Wagram during the Russian campaign, and on 15 March 1814 he was appointed to Napoleon's personal staff.[3]

To say that Laplace enjoyed the patronage of Napoleon is not to say that the Emperor was always considerate or kind to the mathematician or even civil. It was hardly kind to tell Laplace that his wife was too old to wear a pretty dress,[4] but the interview recorded by Chaptal is outrageous in its lack of taste. In 1813 on his return from the battle of Leipzig Napoleon met Laplace and remarked how thin he had become. Laplace explained that his only daughter had died recently—'Oh! That is no reason for losing weight. You are a mathematician; if you work out the mathematics of this event you will see that it all adds up to zero.'[5] Such remarks are not calculated to inspire the unswerving devotion of subordinates and it is not surprising if Laplace sometimes whispered darkly about Napoleon's limitations in mathematics.

The Senate

In order to understand the social and political position of Berthollet and Laplace under the Consulate and Empire, it is

[1] 'Des destinées de la poésie', *Revue des Deux Mondes*, March 1834, *Oeuvres complètes de Lamartine*, vol. i, 1860, pp. 30–1.
[2] P. Marmottan (ed.), *Lettres de Madame de Laplace à Elisa Napoléon*, 1897.
[3] Service historique de l'Armée, Vincennes. Dossier: Général Charles Émile Laplace.   [4] Stendahl, *Vie de Napoléon*, 1929, p. 221.
[5] Chaptal, *Souvenirs sur Napoléon*, 1893, p. 342.

necessary to examine the structure and function of the Senate of which they were both members.

According to the first constitution of the Consulate the Senate was one of four recognized Assemblies, the others being the Legislative Body, the Tribunate and the Council of State. The Tribunate, containing many orators, had the function of discussion without the authority to vote. The Legislative Body was not empowered to debate but only to vote. There is evidence that the other bodies were jealous of the Senate. Its position as the highest ranking of the Assemblies was confirmed by the position of honour accorded to it at Napoleon's coronation in Notre Dame. Yet, if the Senate was first in the hierarchy after the Consuls (or later, the Emperor), the Council of State had more power in the day to day government of France. It is perhaps misleading to compare the two bodies since they fulfilled different functions; the Council of State was like a Cabinet whereas the Senate was the Upper Chamber. In nearly all cases Napoleon Bonaparte got what he wanted from each.

The Senate was to choose the Legislators, the Tribunes and even the next Consuls. Its chief purpose was to safeguard the Constitution and it was to decide whether measures referred to it by the Tribunate or the Government were in accordance with the Constitution. The Senators, of whom there were at first sixty, were appointed for life at an annual salary of 25,000 francs. They had to be at least forty years of age. When we hear of the feeble acceptance by the Senate of all the harsh measures proposed by Napoleon during the latter years of the Empire, particularly legislation relating to conscription, it must be remembered that, although no individual Senator could be removed from office, it would have been possible for the Emperor to have dissolved the Senate, as he did the other bodies, and even to have expected support for this, in view of the high salary of the Senators, as a gesture of public economy. Even more simply, if the Senate had persisted in opposing any important measures which Napoleon wished to introduce, he could have used his right to nominate Senators in such a way as to establish a majority in his favour.

Whereas the Legislature and the Tribunate were composed of able politicians, including prominent members of the Council of

Five Hundred and the Council of the Ancients[1] as well as orators and men of letters who were particularly prominent in the Tribunate, the Senate was reserved for men of distinction, including several men of science and philosophers. At a meeting with Bonaparte on 24 December 1799 a list of thirty-one names of Senators was proposed. The new Senators were to meet the next day to choose the other half of their colleagues. Apart from men of primarily political experience, drawn notably from the Council of Ancients, the first Senators included the scientists Berthollet, Laplace, Monge and Lacépède, the *idéalogues* Volney, de Tracy, Cabanis and Garat and the general Kellerman. Most of the original Senators were proposed by Sieyès. Bonaparte had only just gained political power and knew only very few administrators and men in civilian life and he therefore had to rely on a man of wider political experience. However, he knew Berthollet and Monge particularly well and he would have strongly supported their candidature.

The comparatively small number of Senators was a reaction against the large assemblies of the Revolution. The Senate thus formed an elite and their high salary was calculated to attract ambitious men and to serve as a suitable retiring ground for active politicians, even the Consuls themselves. The fact that the Senate met privately meant that it was not influenced by public opinion. It formed almost a new aristocracy, working in isolation and theoretically free from supervision and criticism. This isolation was a weak point and in the end led to its activities becoming ineffectual. The important place given to the Senate in the Constitution could have made it an effective centre of opposition to the government. It never became this. At the most it sometimes modified Bonaparte's demands. One of the few examples of independent action taken by the Senate occurred in 1806 when it sent a deputation to Berlin to urge Napoleon not to carry the war any further. Yet, despite its general subservience to the Emperor, the Senate maintained its primary position in the Constitution. It was the Senate which declared the First Consul Emperor and in 1814 it was the Senate which officially deposed the Emperor.

The Senate was never distinguished for the political activity of its members. When Roederer was nominated for the Senate,

These Councils had been established under the Directory.

Bonaparte suggested that he should refuse; he could do more useful work in the Council of State with his understanding of public affairs and his authority as a public speaker. Bonaparte is quoted as saying,

> The Senate is alright for men who have finished their career or who wish to write books. Laplace will be very good there, he will be able to work. Berthollet too will be well suited there.[1]

There is here a note of disparagement between a man of action and a politician about academic studies but the main point brought out is that the Senate, while participating in the government, was not thought of as a full-time occupation. It left sufficient leisure for the *savants* to pursue their studies. This point is repeated in Napoleon's reply to Chaptal's letter of resignation as Minister of the Interior. Writing on 6 August 1804 from Calais, Napoleon said:

> I wish to give you a proof of my satisfaction with your services and I have nominated you Senator. In this distinguished office, which will leave you more time to give to your work for the prosperity of our arts and crafts and the progress of our manufacturing industry, you will continue to render useful service to the State and to me.[2]

Berthollet was not a particularly active member of the Senate but his nomination by Bonaparte in February 1804 as vice-president of the Senate is of some historical importance since it enabled Berthollet to play a role in Bonaparte's plan for the acquisition of further power. This was the time of the discovery of a royalist plot to overthrow the First Consul. Moreau, who was suspected of being one of the conspirators, was arrested on 15 February and the news caused a public uproar. Bonaparte was not slow in using the turn of events to his advantage. On 18 February Berthollet had a formal audience with the First Consul at which he expressed the profound indignation of the Senate at the plot. The gravity of the situation justified stern measures, said Berthollet, who continued:

> The wish of the Senate is that, relying less on your courage which disregards all dangers, you should concentrate your attention not

[1] Sainte-Beuve, *Causeries du Lundi*, 3rd edn., Paris, n.d., vol. viii, p. 366.
[2] Napoléon, *Correspondance*, vol. ix, no. 7903.

only on affairs of state, but you should pay some regard to your personal safety, which is the same as that of the state.[1]

Continuing this charade, Bonaparte made a reply in which he suggested that France 'would have been in a sorry plight if the attempt had succeeded because the conspiracy had been chiefly directed against the glory, the liberty [*sic*] and the destiny of the French people'. Bonaparte had long ceased to have any private life; his whole life, he said, was dedicated to fulfilling the duties which the French people had imposed on him. These public statements, prominently reported in *Le Moniteur*, prepared the ground for the end of the Consulate and the beginning of the Empire.

In 1803 Bonaparte founded the system of *Sénatoreries*, fifteen districts into which the whole of France was divided for the purpose of legal appeals. These appointments provided an additional income of 20,000 to 25,000 francs, thus doubling the ordinary senatorial salary. They were given to senators as a mark of special favour. The only men of science to have them were Berthollet, Monge and Lacépède, the latter as an appreciation of his administrative duties in connection with the Legion of Honour. Berthollet was given the *sénatorerie* of Montpellier. The income was derived from land in the departments of the *sénatorerie*, although, as the following details show, in Berthollet's case half the income was derived from land in the Paris region:

Aveyron	641 fr.
Hérault	8180 fr.
Pyrénées Orientales	2492 fr.
Eure et Loir	6855 fr.
Seine et Marne	4522 fr.
TOTAL	22690 fr.

Bonaparte had originally envisaged the duties of such senators to be a minimum period of residence of two months every two years in the *sénatorerie*[2] but this was later increased by a *senatus consultus* to a residence of three months every year. Bonaparte wanted from each senator a report on conditions in all the

[1] *Le Moniteur*, 19 February 1804.
[2] Napoléon, *Correspondance*, vol. viii, no. 6461.

departments of the *sénatorerie*. They were to find out what the local people thought of the government, what was their attitude to religion, conscription, the tax on the upkeep of roads, etc. Such a report could probably have been given with greater authority by the local prefect but an additional duty of the senator was to report directly on the character, conduct and talent of all government employees in the region, including the magistrates and the prefects. Obviously senators given such a task had to be completely trustworthy and have considerable tact.

As the duties required some local knowledge, Bonaparte tried in his appointments to choose Senators who knew something of the region they were to visit. It may seem strange that the *sénatorerie* of Montpellier should be given to Berthollet and not to Chaptal, who was also in favour and who had lived for many years in Montpellier. The explanation is simply that the list of appointments was published on 12 June 1804 when Chaptal was still Minister of the Interior. He did not enter the Senate until 7 August 1804. It was perhaps Berthollet's medical qualifications which suggested his suitability for Montpellier, a university town famous since the Middle Ages for its Faculty of Medicine.

In addition to their extra salary the Senators were provided with a large house, often the most palatial of the region. The official residence of the Senator of Montpellier was the bishop's palace at Narbonne and Berthollet devoted large sums of money to its renovation.[1] Napoleon intended the *sénatorerie* to be a means of enhancing the reputation of the Senate in the provinces and an imperial decree of 24 July 1804 laid down in detail the honours that were to be received by Senators on first entering their *sénatorerie*. The Senator was to arrive in a carriage accompanied by his suite. He was to be met by the local commander, troops were to line the route and there was to be a salute of guns.

Berthollet first went to Montpellier in 1805.[2] On 14 May he presided at a meeting of the Electoral College of the Pyrénées

---

[1] Archives Nationales, O^2. 1351.
[2] This mission interrupted a controversy with Proust on the composition of sulphides: 'Un voyage m'oblige de suspendre la suite de cette discussion', *Journal de physique*, lx (1805), 351.

Orientales department. The purpose of the assembly was to present suitable candidates for the Senate and the Legislative Body. At the time of Berthollet's visit Fourcroy, as Councillor of State responsible for Public Instruction, was on a tour of inspection of schools in the south of France. On 21 May he wrote from Montpellier that he had met Berthollet and his wife there and they had had dinner together with the local prefect.[1]

After 1806 Berthollet continued to enjoy the financial benefits of his *sénatorerie* without fulfilling the duties of residence at Montpellier. The register of attendances of the Institute shows that for the rest of the period of the Empire he was seldom away from Paris and never for more than two or three weeks. One of his absences in November–December 1808 was when he was appointed by Napoleon to preside at the Electoral College of his native department of Mont Blanc from 1 to 11 December. The possession of the *sénatorerie* involved Berthollet in a considerable amount of property dealing. Correspondence now in the *Archives Nationales*[2] reveals that Berthollet was constantly involved in the exchange of property attached to his *sénatorerie*.

Laplace played a rather more conspicuous part in the Senate than Berthollet. In November 1800 he was elected President of the Senate for one year. In 1802 Bonaparte was planning to prolong his tenure of power but only the Senate could give legality to such a change. He was relying on Laplace[3] and a few other favourites to urge their colleagues in the Senate to give him the Consulate for life and the right to nominate his successor. In August 1803, when Bonaparte returned to Paris, he received formal addresses from the Senate, the Tribunate and the Legislative Body. It was Laplace, then vice-president of the Senate, who was the spokesman of that body in welcoming the return of the hero.[4]

In 1800 Laplace was secretary of the Senate. Under a reorganization of the Senate the position of secretary-general was abolished and that of Chancellor created. In September 1803 Laplace was appointed Chancellor, initially for a period of six years, with the duties of responsibility for the records of the

---

[1] *Revue des Pyrénées*, xviii (1906), 364.
[2] Archives Nationales, O². 1351, O². 1379.
[3] J. Thiry, *Le Sénat de Napoléon*, pp. 103–4.
[4] *Le Moniteur*, 17 August 1803.

Senate. If other senators required a certificate of their place of residence or if they needed a passport they had to go to him. Laplace's duties also included affixing the seal of the Senate to all official documents. He had a salary of 6,000 francs a month and was provided with a suite of rooms in the Luxembourg Palace. Laplace first took up residence there in the winter of 1807–8. In 1809, when Laplace's office as Chancellor came to an end, he was re-appointed for a further six years by Napoleon. The creation of the *sénatoreries* brought the annual budget of the Senate to 5 million francs. The regulation of this large sum required a council of administration including the Chancellor and the treasurer (Chaptal). They met Bonaparte several times each year to discuss the finances in detail.

Apart from Laplace's duties as Chancellor, his contribution towards the abolition of the republican calendar is probably Laplace's most notable contribution in the Senate.[1] In July 1800 the consuls had ordered that it should no longer be obligatory to observe the tenth day of each republican *décade* as a day of rest and in 1802 after the Concordat the official day of rest of public servants was made the Sunday. By the end of 1804 when Napoleon had been proclaimed Emperor and crowned in Notre Dame in the presence of Pope Pius VII, the time had come to abolish the secular calendar in favour of one which fitted better with Napoleon's ideas on the close relation between Church and State. So fundamental a change as that of the calendar had to be approved by the Senate and the project of a return to the Gregorian calendar starting from 1 January 1806 was read to the Senate on 31 August 1805. This was presented as desirable because of a minor technical difficulty in the republican calendar and also because France did not want permanently to be out of harmony with the rest of Europe. A special committee under the chairmanship of Laplace was set up by the Senate to examine the question. There was a certain irony in this appointment, since Laplace had helped to devise the republican calendar. Yet he could be relied on to carry out the wishes of the Emperor. Moreover, he could speak, by virtue of his scientific eminence and his position at the *Bureau des Longitudes* with the voice of the technical expert. In his report to the

[1] *Procès-Verbaux du Comité d'Instruction Publique de la Convention Nationale*, vol. vi, pp. 208–13.

Senate on 9 September 1805 Laplace remarked that one of the great advantages of the republican calendar was its unit of ten days. Now that this had been abandoned in practice, there was an additional reason to return completely to the Gregorian calendar. He assured the Senate that no change was contemplated in the republican weights and measures. The Senate obediently approved the reform. Laplace's association with the abolition of the republican calendar stood him in good stead under the Restoration and probably made it easier for Louis XVIII to overlook his close association with the Napoleonic regime.

Bonaparte and Chaptal

Under the Consulate Chaptal played a leading part in France's internal affairs. He was closely in touch with Bonaparte but he was never merely a subordinate ready to carry out the wishes of the First Consul. Like several other of Bonaparte's early ministers he played the role of a tutor. Bonaparte being a young man with exclusively military experience was only too willing to learn from his more experienced ministers.[1] Bonaparte believed in making himself proficient in each department of state and he would closely question every minister so that in the end he understood the principles and even remembered the details of their departments. Chaptal was able to give the First Consul particularly good advice on the needs of French industry. Since the Revolution Chaptal had been a leading advocate of the policy of making France independent of imports from the colonies. This policy was carried to extremes under the 'Continental system' but there is no doubt that it stimulated applied science in France.

Chaptal had been a wealthy man before the Revolution. He subsequently lost most of his money but his business acumen and a lucky turn of events brought about the restoration of his fortune. He was therefore never in the position of Berthollet and Laplace whose fortunes were largely dependent on the favours of Bonaparte. Chaptal consequently had greater independence. Apart from his scientific work he was one of the great men of the Napoleonic age. His administrative ability made him worthy of

[1] Chaptal, *Mes souvenirs sur Napoléon*, 1893, pp. 56, 225.

his key position of Minister of the Interior during the Consulate. A book on Napoleon's ministers classes Chaptal with Talleyrand and Fouché as 'the great'.[1]

Bonaparte and Humboldt

Chaptal tells us[2] that Bonaparte always looked upon Humboldt as a Prussian spy. Every time he met him he asked him his name, although he knew it all the time; he would then pass on to speak to someone else. Another calculated snub was his remark 'You are interested in botany? So is my wife.' Under the Empire Humboldt was said to be the most famous person in Europe after Napoleon. Perhaps Napoleon resented this comparison but probably the hostility towards the foreigner was based on nationalistic and personal grounds.

In view of Napoleon's persistent coldness towards Humboldt it is interesting to have manuscript evidence[3] of an attempt by Humboldt to win some measure of recognition from the Emperor. On 1 February 1808 he sent a copy of the French edition of his *Aspects of Nature*, which had just been published, to Napoleon, accompanied by a letter in which he spoke of his scientific work and his plans for publication:

> Insurmountable difficulties have held up the publication of the historic part of my travels. I hope, however, to be able to present it soon to Your Majesty together with the volume of my astronomical observations and the Political Essay on the Kingdom of New Spain, which is being printed now in Paris. In the meantime I presume, Sire, to submit to the Attention of Your Majesty specimens of three atlases which relate to my travels . . .

He ends:

> . . . Imbued with sentiments of gratitude and admiration which are inspired by the generous interest and the protection which Your Majesty deigns to grant to the sciences that I study, I shall strive unceasingly for a life to which is attached not only the glory of the name of France, but the progress of the civilization of mankind.

---

[1] J. Savant, *Les Ministres de Napoléon*, 1959. Perhaps to classify these three men together does Chaptal less than justice on the moral plane.

[2] *Op. cit.*, pp. 382–4.

[3] Wellcome Historical Medical Library, Humboldt dossier, no. 67101. I must thank M. Théodoridès for drawing my attention to this letter.

This plea for values which rise above nationalism may not have passed unnoticed. Napoleon did not ignore the book. He kept it for a month and then sent it together with Humboldt's letter to Monge with a request that he should let him have his opinion of it.

A crisis came one day in the latter years of the Empire when Napoleon ordered Savary, then Minister of Police, to expel Humboldt from Paris within 48 hours. Humboldt immediately went to Chaptal as a friend who was in close touch with Napoleon. Chaptal found an opportunity that same evening to intervene. At a reception at the Tuileries the Emperor took him to one side and asked for the latest news in the world of science. Chaptal replied pointedly that there was little new work and if Humboldt was prevented from publishing an account of his travels in central America, science in Paris would be at a complete standstill. Napoleon questioned whether this work was really as important as that and Chaptal replied in the same extravagant vein with the following testimonial:

> M. Humboldt has a knowledge of all the sciences and when he travels it is like the entire Academy of Sciences on tour.

Chaptal was also careful to point out that France had become Humboldt's adopted country. His important work had been assembled in Paris; not only did he write in French but he employed French engravers, artists and printers. Chaptal also reassured the Emperor that Humboldt's relationships with foreigners were entirely in connection with his scientific work and had no political implications. He succeeded in persuading Napoleon that Humboldt was an asset to France and the expulsion order was cancelled.

The Patronage Enjoyed by Berthollet and Laplace at the Beginning of Their Careers

Both Berthollet and Laplace as young men had owed their advancement to patronage from persons of influence and it is not difficult to interpret the foundation of the Arcueil circle as a gesture of repayment of their debt to another generation.

Berthollet had arrived in Paris in 1772 without knowing anyone of influence and without even a helpful letter of introduction.

As his interests at the time lay in medicine, he tried to obtain an introduction to one of the eminent medical men of the capital. Remembering that the distinguished physician Tronchin had originally come from Geneva, not far from his native Savoy, he approached him in the spirit of a fellow countryman in a foreign land. Tronchin immediately took to the young Berthollet, whose lack of a formal introduction was compensated for by his upright character and his obvious intelligence. Tronchin was the personal physician to the Duke of Orleans and it was the latter who recommended Berthollet to Madame de Montesson as her personal physician. This post provided not only a salary and a certain security and leisure for scientific work, it also enabled Berthollet to have a room which he was able to fit out as a laboratory. Berthollet was later to help to repay the early patronage of Tronchin by his particularly cordial relations with the younger men of science of Geneva. At one time Geneva almost became one of the outposts of the Arcueil group.

The Duke of Orleans had a reputation as a patron of science and when in 1781 a vacancy occurred in the section of chemistry of the *Académie des Sciences*, Berthollet was able to count on the support of his patron in addition to his own diligence in reading memoirs to the *Académie*, and he was duly elected. It is doubtful whether Berthollet would have secured the appointment in 1784 of superintendent of dyeing (at 6,000 livres per annum one of the best paid scientific posts in the country) if he had not been able to count on the influence of the Duke of Orleans.

Laplace's first patron after his arrival in Paris was d'Alembert, an excellent mathematician and a man of influence. It was through d'Alembert, for example, that Lagrange was brought to Berlin as the star of the Prussian Academy of Sciences under Frederick the Great. Laplace was suitably furnished with several letters of recommendation to d'Alembert but found they were ignored. In 1769 he addressed to the older mathematician a memoir on the general theory of mechanics. When d'Alembert read this he could not help being impressed and sent for the author. A young man who could do work like this deserved his support and within a matter of days Laplace was nominated professor of mathematics at the *École Militaire* in Paris. The school was reorganized in 1776 and although his teaching post was eliminated, he was granted an annual pension of 600 livres.

G

By then he also received an annual income of 500 livres by virtue of his position in the *Académie des Sciences*, to which he had been elected in 1773.

Laplace's first attempt to enter the *Académie* had been in 1772 but he had been beaten by Cousin. Laplace's reaction to this rebuff from the official body of French science was to try through his patron d'Alembert[1] to obtain a salaried position at the Berlin Academy of Sciences. Lagrange in Berlin was very hesitant about taking on the young Laplace and negotiations came to nothing. Fortunately another vacancy arose in 1773 and Laplace entered the *Académie* on 23 April of that year as *adjoint* in the section of mechanics. Ten years later he was promoted to *associé* and on 23 April 1785 he entered the highest grade of *pensionnaire*.

An interesting case of patronage which has already been fully studied[2] is that provided by Laplace's succession to the post of examiner at the *École Militaire*, previously held by Bézout, who died in September 1783. The appointment was in the hands of the Minister of War. Laplace's tactics in organizing support for his candidature were governed by his friend Blouin, a high-ranking civil servant in the Department of the Navy, who was able to provide him with some inside information. He was also helped by Bochard de Saron, an honorary member of the *Académie*, some other members of the *Académie* and a few other powerful friends. It was known that Bézout himself had favoured Laplace as his successor. Although Laplace was successful in obtaining the position at the *École Militaire*, a second post previously held by Bézout and also solicited by Laplace, that of examiner to the Navy, went to Gaspard Monge, who already had two teaching posts. Although this appointment had the effect of bringing Monge permanently to Paris, where he became associated with the Lavoisier circle, it can have done little to win him the friendship of Laplace.

Finally, it was through the patronage of the president of the Paris *Parlement*, Bochard de Saron, that Laplace had his first book published: *Théorie du mouvement et de la figure elliptique des*

---

[1] Lagrange, *Oeuvres*, vol. xiii, 1882, pp. 254–6, 260, 263. D'Alembert wrote of Laplace in the following terms to Lagrange: 'Ce jeune homme a beaucoup d'ardeur pour la géometrie, et je lui crois assez de talent pour s'y distinguer' (1 January 1773).

[2] Duveen and Hahn, *Isis*, xlviii (1957), 416–27.

planètes (1784).[1] Laplace was now firmly launched on his career. After the Revolution he was to be to younger men what d'Alembert and Bochard de Saron had been to him as an unknown and poorly paid junior.

Social Advance through Science

When considering how the various men who came to be associated with each other at Arcueil had entered upon their scientific careers, it is not irrelevant to consider if any social advancement was involved. Was science in France at the beginning of the nineteenth century a career which gave social recognition? In England Sir Humphry Davy was the only man of his generation to be knighted for his services to science, although of the older generation we should not forget Sir Joseph Banks, President of the Royal Society, who had been rewarded with a baronetcy in 1781. In France of the older generation, although rather younger than Banks, were Berthollet, Laplace and Chaptal, who were loaded with honours by Napoleon and given political posts in many ways equivalent to a state pension. Of the possibilities of social mobility from the bottom of the ladder to the top there can hardly be a better example than Laplace, the peasant's son who was honoured with a hereditary title. Of course the overthrow of the aristocracy at the time of the French Revolution followed by Napoleon's plan to create a new nobility, favoured such social mobility. Combined with this social ferment there was in the case of Laplace a more than common pliancy and understanding of political expediency, so that the man who had been made a Grand Officer of the Legion of Honour and a Count of the Empire by Napoleon, was promoted under Louis XVIII to Grand Cross of the Legion of Honour and made a Marquis!

Of all the fifteen members of the Society of Arcueil, only Humboldt had been born into the nobility. Yet he was happier living in a garret in a back street in Paris than in the court circles of Berlin or Potsdam. Humboldt never found class a barrier to scientific communication any more than he felt age to be a barrier. He was prepared, for example, at the age of thirty-five to admit the superiority of Gay-Lussac as his

[1] *Op. cit.*, p. xix.

collaborator regardless of his inferior social position or the fact that he was ten years younger than himself.

Gay-Lussac's father, as *avocat du Roi*, had become a suspect at the time of the revolution and had lost his source of income. Gay-Lussac therefore received his early education under rather straitened circumstances. When he entered the *École Polytechnique* he had to live on the small state allowance supplemented by private lessons. From Berthollet's assistant he became his leading disciple and it was not surprising that when Berthollet died, he bequeathed his ceremonial sword to Gay-Lussac. The gift of the sword which went with the title of Peer of France was intended as a symbolic gesture. The title of Peer was not hereditary but Berthollet felt that his brilliant pupil was worthy of the same honour that he had received. Yet for many years Gay-Lussac received no recognition from the French government for his services to science. According to his biographer Arago, the reason which prevented Gay-Lussac being nominated as a Peer was his daily employment on the manual operations of assaying at the Mint. Eventually in 1839 Gay-Lussac did become a peer for 'services to the State'. It might be tempting to contrast Gay-Lussac's eventual wealth through a variety of appointments and a title with the period when he was reported to have worn clogs. The clogs, however, were not a sign of extreme poverty but merely a protection of which Gay-Lussac availed himself against the damp floor of a basement laboratory.

Thenard was of humbler origins than Gay-Lussac. He was a peasant who had come to the capital in search of an education. With a few *sous* a day he could hardly afford even the cheapest *pension*. The traditional story is that when Thenard was trying to solve the problem of his keep by soliciting from Vauquelin the job of bottle washer, Fourcroy's sisters who kept house for Vauquelin, took pity on him and took him in to help in the kitchen as much as in the laboratory. Thenard gradually rose in the social scale through his research and teaching of chemistry. In 1825 Thenard and Poisson, colleagues at the *École Polytechnique*, were both created barons. Thenard was nominated as a Peer of France in 1832.

Medical Education as an Entry to Science

It is interesting to see how many of the Arcueil group were originally destined for a medical career. If we go back to the sixteenth century, we find men of such various accomplishments as Agricola, Brunfels and Copernicus receiving a medical education. This path into science continued into the nineteenth century, although it is true that not all the members of the Arcueil group described below actually pursued their medical studies very far.

Pride of place must be given to Berthollet, who graduated in the Faculty of Medicine at Turin in 1768. In order to practise medicine in France he had to take the degree of doctor of medicine again and ten years later he graduated M.D. in Paris with a dissertation on wines. He continued to take an interest in medical matters after he had made his name in chemistry. A letter from him on the treatment of various diseases was read at a meeting of the First Class on 5 May 1798, just after the expedition to Egypt set sail. During this expedition Berthollet's medical training was sometimes called on. Back in Paris we find him sitting on committees of the First Class concerned with questions such as the vaccine for smallpox.[1] Nevertheless medicine was very much a subsidiary interest for Berthollet, whose international reputation was based on his chemical work.

Of the same generation as Berthollet was Chaptal, whose uncle in Montpellier was a physician with a considerable local reputation. The high esteem with which he was regarded as well as his sizeable fortune led Chaptal to take up the study of medicine with the idea of succeeding to his uncle's practice. He tells a story, no doubt a common tale in the lore of medical students, that as he was about to dissect a corpse, the hand moved and the head was slowly shaken. After this experience he abandoned anatomy. He continued, nevertheless, with his other medical studies at Montpellier and after three years in 1776 he defended a thesis for his first degree. Three months later he received the degree of doctor of medicine. He then persuaded his uncle

---

[1] Berthollet, Percy and Hallé, 'Exposition des faits recueillis jusqu'à present concernant les effets de la vaccination, et examen des objections qu'on a faites en différens temps, et que quelques personnes font encore contre cette pratique' (Lu le 17 aôut 1812), *Mém. Inst.*, 1812, Pt. 2, 227–88.

to allow him to go to Paris for two years. Here he mixed in literary circles but he did not neglect altogether his post-graduate medical education. He attended courses on gynaecology, but he also attended various courses on chemistry—that given by Bucquet at the *École de Médecine*, another by Mitouard in his private laboratory in the rue de Beaune and another by Sage at the Mint. He associated closely with the crystallographer and mineralogist Romé de Lisle and his enthusiasm for chemistry became such that the archbishop of Narbonne, who was president of the Languedoc parliament, nominated him as the first professor of chemistry at Montpellier. Chaptal prolonged his stay in Paris to acquire a more detailed knowledge of chemistry and on returning to Montpellier his lectures were an immediate success. His career was now clear. His uncle, who still had hopes of making him his successor in his medical practice, died in 1788 leaving him a small fortune.

Poisson too had an uncle in the medical profession. Poisson's family decided that he should become a surgeon and he was sent to his uncle at Fontainebleau to learn the practice of surgery. Poisson relates that his uncle, in order to give him practice in the use of the knife in bleeding, told him to begin by cutting the ribs of a cabbage leaf. Such was Poisson's lack of any kind of practical skill that even this was beyond him. On another occasion he was asked to observe the treatment of a child, who subsequently died. The distress which this caused him convinced him that he could not pursue his medical career any further and he returned to his native village. It happened that his father, a minor civil servant, received the *Journal de L'École Polytechnique*. It was by reading this that the young Poisson realized that his vocation lay in mathematics.

Candolle came to Paris in the first instance to study medicine. This was a reputable career and it was with this object in mind that his father was willing to allow him to leave home and to support him. Candolle was, however, a sensitive person, who could not remain unmoved in the presence of human suffering. In a letter to his parents, for example, in 1798 he reported[1] that he had witnessed two drastic surgical operations at the *École de Médecine* and he could still see in his mind the blood flowing and hear the screams of the patients. Medicine was, moreover, a

---

[1] Candolle, *Mémoires et Souvenirs*, Geneva and Paris, 1862, p. 539.

career which imposed a tremendous responsibility on those who practised it. Candolle already had other interests before he came to Paris. Living for some time in the Swiss countryside, he had conceived a passion for botany. In Paris at the *Muséum d'Histoire Naturelle* there were facilities for pursuing further his studies in this field. Candolle felt a relief that here was an occupation where a mistake could not result in the death of a patient.

Dulong was the youngest member of the Arcueil group to consider medicine as a career. He had originally entered the *École Polytechnique* with the intention of becoming an artillery officer, but his health was badly affected by over-work and he had to abandon the course before the end of the second year. His illness brought him into contact with medicine, which he began to study. Arago describes how Dulong began to practise medicine in one of the poorer districts of Paris. His practice increased as if by magic but his small amount of capital decreased in proportion, since the tender-hearted Dulong did not insist on his patients paying for their treatment. He even opened an account with a local pharmacist so that his poorer patients could get the prescriptions which he made out dispensed there. Finding himself penniless, Dulong turned to the sciences, mistakenly thinking that he could pursue science without continual expenditure. This might have been partly true of botany, to which he first turned, but when he passed on to chemistry and physics, he was to find that the construction of apparatus was to be a continual source of financial worry.

Military Careers and Science

A survey of science at the time of Bonaparte cannot ignore the fact that in the period 1792–1815 France was almost continuously at war. Military considerations and science met in various ways but at the moment we need only consider the effect of the Revolutionary and Napoleonic wars on the careers of the young men of Arcueil. Were they all unmoved by the call to arms to save France from invasion by foreign armies or later by the 'glory' attached to extending the area of French rule in Europe? Was the work of, say, Berthollet and Chaptal in 1793–4 on the exploitation of saltpetre for gunpowder not paralleled by any later military exploits of the younger generation at

Arcueil? The answer is of course that only in exceptional cases would a man on active service have had the leisure in the midst of the Napoleonic wars to contribute to discussions at Arcueil. Malus managed this without formally leaving the army. Yet several other members of the Arcueil group had originally intended to bear arms.

In all cases the transition from a military to a scientific career was possible through the structure of French higher education and notably through the *École Polytechnique*. Biot, originally destined by his father for a career in commerce, had not found the prospect attractive and in 1792, at the age of eighteen, he had volunteered to join the army as a gunner. After a year of active service he was able to return to Paris, where he took the entrance examination for the newly founded *École Centrale des Travaux Publics*, shortly to become the *École Polytechnique*. His mathematical talent soon became obvious and on graduation he was given a teaching post where he could serve his country equally well. Teaching and research were to be Biot's major activities for the rest of his life.

The career of Malus was in some ways similar, with the important difference that Malus was originally intended for a military career and he was the only professional soldier in the Arcueil group. In 1793 he had been brilliantly successful in the entrance examination for the school of military engineering of Mézières. Unfortunately his family connections rendered him suspect to the revolutionary government and, seeing that his career as an officer would be blocked for political reasons, Malus had volunteered as a sapper, in which capacity he helped in the construction of fortifications at Dunkirk. Here his talent was recognized by the officer in charge and he was given the opportunity of entering the *École Polytechnique*. His higher education in science entitled him to a commission in the corps of engineers, where he was promoted to captain in 1796.

Malus was sent with the army to Egypt where he kept a diary. He also took part in the expedition to Syria and we may give his description of the capture of Jaffa by the French troops to show that, although a professional soldier, he was not blind to the miseries and cruelties of war:

> The soldiers, scattered through all parts of the city, killed men, women, children, old persons, Christians and Turks; everything

that bore the human form was the victim of their fury. The tumult of carnage, the broken doors, the houses shaken by the noise of the firing and of arms, the cries of the women, the father and the child overthrown one on the other, the violated daughter on the corpse of her mother; the smoke of dead bodies burned in their garments which had been set on fire, the smell of blood, the groans of the wounded, the cries of the conquerors disputing together over the spoils of their expiring prey, infuriated soldiers responding to the cries of despair by exclamations of rage and redoubled blows; lastly, men satiated with blood and gold, falling down in mere weariness on the heaps of corpses—such was the spectacle which this unfortunate city presented until night.[1]

After Malus' return home he was given various postings in the north of France until 1806, when he was appointed second in command of the fortifications at Strasbourg. He was able to apply his knowledge of higher mathematics to some of the problems of the fort of Kehl commanding the Rhine. In 1809 he was transferred to Paris. Even before this, however, Malus had been able to pay regular visits to the capital in his capacity as examiner in descriptive geometry (1805) and descriptive geometry and physics (1806–11) at the *École Polytechnique*, posts that he no doubt obtained through the good offices of his old friend, Monge. These dates are of some importance, since we know that, although Malus was not living permanently in Paris till 1809, he was staying in Paris at the time of his historic discovery of the polarization of light in 1808.

Descotils, who had come with his father to Paris at the beginning of the Revolution, had begun to receive instruction in chemistry and physics from Vauquelin and Charles respectively. At the end of 1792 at the age of nineteen he was conscripted for service as a naval rating and eventually found himself stationed at Cherbourg. In 1794 a friend advised him to take the entrance examination for the *École des Mines*, which had just been reorganized by the government. He received notice of promotion in the navy on the same day as he heard that he had passed the entrance examination for the *École des Mines*. According to Gay-Lussac, there was no real question of choice. His previous acquaintance with science was enough to convince him that his career lay here rather than at sea. Yet once more it is

[1] Extract from Malus' diary given by Arago, *Biographies of distinguished scientific men*, trans., 1857, p. 367.

interesting to find the higher educational facilities of Paris in the constructive period after the Terror providing an alternative to military service.

It had been the ambition of a military career that had brought Arago to the *École Polytechnique*. He relates in his auto-biography how as a schoolboy he had approached a very young officer of the corps of engineers and asked him presumptuously how it had been possible for one so young to obtain a com-mission. He was told about the *École Polytechnique* and the young Arago devoted all his energies in the next few years to passing the entrance examination. In 1803 the astronomer Méchain had met Arago's father and had given him the advice that his son should take up a career as a military engineer or in the artillery but not in science as this was too difficult and required a special vocation. Such advice stung Arago's pride but soon he had the opportunity of vindicating himself. In September 1804 Méchain died in Spain and his son, who was secretary of the Observatory, resigned his position. Poisson, now on the staff of the *École Polytechnique*, suggested to his brilliant student that he might obtain the post for him. Arago at first refused because this would mean abandoning his proposed military career in which he already had the promise of patronage from Marshal Lannes, a friend of his father. Arago only accepted after Poisson had introduced him to Laplace. Although Arago was flattered to have been supported by the great author of the *Mécanique céleste*, he only accepted the position at the Observatory on the condition that a place in the artillery would remain open to him if he later changed his mind.[1] Thus Arago became a professional scientist only on secondment from the *École Polytechnique* and his name remained on their books for another four years. By then there was no doubt about Arago's true vocation. In the light of his earlier ambitions, it was not inappropriate that Arago should have been appointed in 1821 as examiner in science to the artillery. In the same year Biot was appointed as *Inspecteur d'études* at the military academy of Saint-Cyr.

Other members of the Arcueil group also had connections with the army, Laplace, for example, by his teaching and examining at the *École Militaire* in Paris. The significance of this

---

[1] Letter from Arago to Lacuée, 2 September 1806. *École Polytechnique*, Archives, Section 1803, dossier A.

for us is twofold. In the first place it reminds us of a practical application of mathematics. The art of war had provided a livelihood in the days of Leonardo da Vinci. It continued to do so at the end of the eighteenth century. Secondly, the value of mathematics to warfare in general and to the theory of artillery in particular, provided a common meeting ground for men from military and scientific backgrounds. Without this link Bonaparte's interest in science would have been at no higher a level than that of, say, the English King Charles II.

The fact that the majority of the Arcueil group never carried arms does not mean that the dangers of war were outside their experience. Berthollet had been long enough with the French army in Egypt to have been close to a sudden and violent death on more than one occasion. Nor was scientific work necessarily without extreme physical dangers. When we think of Gay-Lussac's serious accident with potassium metal in the summer of 1808, or of Dulong's repeated investigation of the highly explosive nitrogen trichloride, which cost him two fingers of the right hand and the loss of the sight of one eye, one can hardly consider the pursuit of science in a laboratory much less hazardous than the pursuit of the art of war.

The Politics of the Arcueil Group

It will be argued in this book that the Society of Arcueil was formed at a time of the military, political and economic expansion of France and that although Napoleon was in no sense a direct patron of the Society, he provided both directly and indirectly the financial support necessary for the functioning of such a society. Berthollet and Laplace had provided Bonaparte with technical advice and as members of the Senate they both gave support to the Consulate and to the Empire. For their loyalty they were rewarded by titles and decorations. As Berthollet said[1] he was happy to depend on a fortune which was directly linked with the prosperity of the state.

The loyalty of the two senior members of the Arcueil group to

---

[1] When Berthollet claimed part of the revenue of his *Sénatorerie*, he asked for 'un revenu . . . sur les fonds publics . . . lié immédiatement à la stabilité du Gouvernement'.—*Observations de M. le Sénateur Berthollet sur le Rapport fait au Conseil d'État relativement aux mines de Filiols et de Tauringa*, 20 fevrier 1806.

the Napoleonic regime was not reflected in the attitudes of the younger members, or at least those who were at all politically conscious. The opposition grew stronger as the authority of Bonaparte became more absolute and culminated in hardly concealed hostility when he proclaimed himself Emperor. The students of the *École Polytechnique* were invited to send an address of congratulation to Bonaparte on the thwarting of a plot to assassinate him. This they refused to do, although most of the other officially constituted bodies of the capital including the Institute were quick to do so. Again on the institution of the Legion of Honour, the students refused to demonstrate in support. On the proclamation of the Empire many students refused to add their names to a document supporting the change. When Lacuée as military governor of the school reported this to Napoleon, Napoleon said that the time had come to eliminate the republicans from the school. First, however, he asked for a list of the names of defaulters together with their grades. Seeing that to eliminate the republicans would have been to displace some of the best students, including Arago, he desisted with the remark: 'Ah, if only they had been at the bottom of the list!'[1] When Napoleon complained to Monge of the hostile attitude of the students to his proclamation of the Empire, Monge's embarrassed reply was that the authorities at the school had had a difficult task in making the students good republicans; one could not expect them overnight to become enthusiastic supporters of the rule of an Emperor.[2]

Resistance to Napoleon's newly-assumed powers was one of the bonds linking Arago with Poisson,[3] who lived in the same lodgings. When there was resistance at the *École Polytechnique* in 1804 to supporting Bonaparte's final abandonment of republican principles, it was in the rooms of Poisson, now on the staff of the school, that the students went to organize their opposition. Nor was Biot (despite his detestation of the Jacobins) an active supporter of Napoleon. Biot had visited Madame de Staël at Coppet and his association with this circle, which included Benjamin Constant (removed from the Tribunate in 1802 for his opposition), was not unknown to Fouché's agents. Laplace is said to have asked Napoleon several times to include Biot's name

---

[1] Arago, *Oeuvres, Notices biographiques*, vol. i, p. 15.
[2] *Ibid.*, vol. ii, pp. 505–6.   [3] *Ibid.*, vol. ii, pp. 665–6.

among those honoured with the Legion of Honour, but in vain. The award had to wait until the first Restoration in 1814. Yet in his later life, while many of his former associates, particularly Arago and Gay-Lussac, took part in politics, Biot preferred to devote all his energies to science. The balance of action in the Arcueil group was, however, firmly on the side of the man who was successively First Consul and Emperor. Berthollet, Laplace and Chaptal all gave him their active support. If young men like Arago and Poisson and others from the *École Polytechnique* with liberal views opposed Napoleonic imperialism in their hearts, the question of active demonstration against the regime hardly arose. Under the Empire one was not called upon to have political views. It was clear, moreover, that it was the *École Polytechnique* and not Arcueil which was the centre of republican feeling. It was only under the succeeding constitutional monarchies that someone like Arago was able to sit in the Chamber of Deputies among the opposition.

The Arcueil Group and 'Pre-positivism'

It would take us too far from our main theme to discuss the relations between the later figures of the Enlightenment and the physical scientists at the end of the eighteenth century. Only a passing mention can be made of the 'Society of Auteuil', that group of thinkers which grew out of the meetings at the house of Madame Helvetius at Auteuil in the last quarter of the eighteenth century.[1] The movement continued in the early years of the nineteenth century, led by such figures as Cabanis and Destutt de Tracy. Bonaparte as a young officer had associated with these *idéalogues*, as they called themselves, but he later saw their ideas as a threat to his regime. In 1798 Cabanis had asked Laplace to pass on to Bonaparte a copy of his *Degré de certitude de la médecine* and in 1800 the *idéalogues* Cabanis, Volney, Garat and Tracy were members of the Senate and in this capacity as well as in the Institute they were colleagues (albeit somewhat remote) of Berthollet and Laplace. The interests of

---

[1] Picavet, *Les Idéalogues*, 1891. C. Lehec and J. Cazeneuve (ed.), *Oeuvres philosophiques de Cabanis*, 1956.

the *idéalogues* were directed towards the life sciences and came to be centred on the *École de Médecine* rather than the *École Polytechnique* or Arcueil. Of the physical scientists only the young Ampère had any lasting interest in their brand of psychology and metaphysics. We therefore find Ampère at Auteuil but not at Arcueil. The utopian socialist Saint-Simon is perhaps worth mentioning as a man who made a serious attempt to associate with each group in turn.

In late eighteenth-century French thought there is an obvious link between philosophy and science in the person of Condorcet. It is perhaps significant that when the *Académie des Sciences* finally paid tribute to its ill-fated secretary, it was Arago who composed the *Éloge*. Looking back from the point of view of mid-nineteenth century French thought, it might be permissible to use the term 'pre-positivistic'[1] to describe some ideas and assumptions common to Condorcet, Cabanis and Destutt de Tracy on the one hand and men such as Laplace, Lavoisier and Berthollet on the other. Condorcet's project of applying statistics to the social scene was put into practice by Chaptal as soon as he became Minister of the Interior and the theory of statistics applied to social problems was later developed by Laplace. Lavoisier certainly was strongly influenced by Condillac, adopted a naive sensationalism and excluded 'metaphysical considerations' from his scheme of science. Berthollet was not usually as explicit as his colleagues, Lavoisier and Laplace, but he generally shared their views, Laplace in his *Système du monde* attacked final causes and his ideas were echoed by Biot when he wrote:

> The true object of the physical sciences is not the search for primary causes but the search for laws according to which phenomena are produced . . .[2]

Laplace at one time stated that there was a parallel between the laws of physical science and the social order.[3] This provides an introduction to Saint-Simon.

Saint-Simon has a definite place in French thought leading

---

[1] H. Gouhier, *La jeunesse d'Auguste Comte et la formation du positivisme*, 1936, vol. ii, pp. 2 ff.
[2] 'Sur l'esprit de système' (1809), *Mélanges*, 1858, vol. ii, p. 112.
[3] Laplace, *Oeuvres*, vol. xiv, p. 173.

up to the positivism of Auguste Comte. From 1798 to 1801 Saint-Simon lived in the immediate vicinity of the *École Polytechnique* and even attended some of the lectures there.[1] In an effort to assimilate the ideas of physical science and psychology of his time he used to invite Monge, Berthollet, Laplace and Cabanis to dinner.[2] In 1807 Saint-Simon spoke highly of the work of Laplace, Lavoisier and Berthollet, saying for example that he agreed with Berthollet's ideas on affinity.[3] Although the attitude of Saint-Simon towards Laplace was to change later in the Empire from admiration to hostility after his fantasies had been rejected by the *Bureau des Longitudes*, Saint-Simon's relations with Poisson were happier. Poisson had gone to meetings held at the houses of Destutt de Tracy and Cabanis. He met Saint-Simon there and the older man began to treat him like an adopted son. Saint-Simon later claimed that it was he who had subsidized Poisson up to the time when his teaching appointments made such financial assistance unnecessary.

The Attitude of the Arcueil Group to Religion

There is little information available on the attitude of Berthollet to religion. Perhaps he could most accurately be described as an agnostic. It is around Laplace that the question of religion at Arcueil centres. The problem of his attitude is a complex one. One thing is certain—he was not an agnostic, who left the idea of a personal God to one side while he devoted his life to mathematics and science, although one might get this impression from some of his work. There is his famous statement of determinism that, given an intelligence which could comprehend all the forces of nature, nothing in the future would be uncertain.[4] Newton had brought God into his universe to correct irregularities in the solar system. It was Laplace who showed that these were self-correcting. Laplace considered that there was

[1] M. Leroy, *La vie véritable du comte Henri de Saint-Simon (1760–1825)*, 1925, pp. 188–93.
[2] Gouhier, *op. cit.*, p. 104.
[3] Saint-Simon, *Oeuvres choisies*, Brussels, 1859, vol. i, pp. 85–6, 113–25. An interesting parallel is to be found in Auguste Comte's appreciation of Berthollet's contribution to the theory of affinity. Comte, *Cours de philosophie positive*, 1864, vol. iii, pp. 36–7.
[4] *Théorie analytique des probabilités*, 3rd edn., 1820, *Oeuvres*, vol. vii, pp. vi–vii.

no place for final causes in science and where they had been used in the past, this was because of ignorance of the laws of nature.[1] Religion, said Laplace, was a matter of prejudice.[2] In a manuscript now in the archives of the *Académie des Sciences* in Paris, Laplace gives a survey of his religious views.[3] In this he rejects miracles and speaks of religion as an illusion.

To leave the matter there, however, is too simple. The very existence of this manuscript suggests that Laplace was worried about religious questions. The most remarkable document that bears on his views is a letter from him to his son, written on 17 June 1809. The father regrets that he has not been able to see his son and sends him some money. Laplace hopes that his son in his military career will be a credit to his parents. There then occurs the phrase:

> I pray God that he will watch over your days. Have him always present in your thoughts as well as your father and mother.

If Laplace had really thought that religion was no more than superstition, why should he have brought the mention of God into a private letter? It is true that the first sentence quoted could have been no more than a conventional phrase. The curious thing, if Laplace was an atheist, was that he should link remarks about his undoubtedly sincere parental affection with advice on religious piety.

It was not so much at Arcueil as at the meetings of the *Bureau des Longitudes* that Laplace insisted on bringing the discussion round to religious problems. Through Poisson[4] comes the information that regularly after each meeting of the *Bureau*, walking home along the avenue of the Observatory, Laplace would bring the conversation round to the repugnance which he considered a man's reason must have for certain religious dogmas. There is no evidence that anyone else in the *Bureau* felt the need for this constant discussion of religious fundamentals. It was therefore an internal conflict which Laplace was trying to resolve.

Perhaps it was this basic uncertainty and insecurity that

---

[1] *Oeuvres*, vol. vii, p. vi.   [2] *Ibid.*, pp. cxix, cxlii.
[3] R. Hahn, *Archives int. d'histoire des sciences*, 8ᵉ année (1955), 38–40.
[4] Reported by Cournot, *Souvenirs (1760–1860)*, Paris, 1913, pp. 85 ff.

made Laplace choose religion as a constant target for his criticisms. When the young Swiss scientist Pictet was invited to
dinner by Laplace in May 1802 and again in the following
January he recorded that on each occasion religion was attacked or made fun of, much to his personal embarrassment.[1]
It is true that this was before Laplace had moved to Arcueil
but as Berthollet was present on the first occasion and Biot on
the second, the milieu is not easily distinguishable from that of
Arcueil.

Biot's attitude as a young man to religion seems to reflect that
of Laplace. Yet in his article on Galileo for the *Biographie universelle* (1816), he refrained from a forthright condemnation of the
part of the Roman Catholic Church such as came from the pen
of his contemporary, Brewster. In 1825 when Biot was in Rome
with his son he went out of his way to obtain an audience with
Pope Leo XII. Biot later spoke of the deep impression which this
audience had made upon him.[2] In 1846 he made a formal
return to the Catholic Church, so that one biographer[3] has
been able to present Biot's life as that of a distinguished scientist
who was also a Christian.

On one occasion when Thenard was at the peak of his career,
his lecture audience was joined by a group in clerical garb, who
were immediately insulted vocally by some of the other students.
Thenard intervened and in the name of liberty of conscience he
rebuked the anti-clerics. He reminded them that the great
crystallographer and physicist Haüy had worn a cassock.[4] If
Haüy was never a member of the Arcueil circle, it was not
merely because of anti-religious feeling. Haüy and Laplace
worked amicably together in 1805 and Haüy's absence from the
Arcueil scene is to be interpreted rather in institutional than in
religious terms—he was a professor at the *Muséum d'Histoire
Naturelle* where he lived. Another member of the Arcueil group
who later reacted sharply to an attack on religion was Arago.
Towards the end of his life when the *Académie des Sciences* were
discussing the possible candidature of the Irish-born Abbadie,

[1] M. A. Pictet, *Journal d'un Genevois à Paris sous le Consulat*, pp. 101–2, 113.
[2] 'Une conversation au Vatican' (1858), *Mélanges*, vol. ii, pp. 451–8.
[3] F. Lefort, 'Un Savant Chrétien, J. B. Biot', *Le Correspondant*, Nouvelle
Série, xxxvi (1867), 955–95.
[4] *Un grand français. Le chimiste Thenard*, 1950, p. 126.

H

someone remarked that he was a devout Catholic. Arago replied that their business was to judge his scientific work:

> It is not our province to consider his religious opinions. As for myself, I envy those who are believers.[1]

Despite the reservations mentioned above and the general tolerance of religion shown in their later years, the evidence suggests that the men of Arcueil had little regard for religion. By the early nineteenth century rationalism and anti-clericalism were deeply rooted in French soil. The attitude of the Arcueil group was certainly closer to that of Condorcet than of Chateaubriand. Although Bonaparte had found a use for religion in the state, the period of religious revival in France came only after the death of Berthollet. When later Humboldt in his *Cosmos* came to describe the Creation without mentioning God, we see what was perhaps the influence of the Arcueil group and of Laplace in particular.

Appreciation of the Arts at Arcueil

The meetings at Arcueil were primarily for scientific and social purposes. One might wonder if the dedication of the members of the Arcueil circle to science was to the exclusion of all interest in art, literature or music.

Of Laplace it was said:

> He had not cultivated the fine arts, but he appreciated them. He was fond of Italian music and of the poetry of Racine, and he often took delight in quoting from memory different passages of this great poet. The works of Raphael adorned his apartments and they were found besides portraits of Descartes, Francis Vieta, Newton, Galileo and Euler.[2]

Berthollet was interested in painting and sculpture from an aesthetic as well as a technical point of view. Nor was his library devoted exclusively to works related to science. Like his neighbour at Arcueil, Laplace, he was interested in music. Berthollet retained throughout his life a keen interest in the theatre. Of the other senior members of the Arcueil circle Humboldt had had a particularly wide education and Chaptal had a deep interest in literature and drama.

[1] Quoted by M. Daumas, *Arago*, Paris, 1943, p. 132.
[2] Fourier, *Éloge*.

As regards the younger men of Arcueil, even those whose mathematical talents were developed by the rigorous training of the *École Polytechnique* had not lacked a basic literary education. Arago was later able to make use of his literary talent as secretary of the *Académie des Sciences* in the composition of major biographies of deceased members. In the composition of these *Éloges* he consciously associated himself with a tradition that went back to Fontenelle. When a statue of Molière, raised by public subscription in 1844, was unveiled, it was Arago who delivered an oration[1] which threw a favourable light both on its author and its subject. Biot too had a good command of the French language and was eventually elected to the *Académie Française* (1856). With his previous election to the *Académie des Inscriptions et Belles Lettres* (1841), he had the unusual distinction of being a member of three national Academies.

The Wives of Members of the Arcueil Group

So much of this book is concerned with men that we may be forgiven for turning aside for a few moments to consider the place of women in the Arcueil group. The higher education in science which will be described in Chapter Four was, of course, for men only. It would be easy to conclude that the role of women was purely social and that they had no grasp of the work of their husbands. Madame Berthollet, and Madame Laplace in particular, were charming hostesses but took little part in the scientific discussion at Arcueil.

In the next generation Madame Arago was also to be a well-known hostess to men of science, particularly after her husband's appointment as secretary of the *Académie des Sciences*. Arago himself had two sisters who married his professional friends.

Biot was another scientist who married the sister of a scientific friend. At the age of twenty-three he married a girl of sixteen, the sister of his friend at the *École Polytechnique*, Brisson. The Brisson family lived at Beauvais and there were obviously strong personal reasons why, when Biot was appointed as professor of mathematics in the provinces, Beauvais should be chosen.[2] Biot

[1] Arago, *Oeuvres, Notices biographiques*, vol. iii, pp. 553–67.
[2] Biot was nominated to be professor of mathematics at the *École Centrale* at Beauvais on 13 March 1797. He married on 28 June 1797.

undertook to give his wife instruction in science and mathematics so that she might grace the company of his scientific
friends. Madame Biot was also a competent linguist, being able
to read English, German and Italian without difficulty. When
Berthollet suggested that a French translation should be undertaken of E. G. Fischer's *Lehrbuch der mechanischen Naturlehre* it was
Madame Biot who did a large part of the work with the collaboration of her husband. Biot himself, who might be supposed
to be the translator, admitted in the Preface that he knew no
German and that this task had been performed for him by a
'person very dear to him'. When Biot went to Dunkirk in the
winter of 1808–9 to make geodesic observations, he was accompanied by his wife. During this trip he also studied mirages and
his wife drew the illustrations to accompany his notes.

It was in a shop that Gay-Lussac met the girl who was later to
be his wife. She was one of the daughters of a gentleman living
in reduced circumstances after the Revolution. Being employed
in a draper's shop she was first seen at the age of seventeen by
Gay-Lussac reading a text-book of chemistry behind the coun-
ter! Gay-Lussac, who fell in love with her, was soon to leave for
Italy with Humboldt. Before he left he presented her with a
collection of books on various subjects, so that to the chemistry
of Lavoisier and Fourcroy she could add Euler's *Letters to a German Princess*, Rousseau's botany and several works of literature.
They were married in 1808, a year which was to be one of
Gay-Lussac's most productive in science. Later Gay-Lussac
turned to industrial chemistry to augment his income, feeling
strongly his duty to provide for his wife and five children.

*   *   *

Having observed the position of the leaders of the Society of
Arcueil in the Napoleonic state and having noticed certain
general features of the men who assembled at Arcueil, it is now
time to say something briefly about their individual lives. In
general the aim will be to mention aspects of their lives and
work not covered in later chapters. In most cases this can be done
in a small space but in a few cases, such as that of Humboldt,
the importance of the man and the life he led justify a fuller
treatment. It is appropriate to begin with Berthollet and Laplace, although many aspects of their lives are discussed else-

where in this book. We might consider the others in a roughly hierarchical order, considering first the physicists and then the chemists and ending with those who made least contribution to science. It says much for the high standard of the Society of Arcueil that, even when proceeding according to this plan we arrive at the names of Descotils, Bérard and Amédée Berthollet, we are still dealing with men who made positive contributions to science, even if they lacked the spark of genius.

C.-L. Berthollet

Claude-Louis Berthollet was born in the charming lake-side village of Talloire by the lake of Annecy on 9 December 1748. His father was described in the local baptismal register as 'châtelain et secrétaire de Talloires'.[1] The 'chateau' in which Berthollet was born is now the town hall. At this time Savoy was part of the territory of the King of Sardinia and Berthollet was subject to Piemontese and Italian influence rather than French. He attended school in the nearest large town, Annecy, and then went on to obtain a medical degree at the University of Turin in 1768. The wish for wider experience attracted him to Paris. He was beginning to be interested in chemistry and he took advantage of the facilities offered in the French capital to attend lectures on chemistry by Macquer and Bucquet. His profession, however, was still that of medicine. In 1776 the first of his chemical memoirs was published, the subject being tartaric acid. Berthollet also began to study gases, paying careful attention to the recent experiments of Priestley, Scheele and Lavoisier. In 1778 he was able to present a major memoir on ammonia to the *Académie des Sciences*.

In 1778 Berthollet became a naturalized Frenchman. In order to safeguard his professional position he took the degree of doctor of medicine in the University of Paris, as his Turin degree was not recognized in France. In the same year he married Marie-Marguerite Baur. Berthollet's brother-in-law married in 1791 Anne-Françoise Huart, who was the young sister of Monge's wife. Berthollet's previous acquaintance with Monge now became cemented into a life-long friendship.

[1] Archives de la Haute Savoie, Annecy, *Livre de Batêmes de l'Église Paroissiale de St Maurice de Talloires depuis 10 avril 1717*, f. 128.

On 15 April 1780 Berthollet was elected to a vacancy in the *Académie des Sciences*, caused by the death of Bucquet. Berthollet had been extremely industrious in the previous two or three years, presenting a succession of memoirs to the *Académie* on a variety of chemical subjects including nitric acid, fulminating gold and compounds of sulphur. On 11 March 1780 no less than four reports on different memoirs of Berthollet were read at one meeting of the *Académie des Sciences*. The favourable reports of referees such as Macquer and Lavoisier did much to secure his election.

Macquer's death in 1784 created two further vacancies for chemists, a teaching position at the *Jardin du Roi* (later to become the *Muséum d'Histoire Naturelle*) and the position of director of dyeing. Berthollet had competed with Fourcroy for the vacancy in the *Académie*. Berthollet had won. This time Fourcroy was appointed as professor at the *Jardin du Roi*—an eminently suitable choice, since he was soon recognized as a brilliant lecturer, whereas Berthollet, for all his powers of inspiring his few chosen disciples and co-workers, was never able to present coherently the elements of his subject to a large audience.

Equally just was the choice of Berthollet for Macquer's second major appointment, that of director of the government dye-works. He was soon to write a standard treatise on dyeing and took the important step of introducing scientific principles into what until then had been an empirical craft. Berthollet's most famous discovery was that of the power of 'oxymuriatic acid' (chlorine) to bleach. Previously bleaching had been an extremely slow and tedious process involving treatment of the fabric with alkali and then prolonged exposure to the air. In France an alkaline solution of chlorine is still known as *eau de Javelle* from the place where this was first used, although it was Berthollet who first went to Javelle to demonstrate the use of this solution.[1] It was typical of Berthollet's complete lack of commercial instincts that he refused to try to make any money from the process. The use of chlorine for bleaching was introduced into Britain by James Watt, who had obtained the information from Berthollet during his visit to Paris in 1786. Watt considered that Berthollet should have some financial recognition

---

[1] Berthollet, *Description du blanchiment des toiles et des fils par l'acide muriatique oxigéné* . . ., an 3, pp. 30-1.

of his contribution to the new bleaching works set up in Glasgow but Berthollet was quite happy to see others profiting from his discovery.[1] Similarly in France, instead of exploiting the new process, he supported the project of his former assistant, Bonjour, in setting up a bleaching works at Valenciennes. Berthollet also communicated his discovery directly to Oberkampf. The most permanent recognition received by Berthollet for his discovery was the incorporation of his name into the French language to describe various aspects of commercial bleaching.[2]

Carrying out further experiments with chlorine Berthollet discovered a new salt (potassium chlorate) and he suggested its use as a substitute for nitre in gunpowder. Preliminary trials, however, showed that it was likely to inflict more damage on the user than the enemy. A more successful contribution by Berthollet to the defence of France was in connection with the manufacture of iron and steel. Together with Vandermonde and Monge he analysed different samples of iron and steel and gave advice on its manufacture with the object of improving the production of cannon.[3] In February/March 1794 Berthollet was one of the instructors on an intensive course on the extraction of saltpetre and the manufacture of gunpowder given to a selected group of men brought to Paris from all over France. Berthollet was a member of numerous commissions including the *Commission des monnaies* and the commission on weights and measures. As a member of the *Commission d'agriculture et des arts* he supported the retention of the parks on the outskirts of Paris, which might otherwise have been converted into agricultural land. As a technical expert he was not lacking in courage. During the Reign of Terror he was asked to make an analysis of a sample of brandy which, it was alleged, had been poisoned as part of a plot.[4] He was expected to confirm the conspiracy, but when he drew up his report he stated the simple truth—the brandy was wholesome, although contaminated with a few particles of slate which could be easily removed by filtration. He was summoned before the Committee of Public

[1] Arago, *Oeuvres, Notices biographiques*, vol. i, pp. 464–5.
[2] Descroisilles, *Ann. chim.*, lxxix (1811), 222–3n.
[3] *Ann. chim.*, xix (1797), 13–46.
[4] Berthollet had been appointed with Monge on 15 October 1793—*Receuil des Actes du Comité du Salut Public*, ed. F. A. Aulard, 1889–1951, vol. vii, pp. 420–1.

Safety to explain his lack of co-operation. Here Berthollet was prepared to defy Robespierre to his face, proving that the brandy was not poisoned by publicly drinking a glass.

In November 1789, four months after the fall of the Bastille, Berthollet wrote to Watt that he had retired to the country. He had taken a house at Aulnay,[1] a village on the north east out-skirts of Paris, an obvious prelude to his life at Arcueil. Ber-thollet did not consider that he personally was in any danger, although he foresaw the possibility of losing his salary as director of the dyeworks in the general upheaval of the ad-ministration.[2] Berthollet need not have worried about his future, however. His skill as a chemist made him increasingly valuable to the government and he was to prove himself a capable administrator. By the law of 14 October 1795 a new organization of the Mint in Paris was established with Berthol-let, already one of the *commissaires généraux des Monnaies*, now appointed as one of three directors. He would have been able to contribute more fully to the affairs of the Mint if it had not been for his prolonged absences from Paris on missions in Italy and Egypt. On 29 December 1799, on his nomination to the Senate, Berthollet was replaced at the Mint.

Berthollet had demonstrated his integrity at the worst period of the Revolution. He was selected as one of the commissioners sent to Italy to collect art treasures and objects of scientific value.[3] His second long absence from France was as a member of the expedition to Egypt in 1798–9. Both Berthollet and Monge were nominated commissioners to the general Divan, composed of local leaders from the whole country. Administration, taxa-tion and legislation all became familiar processes to Berthollet. Back in France the new constitution introduced a Senate to which Berthollet was immediately appointed. This brings us, however, to the period of Berthollet's career which is described elsewhere in this book.

In 1814 when the Bourbons returned to France Berthollet

---

[1] Bibliothèque universitaire de Genève, MS. Suppl. 1039, f. 33, 35.

[2] Letter from Berthollet to Watt, 23 November 1789—J. P. Muirhead, *The Origins and Progress of the Mechanical Inventions of James Watt*, 1854, vol. ii, p. 232.

[3] These included manuscripts, machines, mathematical instruments, maps, mineral specimens, plants and animals (Napoléon, *Correspondance*, vol. i, nos. 455 (Art. 8), 663.

was made a Peer of the realm. This was no doubt an acknowledgement of his position as an elder statesman of French science,
although it must have caused some heart searching during the
Hundred Days. In the debates of the Upper House Berthollet
made a few contributions on technical matters—the inferiority
of French steel, the production of saltpetre, and canals.

During the first two decades of the nineteenth century Berthollet was universally respected as one of the leading representatives of French science. Visitors from abroad came to see
him not only as the senior chemist of France but also because
they admired his personal qualities. As Dr Marcet of Geneva
wrote to Berzelius in July 1814:

> Berthollet . . . is the great favourite of all the *savants* who visit
> Paris. There is in his nature something frank, modest and paternal
> which one finds enchanting.[1]

A similar testimonial is provided by one of the most distinguished of Berthollet's guests at Arcueil, Sir Humphry Davy:

> Berthollet was a most amiable man; when the friend of Napoleon
> even, always good, conciliatory and modest, frank and candid.
> He had no airs and many graces.[2]

One of the ironies of Berthollet's life was that the man who
had been called upon to administer the Mint was unable to
organize his own financial affairs. As one of his biographers
remarked:

> Apart from his genius, Berthollet was best known for his lack of
> interest in money. For him gold was nothing but a metal and a
> means of exchange for the necessities of life. It had no value in
> his eyes except in so far as it allowed him to satisfy his love for
> science; and as this love was boundless, his noble generosity was
> hardly limited by the extent of his financial resources . . .[3]

Berthollet also had a reputation for punctuality; even in his
old age he would leave Arcueil sometimes before daylight in
order to be in Paris at a particular time of the morning. One

---

[1] Berzelius, *Bref*, vol. 2, part iv, p. 106.
[2] John Davy, *Memoirs of the Life of Sir Humphry Davy*, 1836, vol. i, pp. 469–
470.
[3] Auger, 'Nécrologie', *Annales de la littérature étrangère*, ix (1822), 297–8.

might have thought that a man of Berthollet's social position would have used a carriage, but according to Jomard and in conformity with his basically simple tastes, he used to cover the distance between Arcueil and Paris on foot, thus taking exercise which he considered good for his gout. Berthollet continued with his usual activities almost up to the end. He died at Arcueil on 6 November 1822.

Laplace

Pierre Simon Laplace was born at the small town of Beaumont-en-Auge not far from Pont l'Évêque in Normandy on 23 March 1749. It is usually said that Laplace was of peasant stock. Certainly his father worked on the land, although it has been pointed out[1] that one of Laplace's uncles was a priest and another a surgeon so that the Laplace family was not without education. The young Laplace went to the local school run by the Benedictine order. The two careers marked out for boys at this school were the army and the Church. Laplace's family intended Pierre-Simon for the Church, but he received a good general education during his ten years at Beaumont with a good grounding in literature and mathematics. At the age of sixteen he was sent to the University of Caen and it was while he was at the College of Arts that Laplace decided that his vocation lay in mathematics. When he decided to go to Paris, it was one of his mathematics teachers at Caen, Pierre le Canu, who provided him with a letter of introduction to d'Alembert.

Through D'Alembert Laplace became professor of mathematics at the *École Militaire* in 1769 and was elected to the *Académie des Sciences* in 1773. Ten years later he became examiner of the artillery cadets and in 1788 with a secure though modest income he married Marie Anne Charlotte Courty de Romange, the grand-daughter of the secretary of state of the king at the parliament of Besançon.

Laplace's main work up to the period of the Revolution was on the movements of the planets and of the moon, of the shape of the planets and of the earth and on the theory of tides. This was the foundation of his monumental *Mécanique céleste*, which was to appear in five volumes over the period 1799–1825.

[1] G. A. Simon, *Biometrika*, xxi (1929), 217–30.

Speaking of his work in physical astronomy, Fourier in his *Éloge* said:

> Laplace was born to perfect everything, to exhaust everything, to drive back every limit, in order to solve what might have appeared incapable of solution. He would have completed the science of the heavens if that science could have been completed.

At the beginning of October 1793 Laplace gave his address as 'chez le citoyen Berthollet, hôtel des Monnaies'[1] but during the Terror Laplace retired to Melun and wrote his *Exposition du système du monde*. By the end of 1794 he was called back to Paris to teach mathematics as assistant to Lagrange at the short-lived *École Normale*. He took a prominent part in the affairs of the First Class of the Institute, founded in 1795. The status and wealth of Laplace, if not his scientific work, in the period 1799 to 1814 were directly dependent on his good relations with Bonaparte, but this aspect of his life has already been mentioned. One might ask what sort of man Laplace was. Typical of the impression which he made on many of his contemporaries was Davy's description of him as 'rather formal and grand in manner with an air of protection rather than of courtesy'.[2]

In 1814 after the banishment of Napoleon to the Island of Elba, Laplace was one of those nominated to the *Chambre des Pairs*. After the second Restoration in 1815 we find Laplace taking an active part in the work of the Second Chamber, not it is true playing a vital role in the government of France, but as a respected *savant* making the contributions that might be expected of a technical expert. Laplace's main speeches in the *Chambre des Pairs* have been conveniently assembled in his collected works.[3] In March 1817 he addressed his colleagues on the utility of the national land survey. In July 1819 in a discussion on the budget Laplace spoke in favour of the suppression of the state lottery, a system which, he said, brought a train of misery and despair to the poor who bought tickets they could ill afford. Laplace also concerned himself with legal reform. The law by which, in the case of a split decision by a jury in a criminal case, it was referred to a higher court, was patently

---

[1] *Procès-verbaux du Comité d'Instruction Publique*, vol. ii, p. 388.
[2] John Davy, *Memoirs of the life of Sir Humphry Davy*, 1836, vol. i, p. 470.
[3] *Oeuvres*, 1878–1904, vol. xiv, pp. 372–87.

unjust. For if only two out of five judges considered the accused guilty, he was condemned on a minority vote. Nor did the mathematician shrink from financial questions and in 1824 and 1825 Laplace spoke on the conversion of government stock.

The man who was called the Newton of his age died on 5 March 1827, the centenary year of the death of Newton himself.

Humboldt

Humboldt became such an influential figure in nineteenth-century science that we may be justified in considering his life in some detail. In particular it is of interest to understand why this Prussian nobleman should have wished to spend so much of his life in France and how he came to have such breadth of interests and yet lack the professional training of most of his colleagues at Arcueil.

Baron Friedrich Wilhelm Karl Heinrich Alexander von Humboldt was born on 14 September 1769 in Berlin. His father, an officer in the Prussian army, had married in 1766 Elizabeth de Colomb, the widow of Baron Holwede. She was of French Huguenot descent and she was to pass on to her second son, Friedrich Alexander, a love of things French, a sentiment which was, however, not uncommon in the Prussia of Frederick the Great. As a wealthy woman she was also able to bequeath to her son an inheritance which made possible his expedition to America. Alexander and his brother Wilhelm were educated by a private tutor. They later had as their mathematics teacher Ernst Gottfried Fischer who was to translate into German Berthollet's *Recherches sur les lois de l'affinité*, in which Fischer incorporated the first table of equivalent weights. Humboldt as a boy, however, was not much interested in science and his mother insisted that his university education should be in economics, which was considered a suitable training for an administrative post in the civil service. Humboldt later wrote:

> Until I was sixteen I had little inclination for scientific pursuits. I was of a restless disposition and wanted to enter the army. This choice did not please my family, who made me take up economics, so that I had no opportunity to attend a course of botany or chemistry. I am self-taught in all the sciences with which I am

now exclusively occupied and I acquired my knowledge comparatively late in life.[1]

In 1787 the two brothers Humboldt went to the University of Frankfurt-on-Oder. The standard of teaching was very low but we may mention that the 'economics' course placed great emphasis on industrial processes: 'They learn to draw plans for a brandy distillery, a tar kiln and a flour mill, they learn the number of threads in the warp and woof of linen and silk, they learn how to make cheese and smelt iron, and how to destroy caterpillars and insect pests.'[2] This content of Humboldt's education meant that in his life in Paris he would have common interests with men like Chaptal.

Humboldt soon left Frankfurt for the more intellectually stimulating university of Göttingen. Here he learned a little physics and chemistry and he became interested in botany and, not least important, he made the acquaintance of George Foster, who had been Captain Cook's companion. It was with Foster that he travelled first to England, where he was introduced to Sir Joseph Banks, and then to France, where he was impressed by the new revolutionary ardour. It was probably the long conversations with Foster, who had travelled the South Seas, which did more than anything to give Humboldt the ambition to be an explorer. Meanwhile, however, he had also become interested in geology and on leaving Göttingen, he attended the theoretical and practical courses of Werner at the School of Mines of Freiburg in Saxony.

Humboldt now began to undertake scientific research and he did experiments on the effect of light on plant life. In 1792 Humboldt became an administrator in the Department of Mines and he soon attracted attention by his enthusiasm, energy and willingness to go down the mines and supervise the workings personally. In his spare time he carried out experiments on galvanism but his work (in common with other work of this period) was spoiled by a failure to distinguish physiological phenomena from those which were purely electrical. During his career as a mining inspector Humboldt's two main external

---

[1] 'Confessions', *Mémoires de la Société de Géographie de Genève*, vii (1868), 180.
[2] K. Bruhns, *Life of Alexander von Humboldt*, trans., 1873, vol. i, p. 45.

scientific interests were in connection with the composition of the atmosphere and magnetism. He had a plan for widespread collaboration to determine the exact composition of the atmosphere in a number of places but the continuation of the war prevented any such international collaboration. He also discovered the magnetic effect of a large block of serpentine in the Fichtel Mountains. He sent a sample of the mineral to Sir Joseph Banks for analysis and he confirmed that it was slightly magnetic.

Meanwhile he had taken a minor part in some diplomatic missions and he had also been offered the post of Director of Mining in Silesia. Humboldt refused the post, saying that he was planning a scientific expedition. It was not until his mother's death in 1796 that he felt free to leave. His father had died when he was nine and it had always been his mother who had directed his education. The death of his mother, although she had been rather a remote figure in his life, linked him all the more closely to his elder brother. Another effect was to provide him with a substantial inheritance which was to make him—a man of modest material aspirations—virtually independent and able to devote his life to scientific discovery with a single-mindedness that was hardly possible for those without independent means of support.

The next two years he spent in preparation for his journey. His original plans included a year in Italy but the Napoleonic campaign made this impossible and it was not until 1805 in the company of Gay-Lussac that he was able to achieve this ambition. Another project, to join an English expedition under Lord Bristol to Egypt had to be abandoned, again because Bonaparte had got there before him. Yet the months he had spent in preparation, learning Egyptian archaeology, were not wasted, if only because they were later to give him one more point of contact at Arcueil with the French *savants* who did go to Egypt —Berthollet, Descotils and Malus. Nevertheless, at the time (May 1798) Humboldt described the situation in the following terms:

> I learned of the arrest of Lord Bristol when I went to Paris, where my brother was. I was so upset and I was so looking forward to seeing other plants and a great country that if I had found MM.

Berthollet and Monge in Paris, I would have accompanied them to Egypt.[1]

It is clear that Humboldt arrived in Paris too late to have any contact with Berthollet. Yet he made the most of a stay of five months in the French capital to make the acquaintance of many leading scientific figures. He met Antoine Laurent de Jussieu and the young Cuvier; he met Laplace and worked with Delambre on geodesic measurements; he received advice from Borda and, not neglecting chemistry, he met Fourcroy and Guyton and worked in Vauquelin's laboratory at the *École des Mines* on the composition of the air. He was invited to become a member of an expedition under the patronage of the French government to the Pacific regions. This too was cancelled and Humboldt determined to cross the Mediterranean from Marseilles to Algiers and then go overland to join up with the French expedition to Egypt under Bonaparte.

With the botanist Bonpland as his companion, he left Paris on 20 October 1798 for Marseilles. Here Humboldt once more had to abandon his plan. He decided to try to obtain a ship in Spain and he and Bonpland set out on foot for Madrid. On their way they passed through Montpellier in January 1799 and Humboldt records that he spent several agreeable days there with Chaptal. In Spain Humboldt was able to put into practice a method of determining altitude by measurement of height of the barometer. He had been instructed in this method by Laplace. The method is, of course, a valid one still used today and by means of it Humboldt was able to make a significant contribution to the physical geography of Spain. We can understand better his immediate sympathy with Arago after the latter's return to Paris in 1809 from a geodesic expedition in Spain when we remember Humboldt's earlier experience. In Madrid Humboldt spent a day with the expatriate French chemist Proust, soon to acquire fame through his controversy with Berthollet.

Humboldt's main business in Madrid showed his skill as a diplomat and he was successful in obtaining the quite exceptional permission to travel in the Spanish colonies in South America for the purpose of obtaining scientific information. He

[1] *Mémoires de la Société de Géographie de Genève*, vii (1868), 186.

was to finance the expedition himself, spending more than he
could really afford but with the expectation that he would
recover at least half his expenses by publication of his travels.
There is no space here to describe in detail the five years that
Humboldt spent away from Europe. We may only mention that
after eighteen months in Venezuela, Humboldt visited successively Cuba, Colombia, Ecuador, Peru and Mexico. He
finally visited the United States, leaving America from Phila-
delphia and arriving back at Bordeaux on 3 August 1804.
During the expedition he was continually able to exercise his
interests and talents in exploration, cartography, oceanography,
geology, meteorology, botany and zoology. Humboldt's own
summing up of his aims was as follows:

> To study the formation of the earth and its strata, to analyse the
> atmosphere, to measure with sensitive instruments its pressure,
> temperature, humidity, the electric and magnetic charge, to
> observe the influence of the climate on the distribution of plants
> and animals, to relate chemistry to the physiology of organized
> beings, these are the aims I have proposed to myself.[1]

Humboldt's instruments were carefully checked in Paris before his departure and again on his return. He put his thermometers, barometer and sextant to continual use. His main work
was meteorological but anything from an electric eel to an
earthquake would be subjected to his keen observation. Of his
astronomical observations he wrote:

> Be indulgent with my astronomical work. Remember it is only
> a by-product of my journey. I am only an apprentice in astronomy
> and did not learn to handle the instruments until two years ago.
> I have undertaken the journey at my expense. Such an expedition
> made by a private person who is by no means wealthy, done for
> his own pleasure and instruction, cannot be compared with those
> undertaken by governments, royally endowed and for which an
> entire society of scholars is assembled to make investigations in
> all the branches of knowledge.[2]

He made observations on deforestation, soil erosion, tropical
rain, volcanoes, and took the temperature of the cold Pacific

[1] Quoted by L. Kellner, *Alexander von Humboldt*, 1963, p. 64.
[2] *Lettres americaines d'Alexandre de Humboldt (1798–1807)*, ed. E. T. Hamy,
1905, p. 43.

5a. Berthollet.

British Museum

5b. Humboldt.

British Museum

6. Laplace in his robes as Chancellor of the Senate.

A

BONAPARTE,

DE L'INSTITUT NATIONAL.

Citoyen premier consul,

Vous m'avez permis de vous dédier cet ouvrage. Il m'est doux et honorable de l'offrir au Héros pacificateur de l'Europe, à qui la France doit sa prospérité, sa grandeur et la plus brillante époque de sa gloire; au Protecteur éclairé des sciences, qui formé par elles voit dans leur étude, la source des plus nobles jouissances, et dans leurs progrès, le perfectionnement de tous les arts utiles et des institutions sociales. Puisse cet ouvrage consacré à la plus sublime des sciences naturelles, être un monument durable de la reconnoissance que votre accueil et les bienfaits du Gouvernement inspirent à ceux qui les cultivent! De toutes les vérités qu'il renferme, l'expression de ce sentiment sera toujours pour moi, la plus précieuse.

Salut et respect,

LAPLACE.

7. Laplace dedicates his *Mécanique céleste* (Volume 3, 1802) to Bonaparte.

8a. Chaptal. Painting by Gros (1824).

8. De Candolle.

current, since known as the Humboldt current. He made a mountaineering record by climbing Chimborazo in the Andes to a height of 19,280 feet. He did not neglect to collect samples of the air at that altitude. It is no wonder that he took a keen interest in Gay-Lussac's balloon ascent after he had been told about it on his return to Paris.

Humboldt's great respect for Berthollet is shown by his choice of the genus name *Bertholletia* for a tree discovered in his exploration, of which the grandest species *Bertholletia excelsa*, the Brazil nut tree, is one of the largest trees in the primeval forests bordering the Amazon in central Brazil. During his travels Humboldt kept his friends in Europe informed of his progress. He always duplicated his news, never sending more than one letter at a time, knowing that the odds were against any particular missive reaching its destination. From Mexico in June 1803 Humboldt sent a collection of minerals to the First Class of the Institute, asking that they should be analysed by one of its members.[1] Several specimens, when they finally arrived, were handed over to Descotils, who was a professional analyst. One of the specimens was a brown lead mineral, in which the Mexican mineralogist Del Rio had claimed to have discovered a new metal. Descotils' analysis showed that it contained chromium but he concluded that no new metal was present.[2] Del Rio agreed with this analysis and it was not until 1830 that the metal vanadium was finally discovered.

Humboldt's travels were published in six parts. Part Five (the first to be published) was on plant geography. Part One was an introduction with atlas. Part Two was on zoology and comparative anatomy; this included contributions by Cuvier and Gay-Lussac. Part Three was political. Part Four was concerned with astronomy and geodesy. The last part in twelve volumes was devoted to botany. It was not until 1833 that the last of these twenty-four volumes was published, although half had appeared by the end of 1815.

The background of the preparation of this ambitious publication must not be forgotten in considering Humboldt's role at Arcueil. Whereas many other members of the group had to share their allegiance to Arcueil with teaching duties, the two great activities in Humboldt's life in Paris were the publication

[1] *Ibid.*, p. 162. [2] *Ann. chim.*, liii (1805), 260–71.

of his travels and his attendance at the Institute and at Arcueil. The First Class of the Institute was too formal and impersonal for Humboldt to be more than a platform for the reading of memoirs. His friendships with the members of the Arcueil group were the really important thing to him and there exist numerous hurriedly written letters by him (many undated) stating that he is just off to Arcueil again.[1] Humboldt was perhaps the perfect member of the Arcueil group. He was willing to extend patronage but the help he gave was not one-sided. He needed scientific companionship and intellectual stimulation. After their Italian journey when Gay-Lussac left him in Berlin to return to Paris, Humboldt wrote how much he missed his friend in that 'moral desert':[2]

> I feel it more every day that I do good work only in an environment where others around me do even better.

When Humboldt returned to Paris in March 1808 he wrote of his close association with Gay-Lussac:

> I pass my time between the *École Polytechnique* and the Tuileries.[3] I work and sleep at the *École*, where I consequently spend my night and mornings. I share the same room with Gay-Lussac. He is my best friend and I find his society most improving and stimulating and this stimulus seems to be mutual.[4]

Soon afterwards Humboldt wrote humorously to Pictet:

> I am living entirely among 'soda' and 'potash'—between Thenard and Gay-Lussac. 'Ammonia', M. Berthollet, comes to see us occasionally . . .[5]

Gay-Lussac married in 1808. Humboldt found a second young companion in Arago. Although they saw rather less of each other after Arago's marriage in 1811, their deep friendship continued up to the death of Arago in 1853. Even after regular meetings at Arcueil had ceased, we find Humboldt reporting in his letters the discussions of the members of the Arcueil circle.[6]

[1] E.g., Wellcome Historical Medical Library, Humboldt dossier, MSS. nos. 33159, 58802.

[2] E. T. Hamy, *op. cit.*, p. 217.

[3] Humboldt's visits to the Tuileries were in connection with his diplomatic mission with Prince William of Prussia.

[4] K. Bruhns, *Life of Alexander von Humboldt*, trans., 1873, vol. ii, pp. 5–6.

[5] *Ibid.*, p. 10.

[6] E.g., 11 July 1819, letter to Pictet, Hamy, *op. cit.*, p. 277.

Humboldt returned to Berlin in May 1827, two months after the death of Laplace. He returned to Prussia largely from a feeling of duty, although he now had the title of Royal Chamberlain and the renewed companionship of his brother helped to compensate for the absence of his Paris friends, notably Arago. That winter Humboldt gave a course of lectures on physical geography to a packed audience in the University of Berlin. He took the opportunity of attacking the speculations of the *Naturphilosophen* and explaining that science must be based on patient observation, accurate experiment and careful measurement. This was surely a lesson he had learned in France.

It was appropriate that when a German congress of science was held in Berlin in 1828 Humboldt should be president. Of the six hundred scientists and doctors who attended, a few came from abroad. Berzelius, whom Humboldt had met at Arcueil, was present and stayed at Humboldt's house, as did Oersted. In his opening address to the conference Humboldt made some remarks about the desirability of personal contact between men of science and the advantage of oral communication both in stimulating the exchange of ideas and in the formation of friendly relations. Humboldt continued in later years to attend such conferences but this ex-member of the Arcueil group was well aware of the disadvantages of large formal gatherings and the fossilization of institutions. Writing to Gauss in 1837 he remarked:

> I prefer a few hours with you to all sessions of the so-called scientists who move in such enormous numbers and so gastronomically that there is never enough scientific contact for me.[1]

Humboldt had not, however, retired from active scientific investigation. He considered that the variation in the magnetic elements could only be investigated by simultaneous observation in different parts of Europe. While Arago and his colleagues at the Paris Observatory made observations, Humboldt in Berlin was tireless in his own magnetic vigils. In 1829 he left Berlin on an expedition to Siberia in the company of Gustav Rose, now professor of chemistry and mineralogy, who examined with him the rich mines of the Urals. Humboldt himself

---

[1] K. Bruhns (ed.), *Briefe zwichen A. von Humboldt und Gauss*, Leipzig, 1877, p. 30.

was particularly concerned with climatic and magnetic observations and for his readings of temperatures he made use of
thermometers constructed and calibrated by Gay-Lussac.

Humboldt was able to calculate the mean height of a large
part of Asia and compare this with data of other continents. The
concept of a mean height of a continent had been introduced by
Laplace in the final volume of his *Mécanique céleste* (1825), where
the relevance was in connection with the effect on the earth's
shape. Humboldt's measurements were significantly different
from Laplace's theoretical estimate and he consulted Poisson
on the reason for this discrepancy. It was, however, with Arago
that Humboldt had the closest contact on the regular visits that
he was able to make to Paris, either on diplomatic missions or
privately. With Arago as one of the two secretaries of the
Académie des Sciences from 1830 to 1853 and Humboldt as one
of the most influential men of science of the period, it was not
easy to gain admittance to the *Académie* without the favour of
this pair. Humboldt, who had always lived modestly, now
found that he was constantly pursued by letters, petitions and
visits in support of various scientific projects. In Paris he found
it advisable to live in obscure back streets where it would be
difficult to find him and solicit his patronage directly. In company with Arago, Humboldt was happy. When separated, he
eagerly awaited letters from him. Humboldt's last visit to Paris
was in 1848.

Humboldt's last great work was his *Cosmos*, a great synthesis,
a 'physics of the world' that he had been planning for fifty
years. He wrote:

> I wished to be able to produce a work after the great model of
> Laplace's *Exposition du système du monde*. I had the good fortune to
> live in the stimulating proximity of Laplace for twenty years both
> at Arcueil and at the *Bureau des Longitudes*, which met at the Paris
> Observatory. Gay-Lussac and Arago were also my companions.[1]

Humboldt's book was to include the poetry of Nature, it was to
describe animate Nature as well as the cold Newtonian universe
of inert masses. Its attempt to be all-embracing is Humboldt's
final gesture, a summary of his own life's work. Yet for all his
respect for numerical accuracy, there is still much of the

---

[1] *Gesammelte Werke*, Stüttgart, 1889, vol. iv, p. 473.

Naturphilosoph in the *Cosmos*. Humboldt, the friend of Laplace and Berthollet, of Gay-Lussac and Arago, had never quite abandoned the habits of thought of his native land and had chosen to dedicate his important book on the geography of plants to Goethe.

Humboldt died on 6 May 1859, a few months short of his ninetieth birthday.

Chaptal

Chaptal was born at Nojaret, department of Lozère, on 5 June 1756. He was educated at the *Collèges* of Mende and Rodez, run by secular priests. In 1774 he enrolled in the Faculty of Medicine at Montpellier and on 5 November 1776 he submitted a thesis for the degree of bachelor of medicine: *Conspectus physiologus de fontibus differentiarum inter homines relative ad scientias*. After qualifying for the degree of doctor of medicine, he persuaded his uncle, who wanted him to go into general practice, to allow him to go to Paris to obtain wider experience. During this time he belonged to an informal literary group, which met at the home of one of its members. His interest in the theatre went beyond visits to the *Théâtre Français*—he actually wrote several plays. During his three-and-a-half years in Paris he became particularly interested in chemistry and he was nominated to teach chemistry at Montpellier. In 1781 he published his first contribution to chemistry—*Mémoires de chimie*—and in the same year he married the daughter of a local merchant. With his wife's dowry and a generous gift from his uncle, Chaptal was comfortably provided for.

About this time he began near Montpellier the manufacture of mineral acids, alum, sal ammoniac, white lead and other chemicals. After a few years he formed a partnership with his former student, Étienne Bérard, to whom he later left the factory. This Bérard was the father of the man who later became a junior member of the Society of Arcueil. Chaptal also began the dyeing of cotton on a large scale. In his autobiography Chaptal claims to have been one of the first in France to have applied chemistry to a wide range of industry. In 1790 he published his *Élémens de chimie* in three volumes, which helped to make his name known not only in other parts of France but in other

European countries and even in America, since in the period of political instability that followed the Revolution, Chaptal received several proposals from abroad that he should emigrate, including one from George Washington, president of the United States.

Although in 1794 Chaptal's political allegiance might well have been in doubt, the Committee of Public Safety appointed him inspector-general for gunpowder and saltpetre in the south of France. This was a responsible position at a time when the revolutionary wars had brought about a shortage of powder. He was then summoned to Paris to take up a similar post there. He was understandably reluctant to endanger his own life by associating himself with the revolutionary movement in Paris when the Jacobins were in power but he received a succession of urgent letters[1] from his friend Berthollet, who warned him that an unfavourable construction would be placed on his delay. If he did not come voluntarily, he would be 'requisitioned'. According to Chaptal's own account, Berthollet's letter gave him confidence and he went to Paris. Chaptal's work on the refinement of saltpetre and manufacture of gunpowder was carried out with Berthollet and other men of science including Monge, Fourcroy and Guyton de Morveau.

After a short period of teaching at the *École Polytechnique*, Chaptal was sent back to Montpellier by the Committee of Public Instruction to organize the school of medicine there. At the same time he resumed his private chemical industrial production. After the Revolution the old Montpellier society that he had known was no more and after several years Chaptal decided to live in Paris, where he had made friends. His decision was not uninfluenced by the vacancy in the chemistry section of the First Class of the Institute, to which he was elected on 24 May 1798, thanks to Berthollet and other friends in the First Class.

Under the Consulate Chaptal was appointed a Councillor of State. On 6 November 1800 he was made acting Minister of the Interior to replace Lucien Bonaparte and his appointment was made permanent from 21 January 1801. As Minister of the Interior Chaptal was concerned not only with the general administration of the whole of France through the system of

[1] Dated 19 March, 20 March, 28 April 1794.

prefects; he was also responsible for public works, education, religion, customs and excise, theatres, state factories, palaces and museums, hospitals and prisons. In the reorganization of the Institute in 1803 Chaptal countered some of the extreme ideas of the Convention and claimed credit for restoring their independence to the separate Classes of the Institute. As Minister of the Interior he exercised patronage towards many who had distinguished themselves in industry and technology. In his concern with the state of French industry, Chaptal claimed to have visited at least one factory a week. His administration was notable for his advocacy of an expansion of technical education, one important centre of which was the *Conservatoire des Arts et Métiers*, where a school for technical drawing was established as well as a school giving practical instruction in spinning and weaving.[1]

In 1804 Chaptal, who was already finding that his opportunities for independent action were diminishing under the growing absolutism of Napoleon, suddenly found the Emperor taking an interest in his mistress, the actress Mlle. Bourgoin. This was too much for Chaptal, who immediately tended his resignation as Minister of the Interior. Napoleon accepted his resignation with some reluctance but compensated him with a place in the Senate.

In 1802 Chaptal had bought a magnificent house at Chanteloup, near Amboise in the Loire valley. His release from the duties of Minister of the Interior enabled him to make use of the house, although he still felt obliged, he tells us, to put in a few appearances in the Senate.[2] Chaptal spent a considerable sum on the restoration of the *château* and in 1808 he claimed it was worthy to receive a king. On the estate he raised sheep, he distilled brandy and he experimented on the cultivation of sugar beet, to which he devoted sixty acres of land. Under Chaptal the annual income of the estate rose from 14,000 to 60,000 francs. Yet Chaptal believed that if anyone was to run an industrial or even agricultural enterprise successfully, even though his workers

[1] R. Tresse, 'J. A. Chaptal et l'enseignenent technique de 1800 à 1819', *Revue d'histoire des sciences*, x (1957), 167–74.
[2] Writing from Chanteloup on 19 June 1808, Chaptal remarked that he would have stayed there another month if he had not been under a moral obligation to attend some of the meetings of the Senate (J. Pigeire, *Le vie et l'oeuvre de Chaptal*, 1932, pp. 459–60).

might live in the country, he himself should live in a town where he would be 'surrounded by technicians and scientists who would enlighten him'.

In 1810 Chaptal was re-elected treasurer of the Senate. This gave him a reason for spending more time in Paris. A second reason was his role as adviser to Napoleon on matters of trade, since he had been nominated a member of the Council on commerce and industry. The Council, which held lengthy weekly meetings, was a small body having the Ministers of the Interior and Foreign Affairs as members *ex officio* and was presided over by Napoleon himself.

At the end of December 1813 Chaptal was sent to Lyons with extraordinary powers to hasten conscription and organize the national guard. Napoleon's confidence in Chaptal's loyalty and ability was again shown during the Hundred Days, when he was appointed Minister of Agriculture, Commerce and Industry. After Napoleon's final exile, Chaptal withdrew to Chanteloup, although in 1818 he was belatedly included in the *Chambre des Pairs*. In this assembly he remained independent of political affiliations. His final years were clouded by the financial ruin of his son who had been running a chemical factory. To pay his debts he sold Chanteloup. Chaptal lived long enough to see Louis-Philippe assume the throne of Charles X. He died on 30 July 1832.

Candolle

Augustin Pyramus de Candolle was born at Geneva on 4 February 1778. His father had been successful in business and was a member of the government of the city. On the approach of the French army in 1792 many of the women and children left Geneva for the country and it was perhaps here that Candolle acquired his first interest in botany. Opportunities of a higher education in Paris attracted the young Candolle and, on the understanding that he would study medicine, he left Geneva for Paris in 1796.

Candolle found himself drawn more and more towards botany and one of his first studies, that of the action of light on plants, aroused considerable interest when presented to the First Class of the Institute in August 1800. Candolle was encouraged to present himself as a candidate for a vacancy in the botany section of the First Class. The attempt was doomed to failure but it brought him to the attention of the *Société Philomatique*, almost as though this society were for unsuccessful candidates to the First Class. Here he met Cuvier, who was later to help him. It was also at the *Société Philomatique* that Candolle met Biot and they collaborated in a series of experiments to determine the thermal conductivity of different gases. They used a large flask filled with the gas under test. The flask had a thermometer suspended at the centre and was placed successively in a cold room and a hot room. They were assisted by another Geneva student, François Delaroche. Despite the patient trials of the three young men repeatedly exposed to a temperature of 60°C for more than an hour at a time, it was not possible for them to obtain much accurate information from their experiments.

In 1802 Candolle married. He was still without regular employment but he took the opportunity offered by Lamarck of preparing a new edition of his French Flora. The publishers had offered Lamarck 12,000 francs for this and Lamarck was willing to give three-quarters of this sum to Candolle for his work. The publishers agreed to pay the young botanist this sum in monthly instalments over a period of three years. Candolle now had a steady income but he had undertaken an immense task. He began with a new classification. He was only personally acquainted with plants in a few regions of France but he organized a national network of correspondents to enable his work to be more representative. One of his ambitions was to become a professor of botany and the opportunity presented itself in 1803 when Cuvier, who had been appointed to help in the organization of the French educational system, found himself unable to continue his course at the *Collège de France*. Candolle was recommended as his temporary replacement. Candolle also gave other lectures later in Paris.

When a vacancy was imminent for a professor of botany at the *École de Médecine*, Candolle realized that he would only be eligible if he had a medical degree. It was true that he had matriculated in the school and had begun courses on physiology and anatomy but he was unlikely to be able to pass the examination. A way of by-passing the regulations was found with the help of several friends and even the connivance of the Minister, Chaptal. When he had obtained his diploma, his friends appropriately acted before him the relevant scene from Molière's *Malade imaginaire*.

In 1805 the new edition of Lamarck's French Flora was published. Candolle realized, however, that there were still several parts of France where no serious study had been made of plants. He drew the attention of the new Minister of the Interior, Champagny, to this fact and he was accordingly given the task of travelling throughout the whole of France partly to observe the flora but also with the more utilitarian motive of noting the connections between botany and agriculture and local conditions. Five years was to be allowed for this programme with 4,000 francs a year for travelling expenses. Candolle started in 1806 and the programme was not completed until 1812.

For the purposes of Candolle's botanical study France was divided into six regions and each summer he would visit one of them. In 1806 Candolle visited the north-west of France, taking the months of July and August. He returned in time to stand as a candidate for a vacancy at the Institute. He was not successful, but the birth of a son later that year made him realize that he should have greater security. An opportunity presented itself in Montpellier where the professor of botany had had a stroke. Moreover, as Chaptal was honorary professor at the medical school and Berthollet was the Senator for Montpellier, Candolle was in a particularly favourable position to be appointed. Yet he was loath to leave Paris and arranged that his botanical exploration for 1807 should be in the Pyrenees, so that he could pass through Montpellier and see more clearly what the position there would involve. He was away from Paris from April to the end of July. When he was nominated for the post, he at first declined on the grounds that he did not wish to abandon the programme of the national botanical survey. Through the good offices of Berthollet and Chaptal, the Minister of the Interior allowed him to keep his first appointment at the same time as the chair at Montpellier.

At the end of March 1808 Candolle left Paris with his family for Montpellier. It was with a heavy heart that he left his friends and the intellectual stimulus of the capital, yet he left under conditions which made it possible for him to return to Paris every year. Candolle gave his lectures on botany six days of the week with field work on Sundays, so that at the end of two months the course was finished and he was free to leave Montpellier. On 1 June he left for Tuscany, then part of the French Empire. He also managed to visit Geneva and Paris. In the autumn of 1808 there was another vacancy for a botanist in the First Class. Candolle failed to secure election despite his assurance that if elected he would immediately resign his Montpellier post and come to live permanently in Paris.[1] Nevertheless, Candolle had spent nearly three months (early October–20 December) in Paris before returning to Montpellier. In 1809 he spent nearly four months in Geneva and Savoy and in 1810 he once more left Montpellier promptly on 1 June, dividing the summer and autumn between his duties in Alsace and north-east France and his interests and friends in Paris. In 1811 Candolle explored the remaining central region of France before going on to Paris, where he spent six weeks. Candolle says that it was not until he returned to Montpellier in November of that year that he regarded himself as established there. Yet in 1812 he again visited Paris, this time primarily to obtain advice about the publication of his *Traité élémentaire de la botanique*, which appeared the following year.

Montpellier had received particularly favourable treatment when Chaptal was Minister of the Interior and its anatomical theatre, chemistry laboratory and the hothouse of the botanical garden had all been built at his orders. Candolle did much to restore and extend the botanical garden in Montpellier and he was also a successful teacher. To his title of professor of botany at the medical school was added in 1810 the title of professor of botany in the newly-established Faculty of Science at Montpellier. The lecture course was common to the two establishments, but he received an additional 1,500 francs for the extra post, half the salary of a Faculty professor. In 1813 he hoped to be appointed Rector of the University, but despite the support of his friends in Paris[2] and his annual visit there he was disappointed. Throughout his residence in Montpellier he had

---

[1] *P.V. Inst.*, vol. iv, pp. 109, 131, 132.
[2] For a letter from Berthollet describing his support see Candolle, *Mémoires et Souvenirs*, Geneva and Paris, 1862, p. 555.

maintained his contacts not only with Paris but also with his native Geneva. In 1816 he decided to return to Geneva, which had now received its independence from France and was a canton of Switzerland. He took up the post of professor of natural history at the Geneva Academy and in 1817 he was appointed director of the botanical garden in Geneva.

In 1816 Candolle had paid a visit to England. He was received by Sir Joseph Banks and he also found Blagden and Marcet most helpful. Candolle spent the rest of his life in Geneva. It was a return home. Yet his years in France had been the formative ones of his life. It was his experience in France that enabled him to aspire to a European reputation. In 1820 Berthollet made one last attempt to bring Candolle back to Paris as a member of the *Académie* but Candolle was now content where he was. In 1826 the *Académie des Sciences* made him one of their eight *associés étrangers*. Candolle died at Geneva on 9 September 1841.

Biot

Jean-Baptiste Biot was born on 21 April 1774 in Paris. His father was an official at the treasury. He attended the *Collège Louis-le-Grand* and after a short time in the artillery he became one of the first students at the *École Polytechnique* in 1794. He proved to be an excellent mathematician and after a short intensive course he graduated and was sent to Beauvais as professor of mathematics at the *École Centrale* there. The *Écoles Centrales* had been established by the Convention in each department of France and an interesting feature of them was the prominent place given to the teaching of science. In the end this venture into the general teaching of science at secondary level proved largely a failure due to the shortage of suitably qualified teachers. In this national campaign, however, Biot played his part.

In April 1803 a large meteorite was said to have fallen near the village of L'Aigle in the Orne department. In view of the general interest in such phenomena, which the rationalist strain in French thought found difficult to accept, the Minister of the Interior, Chaptal, sent Biot to confirm the reports and carry out a full investigation. Biot set out from Paris at the end of June.

He examined the testimony of eyewitnesses and other local people and brought back samples of several meteorites, which Thenard analysed for him when he arrived back in Paris a fortnight later. In a memoir which he read to the First Class on 18 July[1] Biot concluded with the hope that he had 'succeeded in placing beyond doubt one of the most astonishing phenomena which men have ever seen'.

Another of the more unusual projects in which Biot took part was his balloon ascent in 1804 with Gay-Lussac. A further joint venture undertaken by Biot, this time with Arago, was the determination of the arc of the meridian in Spain and the Balearic Islands. They were to take up the task which Méchain had left incomplete at the time of his death in Spain in 1804. The post-Revolutionary metric system was based on the idea of a 'natural' unit, the metre, which was supposed to be exactly one ten-millionth part of a meridian quadrant of the earth. Méchain and Delambre had made measurements over a meridian arc of 10° stretching from Dunkirk to Barcelona and from their readings the length of a standard metre was obtained. It was now proposed that this should be re-determined with greater accuracy by extending measurements further south to the island of Formentera, so that the latitude of the centre of the complete arc should be as near as possible to the forty-fifth parallel. The length of a degree of latitude varies with the longitude in which it is measured owing to the flattening of the earth towards its poles. By choosing to measure a degree mid-way between the poles and the equator the effect of the earth's shape would be minimized.

Biot described the aid he received for the 1806 expedition in the following terms:

> The Emperor gave orders for the expedition and provided gener-ously all the necessary support. Spain gave us a ship and England provided a safe-conduct.

In view of later disputes involving Biot, it is a pleasure to record that Biot's report, which he read at the public meeting of the First Class for 1810, is notable for its generous acknowledge-ment of the help and co-operation of others.[2]

---

[1] Biot, *Mélanges scientifiques et littéraires*, 1858, vol. i, pp. 15–46.
[2] 'Notice sur les operations faites en Espagne pour prolonger la méri-dienne de France jusqu'aux îles Baléares', Biot, *Mélanges*, vol. i, pp. 47–68.

Geodesic measurements were normally carried out by triangulation involving the sighting of a point on near-by high ground. As the Balearic islands were 150 km. from the mainland, the special procedure had to be adopted of carrying out observations at night, using oil lamps and mirrors as targets for observation. Arago was left on the mainland whilst Biot and a Spanish assistant sailed to Iviza to set up the lamps on one of the highest points of the island. It was only after two months of nightly vigils that the observers on the mainland (which formed the base of their triangle) were able to detect a pinpoint of light through a telescope on a night with no moon. This was the beginning of a series of observations which took Arago a year to complete. One of the difficulties experienced by Biot and Arago was the carrying of their instruments up steep mountains, and when Biot returned to Paris in May 1807 it was to obtain another circular scale graduated in degrees to replace one that had broken in transit. Biot did not return to Spain until the late autumn and was therefore present in Paris in the summer when it was decided to call the informal meetings at Berthollet's country house 'the Society of Arcueil'.

Biot's journey to Spain was not his only expedition abroad. In order to extend the measurement of the arc of the meridian to the north, he undertook in 1817–18 a journey through Britain to the Shetland Isles, and in 1824 he was to be found in Italy determining the length of the seconds pendulum. With these diversions Biot continued his life of teaching and research in Paris. A measure of his industry is provided by the list of over three hundred memoirs published in scientific journals, quite apart from the several books he wrote. In his declining years, as doyen of the *Académie des Sciences*, he used his influence to favour many a young man struggling for recognition in the scientific world. At his death in 1862 at the age of eighty-seven, he was the last but one of the survivors of the Arcueil group.

Malus

Étienne Louis Malus was born on 23 July 1775 in Paris. His father was treasurer of France and he had his son educated privately. Malus had a good literary education in the classics; he not only learned Greek and Latin but composed verses and wrote several plays. He was also distinguished in algebra and geometry and passed the entrance examination to the military school of engineering at Mézières. He eventually entered the *École Polytechnique* in Paris and here, by his superior mathematical ability, he attracted the attention of the director, Monge.

On graduation in 1796 Malus went to Metz, where he was cadet sub-lieutenant of engineers and shortly afterwards, captain. In the following year he was posted to active service with the army. For nearly a year he was a member of the garrison in the German university town of Giessen. In the nineteenth century Giessen was to become widely known through the work of Liebig. At that time Giessen was a small obscure provincial university which only enters our story because it was to the eldest daughter of the chancellor of the university that Malus became engaged. In May 1798 he was ordered to Toulon to serve under Caffarelli in an expedition with a secret destination which was later revealed as Egypt.

Embarked on *L'Aquilon*, a vessel of seventy-four guns, he took part in the assault on Malta and he tells us that later, in the battle of the Pyramids, he was in one of the battalions formed in squares on the right wing beside General Desaix. The diary kept by Malus describes other engagements in which he took part and, more peacefully, his work in the Institute of Egypt. At one time he was with Desaix in Upper Egypt and at another he reconnoitred the communications of the Nile with neighbouring lakes. In Cairo Malus supervised the construction of a fort.

In the Holy Land, after sacking Jaffa, the army continued on its way to Acre. Malus was ordered to supervise the emergency hospital set up in a convent for 400 men suffering from the plague. He himself was infected but although all his friends and comrades succumbed, he survived and on 21 April was transferred to a ship returning to Egypt. That summer Malus wrote a memoir on light intended for the Institute of Egypt. In October General Kléber (commander-in-chief after the return to France of Bonaparte earlier that year) conferred on him the rank of major. We will pass over the further military exploits of Malus and come to his return to France where he landed at Marseilles on 1 October 1801. After the regulation period of quarantine he hastened to his relatives in Paris and then to Giessen, where he married the girl who had been engaged to him four years previously.

It was during a stay in Paris in 1808 that Malus discovered the polarization of light. This was hailed as a major breakthrough in the history of science, not only by his contemporaries in France but also abroad. In Britain Brewster wrote:

> The discovery of the polarization of light by reflection constitutes a memorable epoch in the history of optics; and the name of Malus, who first made known this remarkable property of bodies, will be for ever associated with a branch of science which he had the sole merit of creating. By a few brilliant and comprehensive experiments he established the general fact that light acquired the same property as one of the pencils formed by double refraction, when it was reflected at a particular angle from the surface of all transparent bodies . . .[1]

Thomas Young, reviewing the *Mémoires* of the Society of Arcueil in which Malus' discovery was published, hailed it as

> by far the most important and interesting that has been made in France concerning the properties of light, at least since the time of Huygens.[2]

This tribute was paid in spite of Young's antagonism to the corpuscular theory of light advocated by Malus.

Malus was reserved in his manner and once wrote to a friend that he was living like a hermit, spending whole days without uttering a word. His students at the *École Polytechnique* found that when he was correcting their work he would merely point to any part of a solution to a problem that was not clear without speaking. Only in his family circle or with close friends would he reveal the warmth of his personal feelings. On one or two occasions when he considered that others had appropriated his own ideas without acknowledgement he defended his own priority with a vehemence which surprised his friends.

Malus had only a few years in Paris to enjoy the company of his friends at Arcueil and later his colleagues at the Institute. These years are described in subsequent chapters. Malus died on 23 February 1812, his death certificate being signed by his

---

[1] *Phil. Trans.*, 1815, 125.
[2] Young, *Works*, ed. Peacock, 1855, vol. i, p. 247.

9a. Biot.

British Museum

9b. Malus

British Museum

10a. Arago

Musée Carnavalet

10b. Poisson.

Musée Carnavalet

11a. Gay-Lussac.

11b. Thenard.

12a. Dulong.

British Museum

12b. Descotils.

two close friends, Arago and Bérard.[1] His tragic death came when he was not yet forty. By his contributions to optics he was, however, assured of a permanent place in the annals of science.

Arago

Dominique François Jean Arago was born on 26 February 1786 at Estagel in the region of the Pyrenees. His father had a degree in law and during Arago's boyhood was appointed treasurer of the mint at Perpignan. The family also owned a vineyard and a plantation of olive trees, and were therefore of moderate means. Arago was of Spanish descent and when François later joined the Society of Arcueil his lively temperament formed a contrast with the more reserved manner of other members such as Malus.

Arago first came to Paris as a student at the *École Polytechnique.* He proved to be a brilliant pupil and on graduation his obvious merit combined with the friendship of Poisson and the patronage of Laplace won him the nomination to the vacancy for a secretary at the Paris Observatory. Here he entered into an immediate collaboration with Biot on optical experiments, and he also collaborated with Biot in a study of a comet, which they presented at the Institute on 18 November 1805. On 2 May 1806, with the support of Laplace, Biot and Arago were given the task of completing the measurement of the arc of meridian in Spain. The best account of their adventures beyond the frontiers of France has been provided by Arago himself in his 'History of my youth'.

In the course of his adventures Arago found himself carried off to North Africa and it was not until September 1809 that he was able to return to Paris. To most men an absence of three years from the scientific life of the capital would have been a serious handicap to their advancement. Arago was able to present himself as a man who had been accumulating basic scientific data at the risk of his life and this helped him to secure election to a vacancy in the First Class of the Institute at the incredibly early age of twenty-three. He immediately took an active interest in the politics of the First Class and in 1830 he was eventually elected as permanent secretary. Meanwhile he

[1] Archives de la Seine.

K

continued to work at the Observatory, at which he had been given the rank of assistant astronomer during his absence in Spain, and at the *École Polytechnique*, where in 1809 he was appointed to take over Monge's course on analytical geometry.

Arago married on 11 September 1811. It is interesting to find that François Arago led several members of his family towards the world of science. Two of his sisters married scientists. One married the brilliant mathematical physicist Petit, best known for his work carried out in collaboration with Dulong, and the other married the astronomer Mathieu and consequently lived at the Observatory, i.e. in the same establishment as Arago himself. During the Restoration Arago obtained for his younger brother Étienne the post of laboratory demonstrator in chemistry attached to Gay-Lussac's course at the *École Polytechnique*.

Despite his many other duties and obligations, Arago did not neglect research. In 1810 when he was investigating Newton's rings he found that sheets of mica could produce polarization. The experiments he carried out about this time marked the beginning of his dissatisfaction with the corpuscular theory of light and his interest in the wave theory. His friendship with Fresnel is described later. Apart from his scientific research, Arago made important contributions to the popularization of science, both in his lectures on astronomy at the Observatory and as permanent secretary of the *Académie des Sciences*. His election to this post in 1830 gave him a central place in French science for the next two decades.

Arago also took an active part in politics. In 1830 he became a member of the chamber of deputies, representing the Eastern Pyrenees, and took his place on the extreme left wing where he formed part of the opposition to the regime of Louis-Philippe. During the revolution of 1848 he became a Minister in the provisional government. In his short period of office as Minister of War and of the Navy he improved naval rations, ended flogging and procured the abolition of negro slavery in the French colonies. His sudden political defeat was soon followed by partial blindness, although in the remaining five years of his life he still insisted on playing his part as secretary of the *Académie des Sciences*. He died in October 1853.

Poisson

Siméon Denis Poisson was born on 21 June 1781 at Pithiviers, fifty miles to the south of Paris. He was of humble parentage but the death of his father shortly after the Revolution left the family in a state of extreme poverty and Poisson was sent to stay at Fontainebleau with an uncle, who was a surgeon, in the hope that he would take up this career. It was through the *École Centrale* at Fontainebleau that Poisson, who until then had received only the most rudimentary education, came into contact with mathematics. In two years he was ready to take the entrance examination for the *École Polytechnique*. He was not only placed first in order of merit but, because of his exceptional performance, a special category was created for him so that the second in order of merit was deemed to have come first.

Within six weeks of entry to the school he had developed a theorem of Lagrange, generalizing the proposition and extending it to all possible cases. This drew the favourable attention of Laplace. A second patron was Hachette, in whose house he lodged. It was Hachette who secured for him immediately on graduation the post of *répétiteur-adjoint* of mathematical analysis, a vacancy caused by the continual absence in Egypt of Fourier. On 8 December 1800 when he was still only nineteen, Poisson presented his first memoir at the Institute and this made a further favourable impression. He was soon asked by Biot to act as a temporary replacement for his lectures at the *Collège de France* and the association with Biot brought him further under Laplace's wing.

By 1808 he had shown himself to be a mathematician of stature comparable to that of Laplace, since in June of that year he presented an important memoir to the First Class on the invariability of the major axes of planetary orbits, a problem that both Lagrange and Laplace had considered in terms of periodic functions. Poisson was able to demonstrate that the non-periodic terms of the order which he considered would cancel out. In this way Poisson made a major contribution to demonstrating the stability of the solar system.

This memoir in a sense marks the beginning of a career devoted to the application of mathematics to physical problems and the similarity of this programme to that of Laplace was more than a coincidence. Poisson turned from astronomy to physics and in particular the action of molecular forces. He made fundamental contributions to the theory of elasticity, the propagation of heat, the distribution of electricity and magnetism and capillary attraction, to mention only a few fields in which he applied his perfect command of mathematical analysis.

Poisson derived the usual financial benefits from his chairs at the *École Polytechnique* and the Faculty of Science, his post as assistant astronomer at the *Bureau des Longitudes* and his examining duties at the *École Polytechnique* and the artillery school at Metz. In middle age he was appointed to the board of direction for the whole of education in France, with the responsibility for mathematics. He is reported to have made an unwise investment of his savings of about 300,000 francs, a situation which left him in a state of anxiety for many years.

Although Poisson had a short flirtation with politics, it may be said that practically his whole life was his mathematical work. He had simple and regular habits, never missing a meeting of the First Class or a lecture or an examination. As a student at the *École Polytechnique* he had worked particularly hard to the exclusion of social activities. Later, particularly after his marriage in 1817, he received no visitors but worked in his study from early morning until dinner at six, his family and the occasional game of whist with friends in the evening providing his only distraction from his work. By virtue of his mathematical genius allied to his persistent hard work he was able to publish an exceptionally large number of memoirs in scientific journals. If his name is still used today for a ratio of elasticity known to all physicists and engineers, it should be known no less for many other fundamental contributions he made to mathematical physics. His exacting life of study to the exclusion of recreation hastened his death by tuberculosis. He died on 25 April 1840 at the age of fifty-nine after eighteen months of serious illness.

Gay-Lussac

Joseph Louis Gay-Lussac was born on 6 December 1778 at Saint Léonard in the region of Limoges. His grandfather had been a physician and his father was *procureur du roi* and a judge up to the time of the Revolution. The father was then imprisoned because of his supposed aristocratic sympathies but, although he eventually obtained his own release, for a few years the family was living in straitened circumstances. By 1800, however, the father had obtained a position as director of posts.

In November 1794, when he was nearly sixteen, young Gay-Lussac was sent to Paris to the *pension* Savouret, one of the few educational establishments which had survived the rigours of the Revolution. Here he continued his general education and also received special coaching in mathematics to enable him to take the entrance examination for the *École Polytechnique*. He was successful and spent three years there, graduating on 22 November 1800. In 1801 he joined Berthollet as his assistant and there followed an association which was the very kernel of the Society of Arcueil.

The period of the first Empire, which Gay-Lussac divided between Arcueil and the *École Polytechnique*, witnessed many fruitful collaborations of Gay-Lussac, not least with Thenard, and also one great rivalry—that with Davy. Davy's isolation of sodium and potassium was countered by a more effective method of preparation carried out by Gay-Lussac and Thenard, who were also at some pains to challenge (unjustifiably) the elementary nature of the new substances. In the examination of the simple nature of chlorine, it was the two French chemists whose work came first but it was left to Davy to insist that chlorine was an element. The rivalry was even continued on French soil during Davy's visit in 1813–14 when he was the first to announce the existence of the new element iodine (December 1813). Gay-Lussac's major memoir on iodine was not ready until 1 August 1814.

The results achieved by Gay-Lussac were less spectacular than the most famous of those of Davy, but the French chemist was perhaps more systematic. Davy was probably weakest in quantitative work, in which Gay-Lussac excelled.[1] Among the most brilliant contributions made to chemistry by Gay-Lussac

[1] Berzelius writing in 1818 to Marcet commented: 'Davy ne devrait jamais s'occuper de faire des expériences où il faut de l'exactitude, ce n'est point son côté fort.'—Berzelius, *Bref*, vol. 1, part iii, p. 186.

we may include his work on hydracids, vapour density, combining volumes of gases, volumetric analysis, organic analysis and an anticipation of the law of mass action. He thus became the leading figure in French chemistry after the virtual retirement of Berthollet at the end of the Empire. Gay-Lussac held a number of important teaching posts in higher education and was also prominent as a consultant in applied chemistry. He died on 9 May 1850.

Gay-Lussac was attended in his last illness by Magendie, who had rendered a similar service a quarter of a century previously to Laplace. Arago wrote for news of his old friend's health. Arago and Thenard each spoke at the funeral and, shortly after, a third member of the Arcueil group, Biot, had the opportunity of paying public tribute to his former friend and colleague when he was asked by the Royal Society to write an obituary of Gay-Lussac, who had been a foreign member.

Thenard

Louis Jacques Thenard was born on 4 May 1777 at the village of La Louptière, in what is now the department of Aube. His parents were farm workers and Louis Jacques was one of six children. His ability gained him a place in a church school, where he received a literary education. By his early teens Thenard had decided that he would like to become a pharmacist, and it was to pursue these studies that he went to Paris, where he at first lived in a garret before lodging with Vauquelin, his teacher. Through Vauquelin he was introduced to a wider world including Conté (who accompanied Bonaparte to Egypt) and Charles (whose lectures on physics he attended). Thenard, having shown evidence of unusual ability, was soon treated by Vauquelin as an equal. Vauquelin was closely attached to Fourcroy and it looked as though Thenard was to become a third permanent member of this alliance when he had occasion to challenge some of Berthollet's work.[1] Far from alienating Berthollet, the latter was impressed by the ability and enthusiasm of the younger man and after 1804 Thenard became a member of the Arcueil circle.

Thenard's most important work in association with the

[1] *Ann. chim.*, xliii (1802), 176–84.

Arcueil group was done in collaboration with Gay-Lussac. From the beginning of 1808 Thenard published no memoirs of his own for two years. Their fertile collaboration produced several new compounds and one new element—boron. Their work on the alkali metals led incidentally to the preparation of their peroxides. It was from barium peroxide that Thenard in 1818 prepared hydrogen peroxide, perhaps his most famous discovery.

In 1830 Thenard was appointed together with Poisson and Cuvier to represent the sciences in the reorganization of French education and after science it was in the field of education that Thenard made his second major contribution to his country. In 1825 he was made a baron and in 1832 a peer. By now he had become an elder statesman of science and a patron rather than an active scientist. He died on 21 June 1857.

Dulong

Pierre Louis Dulong was born on 12 February 1785 at Rouen. Although he was orphaned at the age of four, he was well cared for by an aunt. He became a pupil at the *École Centrale* founded by the Convention at Auxerre. His ability in mathematics enabled him to pass the entrance examination to the *École Polytechnique* in 1801 at the minimum age of sixteen. He worked excessively so that he had a breakdown at the beginning of his second year and had to leave the school without graduating. Having recovered his health, he studied successively medicine, botany and chemistry. It was finally in chemistry that he found his *métier*, although his subsequent work in physics and physical chemistry shows the value of his earlier training at the *École Polytechnique*.

Dulong worked for a short time in Thenard's laboratory before Berthollet suggested that he should go to Arcueil. His first published paper[1] was an interesting study of chemical equilibrium, clearly inspired by his patron. So much of his work in the period 1811–16 derived from the work of others in the Arcueil group, particularly Berthollet and Gay-Lussac, that we may call attention to his revolt on the subject of atoms. In 1820 he wrote as follows to Berzelius:

[1] *Ann. chim.*, lxxxii (1812), 273–308.

I am convinced, notwithstanding the objections of M. de Laplace
and of some others that this [atomic] theory is the most important
idea of the century . . .[1]

Dulong had to struggle to do most of his research against a
background of ill-health and teaching duties that he found an
undue burden. Dulong was not uncomplaining but he consistently avoided personal quarrels. Chevreul considered it
remarkable that in thirty years of scientific life no one had
published any attacks on him. Thenard found the explanation
in his great modesty: Dulong always spoke well of the work of
others and with reserve about his own achievements.

His own research was not insignificant. He discovered nitrogen trichloride and hypophosphorous acid. In collaboration
with his friend Petit, he formulated the law relating the specific
heats of solid elements to their atomic weights (1819) and did
other important work on heat. He collaborated with Thenard
on the use of platinum as a catalyst (1823) and with Arago in
a long and dangerous series of experiments on the elastic force
of steam at high temperatures (1830).

In 1832 Dulong was elected permanent secretary of the
Académie des Sciences for the physical sciences, thus joining Arago,
who represented the mathematical sciences. The duties were
more exacting than he had anticipated, however, and after one
year he resigned. He died on 19 July 1838, leaving a wife (whom
he had married in 1803) and three sons.

Descotils

Hippolyte Victor Collet-Descotils was born on 21 November
1773 in Caen, the son of a barrister. He attended a local
Collège and then in 1790 he went with his father to Paris, where
he not only survived but managed to acquire a general scientific
education. He was taught physics by Charles and chemistry by
Vauquelin, who took a particular interest in his young student
and friend. At the end of 1792 he was conscripted into the navy.
The foundation of the *École des Mines* was to provide for him not
only a means of escape from military service but a means of
continuing his scientific education. Having passed the entrance
examination to the *École des Mines*, he returned to Paris in

[1] Berzelius, *Bref*, vol. 2, part iv, p. 12.

1794. In 1798 he was given the rank of *ingénieur*, but his career at the school was interrupted when he was asked by Berthollet to go on a scientific expedition. Descotils accepted and later the same year he found himself in Egypt. On his return to France he was put in charge of the laboratory at the *École des Mines* and in 1809 he was promoted to *ingénieur en chef*, a grade for which the salary was 5,000 francs.

From his laboratory Descotils was able to contribute to the national economy, for example, through his analysis of tin ores from the department of Haute Vienne, which showed that these deposits were worth exploiting. He was made a member of the Consultative Committee of Arts and Manufactures established by the Ministry of the Interior and he was later on the governing board of the society for the encouragement of national industry. In 1813 Descotils was sent to Italy to inspect and re-organize the famous alum mines at Tolfa. At the beginning of 1815 he was nominated provisional director of the *École des Mines*. In the course of his work at the *École des Mines*, Descotils carried out a large number of analyses of minerals. A few of these were published in the *Journal des Mines* and the *Annales de chimie*.

The name of Descotils is inseparably linked with the history of the platinum metals. Descotils in 1803 was the first to investigate the coloured precipitate formed by the addition of sal ammoniac to a solution of native platinum in aqua regia.[1] He concluded that this was due to a new substance. Simultaneously in England work had been started on the same problem by Smithson Tennant. He carefully studied the paper published by Descotils and also the work carried on independently in Paris at the same time by Fourcroy and Vauquelin. Although it was Tennant who formally announced in June 1804 the discovery of the new metal which he named 'iridium', it is reasonable to claim for Descotils the independent discovery of the metal.[2]

In 1807 Descotils published a method of extracting platinum without using large quantities of aqua regia.[3] He also devised a method of separating more efficiently iridium from platinum.

[1] *Ann. chim.*, xlviii (1803), 153–76.
[2] J. R. Partington, *History of Chemistry*, vol. iii, 1962, p. 704.
[3] *Ann. chim.*, lxiv (1807), 334.

A recent historian of platinum describes this as 'a rudimentary form of the now universal practice of using the hydrolytic decomposition of iridic chloride in alkaline solution. It took, however, the passage of more than a century to bring such a process into use and Descotils remained a pioneer without followers.'[1]

Not long after his return from Egypt Descotils began to suffer from peritonitis, which often made his laboratory work painful. He was able to carry on for another ten years, but on 6 December 1815 he died at the age of only forty-two.

Bérard

Jacques Étienne Bérard was born at Montpellier on 12 October 1789. The name Bérard was shared by several fairly prominent figures in French science and medicine at the beginning of the nineteenth century and we must not confuse the Bérard of the Society of Arcueil with other men of that name.[2] The elder Bérard (Étienne), who does not appear in any of the standard French biographies, was at one time professor of chemistry at the medical school at Montpellier. He had been first the pupil of Chaptal and then his associate in a chemical factory in the Montpellier region. In the opening years of the nineteenth century, when Chaptal had moved permanently to Paris and Bérard had given up his teaching career, he was still engaged in the manufacture of acids and other products. He also contributed papers to the *Annales de chimie*.[3]

His son, Jacques Étienne, liberated from provincial obscurity by the decision of the father to send him to Paris, achieved a national if not an international reputation through his association with the Arcueil group. From a laboratory assistant he became a full member of the Society of Arcueil and collaborated particularly with Gay-Lussac and Malus. Bérard took advantage of his proximity to Paris to follow courses at the newly-established university and was successively bachelier-ès-lettres (1811) and licencié-ès-sciences.[4]

[1] D. McDonald, *A History of the Platinum Metals from the Earliest Times to the 1880's*, 1960, p. 138.
[2] See e.g. *Royal Society Catalogue of Scientific Papers*, which confuses father and son.   [3] *Ann. chim.*, xxxix (1801), 65–73; lxviii (1808), 78–87.
[4] *Registres de la Faculté de Médecine de Montpellier*, 1804–20, p. 152 (Information from Mlle Y. Vidal).

Bérard is not lost sight of after his return to Montpellier in 1813. Sir Humphry Davy had been in Paris from the end of October to the end of December 1813, and he not only passed through Montpellier on his way to Italy but found the atmosphere so congenial that he stayed there for about a month, during which time he received every assistance from Bérard.[1] It was in Bérard's laboratory that Davy continued his experiments on iodine, which he had so successfully begun in Paris. Davy was particularly interested in the possible iodine content of Mediterranean marine plants and Bérard had large quantities of seaweed burned so that he could subject the ashes to chemical examination, help which was acknowledged by Davy.[2] When Davy finally left Montpellier on 7 February 1814 to visit the fountain of Vaucluse, it was in the company of Bérard.

We also have the testimony of the British chemist, Smithson Tennant, who went to France in October 1814 in the peace following the defeat of Napoleon. In October and November he made a tour of southern France including Montpellier. He wrote:

> At Montpellier I had the peculiar advantage of a most attentive acquaintance (M. Bérard), who is one of the best chemists in France. The country affords few such; but he was brought up at the feet of Berthollet, who gave me a letter to him. He succeeded to the chemical works of Chaptal, which are now very extensive and carried on with great intelligence.[3]

After his life at Arcueil, however, Bérard was not content with a life devoted entirely to industrial chemistry. On 9 July 1817 he submitted a thesis at Montpellier, on the analysis of animal substances,[4] for the degree of Doctor of Medicine. The thesis was not remarkable for its originality, but the degree enabled him to accept immediately afterwards the position of professor of chemistry at the school of pharmacy at Montpellier. He later became professor of chemistry in the Faculty

---

[1] J. A. Paris, *The life of Sir Humphry Davy*, 1831, vol. ii, pp. 32–3.
[2] *Phil. Trans.*, 1814, 505.
[3] Letter written by Tennant in November 1814 from Lyons, quoted by T. Thomson, *Annals of Philosophy*, vi (1815), 95.
[4] *Ann. chim. phys.*, v (1817), 290–8.

of Medicine. His few publications in this period include studies on mineral waters.

In 1837 Bérard was elected as a member of the Chamber of Deputies for the department of Hérault and sat as a liberal. His political career was short-lived, however, and his opposition to the government resulted in his not being appointed Dean of the Faculty of Medicine at the University of Montpellier until 1846.

The death of Bérard on 10 June 1869 removed the last living link with the Society of Arcueil.

A. B. Berthollet

Amédée Barthélemy Berthollet was born on 8 October 1780.[1] He entered the *École Polytechnique* in December 1796 but he left in September 1798, abandoning the rigorous mathematical training of the *École* in favour of a general study of chemistry and chemical industry. When his father bought the property at Arcueil in 1801, Amédée Berthollet began a small trial chlorine bleaching works in collaboration with Gay-Lussac. The Bièvre stream which ran through the village had been used for generations by the local inhabitants for the traditional method of bleaching by exposing cloth to the air and sunlight, followed by washing, the whole process being repeated many times. Arcueil was now to be one of the centres of the new science, although on the practical plane the village of Jouy near Versailles was to be of greater importance. Here Oberkampf had set up a larger bleaching works attached to his textile printing factory and it was here that Amédée Berthollet went to widen his industrial experience. His connection with Jouy lasted four years. In the period 1801–5 he had set up a small laboratory, where he had carried out experiments on the whole range of dyeing and bleaching.

Amédée Berthollet's ambitions, however, extended beyond industrial chemistry. He wished to contribute to pure research and in March 1803 he read a memoir at the Institute, work which revealed the influence of his father's ideas on variable proportions. In January 1807, just before the founding of the

[1] École Polytechnique, *Registre de Matricule des Élèves*, vols. 1–2 (1794–1802).

Society of Arcueil, he joined the *Société Philomatique* in order to have more of the company of other young men interested in science. On 24 March 1808 he read a memoir to the First Class on ammonia, the composition of which had been discovered by his father.

Later that same year he went to the Carmargue in the south of France to set up a chemical factory in collaboration with Chaptal's son. The climate and the proximity of raw materials made Provence a suitable region for chemical industry at that time but Amédée Berthollet probably missed the company of his Parisian friends. In 1810 (the beginning of a period of general economic depression in France) the failure of the factory drove him to suicide. The man who had been brought up in a scientific environment chose to die in a way that might be of use to science. His tragic end at the age of twenty-eight by carbon monoxide poisoning is described by Thomas Thomson in the following words:

> Retiring to a small room, he locked the door, closed up every chink and crevice which might admit the air, carried writing materials to a table on which he placed a second-watch, and then seated himself before it. He now marked precisely the hour, and lighted a brazier of charcoal beside him. He continued to note down the series of sensations he then experienced in succession, detailing the approach and rapid progress of delirium, until, as time went on, the writing became confused and illegible, and the young victim dropped dead upon the floor.[1]

Amédée Berthollet cannot be described as a great scientist, although it is impossible to say what he might have accomplished had he enjoyed more than a brief adult life. In the history of science Amédée Berthollet has no important place, but in this book his contribution assumes greater proportions. After all, it was to further the scientific career of his son and of other young men that Berthollet founded the Society of Arcueil.

If the Society of Arcueil survived the death of Berthollet's son, it was not because Berthollet did not feel the loss very deeply. Cuvier reports on his subsequent morose and withdrawn expression and when Berthollet returned to science it was partly as a distraction to make him forget his grief. We may note the

---

[1] T. Thomson, *History of Chemistry*, 1830, 31, vol. ii, p. 151.

following significant remark in a letter written by Berthollet soon after the downfall of Napoleon:

> It seems to me that our calamities will have the happy effect of increasing our zeal for *science, which is the least deceptive refuge in this life.*[1]

'Associate Members' of the Society of Arcueil

Apart from the fifteen men who were considered to be full members of the Society of Arcueil, there were a number of others who were definitely more than mere visitors to Arcueil. Their presence at Arcueil and their collaboration with members of the Arcueil circle would entitle them to be considered as 'associate members' of the Society. The possible claim of five men to this description will now be briefly examined. It is interesting that two of them should originate from Geneva, an important centre of scientific intelligence at the beginning of the nineteenth century. Candolle too came from Geneva and Biot, Humboldt and later Arago were to visit that city, temporarily incorporated into the French Empire as the department of Leman.

Marc Auguste Pictet (1752–1825), the oldest of the five to be considered, although a citizen of Geneva, was so frequently in Paris during the Consulate and Empire that there was some doubt as to his qualifications to remain a correspondent of the First Class of the Institute.[2] He was interested in astronomy, physics and chemistry and he made several visits to Britain, but it is above all as one of the editors of the *Bibliothèque britannique*[3] that he deserves to be remembered in the history of science. After his third visit to England in 1801 he returned to Geneva by way of Paris, where at meetings of the First Class on 8 and 13 October he gave news of British science and industry and displayed instruments he had brought back. In 1802 he was back

[1] Royal Society, *Blagden Letters*, B.143. Letter from Berthollet, 3 February 1816 (my italics).

[2] On 11 April 1802 Pictet was elected 'Associé, Section de Physique' but according to the government decree of the following year 'Pictet à Genève' is named as a correspondent. In March 1807 he was further nominated as a correspondent of the Institute in the Section of Rural Economy.

[3] A unique journal, important during the Napoleonic wars for its role in disseminating on the continent news from Britain. The author is preparing a study of this periodical.

again in Paris and this time he stayed for a whole year. Thanks to his diary[1] we know something of his social activities in addition to his strictly scientific work.

In May 1802 he was invited to dinner by Laplace and he found Blagden, Berthollet and Fourcroy among the guests; the following December and January finds him again dining with Laplace. On these occasions it was the custom to hold religion up to ridicule, whether the discussion originated from Chateaubriand's writings or otherwise. At one of these dinners Pictet met Chaptal —at that time not only Minister of the Interior but president of the First Class of the Institute. Pictet also dined at Berthollet's house in July 1802[2] and one gathers from his correspondence about this time that he saw Berthollet fairly frequently and discussed scientific matters.[3] At this time too Berthollet contributed regular extracts from the *Bibliothèque britannique* to the *Annales de chimie*. Pictet spent a further three months in Paris at the beginning of 1804 and he refers to dining with Biot. In the autumn of 1804 Pictet was able to play host to Biot when the latter passed through Geneva in his capacity as entrance examiner for the *École Polytechnique*. Biot's friendship with Pictet is also illustrated by the numerous contributions he made to the journal edited by Pictet. During Pictet's visit to Paris in 1804 he went to see Talleyrand to offer his services in his capacity as editor of the *Bibliothèque britannique* to send messages to England.

We find Pictet once more in Paris in 1805. He continued to see Berthollet, to whom he passed on the discoveries by Smithson Tennant and Wollaston in England of osmium, iridium and palladium, and he dined with him at Arcueil.[4] In a letter to his friend Marcet he spoke of his admiration for the great traveller Humboldt, whom he had met and whom he visited regularly.[5] In the following years Pictet continued to live as much in Paris as in Geneva. He attended meetings of the First Class of the Institute regularly when in Paris and on 1 October 1810 Gay-Lussac, who was in the habit of seeing Pictet regularly at the

[1] 'Journal d'un Genevois à Paris sous le Consulat', *Mémoires et documents publiés par la Société d'histoire et d'archéologie de Genève*, 2e série, v (1893–1901), 98–133.
[2] Letter from Pictet to A. Marcet, Paris, 20 July 1802, *Bibliothèque universitaire de Genève*, MS. fr. 666, f. 133.   [3] *Ibid.*, f. 129, 135.
[4] Letter dated Geneva 17 July [1806], *ibid.*, f. 162.
[5] Letter dated Paris 19 January 1805, *ibid.*, f. 151.

meetings at the Institute, wrote to him, remarking that he had
not seen him lately. Pictet, who was a correspondent of Davy,
translated into French his memoir on the decomposition of the
fixed alkalis and read this at three successive meetings of the
First Class in September 1808. Pictet's interest in Davy's work
would bring him close to Gay-Lussac and Thenard at this time.
Also in July 1809, Pictet, Gay-Lussac and Thenard were
appointed examiners in science to the four Paris lycées.

From the above it is clear that Pictet was on good terms with
Berthollet and many other members of the Society of Arcueil,
including his fellow-citizen of Geneva, Candolle. Only Laplace
may have taken an objection to him.[1] It is probable that only
the policy of severely restricted membership of the Society of
Arcueil and Pictet's vacillations between Geneva and Paris
prevented him from obtaining formal membership of the Society.
In any case Pictet's age, his membership of the First Class and
his important position as the editor of a leading scientific journal
would hardly have allowed him to fit in among the junior
members. Nevertheless, in a paper published in the *Mémoires* of
Arcueil by Berthollet on the heat produced by the impact and
compression of metals, he acknowledged the assistance of Pictet
and Biot and even used a particularly sensitive thermometer
belonging to Pictet.[2]

Another son of Geneva, whose name does not appear among
the fifteen 'official' members of the Society of Arcueil, but who
nevertheless attended meetings, was François de la Roche. The
fact that he attended some of the meetings of the Society of
Arcueil is clear from Candolle's account.[3]

The father of Delaroche (as his name was usually written)
had been born in Geneva but had come to Paris where he was
employed as a doctor at the *maison de santé* in the Faubourg St
Martin. The son, born about 1775,[4] also studied medicine and
at one time helped Biot and Candolle in their experiments on the
body's transpiration at high temperatures.[5] Delaroche became

---

[1] At a meeting of the First Class in 1803 Pictet had objected to some remarks by Laplace—'Laplace a repliqué avec aigreur. Il se pourrait qu'il
m'en voulut', 'Journal d'un Genevois' etc., p. 113.

[2] *M.S.A.*, ii (1809), 441–8.

[3] Candolle, *Mémoires et Souvenirs*, 1862, p. 165.

[4] A. de Montet, *Dictionnaire biographique des Genevois*, Lausanne, 1877, 78.

[5] Candolle, *Mémoires*, p. 116.

particularly interested in this subject and in 1806, the year of his graduation in Paris as a doctor of medicine, he published his first memoir, which was concerned with the effect of heat on animals. His scientific interests and his friendship with Biot and Candolle gained him the membership of the *Société Philomatique*, to which he was elected on 24 January 1807, the same day as Amédée Berthollet.

It was Delaroche who was nominated as a naturalist attached to the expedition on the extension of the meridian. He probably obtained this post through the good offices of his brother-in-law Duméril, an icthylogist at the *Muséum d'Histoire Naturelle*. He was all the more acceptable as the expedition was led by his friend Biot. Biot had already published in the first volume of the Arcueil *Mémoires* an analysis of air contained in the swim bladder of Mediterranean fish. This was one of the subjects Delaroche intended to investigate further when he left Paris with Biot for the Balearic Islands in October 1807. During the winter months Delaroche carried out a systematic investigation of the air contained in the swim bladder of fish caught at various depths and concluded that the quantity of oxygen present for different fish of the same species was proportional to the depth at which they were found.[1]

On his return to Paris in 1808 Delaroche took up again his previous work on body temperature and environment and in November 1809 he read his first paper to the First Class on this subject. Meanwhile he took over from Candolle the publication of further volumes of *Les Lilaciées*. In 1811 his work was turned towards physics by the announcement of a prize to be awarded by the Institute for research on the specific heat of gases. In June 1811 Delaroche read a memoir to the First Class on radiant heat and there followed an active collaboration with Bérard on the subject of the prize. On 3 February 1812 they deposited a sealed note on the specific heat of gases with the secretary of the First Class and when the award was made, it was Delaroche and Bérard who received the prize.

The last memoir that Delaroche read at the Institute was on 12 May 1812 on the influence of air temperature on respiration. He said that when he had presented a memoir on animal heat two-and-a-half years previously, the problem of respiration at

[1] *Annales du Muséum d'Histoire Naturelle*, xiv (1809), 184–217; 245–89.

different temperatures had been raised again at the end of the meeting by some leading members, and in particular Laplace, who suggested that he should carry out further experiments on this.[1] Berthollet offered him full facilities for carrying out the experiments and Delaroche began them immediately at Arcueil with the help of Bérard. It was in this way that the two young men came to know each other and this was the beginning of the association which led to the important work on the specific heat of gases.

We may wonder why the name of Delaroche is not to be found in the lists of members of the Society of Arcueil included in the volumes of *Mémoires* of the society published in 1807, 1809 and 1817. In 1807 he knew Biot and Candolle but probably none of the senior members of the Society. It was not until November 1809 that he drew the attention of Berthollet and Laplace. In the following years he was to be found not infrequently at Arcueil but at the end of 1813 he died suddenly of a fever. One of the last investigations carried out by Delaroche was on the influence of the wind on the propagation of sound. It was read at the First Class on 15 November 1813 and published posthumously by Arago in the first volume of the *Annales de chimie et de physique*. Delaroche had carried out his experiments in the autumn of 1813 in the vicinity of Arcueil with the help of a friend from Montpellier.

Another young man who associated with the Arcueil group was Jean Louis Roard. He was one of the first students at the *École Polytechnique*, which he entered at the age of nineteen, and he left three years later in 1797. He was appointed as professor of physics at the *École Centrale* at Beauvais, where he had Biot as a colleague. Roard's main interest was chemistry. His first published paper[2] was concerned with pigments and by 1804 he had been appointed director of dyeing at the Gobelin works. He wrote a memoir on the dying of wool, which was presented at the Institute on 31 December 1804 and which Berthollet examined.[3] He now entered into a period of collaboration with Thenard and on 23 June 1806 they presented the results of their joint work (in which they had been assisted by Amédée Berthollet)

---

[1] *Journal de physique*, lxxvii (1813), 5–16.
[2] *Ann. chim.*, xl (1801), 133–44.
[3] *P.V. Inst.*, vol. iii, pp. 172, 177–8. *Ann. chim.*, liii (1805), 184–207.

in a memoir read to the First Class and praised by Chaptal.[1] The following year he was collaborating with Gay-Lussac on the treatment of silk and it was Gay-Lussac who proposed him as a candidate for a vacancy in the chemistry section of the First Class in 1810.[2] He wrote another joint memoir with Thenard about this time.[3] Thus to the well-known partnership of Gay-Lussac and Thenard a third figure is added and in the *Recherches physico-chimiques* of 1811 Gay-Lussac and Thenard acknowledge the co-operation of Roard in their studies of the effect of light on dyes.[4]

Next a brief mention must be made of Provençal, if only because he was Humboldt's collaborator in a study of the respiration of fish, published in the Arcueil *Mémoires*.[5] Provençal (like Roard) is not included in any of the standard French biographies. He is mainly of interest as a further link of the Arcueil group with Montpellier. Jean Michel Provençal (1781–1845) was appointed professor of zoology when the *Faculté des Sciences* was established at Montpellier in 1810. He was a colleague and friend of Candolle[6] and in 1810 he was elected a correspondent of the First Class of the Institute in Paris. Ampère, writing in 1811, spoke highly of him and said that he was very friendly with him.[7]

The chemist Chenevix was also associated with Arcueil. Richard Chenevix (1774–1830), an Irishman of French ancestry, had been imprisoned in Paris during the Reign of Terror. If we are to believe Thomson,[8] he shared a cell with several French chemists, who passed the time by explaining the principles of chemistry to him. On his release Chenevix studied chemistry seriously and began to make a name for himself as an analytical chemist back in Britain. In April 1803 appeared an anonymous announcement of a new metal, palladium, which was on sale at a private house in London. Chenevix, suspecting from the

[1] *Ann. chim.*, lix (1806), 58–95. *P.V. Inst.*, vol. iii, pp. 617–18.

[2] *Mém. Sav. Etr.*, ii (1811), 518–45. *P.V. Inst.*, vol. iv, pp. 314–15.

[3] 'Sur les mordants employés dans la teinture', *Ann. chim.*, lxxiv (1810), 267–99.

[4] *Op. cit.*, vol. ii, p. 200.

[5] *M.S.A.*, ii (1809), 359–404.

[6] Humboldt writing to Candolle on 24 March 1812 sends his regards to Provençal, *Mémoires de la Société de Géographie de Genève*, vii (1868), 265–6.

[7] *Correspondance du Grand Ampère*, ed. L. de Launay, 1936, 43, pp. 362, 407.

[8] T. Thomson, *History of Chemistry*, 1830, 31, vol. ii, p. 215.

unorthodox method of announcement that it was a fraud, bought up the entire stock. Convinced that this was no element, Chenevix made repeated trials to synthesize it from platinum and mercury and eventually claimed success. He presented his results at a meeting of the Royal Society on 12 May 1803. Chenevix continued to maintain this position and it was not until February 1805 that Wollaston, now secretary of the Royal Society, admitted that he had been responsible for the discovery and the unorthodox method of announcement. It was unfortunate that Chenevix should have staked his chemical reputation on the mere suspicion of a fraud and that he should have been in such a hurry to claim that he had synthesized palladium.

In December 1802 Berthollet reported to the First Class on a book by Chenevix criticizing the new chemical nomenclature. According to Blagden,[1] who was present, Berthollet 'spoke very favourably both of the work and of the author'. Accordingly, when Chenevix was travelling on the continent in the late summer of 1803, he was already well in Berthollet's favour and it was through the good offices of the latter that he obtained a passport to leave Paris.[2] Again in June 1806 he obtained a passport to enter France through the recommendation of Berthollet and Laplace.[3] The travels of Chenevix on the Continent of Europe during the Napoleonic wars illustrate what was possible for a man of science provided he had friends in high places.

The research of Chenevix on the combination of platinum and mercury had been influenced by Berthollet's ideas on affinity and Berthollet for his part had been interested to read Chenevix's memoir in the *Philosophical Transactions*,[4] in which he had suggested that platinum could combine with mercury in several proportions to form a compound body from which even the strongest fire could not separate the mercury. Berthollet offered the hospitality of his laboratory at Arcueil to enable Chenevix to continue research on these alloys and Descotils

[1] British Museum, Additional MS. 33272, f. 214v.

[2] Natural History Museum, *Collection of copies of the correspondence of Sir Joseph Banks made for Dawson Turner*, vol. xiv, f. 141 (letter from Chenevix to Banks, Leipzig, 25 September 1803).

[3] E. d'Hauterive, *La police secrète du premier Empire*, vol. ii, 1913, p. 386. Chenevix had spent 18 months at Freiberg, where he had attended Werner's lectures, but in the later controversy between Werner and Haüy, he supported the latter.

[4] *Phil. Trans.*, 1803, 290–320, especially pp. 297, 307.

was also willing to collaborate in this work.[1] The final role of Chenevix in the Society of Arcueil was as the bearer of several copies of the latest volume of the Arcueil *Mémoires* to Britain in the summer of 1809.[2] The responsibility of Chenevix for making Dalton aware of the work of the Arcueil group does something to compensate for his unfortunate role in the palladium affair.

Finally one might ask about some of the scientists who lived in Paris but were *not* associated with the Arcueil group. Perhaps if Monge and Laplace had liked each other more, Monge would have become a member of the Society of Arcueil, but in any case he was busy enough with his beloved *École Polytechnique*. Fourcroy tended to be a colleague and even a rival of Berthollet rather than a friend and he would not have come to terms easily with the physical approach of the Arcueil group; in any case he had a violent dislike for Chaptal.[3] Guyton was seventy years old in 1807 and his work at the *École Polytechnique* and at the Mint was enough for him. If Guyton was too old, Petit might have been too young, since in 1807 he was only sixteen and was about to enter the first year of his studies at the *École Polytechnique*. His first publication dates from 1814, when the formal meetings at Arcueil were at an end. Petit's fruitful collaboration with Dulong in the Restoration came at a time when the Arcueil association was much less well-defined. Rumford had come to live permanently in Paris in 1805 on his marriage to Madame Lavoisier. Rumford became particularly friendly with Lagrange but offended Laplace by rejecting his theory of capillarity in favour of a theory of his own. Berthollet's great friend Blagden too had quarrelled with Rumford and he therefore had little contact with the Society of Arcueil.

An almost exact contemporary of Petit at the *École Polytechnique* was Cauchy, who was to become one of the most brilliant mathematicians of the next generation. The Cauchy family had lived in the village of Arcueil since the time of the Revolution but in much more modest circumstances than Berthollet. In January 1800 Cauchy's father became secretary to the Senate and he did not neglect the opportunity of mentioning to Laplace (whom he naturally met in the course of his work) the

[1] *Ann. chim.*, lxvii (1808), 86–90.
[2] Royal Society, *Blagden Letters*, B.135 (9 July 1809).
[3] Candolle, *Mémoires et Souvenirs*, 1862, p. 186.

mathematical talents of his son Augustin, who entered the *École Polytechnique* in 1805 at the age of sixteen. The differences of social positions between Cauchy *père* and Laplace probably meant that they were neighbours in no more than the literal sense of the term. Moreover, the Cauchy family were devout Catholics. Nevertheless, Laplace was fully aware of the mathematical ability of young Cauchy and when a vacancy arose in the First Class of the Institute at the end of the Empire, Laplace was prepared to support him. In the event Cauchy entered the newly constituted *Académie Royale des Sciences* in 1816 by royal proclamation.

The Organization of Science in France at the Beginning of the Nineteenth Century

IN THE previous chapter all the characters of the Arcueil group were introduced. But to understand Arcueil it is not sufficient to know something of the *people* involved; we must also consider *institutions*. The place of the Society of Arcueil can only be judged against the background of other societies concerned with science and functioning in the Paris region in the opening years of the nineteenth century.

The first point to be made is about the number of such societies. It has been thought worthwhile to mention briefly some of the more trivial organizations in order that the whole spectrum should be available for examination. At one end of the spectrum was the section of the Institute concerned with science, the 'First Class'. A capable man might aspire to membership for a whole lifetime before actually being elected. An equally able man might fail to secure election for lack of support from one of the powerful factions within the First Class. The honour of being a member was proportional to the difficulty of securing election. At the other extreme were minor societies which, at their worst, aped the formal organization of the Institute and at their best provided some contact for ordinary Frenchmen with the science and general culture of the age.

The First Class of the Institute

It is impossible to understand the position of science in France at the beginning of the nineteenth century without a study of the *Institut de France*, or to be more precise, the First Class of the Institute, since it was as this section of the Institute that the old *Académie Royale des Sciences* was re-born under a new name. Although we are primarily concerned with the first decade of the nineteenth century, it is necessary first to consider the earlier years of the Institute. The first meeting of the newly created Institute was held on 6 December 1795 as one outcome of the law relating to public instruction passed by the National Convention six weeks earlier. The Institute was to be divided into three sections or 'Classes'; the First Class was that of the so-called 'mathematical and physical sciences' (which included the life sciences), the Second Class was for 'moral and political sciences' and the Third for 'literature and fine art'.

The union of the academies into one body was an application of the principles of the *Encyclopédie* of Diderot and d'Alembert and had been advocated by Mirabeau, Talleyrand and especially by Condorcet. Previously there had been quite separate academies; now the bonds between the different 'Classes' was so close that one might say that it was really a single academy which sometimes met in separate sections merely for the convenience of carrying out a specialized task more efficiently.

The First Class was to comprise ten sections, each having six members resident in Paris and six associates in the provinces. This was an attempt to strike a fair balance between the capital and the rest of France, as implied by the opening sentence of the statute which brought the Institute into existence: 'The National Institute of science and arts belongs to the whole Republic.' In practice the centralization of talent in Paris not only continued but increased, particularly under the Consulate and Empire. Cretet, Minister of the Interior in the period 1807–9, is reported[1] to have shocked Laplace by saying:

> Do you know that I would sometimes like to fire a cannon into your Institute . . . to disperse its members throughout France. Is it not deplorable to have all the best brains in Paris and the provinces in ignorance?

The First Class of the Institute was thus to have a total of sixty resident members compared with thirty-six in the Second Class and forty-eight in the Third Class. Not only was the Class of 'mathematical and physical sciences' the largest; it was also given primacy of place in the Institute. Whereas the *Académie des Sciences* (founded 1666), despite its distinguished history, had always been the junior institution in relation to the *Académie Française* (founded 1635), under the Directory, Consulate and

---

[1] Flourens, 'Éloge de . . . Candolle', *Mém. Acad. Sc. Inst.*, xix (1845), xi.

Empire the precedence of science and literature were reversed. This was in conformity with the Enlightenment ideal of science as a liberating force, and on a more practical plane, science had already proved its utilitarian value in the crisis of 1793–4. Judged by the criterion of immediate utility, science could have no other place than first. Under Bonaparte the value of science to the national economy became increasingly clear but there was a sharp reversal of policy under Louis XVIII. With the restoration of the monarchy, the seniority of the *Académie Française* was reasserted. A document entitled 'Royal decision on the honours to be accorded to the *Académie Française*' gives a list of six special privileges (particularly in relation to the court) which were to be accorded to members of the *Académie Française* only.[1] These honours were not granted to members of the other academies. The re-formed *Académie des Sciences* took its place as third in order of seniority. Science and its practitioners continued to be respected but the precedence of science was at an end.

We must return, however, to the organization of 1795. The First Class was divided into ten sections and from the following list it will be seen how misleading was the title 'mathematical and physical sciences':

1. Mathematics.
2. Mechanical arts.
3. Astronomy.
4. Experimental physics.
5. Chemistry.
6. Natural history and mineralogy.
7. Botany and plant physiology.
8. Anatomy and zoology.
9. Medicine and surgery.
10. Rural economy and the veterinary arts.

One third of the original members of the Institute were nominated by the Directorate. In the First Class these included Lagrange, Laplace, Berthollet and Guyton. Indeed when Bénézech, the Minister of the Interior, addressed the newly-formed Institute, he pointed out that, despite the two years of social and political upheaval, France could still boast of her scientists, of

[1] Aucoc, *L'Institut*, pp. 208–9 (10 July 1816).

whom he named ten including the first three mentioned above. Guyton de Morveau, by his nomination to the Institute, now became officially recognized for the first time, since he had not been successful in his previous candidature for a vacancy in the old *Académie des Sciences*.[1] It was the task of the nominated members to elect the remaining two thirds of the members and it was in this way that Fourcroy was proposed on 9 December 1795. Three of the great chemists of the period had now become members. A fourth, Chaptal at Montpellier, was first elected as one of the non-resident associates in the chemistry section but was finally elected as a resident member on 24 May 1798.

One of the most significant differences between the First Class of the Institute and the *Académie des Sciences* was the abolition of a formal hierarchy of title of membership. The former distinction in status and salary between *honoraires*, *pensionnaires*, and *adjoints* was abolished. This was to a certain extent replaced by an order of seniority within each section. Thus if we look at the list for 1803[2] we find the Mathematics Section of six members headed by Lagrange with Laplace in second place and Delambre (about to be elected as one of the two permanent secretaries) in fifth place. The Mechanics Section was headed by Monge, the Mineralogy Section by Haüy. The six members of the Chemistry Section in order of seniority were Berthollet,[3] Guyton, Fourcroy, Vauquelin, Deyeux and Chaptal. Chaptal, despite his key position in the government as Minister of the Interior, was only a junior member as far as the decisions of the Chemistry Section were concerned. The First Class had, nevertheless, shown its tact by electing Chaptal as president in 1802.

A serious criticism of the regulations of 1796 was that new members were elected by the Institute as a whole and not by the Class concerned, although the latter had the right to prepare a preliminary list of candidates. This meant that more than half of the electing body would not be properly qualified to assess the relative merits of the candidates. A second serious fault, a reflection of the political climate, was the withdrawal of

---

[1] Guyton had, however, been a correspondent of the *Académie*.

[2] The list drawn up at the reorganization of 1803 is nearer to the period which is the main concern of this book than the original list.

[3] Guyton had been placed first and Berthollet second in the list of 1795. This was probably due to Guyton's greater age—he was nearly twelve years Berthollet's senior.

authority from the president and secretary of each Class, who were elected for six months and twelve months respectively. (Actually there were two secretaries, who had to be elected at intervals of six months.) This system had two disastrous results. On the one hand the Institute spent a large amount of its time on administrative matters owing to the frequency of elections of all kinds. On the other hand, the efficiency of the administration was low, since there was no continuity of office, as in the days of the *Académie des Sciences*, whose permanent secretaries had included such famous names as Fontenelle and Condorcet. Despite the dangers of abuse of authority by an oligarchy, it was probably preferable to the anarchy which prevailed in the administration in the first years of the Institute.

In the revolutionary calendar, the week with its Sabbath was replaced by a unit of ten days called the *décade*. Each Class of the Institute was to meet twice every *décade*, the First Class, for example, meeting on the first and sixth days. In July 1796 it was laid down that each resident member should receive an annual salary of 1,500 francs in principle. In practice it was felt that, as in the old academies, some financial inducement should be used to encourage the regular attendance of members. It was agreed to deduct a sum of 300 francs from the annual salary and use this to make up a fund which would be divided in proportion to the actual attendance of members at meetings. A quarter of an hour after the beginning of a meeting a line was drawn below the last name signed in the register. Only those who had signed above the line were entitled to payment known as a *jeton de presence*. The usual value of a *jeton* was about five francs.[1] Those members of the Institute who, through motives of need or greed, attended all the meetings of the Institute in order not to miss their *jetons* were known as *jetonniers*. As the attendance registers of the First Class reveal that when Bonaparte attended he was usually late, it is clear that he at least was no *jetonnier* !

The budget for the Institute was not passed without comment. With individual salaries of 1,500 francs and administrative costs the budget came to 280,000 francs, which to many members of the Council of Five Hundred in July 1796 seemed excessive. It was passed, however, on the assurance that this

[1] The equivalent of about two days wages of the average working man in Paris in the period 1800–10.

sum would be deducted from the 600,000 livres allowed annually to the Minister of the Interior for the support of science
and arts. In the first few years of the Institute, salaries were not
paid as regularly as they should have been and by March 1800
they were eleven months in arrears. The Institute set up a
commission to inform Bonaparte (now First Consul) of the plight
of the members, some of whom had no other source of income.
No doubt the members of the Institute congratulated themselves on their foresight in electing the young General Bonaparte
to their ranks two years previously.

We have mentioned that the salary of members of the Institute was 1,500 francs. In practice the salaries were distributed so
that their *average* was 1,500 francs. The original members
appointed, such as Berthollet, were to receive 2,100 francs, the
second group elected (e.g., Fourcroy) were to receive 1,500
francs and the final group elected (e.g., Vauquelin) were to
receive only 900 francs. By the statutes of 1803 a return was
made to the principle of equality. Each member now received
1,500 francs less 300 francs which was to be divided according
to the attendance. This did not go without opposition, however, and at a meeting of the First Class on 21 February 1803
one member suggested that allowances should be given to
members in respect of their seniority.

In the Council of Five Hundred in 1796, Villers, presenting
the report, insisted that those with private incomes should not
be allowed to forgo their salaries, otherwise the way would be
open to the re-establishment of honorary members as in the old
Academies, such members being appointed because of their
rank rather than their abilities. Difficulties arose in the application of this principle in the case of members who in some other
capacity received a substantial salary from the State. By a
resolution of the Institute on 6 August 1796 the Institute salary
was to be suspended in the case of members of legislative bodies,
but the whole thing was rather vague and on 7 April 1801 the
Institute passed the following resolution:

> Those members of the Institute who hold public offices and who
> receive in this capacity a salary of 10,000 francs or more will have
> their salary from the Institute suspended, so that . . . they will
> receive only the payments in respect of attendance.

In May 1803 Bonaparte countermanded this resolution so that, for example, wealthy Senators such as Berthollet were no longer to be deprived of their salaries as members of the Institute.

On the foundation of the Institute the first members, nominated by the government were exhorted 'in conformity with the laws and decrees of the Directorate, to follow scientific and literary work which has as its object general utility and the glory of the Republic'. The theme of utility was dominant under the Directory and is reflected in much of the activity of the First Class including its initial choice of subjects for the annual prizes. Condorcet had used the term *fonctionnaire publique* to describe the position of members of an institution such as the Institute and when we find them behaving with obedience and even servility towards the representatives of the government, we should remember that members of the Institute, unlike members of the Royal Society, were, in the broadest sense of the term, civil servants.

The early Institute was required to justify itself by works and we find a variety of communications from different ministries which corresponded with the First Class as if it were just another government department. In the first six months of the existence of the Institute it was asked to draw up reports on objects or memoirs sent not only by the Directorate (a variety of topics including the examination of minerals, machines and a boat) but also the Ministry of Foreign Affairs, the Ministry of the Interior, the Ministry of Finance and the *Bureau Central de la Commune de Paris*. We find the Institute concerned with topics ranging from education to a new geographical division of France. Sometimes the subject involved collaboration between various Classes. When the Minister of the Interior in August 1799 asked for advice on the cleaning of marble statues, the chemists of the First Class combined with the sculpture section of the Third Class.

Heavy demands were made on the First Class of the Institute. The members of the Class had a meeting twice each *décade* and in addition there were the twelve monthly general meetings and four quarterly public meetings. There were extra meetings of the sections and, most onerous of all, the innumerable committees. Not only were committees elected to consider govern-

ment matters, the appointment of a committee was the normal
procedure for the examination of a memoir submitted by any
outside individual. This committee would report back to the
First Class at a later meeting. At many of the early meetings of
the First Class work was postponed to a later meeting because of
the time taken by administration and other business, and from
31 May 1798 the First Class was forced to meet earlier in the day
because of the pressure of work. There were so many time-
consuming committees that on 28 March 1800 a further committee was appointed to speed up the work of the other committees! A picture of the members of the Institute meeting
almost daily and spending half their time on administrative
matters would be only a slight exaggeration. Certainly the
continual elections for members of committees and ballots for
offices and for vacancies in the sections either as residents or
correspondents was the most prominent and time-consuming
feature of the meetings of the Institute. Of the lobbying that
preceded many of these elections more will be said later.

The four quarterly public meetings of the Institute were
intended to give the general populace an idea of the work of all
the Classes of the Institute. Consequently each Class made its
own contribution and a memoir on physics would be followed
by a dissertation on human happiness and a memoir on ele-
phants by a piece of epic poetry—a veritable *pot pourri*, lasting
three to four hours, far longer than the patience or attention of
much of the audience. If the Classes had held their public
meetings separately, people would have been able to choose
between science and literature, but the idea of unity of knowledge did not permit this. The choice of subjects was often bad
and even singularly unfortunate—as even the *Moniteur* remarked when Fourcroy (no doubt chosen because of his ability
as a lecturer) delivered to the public on 4 April 1797 a memoir
on the comparison of human urine to that of a horse. Another
memoir, read at the same meeting by a member of the Second
Class on the social habits of dogs, may well have been received
by the general public with more levity than was intended by
the author.

The Institute under the Consulate and Empire

In 1801 Bonaparte, wishing to carry out various improvements in the Louvre, realized that the Institute would have to move. A new place was sought as near as possible to the centre of Paris. By the decree of 20 March 1805 Bonaparte transferred the meeting place to the Palais des Quatre Nations on the left bank (i.e. the south side) of the Seine. In comparison with the spacious splendour of the Louvre this was a modest building, but most of the members of the Institute were glad to be in a home of their own and not in shared apartments under the surveillance of a host of minor functionaries. The First Class met for the first time in the Palais des Quatre Nations on 9 February 1807, and the *Académie des Sciences* continues to meet there today.

On 30 July 1800 the First Class appointed Laplace and Fourcroy as its representatives to meet representatives of the other Classes to consider whether members of the Institute should have a recognized means of identification. They eventually decided that a uniform was desirable. A decree signed by Bonaparte on 13 May 1801 gave details of the uniforms, one for the most formal occasions and another for ordinary meetings. The Rev. William Shepherd, one of many visitors to Paris during the peace of Amiens, described their uniform as 'very odd':

> It consisted of a dark green coat richly embroidered with light green lace, a yellow waistcoat and green breeches. The attire gave them the appearance of a company of respectable old English butlers.[1]

Shepherd was not very sympathetic, however, towards the formal meetings of scientific societies:

> I found the proceedings of the National Institute as tedious as those of the Royal Society of London; and I was heartily glad to escape from the assemblage, which, in my opinion, was chargeable with a profusive waste of time. For what benefit can be derived from the hearing of mathematical calculations, the details of chemical experiments and long series of profound argumentation, the comprehension of which can only be the result of patient study in the retirement of the closet?

---

[1] W. Shepherd, *Paris in 1802 and 1814*, 2nd edn., 1814, pp. 101–2.

In 1802 Bonaparte as First Consul called for a reorganization of the Institute. His motives were largely political and the reorganization enabled him to suppress the potential opposition of the political theorists. At the same time a genuine need for reform had been felt, not least by the First Class. The report on the Institute presented to the Consuls on 7 January 1803 is all the more interesting as it was presented by Chaptal. Although Chaptal was Minister of the Interior, he was also a man of science and a member of the First Class and indeed its president in the republican year XI, i.e. at the time of this report.

Chaptal admitted that, while the aim of an Institute intended to bring together science, literature and the arts was well intentioned, in practice many difficulties had been found. Chaptal spoke of a forced association between subjects which had nothing in common. The system of elections which depended on members of the Institute as a whole rather than those who had knowledge of the qualities of the candidate was ludicrous. A division into four Classes was proposed, each with considerable autonomy. As a gesture to the principle of unity there were to be four general meetings each year at which each of the Academies would take it in turn to give an account to their colleagues of work in that Class during the previous year. A most important proposal involved the reintroduction of the permanent secretaries. This was even seen as making a contribution to the history of science:

> The re-establishment of these positions will bring about a rebirth of a branch of eloquence too much neglected in the past ten years and will give to the work of the Academies that spirit of continuity, that linking of facts and ideas which alone is able to establish the period of a discovery and to trace with precision the history of human knowledge.

The importance of the permanent secretaries may be inferred from the salary of 6,000 francs, four times that paid to ordinary members. The post of permanent secretary was obviously a full-time appointment, as opposed to ordinary membership which left some time for research, administration, teaching or politics.

The duty of the Institute to present periodical reports to the government was soon forgotten, but it was revived by Napoleon. Under the Consulate and the Empire the head of State did not neglect to approach men of science directly to solve particular scientific and technical problems. Considerably less demands, however, were made by government departments on the time of the First Class than under the Directory. A few of these will be mentioned as representative examples of the area in which the advisory capacity of the official body of French science was considered valuable. On 6 April 1800 there was the first of several approaches by the Minister of the Navy to examine pumps. At the same meeting of the Institute the Minister of War asked for a report on a proposal to set up a line of signalling stations from Paris to the English Channel. Laplace was on this committee. On 27 June 1803 the Minister of Finance asked for technical advice on coinage. On 19 November 1804 the Minister of the Interior asked for a report on unpleasant fumes emitted from factories, with particular reference to the effect on public health. Chaptal and Guyton were appointed to examine the question. On 3 March 1806 a further request came from the Minister of the Interior, who wanted advice on the use of cast iron for columns of the Panthéon. Laplace and Monge were members of the committee on this problem.

At a meeting on 28 September 1806 it was announced that the Minister of War had sent a copy of the current instructions on the construction of lightning conductors for the comment of the First Class. A committee was appointed including Laplace, Charles, Montgolfier and Gay-Lussac and the report was read by the latter at a meeting five weeks later. Whereas on a previous famous occasion in the history of science, the Royal Society had to choose between knobs and points for lightning conductors, the French scientists were concerned with the number of points and the material used for them. They considered the suggested use of gold and platinum to be unnecessarily extravagant and proposed gilded copper instead. Attention was also given to the earthing of the conductor. On 11 November 1811 the question was the dyeing of sheep skins for the army without damaging the wool and Chaptal, Berthollet and Tessier were appointed to examine this. Berthollet was again a member of a committee appointed on 1 February 1813 to provide the Minister of War with information on the

M

use of zinc for utensils in military hospitals. These were all comparatively trivial affairs when compared, for example, with the services of some of the same scientists, notably Berthollet, to the Republic in the refining of saltpetre and the production of iron and steel.

At a time when Napoleon had pushed conscription beyond the point of reason, the Institute was able to obtain a special concession. On 14 March 1814 the Minister of the Interior was able to forward to the Institute a copy of a decree by which Napoleon had exempted from military service certain young men who were outstanding in the sciences and the arts and had been specifically listed by the Institute. The physiologist François Magendie, then aged thirty, although not yet a member of the Institute was one of those exempted,[1] thanks to the good offices of Laplace and the minutes for the meeting of the First Class of 21 March record his thanks to the official body of French science.

Another constant point of contact between the government and the *Académie* or Institute was in the election of members. The election always had to be confirmed by the head of state although in the old *Académie des Sciences* for the high rank of pensioner the power of the members of the *Académie* was limited to proposing three candidates; they then awaited the king's pleasure to fill the vacancy from these. In the First Class of the Institute the ratification of elections by Bonaparte became little more than a formality. Later under Louis XVIII there were the cases of Hachette and Fourier, whose election to the *Académie* was at first refused confirmation by the king. A crueller case of political discrimination was that against the aged Monge, the devoted servant of Napoleon. Monge was expelled from the *Académie* on the restoration of the monarchy.

A Crisis within the First Class

So far the work of the First Class of the Institute in general has been discussed and, in particular, its relations with the government. As the official body of French science, it included a galaxy of talent and was admired in other countries. In England, for

---

[1] Magendie had already obtained exemption from military service, e.g. in August 1805.

example, the professional competence of the First Class was acknowledged despite political hostility to the Napoleonic regime. This was from a country in which what should have been the organized focus of science, the Royal Society, was suffering from an inflated membership, in which men who could make a genuine contribution to science were in a distinct minority. A body such as the Institute, which had no place for the wealthy amateur or the dilettante aristocrat, therefore became the object of admiration.

It has been seen, however, that there were many inherent weaknesses in the original Institute and although the reorganization of 1803 brought about some improvement, the resulting society was far from perfection. Attendance of members was more or less guaranteed by moral pressure and financial inducement. But attendance was one thing and active participation another. In 1809 a crisis in the affairs of the First Class was admitted. We shall be particularly concerned to discover if the temporary decline in the affairs of the First Class was related in any way to the Society of Arcueil.

It was the custom for authors and editors to present copies of their publications to the appropriate Class of the Institute. Berthollet's presentation of volume two of the *Mémoires* of the Society of Arcueil to the First Class was perhaps a little tactless in its timing. It was at the meeting of 12 June 1809 that the First Class of the Institute recorded the receipt of this volume. At its previous meeting the members had met in secret session to discuss the decline in the quality and quantity of the memoirs presented at the weekly meetings. A committee consisting of Fourcroy, Laplace, Cuvier, Legendre and Lacépède was appointed to draw up a 'report on the means of making the work of the Class more active' and six weeks later it presented its report.[1]

The report began by recalling some of the circumstances which had caused concern to members. Earlier that summer there had been two consecutive meetings which had had to be adjourned within a few minutes as there was no worthwhile correspondence and no memoirs to be read. Three causes were assigned to this decline in activity. The first was that too many non-members were present at meetings and that many

[1] *P.V. Inst.*, vol. iv, pp. 227–9.

members did not wish to present memoirs in such company, since their work could be criticized outside the Institute before it had been published, or worse, their discoveries could be seized upon by total strangers. What was more, when memoirs were presented, the spontaneous comments and discussions on a high level which these had once provoked, were no longer forthcoming. Another reason was related to the long delays in publication, which were experienced by everyone who read memoirs at meetings of the Institute. The committee realized that many members of the First Class preferred to have their work published immediately after they had written it by by-passing the official *Mémoires* of the First Class in favour of one of the other scientific journals.

These two arguments provide an interesting criticism of the functioning of the Institute, but it was a third reason given for the falling off of memoirs presented to the First Class that was most relevant to the Society of Arcueil and was indirectly a great compliment to it:

> . . . the number of special societies which have been formed in Paris and where members of the Institute go to read their memoirs; this makes the reading of memoirs in the Class a matter of indifference to them, because these societies, composed of persons more particularly devoted to special subjects, form an audience more fitted to appreciate detailed memoirs.

No society was mentioned by name. The Philomatic Society might have been included in these remarks, but its attendance was largely drawn from younger men, aspirants to the Institute and camp followers rather than members; also it was hardly specialized. The membership of the Society of Arcueil (its four leading figures: Berthollet, Laplace, Biot and Gay-Lussac were then members of the First Class) and its concentration on problems of chemistry and physics make it the obvious target of this criticism. Yet the committee appointed by the Institute had to admit the advantages of a small select society:

> Thus the presence of a few chosen persons often gives to memoirs an audience of a kind it would not have among members of the Institute, because today so much of science is so specialized that it cannot enter into a general education and the most highly educated man does not understand what is said unless he has devoted himself to the particular subject.

Although this report provides a revealing glimpse of the difficulties of scientific organization at the beginning of the nineteenth century, it would be a mistake to conclude from it that the Society of Arcueil can be summed up simply as an answer to the increasing need for specialization.[1]

Various reforms were proposed by the committee of the First Class. The easiest to enforce (since members could not be prevented from going to the meetings of other societies or publishing their work elsewhere) would be a revision of the procedure for publication. Also there should be a periodical appearing at regular short intervals and devoted to the work of members of the First Class. Yet a quarter of a century was to elapse before the publication of the first number (August 1835) of the *Comptes Rendus Hebdomadaires des Séances de l'Académie des Sciences*.

The Election of Members of the Arcueil Group to the First Class and to the Académie des Sciences

Perhaps the most interesting of the various ways in which the Arcueil circle interacted with the Institute was in the elections to vacancies in the First Class. Appropriate vacancies occurred so seldom that the ambition to join the severely limited membership of the First Class with its international prestige prompted careful preparation. There is no doubt that the Arcueil circle constituted a pressure group within the First Class and this group was powerful enough to influence the drawing up of lists of candidates for election and the election itself. Some of the events portrayed here may be capable of a different interpretation but the mass of evidence favours the view that elections were often not won simply on the merits of the candidates. Experienced members of the First Class knew how to prepare the ground for their friends and appreciated above all the importance of timing. Of the various groups and coalitions that

---

[1] The Society of Arcueil deliberately proceeded on two fronts, the study of physics and chemistry, and there is therefore no valid simple comparison with the situation in England, where the Royal Society appeared to be threatened by the emergence of very specialized societies such as the Geological Society (founded 1807) and the short-lived 'Society for improving Animal Chemistry' (founded 1809)—C. R. Weld, *History of the Royal Society*, 1848, vol. ii, pp. 237–50.

came into being in French academic politics in the nineteenth century the Arcueil circle has a definite place.

In order to understand the peculiar circumstances of some of the elections to the First Class, we might first examine how Gay-Lussac became a member of the Institute. In the first few years of the nineteenth century there was no vacancy or prospect of a vacancy in the chemistry section. Gay-Lussac was fortunate, however, in that his interests and research had not been confined to chemistry. He could also claim to be quite a respectable experimental physicist and could therefore aspire to membership of the Institute through the section of 'general physics'.

One of the members of this section, the elderly Brisson, was ailing at the beginning of 1806. At a meeting on 10 February the First Class expressed its concern about the state of Brisson's health, and further reports to the Institute in March led people to expect that the end could not be far off. The news that Brisson's death was imminent probably decided Gay-Lussac to return to Paris from Berlin a little earlier than he had originally intended.[1] According to the rules of the Institute, however, no matter how ill or incapable a member might be, even if he had lost the use of his reason, a vacancy could not be declared if he was still alive. Brisson died on 23 June. The question of a replacement was not officially raised for two months but even then it was possible to postpone consideration of possible candidates on the grounds that two members of the physics section (Lefèvre-Gineau and Lévêque) were away from Paris. Meanwhile Gay-Lussac had not been idle. On 8 September he and Humboldt presented their joint memoir on magnetism and at the meeting of the Institute a week later Gay-Lussac was ready to present his provisional results on the variation of temperature of gases on expansion, research which he had carried out at Arcueil with the encouragement of Laplace and Berthollet. Here was some more work to Gay-Lussac's credit that was indisputably 'physics'. Yet he need not have hurried quite so much. Lefèvre-Gineau did not return to Paris until mid-November. There was now no longer any excuse to delay the election further.

In December events moved fast. At the meeting on the first of

---

[1] Arago, *Oeuvres, Notices Biographiques*, vol. iii, p. 29.

the month, Gay-Lussac took the unusual step of reading *two* memoirs, one on magnetism and another on 'gases considered in their different relationships with heat'. In accordance with the usual practice in the case of memoirs presented by non-members of the Institute, a committee was appointed to examine them. The committee consisted of Berthollet, Laplace, Haüy and a member of the physics section, Lefèvre-Gineau. The usual time taken to produce a report was several weeks. Yet in this case Haüy was ready to present reports on these memoirs at the very same meeting! The reports were favourable and accordingly ended with the recommendation of publication in the *Mémoires des Savants Étrangers*. More extraordinary events were to follow. As soon as the Class had approved the two reports on Gay-Lussac's memoir, it met in secret session to decide on a successor to Brisson. The section of 'general physics', of which the senior member was Charles, drew up a list of candidates in order of preference headed by two names bracketed together: Gay-Lussac and Tremery. Lower on the list appeared the names of Montgolfier, Hassenfratz and Prieur.

The Arcueil faction had won the first round. Their nominee was on the list in a favourable position. This advantage must now be pressed home. At the next meeting of the First Class a favourable report was read on Gay-Lussac's memoir on the specific heat of gases and the thermal effect of the expansion of gases. This had originally been given to a committee consisting of Laplace, Haüy and Delambre but somehow Berthollet had managed to get on the committee and the useful signature of Lefèvre-Gineau was also at the bottom of the report. At the same meeting a report was read on Gay-Lussac's memoir on magnetism, which was a joint undertaking with Humboldt. The next item in the minutes was the impending election! The first ballot was inconclusive but in the second ballot Gay-Lussac received an absolute majority. The preparatory work of the Arcueil group and the favourable publicity, which they had ensured that their candidate received in the two meetings preceding the election, had not been in vain!

The next member of the Arcueil group to gain admission to the Institute was Arago. Although Arago had only just joined the Society of Arcueil due to his long absence from France, he was definitely associated with the Arcueil circle, having enjoyed the patronage of Laplace and having collaborated closely with Biot. It was Biot who announced at the meeting of the First Class on 17 July 1809 that Arago had returned to France safely and it was Humboldt who extended the warmest welcome to him immediately on his return.

The most curious feature of Arago's eventual election to the Institute was the inordinate length of time which was allowed to elapse before the vacancy in the astronomy section was filled. The vacancy was caused by the death of Lalande on 4 April 1807. After six weeks had elapsed (a decent length of time after the death of the distinguished astronomer) the First Class considered the question of the vacancy but decided by a unanimous vote to postpone the election for six months. This could have been for one of two reasons: there were no suitable candidates or there was a particularly suitable candidate who was not available then but was expected to return to Paris later in the year. There is good reason for believing the second possibility, the candidate being Arago. Biot and Arago had been chosen by the *Bureau des Longitudes* for geodesic work on the Balearic Islands. Biot (already a member of the Institute) had returned to Paris in the spring, leaving Arago to complete the work. The *Bureau des Longitudes* had shown its confidence in Arago by naming him assistant astronomer on 15 July 1807. Again on 7 December 1807 the First Class decided to postpone the election. In 1808 Arago disappeared[1] and if we were to believe his own account he was given up for lost. One might then ask why the Institute should keep open a place for a man presumed dead. A study of the minutes of the *Bureau des Longitudes* shows that only at the meeting of 22 September 1808 was there any serious doubt as to whether Arago was still alive. By 30 September they were reassured by a letter from his father, who kept them constantly informed about his son till the following July, when François Arago finally reached Marseilles. After a period of quarantine he arrived back in Paris in August 1809. At the meeting of the First Class on 28 August Arago was welcomed back and allowed by special invitation to take part in the meeting.

At the meeting of 4 September Arago read a memoir on the

---

[1] Arago had a series of adventures which included capture at sea by a Spanish corsair. Once more on his way back to France, he was driven by a storm to North Africa.

work he had done in Spain. It was at this meeting that it was decided to procede to the election for the vacancy caused by the death of Lalande more than two years previously. If there were any doubt that this place had been kept for Arago, the timing of the decision to elect a successor surely helps to decide the issue. At the same meeting Laplace and Delambre presented a report on a memoir by Arago on the velocity of light. This had waited exactly three years for a report but now that an election was pending there was no time to lose! A fortnight later the election was held and Arago obtained 47 votes as against 4 for his rival, Poisson. Laplace had been put in a difficult position by this election, since the two principal candidates were both his protégés. He had tried to resolve this difficulty by suggesting that the election should be postponed. This, he said, would stimulate the ardour of the young men. To this Hallé replied that Laplace was like a man urging on a donkey with a carrot until the poor beast collapsed by sheer exhaustion.[1] On another occasion, when faced with an embarrassing choice, Laplace had written names on two pieces of paper, folded them and placed them in his hat. He then drew out one, placed it in the urn and told his neighbour that in this way he would never know for whom he had voted. It was unfortunate that his neighbour had been curious enough to look over Laplace's shoulder when he was writing out the names and saw that the same name appeared on each paper![2]

Fourcroy's death on 16 December 1809 provided the first vacancy for ten years in the section of chemistry of the First Class. At the meeting of 15 January 1810 Berthollet, as the senior member of the chemistry section, recommended that the vacancy should be filled by immediate election and at the next meeting a list of six candidates was presented. The presentation was by Guyton and this is perhaps understandable in view of the fact that Berthollet's son was included in the list. The names were (in order of suggested merit): Thenard, Descotils, Amédée Berthollet, Désormes, Chevreul and Darcet. The length of time since the last vacancy in the chemistry section had added to the proven merit of the candidates. Yet, however deserving several of these might have been (and later proved to be), the rules of the

[1] Arago, *Biographies of Distinguished Scientific Men*, trans., 1857, p. 53.
[2] *Ibid.*, p. 58.

Institute allowed only one person to be elected. Thenard was elected, which is not surprising considering his ability and his activity in the previous two years. At the recent meeting of 18 December he had added to his score of memoirs and at the next meeting he had been awarded Napoleon's prize for electricity, a joint award shared with Gay-Lussac. It was perhaps in view of the impending election that Thenard and not Gay-Lussac read their joint memoir on the quantitative analysis of vegetable and animal substances on 15 January.

In April 1810 there was a vacancy for the coveted place of *associé étranger*[1] due to the death of Henry Cavendish. For the sake of brevity we may say simply that a committee of six appointed to present candidates was headed by Laplace, representing the mathematical sciences and Berthollet, representing the 'physical' sciences. The name of Humboldt appeared at the head of the list they drew up. Second came Berthollet's friend and correspondent, James Watt. Last on the list came Gay-Lussac's rival, Davy. The successful candidate was Humboldt.

Four months later Malus was one of the candidates for another vacancy. In accordance with the practice of a well advised candidate, he arranged to read a memoir at the meeting of the First Class immediately preceding his nomination. He was successful in the election of 13 August but not without serious opposition from the engineer Girard.[2] Malus held his position for only eighteen months. His tragic death on 24 February 1812 left a vacancy, to which Poisson was elected, again over the head of Girard, who lacked personal connections in the ranks of the First Class.

Not all the Arcueil candidates entered the First Class or its successor, the *Académie des Sciences*, so easily. Bérard, standing in November 1816 for the place of correspondent in the chemistry section, had to compete with such men as Wollaston, Dalton and Berzelius. It was only in December 1819, when such eminent competition was lacking, that he was finally elected. Yet apart from its own membership, the *Académie* had the power to recommend candidates for vacancies in higher education in science

---

[1] There were only eight *associés étrangers* compared with a hundred *correspondents*.

[2] Girard had been responsible for the construction of the canal of Ourcq.

throughout France. In 1817 there was a vacancy for the chair of pharmacy at Montpellier. The committee of the *Académie* investigating the vacancy was headed by Berthollet and, after hearing his report, Bérard was unanimously elected.[1]

In May 1815 there was a vacancy in the physics section. This seemed to offer an opportunity to Dulong. After all, this was how Gay-Lussac had entered the Institute. The strongest candidate was Girard, who had the title of chief engineer of bridges and highways. We have met him previously as a candidate and he had not yet given up. In fact he had read a memoir to the First Class as recently as 1 May. On 22 May an attempt to postpone consideration of the vacancy was narrowly defeated and at the next meeting a list of candidates in order of merit was due to be presented. On 29 May, however, the physics section[2] asked for further time to prepare this list, saying that they were not yet sufficiently well informed of the respective merits of possible candidates. They therefore postponed for one week the presentation of the list of candidates. This gave an opportunity for Dulong at the same meeting to present a memoir on expansion, the joint work of himself and Petit. Gay-Lussac and Biot were appointed to examine this memoir and their report was ready for the next meeting (5 June), when the election was due to take place. Apart from the usual summary expected in such reports and the recommendation for publication in the *Mémoires des Savans Étrangers*, Gay-Lussac and Biot went out of their way to praise the extreme care taken by Dulong and the originality of his work. When the list of candidates was presented, Dulong appeared first in the list and the experienced Girard was placed third. Yet when the ballot was held, 31 votes were given to Girard as opposed to 21 to Dulong. It is clear that the majority of the First Class had not been convinced of the merits of young Dulong as a physicist. A second attempt to get Dulong elected to a vacancy in the physics section in 1817 was also unsuccessful and he had to wait another six years for a place. Even the election of 1823 had unusual features, which illustrate the politics of the *Académie des Sciences*.

There was a heated discussion at the meeting of the *Académie*

[1] *P.V. Inst.*, vol. vi, pp. 210–11.
[2] Gay-Lussac and Poisson were now members of the physics section.

des Sciences on 20 January 1823 about the election for two vacancies, one each in the sections of chemistry and physics. Thenard, now president as well as the representative of the chemistry section, proposed that the nomination of candidates for the vacancy in the section of chemistry should be postponed. Some members protested that there should also be a postponement in drawing up the list of candidates for the physics section, but the stronger party was successful in presenting at this meeting a list for the physics vacancy. The first two names were Dulong and Fresnel, the order of nomination being based on Dulong's seniority by virtue of the date of his publications. At the following meeting Dulong was elected by 36 votes to Fresnel's 20 votes. It was only after Dulong's election that the disputed list of candidates for the chemistry section was presented and their respective merits discussed by the *Académie*, and the election finally took place on 3 February. Had Dulong been unsuccessful in the first election, he would have been an obvious candidate for the second. Yet with strong competition from Darcet and Chevreul (both of whom had crossed swords with the Arcueil group), Dulong's chances of election to the *Académie* were possibly stronger in the physics section. It was the stratagem of separating the two elections which gave Dulong a double chance of election. It would have been fitting for Dulong to have succeeded to the vacancy in the *Académie* caused by the death of his teacher, Berthollet. Certainly Dulong was more of a chemist than a physicist. But political expediency decreed that he should be presented for the first vacancy. It was unfortunate only that Dulong's success was gained at the expense of Fresnel. (Fresnel, however, was exceptionally fortunate in there being another vacancy in physics a few months later and this time he was successful.) Fresnel had had vigorous support from his friend Arago, but the combined support of the other members of the Arcueil faction was sufficient to win a place for Dulong. With this election the last of the members of the former Society of Arcueil had arrived on the official stage of French science.

The Philomatic Society

Another society which functioned regularly in the early nineteenth century was the *Société Philomatique* or Philomatic Society. In its importance it cannot be compared with the First Class of the Institute, yet, like the latter, its place in the scientific scene in France at the beginning of the nineteenth century cannot be understood except by some detailed consideration of its origins.

On 10 December 1788 there took place the first meeting of a society, earnest in its intentions but hardly impressive in its membership. There were six young men present at this meeting and they had in common the desire to learn and understand all branches of contemporary science. The inspiration for the formation of the society came from Riche and Silvestre, both aged twenty-six and both recently qualified as physicians. Two other physicians were present, Audirac and Petit and the remaining two members of the group were Broval, who was interested in mathematics and Alexandre Brongniart (then aged eighteen), who was later to make a name for himself in mineralogy. Brongniart became in turn treasurer and president of the society.

Claude Antoine Gaspard Riche (1762–97) had become a doctor of medicine at Montpellier in June 1787. Throughout his short adult life his passion was natural history. In 1788 he came to Paris and almost immediately his association with Silvestre led to the formation of the Philomatic Society. Riche was the first secretary of the society but he only features in its early history, since in 1791 he left on a scientific expedition to Australia and although he survived to return to France, he had never enjoyed good health and he died shortly afterwards. In his short association with the Philomatic Society, Riche read numerous reports at meetings.

Riche was succeeded as secretary by Augustin François Silvestre (1762–1851). Silvestre is best remembered for his contributions to agricultural science; he was made a member of the *Société d'Agriculture* in 1792, later becoming its secretary having, one might say, served his apprenticeship in the Philomatic Society over the period 1791–1802. Eventually in 1806 Silvestre was elected to a vacancy in the Institute in the section of 'rural economy'.

The principal objects of the Philomatic Society are revealed in a general survey made by Riche in May 1790. He emphasized that members were above all concerned with self instruction:

> Let us make it a point of honour to instruct one another and to follow together the rapid progress of the different sciences and arts, which an individual alone would soon lose track of, if he did not unite his efforts with those of others.

To this end members were required to be active. They were obliged to contribute reports on scientific books and periodicals and present memoirs regularly at meetings. This was an admirable rule to discourage the passive and indifferent, but the element of obligation had the inevitable disadvantage of producing much work of a very mediocre standard.

There was a second method of keeping in touch with current scientific developments and this was to send representatives to attend meetings of other societies in Paris concerned with science, natural history, medicine or agriculture. This activity of the society had been stipulated in Article 2 of its Rules but it was soon found that other societies were opposed to admitting strangers to their meetings and in May 1790 Riche reported that despite the efforts of its members, they had only been able to gain admission to the meetings of the *Société d'Agriculture*. The *Académie des Sciences* was particularly sensitive to the intrusion of these outsiders, and when representatives of the Philomatic Society were later admitted, they at first felt obliged to treat as confidential what they heard. After the foundation of the Institute the Philomatic Society sent two representatives to meetings of the First Class, but their position was not regularized until 27 December 1800. The minutes of the First Class ten days later record the thanks of the secretary of the Philomatic Society for permission to send two representatives, who are named as Baillet and Daudin. The rights of the Philomatic Society in this matter were again confirmed at a meeting of the First Class in July 1809.

Members of the Philomatic Society resident in Paris were required to attend meetings regularly once every week, failing which they were liable to a fine. All members paid an annual subscription. Anyone interested in the aims of the society who lived in the provinces could become a corresponding member. These members were expected to contribute to the society by correspondence and they also had the right to address requests for information to the society. At first a journal of the activities of the society was circulated in manuscript form for the benefit of correspondents but by 1792 the increase in the number of correspondents had made this impracticable. Also an increased membership had improved the finances of the society so that from October and November 1792 it was able to publish its *Bulletin des Sciences*. This constituted a kind of scientific news letter and consisted of a few quarto pages. In principle it appeared monthly but some of the later issues covered periods of two, three or even four months.

At the very beginning the Philomatic Society made slow progress. It was not until November 1789 that any further members joined the original group. Even then the reports for 1790 record the deaths of two of the original members, Petit and Audirac. The fact that the first general report on the activities of a 'term' (*semestre*) was only in May 1790, suggests that the society had only begun to function seriously in the winter of 1789–90. On 9 November 1789 three new members joined the society. It was thus that the Philomatic Society made the valuable acquisition of Vauquelin, then at the beginning of his great career in analytical chemistry. He was to prove an asset to the society in its early years not only by his great industry but also by his talent. The next new member was Séguin, who joined in March 1790. Throughout 1791 there was a steady stream of new members so that by the end of the year the society had eighteen resident members as well as seventeen correspondents. It was also in 1791 that the society began to issue its *Bulletin*, although it was not until the following year that it was printed. On looking through the lists, however, one is struck less by the number of members than by their quality. These are not the men who left their mark in the annals of science. If we except Vauquelin, Brongniart and Lavoisier's collaborator, Séguin, who may be known to students of the history of science, the remainder might be regarded as nonentities. After all, no great scientific competence was demanded of members; all that was expected was genuine interest.

One also notices the dominance of medical men. Of the six

founder members, four were physicians. Of the next thirteen members to join up to the end of 1791, nine had medical qualifications, being described variously as 'doctor', 'physician' and even (one) 'surgeon'. Of the seventeen correspondents enrolled in this period, six were medical men, seven were described as 'naturalists' and four were chemists. The first secretary, Riche, was primarily interested in natural history. Medicine, natural history and chemistry seem to have been the primary subjects studied by the society. In its rules the sciences to be studied were headed by natural history and anatomy. Silvestre's interest in agriculture was also present under the heading 'rural economy'. The mathematical and physical sciences were represented largely by one man, Broval, and we find him at one meeting doing his best to expound on a point from the *Traité de mécanique analytique* of Lagrange to his non-mathematical colleagues. The continual difficulties of members in understanding current developments in sciences of which they had not even studied the elements, led to the introduction of elementary courses of instruction as a subsidiary activity of the society. By the end of 1791 these were functioning in mathematics, physics and anatomy and courses of chemistry and zoology were planned. Although these events belong to the decade before our period of special interest, two features of the Philomatic Society emerge which were to persist in the early nineteenth century. The first was the bias away from mathematics and physics towards the life sciences. This bias may also be seen later by looking at the journals which were chosen as the source of extracts published in the *Nouveau Bulletin* of the society. The second feature was the aim of self-education. Although the standards of admission of the society were later raised, there persisted the ideal of mutual instruction which makes a fundamental distinction between its meetings and those of the Institute.

After more informal beginnings a definite procedure was adopted for the meetings of the society. When members arrived, they would sign the attendance sheet and at the beginning of the meeting this sheet would be removed and signed by the president. The secretary then read the minutes of the last meeting and new business began with correspondence. Reports were read on topics previously selected by the society. The representatives who had attended the meetings of other societies then reported on their activities. Finally came the compulsory contributions of members whose turn it was and any other memoirs that had been sent to the society, for example, by corresponding members. One of the functions of the president was later laid down to be the suppression of conversations between individual members. The society had definite business to perform and gossip was not encouraged. More prominent in the rules was one, the full significance of which to the continued existence of the society will soon be clear:

> All political discussion, or discussion not related to the sciences studied by the society is rigorously excluded during meetings. (Art. VIII.)

In September 1793 something happened which changed the position of the society completely. It is important that this change should be seen in its proper perspective. The Philomatic Society was to prove a refuge for organized science in France between the period of the suppression of the *Académie des Sciences* and the formation of the Institute. The spirit of iconoclasm of the Revolution turned in 1793 to the Academies. In May 1793 the Convention agreed, on the report of Lakanal, to allow the *Académie des Sciences* to proceed to the election for vacant places and also to continue to pay the members of the *Académie* their salaries. The *Académie des Sciences* alone among the Academies was in an ambiguous position. On the one hand all Academies were looked upon as royalist institutions, whose members formed a class with special privileges. Not only were members provided with an income by the king but among the honorary members of the *Académie des Sciences* were numbered a cardinal and several dukes and marquesses. On the other hand the *Académie des Sciences* had rendered undoubted service to the state by supplying technical experts to deal with such matters as the new weights and measures and the supply of saltpetre.

Lavoisier and his fellow-members of the *Académie des Sciences* found that their only right to collective action accepted by the Convention was as members of the commission on weights and measures. Lavoisier could have adopted the expedient advised by Lakanal, that of forming the ex-members of the *Académie* into a new *Société libre*. This would have had the effect of obeying the letter of the law which had suppressed the Academies rather than its spirit, and the members of the *Académie* preferred to take an alternative course of action—to merge into a previously existing society, the Philomatic Society. Lavoisier and Silvestre were already known to each other; both were active members of the *Société d'Agriculture* and the *Bureau de Consultation des Arts et Métiers*. Apart from this there had been a regular contact between the representatives of the Philomatic Society who had attended meetings of the *Académie*. This then is the background of the entry in the minutes of the meeting of the Philomatic Society on 14 September 1793 which records the new membership of Berthollet, Lavoisier, Vicq d'Azyr (1748–1794), Ventenat (1757–1808) and Lefèvre-Gineau (1751–1829). The example of Lavoisier and Berthollet was followed by other members of the *Académie*. At the next meeting of the Philomatic Society on 21 September Fourcroy and Lamarck (1744–1829) were among those admitted. A week later Monge and Prony joined and finally on 3 November Laplace and Deyeux were numbered among the new members.

Thus in the autumn of 1793, political events led to a complete transformation of the modest Philomatic Society. We know that for a short period the leading *savants* of France were associated with this society. There remains the question of how active this association was. Lavoisier's membership, though a crucial one, was short-lived, since on 28 November 1793 he was imprisoned and on 8 May 1794 he was led to the guillotine. There is no evidence that Berthollet ever took an active part in the affairs of the society, nor is there any record in the annual reports of any memoirs read by such other leading figures as Laplace and Monge. Yet other prominent former members of the *Académie des Sciences* including Prony, Lacroix, Hallé, Daubenton and Lamarck did contribute several memoirs each, as did Fourcroy either alone or in conjunction with his younger collaborator and protégé, Vauquelin. Among the younger members of the society Cuvier became particularly active and contributions were also received from men whom we shall meet later at Arcueil, Candolle and Descotils. Humboldt first corresponded with the society and later, when he came to Paris, he read a memoir on the analysis of the air at a meeting of the society. Biot too at first contributed to the society by correspondence but in 1799 when he visited Paris he was able to read two mathematical memoirs in person. From what has been said we may conclude that some former members of the *Académie des Sciences* pursued in the Philomatic Society an activity comparable with that which they would have followed in the *Académie* had it still been in existence. Their contributions in this period constitutes the highlights in the society's activities.

Yet the picture of the Philomatic Society as the temple of French science during the whole period of the suppression of the Academies is one which cannot be accepted without reservations. The enrolment of new members to the society came to a sudden halt after 13 December 1793 and was not resumed for nearly nine months. The uneven distribution of the dates of reception of new members during the next five years suggest that the meetings of the society were far from regular. Although it had been decided to hold an annual general meeting at which the secretary would read a report of the society's activities, it was not found possible to hold such a meeting after the end of 1791 until 1797. In his report read on 13 December 1797, which covered this period of six years, Silvestre referred to the long time which had elapsed since the last anniversary meeting and is evident that although the society was nominally in existence all this time (and it was never officially condemned), it too suffered from interruptions in the continuity of its effective existence.

Political events had not only brought eminent men of science into the society, they had brought about an increase in numbers, so that in 1795 there were fifty-six members. This brought the prospect of limiting membership and thus increasing the value placed on becoming a member. At the same time the Philomatic Society could continue to trade on the names of the great men, regardless of whether they were active members. A rule was drafted (Art. XX) to excuse such senior members:

> Members who have reached the age of sixty, and whose business or other circumstances prevent them from contributing actively to the work of the society, will be placed as a right among the *associés libres*.

Such members were not required to pay subscriptions or read papers to the society but they were sent copies of the *Bulletin*, and we know that when Berthollet was in Egypt the *Bulletin* did something to keep him in touch with the developments in science in Paris. After 1807 a further method of regularizing membership was arrived at. Distinguished men of science, who had at one time been associated with the society, were designated 'Emeritus members'. By 1810 there were six such members headed by Berthollet; the others were Lamarck, Monge, Haüy, Duchesne and Laplace. It was laid down that any member who had been associated with the Philomatic Society for ten years could become an honorary member with no obligation to pay subscriptions. This rule led to a significant increase in the nominal members of the society, so that by the mid-nineteenth century half the 'members' were in fact honorary members.

The membership list shows that the Philomatic Society at the beginning of the nineteenth century was a stepping stone to higher honours in the First Class of the Institute. Nevertheless, in contrast to the early days when willingness was more relevant than ability, the rules now included the stipulation that candidates for membership should have at least one publication to their credit. This condition, coupled with the numerical limitation of membership, did much to raise the standards of the society. It became in many ways a parallel society to the First Class of the Institute, but on a lower plane. It provided young men with experience of scientific controversy.

When Fresnel was elected to membership in 1819, shortly after his arrival in Paris, he wrote:

> I see a great advantage of membership in connection with [my own] education and the experience I could gain of speaking and discussing matters in public.[1]

When it instituted *jetons de presence* and decreed that no individual member had the right to use the name of the society without general consent, and even divided into sections, we have evidence of hardening of the arteries. The spontaneity and enthusiasm of youth had gone and had been replaced by a formal society conducted according to a formidable list of regulations.

There does not appear to have been any rivalry between the Philomatic Society and the Arcueil group. This rather sur-

---

[1] Fresnel, *Oeuvres*, 1866, vol. ii, p. 846.

prising statement throws some light on each of the two associations. Membership of the Philomatic Society was formal. It dated from a particular day in a particular year and gave each member a certain seniority. This was not a group with which one could be loosely associated. On joining, members were given a diploma, to which the seal of the society was attached. In many ways it was the junior forum of the First Class of the Institute. Arcueil, as we shall see, was never a *formal* society. The majority of active members of the Philomatic Society were to be found in a particular part of the spectrum of scientific talent. One would not expect to find there the senior members of the Institute. On the other hand, after the first few years of the society, one would not be likely to meet the most incompetent beginner. The typical new member of the Philomatic Society was in his twenties or thirties, had done some scientific work but was not yet far enough advanced in his career to aspire to membership of the First Class. The Arcueil group, despite its much smaller size, included a wider range. At one end it was continually inspired by Laplace and Berthollet who had become in a sense the two *doyens* of French science. At the other end there was young Bérard, who first came to Arcueil as a laboratory assistant and gradually gained acceptance as a full member of the group. Such differences being borne in mind, we shall find it easier to understand the junior members of the Arcueil circle attending the Philomatic Society and even presenting the results of some of their research there.

It has been observed that Berthollet and Laplace joined the Philomatic Society during the period of the suppression of the Academies. Later they ceased to be active members. Other members of the Arcueil group joined the Philomatic Society in the following order:

Descotils	(3 December 1796)
Chaptal	(21 July 1798)
Candolle	(5 October 1800)
Biot	(2 February 1801)
Thenard	(12 February 1803)
Poisson	(5 December 1803)
Gay-Lussac	(23 December 1804)[1]

[1] Different issues of the *Bulletin* of the Philomatic Society give different

A. B. Berthollet   (24 January 1807)
Malus   (April 1810)
Arago   (April 1810)
Dulong   (21 March 1812)

With only two exceptions, all these men joined the Philomatic
Society several years before they could seriously think of election to membership of the First Class of the Institute. The
Philomatic Society, let us repeat, was a junior Academy. One
exception to this generalization was Chaptal, who on deciding
to come to live permanently in Paris from 1798 was eager to
join in as much of the scientific life of the capital as possible. He
had, however, hardly more than a year of active membership,
since under the Consulate he was called to take part in the
government. The second exception was Arago who joined at the
same time as Malus and possibly because of his friendship with
him. It had been exceptional good fortune which had enabled
Arago to gain a place in the Institute seven months previously
and still being only twenty-four, he was probably more at ease
with the young men who formed the core of the Philomatic
Society than with the greybeards of the First Class.

Not only did all the younger men of Arcueil (except Bérard)
belong to the Philomatic Society, but at one time several of
them took a prominent part in the running of the society's
Bulletin. When the *Bulletin* was published again in October 1807
after an interval of two-and-a-half years, the botany contributions were partly edited by Candolle, chemistry was edited by
Thenard and Descotils, physics by Gay-Lussac and mathematics by Poisson. This shows in a way the keen spirit of these
young men. The timing of this renewed publication suggests
that there was no essential rivalry between the newly-founded
Society of Arcueil and the Philomatic Society. There was no
feeling of incompatibility. In a sense their publications were
complementary. The Arcueil *Mémoires*, appearing every few
years, was to publish in full memoirs connected with the society
and its select members. The *Bulletin* covered a much wider field.
Its value lay in its regular monthly publication. It gave prompt
reports of memoirs read at the First Class of the Institute as well

---

dates, varying from 12 February 1803 to 26 March 1805. Despite this wide
discrepancy, the order of joining the society is not affected.

as at its own meetings. It gave extracts from other journals (a marked bias here towards the life sciences) and constituted a valuable contribution to scientific journalism rather than a permanent collection of scientific memoirs.

The 'Société d'Encouragement'

Another association, members of which were later associated with the Society of Arcueil, was the *Société d'Encouragement pour l'Industrie Nationale*. This was very much Chaptal's society and he was repeatedly elected president from the very first meeting at the Paris Hôtel de Ville on 18 November 1801.

The object of the society was to collect and disseminate information on techniques and discoveries useful to industry, to encourage technical education, to help artisans living in poverty, and to encourage new developments and discoveries by the award of prizes. From the beginning it offered prizes ranging in value from 600 to 3,000 francs on such subjects as the economical production of enamelled utensils, the manufacture of fishing nets and the production of Prussian blue and white lead. Bonaparte as a gesture of practical support for the work of the society took out a hundred shares. The society began with about three hundred members, each of whom paid a subscription.

At a meeting on 28 June 1802 Berthollet was elected president of the committee on applied chemistry. This committee included among its members important figures in chemistry such as Fourcroy, Guyton de Morveau and Vauquelin as well as the younger Descotils, recently returned from Egypt. Descotils was soon investigating a case in which iron had been supposed to have been converted into steel without the addition of carbon, but, of course, he was unable to confirm that this was possible. A prominent member of the society from its foundation was Candolle, who was particularly interested in economics and social welfare. Thenard was a member for a short time and Gay-Lussac joined later. Rumford[1] and Blagden, who attended some of the early meetings, were elected foreign correspondents

[1] Rumford with his experience of the Royal Institution may well have been an important influence on the direction of technical education and the encouragement of technological advance in France at the beginning of the nineteenth century.

of the society and Humboldt was elected to the same title not long after his return from America.

The society decided to publish a journal and in August 1802 Candolle announced that his friend Frédéric Cuvier would undertake to edit this. In addition to reports of meetings, the *Bulletin* contained memoirs on a variety of subjects related to economics, industry and applied science. This included memoirs on Berthollet's discovery of the use of chlorine for bleaching and a report on a new blue pigment, which had been discovered by Thenard. Chaptal, as Minister of the Interior, had summoned this young chemist from the *École Polytechnique* and commissioned him to prepare an ultramarine pigment, which was required by the porcelain factory at Sèvres. He was given some money for his expenses and told to begin immediately. Thenard is said to have discovered the blue pigment which bears his name only a fortnight later.[1] Bonaparte's minister was singularly fortunate in this early example of state-subsidized research!

In 1804 the society agreed to meet every Tuesday afternoon at the Hotel des Monnaies in Paris. We know that Candolle was a regular attender and that Chaptal made a point of being one of the first to arrive. It is doubtful if Berthollet gave much more than nominal support to the society. Guyton usually spoke on behalf of the sub-committee on applied chemistry and in 1804 he replaced Berthollet as its chairman. Berthollet still continued to be a member of the committee. Thus although Chaptal, Candolle, Thenard, Gay-Lussac, Humboldt and Berthollet, all later members of the Society of Arcueil, were at one time associated with the *Société d'Encouragement*, it is doubtful if any, apart from the first two named, took it very seriously. Berthollet's lack of positive interest in the *Société d'Encouragement* relegates it to a position of minor importance as a forerunner of the Society of Arcueil. From the point of view of French industry, however, Chaptal's society made a major contribution and deserves fuller treatment than we are able to give it here.

Minor Scientific Societies in Paris

In order to obtain a more representative idea of the situation in French science, we must now turn our attention to a number

[1] *Un grand Français. Le chimiste Thenard*, 1950, pp. 87–8.

of minor societies, all of which were at least ostensibly concerned with science and which were in existence in Paris during the first decade of the nineteenth century. Societies in provincial France are not without interest and there were occasional contributions of at least national importance made at some of their meetings, particularly in the second half of the eighteenth century. Yet in the confines of this chapter the aim will be no more than to provide a picture of scientific societies in the capital.

The relationship of scientific societies to the First Class of the Institute is particularly worthy of comment. The Society of Arcueil became almost an Academy within an Academy, preparing reports to be submitted to the First Class, discussing experiments and the memoirs of their colleagues, which were later to be presented to a wider audience at the Institute. The Philomatic Society was more of a society for aspirants to the First Class, the rigidity of rules for election to the Institute giving scope to a society of young men, the best of whom were to be the next generation of scientists in the Institute. The other societies, with a few exceptions, were not notable for the quality of their membership. In some cases it is almost as if they were children playing at the game of holding their Institute. Bonaparte had been able to have his Institute in Egypt. Lesser men, geographically closer to the meetings of the Institute in Paris, were nevertheless intellectually far removed from the brilliant achievements of its members. Yet, provided there was no suspicion of a political motive, there was always the freedom to belong to a society which might have a formal code of rules and elections and which might model itself on the Institute to the extent of dividing into several 'Classes', meeting sometimes together, sometimes separately. There were obvious social advantages in belonging to a club and to these were added certain intellectual pretensions and even perhaps the possession of a formal certificate of membership with the crest of the society and a wax seal. Such certificates did no harm and had the advantage of providing a source of revenue for a group which usually depended entirely on its members for finance.

The societies may be conveniently divided into two groups, the general and the specialist. The general societies considered here were all in name, if not in fact, concerned with science, often with applied science. Of the specialist societies probably the most important were the medical. There was the *Société de Médecine* which met at the Louvre. This society, founded in 1796 as the *Société de Santé*, was concerned with all branches of sciences relating to the art of healing. Less demanding in its standards of membership was the *Société médicale d'Émulation* which was founded in Paris in 1798. Magendie became a member of this in 1808 when he was still too young and obscure to be more than an ordinary member of the public at the meetings of the Institute.[1] Among later medical societies were the *Société medico-pratique de Paris* (1806) and the *Société de Médecine pratique de Paris* (1808). A *Société anatomique* had been founded in Paris in 1803. The *Société Royale de Médecine*, founded in 1778, had been suppressed with the other 'royalist' academies in 1793 and was only re-established in 1820 as the *Académie de Médecine*. With the details of these societies we are not concerned here. Their dates of foundation, however, serve to illustrate the social and professional tendency in France in the period immediately after the Revolution to form organized groups. The dissolution of the academies in 1793 increased the size of the vacuum requiring to be filled.

In the field of natural history there had been a *Société Linnéenne* founded in Paris in 1788. Political troubles soon led to its dissolution although in 1792 it managed to publish a volume of proceedings (*Actes*). By 1798 conditions had become more favourable in France to the disinterested pursuit of science free from political interference and the society, which had by now changed its name to *Société d'Histoire Naturelle de Paris*, elected Jussieu as president for two years and Cuvier as secretary. The society included among its members a number of distinguished men of science including Fourcroy, Haüy, Lacépède, Lamarck and Vauquelin. They decided to publish a journal and the first number of their *Mémoires* appeared in May 1799. The society undertook to continue this publication if it were favourably received, but in fact no more appeared after the first number. It was not until June 1820 that the society was reconstituted, taking its original title of *Société Linnéene de Paris*. Meanwhile interest in the biological sciences was catered for by the publications of the *Annales du Muséum National d'Histoire Naturelle*. The

[1] J. M. D. Olmsted, *François Magendie*, New York, 1944, p. 20.

first volume of this was published in 1802 and successive volumes followed fairly regularly, so that by 1813 twenty had appeared. A new series began in 1815 under the Restoration. The *Annales* was not an open publication like, for example, the *Annales de chimie*. It was edited by the staff of the Museum, who contributed the vast majority of the contents.

We might also mention the *Société des Pharmaciens de Paris*, which was related on the one hand to natural history and on the other to chemistry. Various agricultural societies had been founded in the provinces in the eighteenth century and Paris too had its *Sociétéd' Agriculture*. In this sampling of specialized scientific societies might be included the *Société de statistique*, founded in February 1803. Meetings were held in the house of one of its members, Ballois, who was also editor of the *Annales de statistique*.[1] Finally, in an age in which electricity seemed to open a whole new field of investigation, we should not neglect to mention the *Société Galvanique*, which was particularly interested in the medical effects of electricity. The society first met in the former Oratory in 1802 but its activities in succeeding years suggest a rapid decline.

General Societies Ostensibly Concerned with Science

An interesting society in existence in Paris in the early nineteenth century was the *Athénée des Arts*. This society, founded in 1792 as the *Lycée des Arts*, began primarily as an educational institution but it developed into a society and probably a more genuine scientific society than several other societies which claimed to be interested in science.

The chief objects of the *Lycée des Arts* were to establish courses on scientific subjects open to members of the public, and to honour men responsible for useful discoveries and inventions by the award of medals or crowns of honour. Both aspects of the functioning of the *Lycée* laid stress on the practical applications of science. This institution provides a remarkable example of the application of private enterprise in republican France. It was Charles Gaullard Desaudray who provided not only the idea and energy but also the money for the installation of the society in the Palais Royal. The problem of finance was one of the

[1] Aulard, *Paris sous le Consulat*, vol. iii, pp. 686, 730; vol. iv, pp. 51–2.

chief obstacles to the success of the *Lycée*. Appeals to the government for subsidy were generally unsuccessful, although the records of the Committee of Public Safety meeting on 17 August 1795 include a decision to subscribe at government expense to 2,500 copies of the journal of the *Lycée des Arts*. A more direct example of government subsidy was the 'titre d'encouragement' of 60,000 francs approved by the Convention in September 1795.

Awards for discoveries and inventions were made by a directory which included Berthollet, Fourcroy, Lalande, Lamarck, Nicolas Leblanc and many others. Lavoisier was a prominent early member of the *Lycée* and in May 1793 he read a report (by Fourcroy and himself) on Berthollet's process for bleaching. He emphasized the utility of this invention, which had been profitably exploited by many, but pointed out that Berthollet had received no official recompense for his work. Lavoisier said that, if the government was slow to reward Berthollet, he hoped that the award which the *Lycée* had decided to make of a crown (of laurel and oak leaves) would serve as a symbol of the value attached to Berthollet's work by his fellow-scientists.

In December 1798 the premises of the *Lycée des Arts* were destroyed by fire. The *Lycée* moved to the former Oratory, now a secular building, but it abandoned its formal courses of lectures which had now become superfluous because of the recent development of scientific and technical education. In 1802 the name was changed to the *Athénée des Arts* and we must now consider briefly the activities of this society, taking as a guide the constitution drawn up in 1803. The *Athénée* then consisted of 240 ordinary members as well as honorary members, associate members and correspondents. The ordinary membership was divided into three classes each of 80 members: a Class of Mathematics and Physics, A Class of Literature, and a Class of Fine Arts. Each Class met once a week, the science Class, for example, meeting on Wednesdays. The subjects studied by this group were officially listed as: 'Arithmetic, geometry, physics, mechanics, astronomy, geography, navigation, military technology, optics, acoustics, natural history, chemistry, medicine, rural economy, industry.' There was an annual subscription of 36 francs. An additional charge was made for the certificate presented on admission. It was recognized that a financial barrier might impede able and interested prospective members and there was a clause in the constitution of the society which permitted the admission of such talented but impoverished members up to a maximum of one fifteenth of the total membership. The society's goal of encouraging the artisan and inventor was always looked upon with favour, if not with actual cash, by the government. Because of official interest, we find public meetings presided over not by self-important nonentities but by members of the government, Fourcroy and Abrial (Minister of Justice) successively in the republican year X, Chaptal and Berthier (Minister of War) in the year XI and in the year XII even the famous Talleyrand (Minister of Foreign Affairs) agreed to preside.

In conclusion we may repeat that the main activity of the *Athénée des Arts* was the encouragement of innovations in industry. It attempted to bring together the creative talents of men of science and the arts with the practical ability of the craftsmen and mechanic. The finances of the society, after several ingenious efforts of the founder of the *Lycée*, Desaudray, were met by the subscriptions of members, who were encouraged to attend by the device of counting their attendance towards their future subscriptions. In the long run the effectiveness of the society depended on the quality of its members. Whereas many men of the first rank were associated with the *Lycée* in its early years, and some continued as honorary members, the ordinary members were largely undistinguished and although the *Athénée* continued in existence beyond the mid-nineteenth century, it failed to live up to some of its earlier promise.

Another minor society which met at the turn of the century was the *Société libre des Sciences, Lettres et Arts de Paris*, which held regular weekly meetings for members and a public meeting every quarter. The members of the society (who were required to pay a subscription) were distinguished by their obscurity or at most by their mediocrity. Societies with intellectual interests had become fashionable and the so-called *Société des Sciences, Lettres et Arts* added to its attractions by meeting at the 'Palais National des Sciences et Arts' (a part of the Louvre) which was also the meeting place of the Institute. The society was therefore modelled on the famous Institute not only in its professed range of interests but also in its locale. An examination of the memoirs presented to the society, however, shows that in practice it was hardly concerned with science at all.

Another society, the name of which suggests a particular concern with applied science, was the *Société Philotechnique*. Its claim to be considered as a scientific society would seem to be further enhanced by being able to boast among its members a group from the *Muséum d'Histoire Naturelle*: Fourcroy, Cuvier, Lamarck, Geoffroy Saint-Hilaire and Lacépède. Again, however, neither the origins nor the activities of the society substantiate this preliminary impression.

In 1795 a minor dramatist, Hector Chaussier, decided to start a journal devoted to literature and the arts. He associated with other writers to obtain material for the journal and soon a group of eight men began to meet regularly for this purpose. The interest of some dwindled and in order to obtain a regular supply of copy, membership of the club was extended. It was called the *Société Philotechnique* after the rather misleading title of the journal which it had begun to publish but which had lasted less than a year. Nevertheless the general climate of opinion was favourable to the establishment of cultural societies and the society continued to exist for most of the nineteenth century.

Although the society managed to attract a reasonable number of eminent figures of the period, it is not clear that they took an active part in the society. Napoleon's generals Kléber and Moreau were among the best-known figures to take an interest in the affairs of the society. The young Cuvier was obviously a valuable acquisition and his resignation in 1804 on the grounds of pressure of work was a blow to the group. Cuvier had been president of the society twice, as had Lacépède. Apart from its weekly meetings, the society held the usual public meetings twice a year. The meeting might include the performance of music and would conclude with a dinner. This was very much a male club and women were explicitly excluded from membership.

In imitation of the Institute the *Société Philotechnique* grouped itself into three Classes: 1st: French Literature, 2nd: Physical and Moral Sciences, 3rd: Fine Art. It is evident that the primary interest of the society was in the first of these subjects, the others being included to give a broader basis to the group. The *Société Philotechnique* made continual efforts during the first decade of the nineteenth century to make the Institute aware of its existence. For example it regularly sent the First Class a small number of tickets for its public meetings. On one occasion the official answer of the Class was that, whilst it thanked the society for the five tickets received, it would be preferable if members of the Institute were automatically admitted on furnishing proof of identity.[1] In conclusion we may consider the existence of the *Société Philotechnique* as an interesting aspect of early nineteenth-century society in France. In the history of French literature it may well have a small place but as regards the physical sciences, the society had no significant contribution to make.

We must not neglect to mention a society which was definitely concerned with science and is of all the more relevance to a study of the Society of Arcueil since it too became established as a society with its own journal in the summer of 1807. This was the *Société des Amateurs des Sciences physiques et naturelles de Paris*. The society deliberately took an unpretentious name and announced that its object was the mutual instruction of its members. Some considerable time had been given to drawing up a formal list of rules: It was stated that the society was particularly (*sic*) concerned with mathematics, physics, astronomy, chemistry, natural history and medicine. Ordinary resident members were expected to pay a subscription and read at least one memoir a year.

In 1807 there were actually forty resident members of the society but the regulations permitted up to sixty. A quarter of the resident members were described as doctors of medicine and this represented the dominant profession in the society. Despite the avowed range of interest in the society, its published memoirs show a preponderance of interest towards natural history and medicine. The most important figures in the history of science among the ordinary members included the young doctor Delaroche, the chemists Darcet and Despretz and the brilliant Alexis Petit, then at the age of sixteen having just been accepted as a student at the *École Polytechnique*.

---

[1] *P.V. Inst.*, vol. ii, p. 210.

Particularly keen members were Brard, an assistant at the *Muséum d'Histoire Naturelle* and Lucas, the son of a keeper at the *Muséum*. The society had a special category of honorary members and among these were to be found several members of the First Class of the Institute. The honorary members included Jussieu, Desfontaines, Haüy and Vauquelin, all possibly persuaded by their young associates at the *Muséum* to permit the use of their names. The contribution of honorary members to the society hardly extended beyond a vague and distant patronage. Nevertheless by 1808 the number of such members had been increased from fourteen to twenty, now adding, for example, Gall of medical fame and Thouin from the *Muséum*.

In the course of one year the society decided to change its title, thereby unwittingly adding to the labours of future historians. In 1808 it became the *Société des Sciences physiques et naturelles*, since it was considered that it had now achieved a measure of recognition in France and was now in a position to contribute to the advancement of science. This hope proved to be unduly optimistic and the society ceased to publish after 1808. On 21 August 1809 we find the society asking to be allowed to send two representatives to the meetings of the First Class of the Institute. Despite its ambition the society was, however, doomed to extinction and oblivion, run as it was by men who had no original contribution to make to science. None of the officers of the society was of any notability. They could only shine by comparison with the even more obscure figures from the provinces. This can be seen from the list of societies to which the permanent secretary of the *Société des Sciences physiques et naturelles* could claim to belong. He had been concerned with correspondence with the provinces and provincial societies had responded by granting him membership of their respective associations. The list which follows the name of the secretary, Jacquelin-Dubuisson, serves as a reminder of the existence of a group of societies concerned with science, medicine and literature in the major French provincial towns. Jacquelin-Dubuisson was not only a member of the *Athénée des Arts* in Paris and the *Société académique des Sciences de Paris*. He was also a member of the following seven provincial societies: the *Académie des Sciences, Arts et Belles Lettres de Caen*, the *Athénée de Niort*, the *Société de Médecine pratique de Montpellier*, the *Société des Sciences physiques et médicales de Liège*, the *Société des Sciences, Lettres et Arts de Rennes*, the *Société des Sciences, Lettres et Arts de Rochefort* and the *Société d'Émulation de Poitiers*.

The situation during the Consulate and Empire in which numerous small societies were meeting regularly and preparing memoirs raises the question of publication, and in 1801 there appeared the first volume of *Mémoires des sociétés savantes et littéraires de la République Française*. It began with high hopes and with two members of the Institute, Prony and Parmentier, on the editorial board. The publication was intended to serve as a point of contact for the many minor societies then functioning in France whether they were concerned with science, technology, agriculture, commerce or literature. The journal, however, failed to make its mark and ceased publication in 1802.

In 1809 a further attempt was made to provide a general review of memoirs on science and related subjects. The *Annales des sciences et des arts*[1] was edited by Dubois-Maisonneuve and Jacquelin-Dubuisson. The editors hoped to produce a general synthesis of scientific memoirs going back to 1800 but there was insufficient support for this project and publication of the journal ceased in 1810.

---

[1] *Annales des sciences et des arts contenant les analyses de tous les travaux relatifs aux sciences mathématiques, physiques, naturelles et médicales; aux arts mécaniques et chimiques; à l'agriculture, à l'économie rurale et domestique, a l'art vétérinaire, etc., et présentant ainsi le tableau complet des acquisitions et des progrès qu'ont fait les sciences et les arts, les manufactures et l'industrie, depuis le commencement du 19e siècle. Avec l'indication des prix décernés et proposés par les Académies et sociétés savantes, la nécrologie des savans les plus connus et la notice bibliographique des ouvrages publiés dans l'année.*

CHAPTER FOUR

Scientific Institutions for Teaching and Research in Early Nineteenth-century France

Introduction

THE SCIENTIFIC societies which have been described in the previous chapter each provided a potentially valuable forum for discussion. They were, in the broadest sense, rival institutions with respect to the Arcueil group, particularly when the latter established itself as a society. There was another group of institutions concerned primarily with teaching, but also in some cases with research, which were not so much in competition with the Arcueil group as complementary to it. Yet it is not possible to make a complete distinction between these two kinds of institutions. There were the two extremes: on the one hand there were societies like the *Société Philomatique,* which were clearly societies and nothing else; there was almost always an element of honour in belonging and there might be a subscription for membership. On the other hand, there were paid teaching positions as, for example, in the *Faculté des Sciences,* which provided a means of livelihood for men of science. The distinction becomes blurred, however, when we consider the Institute in the first category, since its members were salaried. In the second category we have the *Bureau des Longitudes,* which provided a substantial salary for its members and yet met regularly in the same way as a scientific society of the first group.

The distinction may be worth retaining, however, since appointments to scientific research and teaching institutions seem very germane to our theme of patronage. As these institutions provided the main source of financial support for most of the leading figures in the scientific life of early nineteenth-century France, it is worth asking the blunt question 'how much was

190

the job worth?' and investigating how suitable candidates were chosen for these appointments. In the *École Polytechnique* Laplace and Berthollet appear to have exercised a powerful influence and in the *Bureau des Longitudes* Laplace nearly always got his own way. The patronage of Humboldt was instrumental in obtaining an appointment for Gay-Lussac in 1808 at the inauguration of the Faculty of Science in Paris.[1]

There is another aspect which puts the teaching institutions in a different category from the societies and this is the question of time. Few people would grudge spending an afternoon or evening a week at a society meeting, particularly if the standard of contributions was high. The responsibilities of teaching were greater and were sometimes supplemented by administrative duties. Where several posts in different institutions were held by the same person, very little time was left for original research. We shall see that this general problem was particularly acute for Dulong, who was dogged by ill-health.

In this chapter, while describing some of the main educational and research establishments in Paris at the beginning of the nineteenth century, particular emphasis will be laid on the activities of the members of the Arcueil group. From the outset the association of Berthollet and Laplace is a matter of interest. Their friendship developed in various ways and an obvious opportunity lay in the teaching and administrative duties which they both shared in the *École Normale* and especially in the *École Polytechnique*.

The 'École Normale' of the Convention

In January 1795 a group of the most distinguished French scholars was appointed to give a course of lectures to prospective teachers from all over France. This was to be the *École Normale*. Every five days (i.e. twice every *décade*) Lagrange and Laplace were to lecture on mathematics, Haüy on physics, Monge on descriptive geometry, Berthollet on chemistry, etc. Half the course was devoted to scientific subjects. Students were expected to be familiar with the elements of each subject in the curriculum and it was hoped that they would assimilate the advanced work taught at the school and bring about the

[1] Wellcome Library, Humboldt MSS. 67391, 67799, 64702.

diffusion of their newly-acquired knowledge throughout the Republic.

Berthollet in his course discussed in detail the current theory of chemical affinity. He later said[1] that it was during his hurried preparation for these lectures that he first began to realize that the current ideas about affinity could not be correct. Looking through the lectures given at the *École Normale*, we find Berthollet taking an opportunity to compliment Laplace[2] and Laplace more surprisingly outspoken when on 30 April 1795 he lamented the death of Lavoisier by 'the most bloody tyranny'.[3] In May the school was closed since, although it was providing instruction at a high level, the majority of its pupils were insufficiently prepared to derive any benefit from the courses.

The 'École Polytechnique': Foundation and Curriculum

In contrast to the short-lived and experimental courses of the *École Normale*, the association of both Berthollet and Laplace with the *École Polytechnique* was to be long and fruitful. Founded originally in December 1794 as the *École Centrale des Travaux Publics*, the school was renamed the *École Polytechnique* in the following September.

The *École Polytechnique* was founded with the idea of giving a common training to civil and military engineers; it was also hoped that it would provide suitable basic instruction for mining engineers, geographers, naval architects, etc. Finally it was thought that the training given would be suitable for young men who would later teach mathematics or the physical sciences. For these quite diverse careers, it was considered that students should be trained in mathematics and 'physics', the latter term being used in the widest possible sense. A prominent part of the mathematics taught was descriptive geometry, a subject virtually founded by Monge, who was also one of the founders of the *École Polytechnique*. 'Physics' was the name given to a study of matter and was divided into general physics and chemistry. An analysis of the time spent on various subjects by students at the *École Polytechnique* in 1801 shows that chemistry

[1] *Ann. chim.*, xlvi (1803), 288–9.
[2] *Séances des Écoles Normales*, vol. ii, p. 383.
[3] *Ibid.*, vol. v, pp. 214–15.

was one of the principal subjects taught, as much time being spent on this as on mechanics, analytical geometry and architecture put together. The explanation of the prominence of chemistry in the training programme of civil engineers, artillery officers, etc. lies partly in the importance this study had acquired in France in the previous decade both as a pure science and for its many applications to the French economy. It must also be pointed out that chemists had been strongly represented on the committees which drew up successive plans for the school. Fourcroy was a prominent and influential figure among the founders of the *École Polytechnique* and Guyton was its director for three years during the absence of Monge. Both these chemists lectured at the school as did Berthollet, who had been associated with it from the beginning. After 1800 Berthollet was a permanent member of the governing body of the school.

In the first years of the existence of the *École Polytechnique* the teaching of chemistry was to be divided as follows: Fourcroy was to lecture to the first-year students with Vauquelin as his assistant, Berthollet with Chaptal had the second-year course and Guyton with Pelletier were assigned to the third year. Chaptal left the school after a few months to return to Montpellier and was replaced as Berthollet's assistant by Chaussier, who also had other duties in the school. When Berthollet was called to Egypt, Chaptal returned to the *École Polytechnique* to take his place as professor. The long absences of Monge and Berthollet, first in Italy in 1797–8 and then in Egypt in 1798–9 obviously affected the staffing of the school but it affected its morale even more. In November 1799 the minutes of the governing body of the school record that the members suspended their meeting to express their joy at the safe return of Monge and Berthollet from Egypt.

In 1799 there was a fundamental reorganization. This had been approved in principle earlier in the year, but Bonaparte's *coup d'état* of 18 brumaire dissolved the constitution which had favoured it. The reform might have been postponed indefinitely but for the good offices of Laplace during his short tenure of the Ministry of the Interior. Although Laplace did not give lectures at the *École Polytechnique*, he had been asked as an examiner for entry to the artillery to become one of the examiners for the school, an appointment which he kept until

1799. Laplace had therefore kept in touch with the school during the whole of its development and was fully aware of all its problems. The law which brought new life and enthusiasm to the *École Polytechnique* was passed on 16 December 1799. The unsatisfactory position of the previous two or three years was rectified. The teaching was reorganized with reasonable financial support. In particular the three-year course was replaced by a two-year course, followed by instruction in one of the several specialized schools, the *Écoles d'application*. The relationship of the *École Polytechnique* with these schools, always a sore point, was clarified.

The function of the *École Polytechnique* was described by the law of 1795, which had restricted admission to the specialized schools of Artillery, Military Engineering, Civil Engineering, Mining, etc. to graduates of the *École Polytechnique*. There were, however, many protests that this placed the *École Polytechnique* in a specially privileged position. This was true and it increased the importance of the school in the life of France. Originally students did not have to select their future careers until after they had followed the general course of instruction at the school, but the army complained that this system resulted in their obtaining only a few students and these of low calibre. From 1799 students had to state on admission to the *École Polytechnique* which military or public service or graduate school they wished to enter on completion of their studies there.

After the reorganization chemistry continued to be taught in the first and second years and Berthollet, who had previously lectured on organic chemistry, now gave a course of lectures on chemistry on an industrial scale. From 1802 he gave a course of theoretical chemistry applied to industry. This was an advanced course closely related to his *Statique chimique*. It proved too difficult for the students and in 1805 Berthollet resigned his teaching appointment at the *École Polytechnique* but continued to be a member of the board of governors.

An important feature of the early curriculum had been practical work and this was made to alternate with theoretical work in the students' day. During the first decade of the nineteenth century the emphasis on many subjects was changed. Practical work was abandoned in 1807. An examination of the timetable for 1812 shows that the subjects to which most time was devoted were mathematical analysis and a study of mechanics and machines. More than ten per cent of the timetable was still devoted to chemistry. There had been complaints, not unknown in the twentieth century, about the low standard of literacy of some of the students. Since 1802 all candidates for admission had been expected to write good French and from 1804 there was a short course on grammar and literature. It is only fair to add that another analysis[1] of the curriculum during the period of the Consulate and Empire has been in terms of increased militarization as shown, for example, in the increased prominence given to the course on fortification. The question of the relation of the *École Polytechnique* to the armed forces of France will be discussed later.

The first course at the *École Polytechnique* was an emergency programme, called a *cours révolutionnaire*. This was a course which in three months was supposed to summarize the work of a normal three-year programme. Students were to be examined at the end of the three months and then divided into three groups. The ordinary three-year course was to begin in May 1795 with the best students promoted to the third-year course, the next best put in the second year and those who had profited least from the rapid course of lectures, together with late entrants, were entered for the first-year course. This had the effect of producing reasonably able men to be military engineers and artillery officers, who were so urgently required by the revolutionary armies, which could hardly have waited for the full three years. It was because of the national emergency that Biot left the *École Polytechnique* in 1795 after only one year to take up a teaching post. Malus graduated after only two years and returned to the army in the Corps of Engineers.

The *École Polytechnique* acquired much of the scientific apparatus required for instruction by means which could hardly have a parallel in the history of any scientific institution. A ready source was available through the revolutionary confiscations, particularly from the crown, the clergy and the Academies. A large number of physical instruments had been assembled together and Barruel on behalf of the *École Polytechnique*, made a selection of 260 different items valued at 30,000 francs. A major source was obviously the former *Académie des Sciences* but

[1] L. Pearce Williams, *Isis*, xlvii (1956), 376–9.

probably a fair number of the instruments had belonged to wealthy amateurs. The chemistry laboratory, the mineralogy collection and the library were assembled from similar sources. The brass required to make new apparatus came from six thousand pounds of copper and two thousand pounds of zinc requisitioned by the Commission of Commerce. The victories of the republican armies furnished further chemical supplies, notably alum and mercury. Twelve thousand pounds of mercury were brought back to Paris from the Palatinate and a sixth of this was presented to the *École Polytechnique*. Mercury, a basic requirement for much physical and chemical apparatus, was an expensive commodity and before the Revolution there were only a few people like the wealthy Lavoisier who could afford large supplies of mercury, a fact that had not escaped the attention of some of his envious visitors. On a later visit to the *École Polytechnique*, Bonaparte took the opportunity of presenting a further quantity of mercury obtained as war booty to the school. It may also be noted that Monge and Berthollet did not forget the *École Polytechnique* during their requisitioning expedition in Italy in 1797–8.

The Entrance Examination

The entrance examination for the *École Polytechnique* tested in particular the candidates' knowledge of mathematics. All entrants had to be judged of good character and 'attached to republican principles'. With nearly four hundred students in 1795 there was a shortage of teaching staff. Biot, who was in the first batch of students, found himself made a monitor with teaching duties. This was on the strength of a few months study at the *École des Ponts et Chaussées* and the fact that, at the age of twenty, he was one of the senior students. Malus was also a student in the first year of the school's history. He was nineteen years old and expected to help with instruction. It was later admitted that the whole system of monitors was pernicious, since young men were expected to teach their comrades during time which they should have spent on their own learning. In this first year there were forty-three monitors altogether and they voted among themselves to decide on twenty-five section

leaders (*chefs de brigade*). Malus obtained more votes than anyone else, Biot being tenth on the list.

The regulations for admission to the school laid down the age
limits of sixteen to twenty. Later, admission up to the age of
twenty-six was permitted in the case of students who had done
military service. It was rather unusual to enter at the age of
sixteen, although the sons of both Berthollet and Laplace
gained admission at this age, as did Dulong, without family connections to help him. The age of entry naturally depended
largely on the ability of young men, particularly in the provinces, to acquire the necessary mathematical knowledge.
Although the examiners were instructed to look for intellectual
promise as much as attainment, it would be harder for a lad
from a remote country village to impress the examiners than
one who had followed a mathematics course at one of the
Écoles Centrales. Most fortunate of all were those who could
come to Paris and enter a specialized establishment which provided preparation for the entrance examination of the *École
Polytechnique*. The so-called *École Polymathique* in the Rue de
Clichy, for example, could claim in 1806 that, in the previous
five years, thirty of its pupils had been accepted by the *École
Polytechnique*.[1]

The case of Arago is unique.[2] As a young boy he found the
syllabus for the entrance examination to the *École Polytechnique*
in the library at his school at Perpignan. He saw that the study
of the classics of French literature and even the elementary
mathematics he was taught at school would be quite inadequate.
He therefore decided to teach himself and sent to Paris for
mathematical books. Fortunately he made the acquaintance
of a local man who studied higher mathematics as a pastime and
was prepared to advise him. Arago, however, later insisted that
he was essentially self-taught. Prevented by accident from taking
the examination in 1802 at the age of sixteen Arago applied
himself with renewed vigour to an intensive study of mathematics. He now added to his library books by Euler, the *Théorie
des fonctions analytiques* of Lagrange and the *Mécanique céleste* of
Laplace (Volumes 1 and 2). Arago read a memoir by Poisson,

---

[1] *Revue philosophique, littéraire et politique*, new series, iii (1806), 571–2.
[2] Arago, 'The history of my youth', *Biographies of distinguished scientific men*,
trans., 1857, pp. 2–6.

written when he was still a student at the *École Polytechnique*, and, imagining that this was typical of the standard required, he set his sights very high. By the time the examination took place, he had Lagrange's work at his finger tips and after an exceptional oral examination of more than two hours, during which he answered a series of mathematical problems of a high standard at a blackboard, he was declared to have passed. His name was placed first in order of merit on the list of successful candidates for that year. This was obviously an exceptional case and Arago later admitted that before admission he had reached a higher standard in mathematical analysis than that required from graduates of the *École Polytechnique*.

Gay-Lussac and Thenard

Gay-Lussac came to Paris in November 1794 as a young country lad. At a *pension* in the capital he studied for entrance to the *École Polytechnique*. Three years later, at the age of nineteen, he passed the entrance examination with distinction. On his admission on 27 December 1797, he was the first student from his home department to gain a place. After graduating in 1800 Gay-Lussac was one of four students who chose to pursue further studies at the *École des Ponts et Chaussées*, one of the *Écoles d'application* which had the reputation of attracting the best students. Later in the same year, however, he withdrew from the course to work in Berthollet's laboratory. This was a private position but later Berthollet was able to have him appointed not as a full *répétiteur* (demonstrator), since there were no vacancies, but as an *adjoint* (assistant), an appointment which dated from 31 December 1802. When Fourcroy's demonstrator, Thenard, left the *École Polytechnique* to take up the chair of chemistry at the *Collège de France*, Gay-Lussac was appointed in his place (23 September 1804), although he was still able to continue as Berthollet's assistant at Arcueil. Berthollet later obtained quarters for Gay-Lussac at the *École Polytechnique* on the grounds that this would give him more time for his research and teaching.[1] Gay-Lussac lived at the school from 1806 to

---

[1] Letter from Berthollet to Lacuée, Governor of the *École*, 23 September 1805—*École Polytechnique*, Archives, Section 1794, dossier Berthollet.

1808 when, after his marriage, he moved to a house in the Rue d'Enfer near Berthollet's town house.

Thenard had been at the *École Polytechnique* as demonstrator from December 1798 until April 1804. Yet despite his long association with the school, it was not until the end that he became friendly with Berthollet. Thenard's early patron was Fourcroy and it was through the latter that Thenard had obtained the post of demonstrator. Thenard's attachment to Fourcroy was not restricted to his official duties at the school; until about 1804 much of his research was closely linked with that of Fourcroy and his friend Vauquelin. Gay-Lussac's post as demonstrator to Fourcroy had no personal significance. Thenard's resignation offered the opportunity of promotion from assistant demonstrator and Gay-Lussac would have been foolish to have refused this step up the ladder, which in no way affected his fundamental loyalty to Berthollet. Probably Thenard's early interest in organic chemistry can be credited to Fourcroy but Thenard lacked one of the advantages of Gay-Lussac. He had not himself undergone the rigorous mathematical training of the *École Polytechnique* and here we see one of the fundamental differences which separated him from the physical chemist Gay-Lussac, who was also to be his close friend and colleague in the Arcueil circle.

In 1808 and 1809 Gay-Lussac was engaged on some major research, including work on the alkali metals and the isolation of boron, all in conjunction with Thenard. It was presumably in recognition of this work, carried out at the *École Polytechnique*, that, by an imperial decree of 31 March 1809, the title of Professor of Practical Chemistry was conferred on Gay-Lussac. There were, however, no funds available at the time for the remuneration of the holder of this new post. On the death of Fourcroy in December 1809 Gay-Lussac was unanimously elected by the *Conseil de Perfectionnement* on 17 February 1810 to succeed him at a salary of 6,000 francs. Although Gay-Lussac's chair had been a personal one, it was considered that, once established, it might be used to attach able men to the school and accordingly Thenard was brought back to the *École Polytechnique*. From October 1811 Thenard took over Guyton's teaching duties at the *École*.

Examiners

Examinations were very prominent at the *École Polytechnique*. In the first place there was an entrance examination and the number of candidates presenting themselves for the limited number of places increased steadily as the fame of the school grew. Further examinations were held at the end of each year of study and there was, of course, a final examination for graduation. The holding of these examinations placed a considerable burden on the staff of the school, a burden which was multiplied by the system of conducting individual oral examinations. Some examiners tried to cut down the time by examining students in pairs, but this was obviously not a satisfactory solution. Not all the examiners were on the teaching staff of the school. Malus, for example, was not even living in Paris when he was appointed as examiner for the intermediate and final examination in descriptive geometry (1805), an appointment to which the subject of physics was added in the following and succeeding years. For this duty he received 2,000 francs. Malus' history, however, shows that the visits to Paris which he was obliged to make, were to be most beneficial to him as a means of keeping in touch with people and ideas at the focus of French science.

A complementary duty was that of Biot, who from 1799 to 1805 was one of the examiners for entry to the school. This involved an annual tour of the provinces. When the *École Polytechnique* was founded, it was stipulated that entrance examinations should be held simultaneously in twenty-one provincial centres as well as in Paris. The difficulty of obtaining a score of appropriately qualified examiners and of comparing their assessments of candidates led to the division of France into four regions, each of which was covered by one examiner, who travelled from one centre to the next. Biot's region was the south-eastern part of French territory which then included parts of what are now Italy and Switzerland. His journeys must have been of interest to Berthollet, who had lived in this region as a young man. At that time Geneva was at the centre of scientific intelligence and Biot's visits cannot have been without profit to himself and his associates in Paris on the one hand and to the *savants* of Geneva on the other. When Biot visited Geneva in

1805, it was in the company of Candolle, then engaged in compiling his collection of French flora.[1] On another visit Biot regretted how few days he would be allowed to spend with his friends in Geneva.[2] He always had to keep to a strict schedule, which in 1805 was as follows: After conducting the examination in Geneva on 7 September, he had to be in Turin by the 18th and on 29 September it was the turn of Grenoble. He returned to Paris by way of Lyons, where he examined candidates on 7 October and Dijon, where he passed a week later.

Student Finance

From the beginning provision had been made to give financial support to students at the *École Polytechnique*, although the money paid in *assignats* was worth little in practice. In the summer of 1795 many of the students were no longer able to get enough to eat and left the school. Their grant was divided among the neediest students remaining. At this time the Committee of Public Safety was distributing one pound of bread a day to 150 students and later government assistance included military rations and even clothing. It would not be just, however, to judge the problem of student finance from the evidence at a time of national crisis. Passing on to the reorganization of 1799, we find that students received the pay of an artillery sergeant—360 francs a year. Even then nearly half the students received further assistance from the State, bringing their total grant to about 500 francs. Students with the responsibility of section leader were given about 700 francs. There were some who, like Gay-Lussac, found an opportunity of giving tuition privately as a means of supplementing their income. In 1798 more than three dozen young men, who were supposed to be undergoing full-time education at the *École Polytechnique*, were in fact spending a large part of their time as teachers of mathematics and science in the *Écoles centrales* in the Paris region. In the same year about forty students left the *École Polytechnique* without graduating. Probably this 'leakage' was due less to straightforward academic failure than to personal problems,

---

[1] *Bibliothèque universitaire, Geneva*, MS. fr. 666, f. 159.
[2] *Bibliothèque universitaire, Geneva*, Autog. Rillier. Biot's letter to Pictet of 6 September 1804.

illness and overwork as well as dissatisfaction with the poor grant and living conditions.

A most interesting document[1] was provided by the administration of the *École Polytechnique* in reply to an accusation that most of the students belonged to wealthy families, or at least had families in Paris, and therefore did not require a subsistence allowance. This document shows that by far the largest group of students (46 per cent) were the sons of artisans and peasants and that nearly sixty per cent were estimated to have no means of support other than that provided by the State. Malus was one of the early students of the school who could not have remained without a grant and a formal statement to this effect signed by Malus, has survived.[2]

For the first ten years of its existence the *École Polytechnique* was an outstanding example of 'a career open to talents' irrespective of wealth. In 1805, however, it was decided that students should no longer be subsidized by the state. Instead of receiving a minimal grant, they were to contribute a sum of 800 francs a year for their board and lodging. From this time on the *École Polytechnique* ceased to be freely open to students from poor homes. Gay-Lussac's father, who had lost his money in the Revolution, would probably not have been able to support his son at the *École Polytechnique* under the new regulations. Certainly Poisson's widowed mother would never have been able to finance her son's scientific education. The governing body of the school, however, did what it could to soften these harsh new regulations, and they were able to obtain partial remission of fees for poorer students. But if the Emperor Napoleon was sometimes short-sighted, it might seem that King Louis XVIII was blind. In 1816 under the Restoration the cost of *pension* for students at the *École Polytechnique* was increased from 800 to 1,000 francs and the reason was stated explicitly. It was the hope that young noblemen and the sons of wealthy families might be attracted to study there and form an educated elite. Graduates of the school with suitable backgrounds would be eligible for important government appointments. Twenty-four scholarships were founded (less than one place in ten) for students without means. Genius then, as always, could break the

[1] Quoted by Fourcy, *Histoire de l'École Polytechnique*, 1828, p. 177.
[2] *École Polytechnique*, Archives, Section 1794, dossier M.

barrier of money and class but competence might well be passed over and France was to be the poorer as a result.

Staff Finance

Under the Directory the *École Polytechnique* was constantly beset by financial problems and when the school asked for more money, a member of the Council of Five Hundred attacked what he considered to be the over-staffing of the school. Why, for example, were there so many people teaching chemistry? The budget for the school could be reduced not only by decreasing the number of staff, but also by decreasing the number of students. In 1797 it was decided that as an economy measure the number of students was to be cut to 200 with an overall budget for the school not exceeding 300,000 francs. Eventually a supplementary grant of 180,000 francs was passed and this allowed the student numbers to remain at 250. This also allowed staff salaries to be raised to their original level, since by a decree of the Directorate of 30 January 1797 these had been uniformly reduced as an economy measure. The teaching staff of the *École Polytechnique*, which was habitually asking for increased funds, now stated that they would have been quite content with a salary of 5,000 francs per annum. It had come to their notice, however, that professors at the *Collège de France*, the *École de Santé* and the *École des Mines* were to receive 6,000 francs per annum and the teachers at the *École Polytechnique* did not wish their positions to be considered inferior.

Matters were not improved much during the Consulate. In 1800 the publication of the *Journal de l'École Polytechnique* was suspended due to lack of funds. In 1801 and 1802 further economies were necessary, and at one time the staff and students were five months in arrears with their salaries. On several occasions members of the staff offered to forgo their salaries, so that this money would be available for general use. Monge and Berthollet on their appointment as members of the Senate immediately offered to continue their teaching duties without salary, but it was found that Senators were not eligible to draw money from any other government appointment and so the hoped-for additional source of revenue did not materialize.

Militarization

Bonaparte and his ministers were fully aware of the military value of the *École Polytechnique* as a source of potential officers. On 2 March 1804 it was suggested that some young men who were academically not quite good enough for the *École Polytechnique* might be passed on to the army as suitable material for future infantry officers. For the artillery more mathematical knowledge was required, but the French army could not always wait until the men had finished their course. On 23 December 1803 Berthier, Minister of War, asked that the sixty-two students in the second year registered for the artillery should be given an intensive course lasting not more than six weeks and then join the army. Bonaparte himself had a rather peculiar idea of the function of the school when he gave orders that, as a reward for bravery in battle, a fifteen-year-old boy should be admitted to the school until he was old enough to become an officer in the cavalry. It was in ways such as these that the government under the Consulate tended to treat the *École Polytechnique* as a military academy.

In July 1804 a sudden change took place in the organization of the *École Polytechnique*. Napoleon ordered that it should be reorganized on military lines, despite strong advice to the contrary from Monge, Berthollet and Fourcroy. The excuse for the militarization was the lack of discipline among the students. There had been trouble outside the school and, even inside, the system of section leaders had not proved a success.

Students now had to wear a military uniform, do drill and live in barracks. Harder work was demanded of them. Previously students had been expected to arrive at the school from their lodgings by 8 a.m. ready for the first lecture and the working day had lasted about nine hours. Under the new regime with all students living in, they rose at the summons of a drum at 5 a.m. and they managed to do eight hours' work before lunch at 2 p.m. A further three hours' work in the evening was expected.

The director of academic studies was made subservient to a military governor, although the appointment of Lacuée to this post from 1804 to 1814 made this provision less severe in practice. For example, in 1807, when an attempt was made by the

Minister of War to conscript students in the middle of their courses, this interference was successfully resisted by the governor. By a decree of 1811 the traditional right of choice of career by the students was replaced by a system in which the best students were drafted as military engineers. The artillery too drew heavily on the school and in the course of two years (1811–1813) more than two hundred students of the *École Polytechnique* became officers in the artillery. Yet, while undermining the school from within, Napoleon by the same decree of 1811 attacked it from without. In future artillery students would attend military academies instead of the *École Polytechnique*. There was no intention, however, of allowing the *École Polytechnique* to pursue scientific and technological education in isolation from Napoleon's growing need for military manpower. It seems plain that under the Empire, when there was a clear conflict between the interests of science and war, as in the *École Polytechnique*, Napoleon and his ministers always favoured the short-term military view. The case of the *École Polytechnique* shows that Napoleon's claim to have been a patron of science is weakened considerably by his overriding military ambitions.

Because of its value in relation to military training, the number of places in the *École Polytechnique* was increased under the Empire and this inevitably lowered the standard of admission. The standard of teaching, however, had probably improved considerably since the early days of the experimental courses. The school also began to benefit by the services of its own graduates. The case of Poisson comes instantly to mind. Immediately on graduation in 1800 he obtained a teaching post at the *École Polytechnique* as assistant lecturer in mathematical analysis. In 1802 at the age of 21 he was provisionally appointed professor of analysis and mechanics, a position which was later confirmed. The young professor was greatly respected by his students. When the students had been determined to withhold their formal approval for the legislation creating Bonaparte Emperor of France, Poisson used his influence to make them change their mind, since it seemed likely that such an act of defiance would have resulted in the closing of the school. Poisson was at once a brilliant mathematician and a vigorous and capable teacher. Other members of the staff of the school

P

illustrated only too well that men of high intellectual qualities are not always good teachers. Ampère, for example, who taught at the *École Polytechnique* from 1807, was completely ineffectual as a teacher. On the other hand Hachette, whose right to a place in the general history of science might be questioned, was a careful and successful teacher of descriptive geometry at the school.

The 'Conseil de Perfectionnement'

It has been mentioned that one of the achievements of Laplace as Minister of the Interior was to secure the adoption of a new organization for the *École Polytechnique*. The law passed on 16 December 1799 may be regarded as the real charter of the school. It created a governing body for the *École Polytechnique* called the 'Council of Improvement' (*Conseil de Perfectionnement*). There had previously been a *Conseil d'Instruction et Administration*, concerned with the details of running the school. This was now made subordinate to the Council of Improvement, which in any case was to include four delegates from the teaching staff of the school. The four passing-out examiners were also included in the Council, as was one representative from each of the specialist schools (Artillery, Civil Engineering, Mining, etc.), which students of the *École Polytechnique* would enter on graduation. Finally there were three members of the First Class of the Institute. The three members elected by the First Class in 1800 were Monge, Berthollet and Laplace and they continued to be re-elected annually, although when Monge was appointed Director of the school, his place was taken by Lagrange and later by Carnot.

Berthollet presided over the very first meeting of the Council on 23 October 1800. At the following meetings Laplace was president but Berthollet again presided for all the meetings of 1802. During the whole period of the Consulate and Empire both Berthollet and Laplace continued as members of the Council to influence the policy of the *École Polytechnique*, including the appointment of staff. The Council had an enormous value as a permanent commission of experts who could safeguard the interests of the school and exercise a continuity of policy, which the intervention of a succession of government ministers would have made impossible. The powers of the Council continued under the reorganization of 1804, although it was now presided over by the military governor of the school. Poisson, Gay-Lussac and Thenard were all at one time members of the Council, having been chosen by their colleagues on the staff of the school to represent them. Malus, Descotils and Dulong were also successively members of the Council in their capacity as passing-out examiners.

The Council held an annual series of meetings, usually starting about the end of October. It had been hoped that a few meetings at this time of the year would be sufficient to deal with most of the major administration and teaching problems of the school for the whole year. In practice these sessions became more and more prolonged. In 1806 they occupied the months of November and December. In 1807 the first meeting was held on 23 October and the last of the series three months later. In 1808 the series of meetings lasted from 19 October until 11 March the following year. These dates have some relevance to the Arcueil 'season' as will be seen later. It is evident that Laplace and Berthollet had this regular administrative duty in Paris each winter and other members of the Arcueil circle were affected in different years.

One of the first tasks of the Council when it was established was to clarify the relationship between the *École Polytechnique* and the specialist schools, but as the name of the Council suggests, its primary function was to modify and improve the teaching programme and examinations. It was also responsible for staff appointments. The Council did much to preserve the spirit of the *École Polytechnique* as an establishment of higher scientific and technological education when the organization imposed by Napoleon could easily have reduced it to little more than a military academy.

As a later example of the influence of the Council in the teaching at the school, we may take the case of Ampère and Cauchy, whose students had been unable to understand their lectures. The two instructors were ordered in 1823 by a sub-committee of the Council under the chairmanship of Laplace to submit to it printed copies of the contents of their lectures and these were to be distributed to students in advance. The following year Ampère and Cauchy were told to base their lectures on a published work, which the students could have in front of them.

The 'École Polytechnique' and Arcueil

In the early nineteenth century the *École Polytechnique* was one of the leading institutions in the world which provided a higher education in science. It has been of special interest to consider it more particularly in relation to the Arcueil circle. We have seen that Berthollet, Laplace and Chaptal were all appointed to the original staff of the school and that Gay-Lussac and Arago had been students there. Both Gay-Lussac and Thenard did important work when they were on the staff of the school. Biot had been one of the original students and from 1799 to 1805 he carried out the onerous duties of examining prospective students. In 1806 this task was taken over by Poisson, who had himself been a student there from 1798 to 1800 and who was taken on to the teaching staff of the school immediately after graduation. Malus had been one of the first intake of students; he had subsequently visited the school regularly as an examiner and in 1812 he was appointed director of studies and second-in-command of the now militarized *École Polytechnique*. Descotils was examiner in chemistry from 1810 to 1812. Other students at the school included Dulong (1801–2) and Arago (1803–5). In 1810 Monge's health no longer permitted him to lecture regularly and Arago was appointed to replace him, first temporarily and then permanently as professor of descriptive geometry. In 1812 Dulong returned to the school as an examiner and became successively professor of physics (1820) and director of studies (1830).

Berthollet and Laplace as representatives of the Institute became permanent members of the governing body of the school. It is obvious that they had a high regard for the training given, as they both sent their sons there. Amédée Berthollet stayed for nearly two years but did not graduate. Humboldt, who never had any official position at the school, is sometimes listed among the distinguished visitors but, far from paying a formal visit, he actually worked and even slept there. He shared Gay-Lussac's room and carried out experiments in the laboratory in 1808. Of the fifteen members of the Society of Arcueil only two, Candolle and Bérard, had no connection with the *École Polytechnique*. The collapse of the First Empire did not end the association of members of the Arcueil group with the *École Polytechnique*. After the Restoration of 1815 we find the resilient Laplace as president of a commission appointed to advise on the reorganization of the school. The commission drew up a long memoir to suggest the lines on which the school should be run to train young men in science and engineering 'for the glory of the monarchy'.

The 'Bureau des Longitudes'

In England a Board of Longitude has been established in 1714 with the object of encouraging research into the best method of determining longitude at sea, a problem of considerable importance to a naval power. It was not until after the Revolution in France that the desirability of following the English example was appreciated, although when the *Bureau des Longitudes* was founded, its terms of reference were rather wider than those of its English counterpart.

Laplace played a prominent part in the founding of the *Bureau*. In a letter written by Laplace to Lakanal on 22 December 1794, he suggested that three astronomers should be attached to the Paris Observatory, each astronomer having one pupil.[1] An astronomical commission consisting of three mathematicians and four astronomers should be appointed to direct the various French observatories and to collect and publish observations and tables. This commission was to be the *Bureau des Longitudes*. An interesting passage in Laplace's letter is one in which he urged the value of astronomy not only for its utility in navigation, etc. but also as a means of combating the superstition of astrology. Subsequently on 10 April 1795, Lakanal in his report to the Committee of Public Instruction included a sum of 60,000 livres for the establishment of a *Bureau des Longitudes* 'as in England'.[2] A decree presented by Grégoire and passed by the Convention on 25 June formally established the *Bureau*. It was to consist of two mathematicians (Lagrange and Laplace), four astronomers, two naval experts, a geographer

[1] *Procès-Verbaux du Comité d'Instruction Publique*, 1891–1957, vol. v, p. 309.
[2] *Ibid.*, vol. vi, p. 67.

and a technician. Each of the members was to receive a substantial salary.

The first meeting of the *Bureau* was held in the Petit Luxembourg and it later met in the Louvre. From 27 January 1804 meetings were held at the Observatory. The location of the Observatory, near what was then the southern extremity of Paris, is not without interest. It was significantly nearer to Arcueil than the *Bureau* had been when it met at the centre of Paris. In the seventeenth century a few of the early meetings of the *Académie des Sciences* had been held at the Observatory, but the inconvenience caused to members by its distance from the centre of the city had led to its abandonment for this purpose. In the early nineteenth century the location of the Observatory was to be a positive advantage to members of the Arcueil group such as Laplace, Biot, Arago and Poisson who were connected with the *Bureau*.

The *Bureau* was originally to meet on the second and seventh days of each *décade*, but when the Institute chose these same days for the meeting of its First Class, the days of the *Bureau* were changed to the fourth and ninth of each *décade*. It was not only the Institute that clashed with the meetings of the *Bureau des Longitudes*, but also the Senate, of which Laplace was a prominent member.

From the autumn of 1802 the *Bureau* met only once a week, although the day of the week chosen was changed repeatedly. After meeting on Mondays and then Tuesdays, Laplace suggested Fridays and this was confirmed by a decree of 20 January 1804. In 1806 Prony, who was then president, pointed out that his duties as director of the *École des Ponts et Chaussées* would often prevent him attending on Fridays and it was therefore agreed provisionally to meet on Saturdays. In February 1807 (when regular meetings of the Society of Arcueil had begun) Wednesday was chosen as the day and this continued fairly regularly until the death of Laplace. It is interesting to observe that the *Bureau* never met regularly on Thursdays and this must have been one reason why the Arcueil group sometimes chose this day—at least in 1807—for their meetings. Later the many duties of the members of the Society of Arcueil made even Thursday impossible and most subsequent meetings at Arcueil were held on Sundays.

The meetings of the *Bureau* took place in the afternoon. The length of the meetings, 1.30 p.m.–3.30 p.m., was even laid down by ministerial decree (20 January 1804). Yet it would be misleading to regard an appointment to the *Bureau* as a sinecure demanding only two hours' work a week. As such it would have been less demanding than membership of the Institute. Yet the members of the *Bureau* themselves insisted that their appointment was a full-time occupation and that they considered it their duty to devote their complete working day to the advancement of astronomical theory and the calculation of accurate astronomical tables. A further duty was to publish regularly the *Connaissance des Temps*. Apart from its astronomical and geodesic work, the *Bureau* was concerned with the related problems of standards of mass and length. In September 1803 Chaptal as Minister of the Interior had given the *Bureau* charge over these standards. In 1805 and 1817 the *Bureau* was engaged in comparisons of its standard of length and in 1811–12 the Bureau was concerned in an alleged discrepancy in the kilogram.

The members of the Bureau were paid 8,000 francs per annum (*adjoints* 4,000 francs), as compared with the 1,500 francs paid to members of the Institute. It was clear to the members of the *Bureau* that whereas the members of the Institute, having attended meetings and drawn up reports, were free to supplement their income if they wished in their remaining time, the members of the *Bureau* were full-time employees of the State. It was true that there were exceptional cases, such as that of Lalande who, apart from other duties, suffered from poor health which prevented his regular attendance at meetings of the *Bureau*. He employed several calculators to do some of his work for the *Bureau* for him and he paid them from his salary.

If Lalande took less than his proper part in the activities of the *Bureau*, Laplace took more. Laplace had taken advantage of his short tenure of the Ministry of the Interior to provide further facilities for the *Bureau* and, most important, to assign a sum of government money for this purpose. Another and later example of Laplace's patronage is provided by his gift to the Observatory of a repeating circle, which he had had specially made by the instrument-maker Reichenbach in 1810 for use in the determination of the declination of stars eclipsed by the moon. This instrument (rather like a large theodolite) cost Laplace 6,546 francs with a further charge for carriage to Paris.

Delambre quoted Monge as saying that, although he admired the energy of Laplace, he was too fond of directing his colleagues. Laplace was elected several times as president of the *Bureau* but the minutes make it clear that apart from this function, he was particularly prominent in making proposals and using his influence to see that they were accepted. At the meeting of 2 May 1806 Laplace reported that he had asked both the Minister of the Interior and Napoleon himself to authorize the resumption of the measurement of the meridian, work which had been suspended since the death of Méchain in Spain in 1804. This approval was doubly important since it ensured that state finance would be available to finance the enterprise. It was Laplace who proposed Biot and Arago to undertake this work and the *Bureau* agreed to this. It may be more than a coincidence that it was under the presidency of Laplace in 1811 that he was able to announce to his colleagues in the Bureau (6 March) that Napoleon had granted 50,000 francs to complete the extensions to the Observatory.

Laplace was, of course, no mean politician. Despite his close association with Napoleon, he found favour with Louis XVIII and the minutes of the *Bureau* for 9 April 1817 report that Laplace and Arago had taken a telescope to the Tuileries, ostensibly to show the Royal family the phases of Venus. Laplace had taken the opportunity of urging the Duke of Angoulême, Minister of the Interior, to undertake the planning of a military map of France. When this was agreed, it was only natural that Laplace should be made the president of the commission appointed to prepare the map. Laplace also used the resources of the *Bureau* to investigate his own interests. It was, for example, Laplace who arranged for the *Bureau* to determine the velocity of sound for him in 1822.

The hand of Laplace is also evident in the making of appointments to the *Bureau*. There were no new appointments between 1799 and 1806. Then the occurrence of a vacancy enabled Biot to be nominated *adjoint* on 29 August 1806. This was followed by the nomination of Arago as *adjoint* from 15 July 1807 and of Poisson on 24 August 1808. No further vacancies occurred in the next five years. The succession of appointments of these three protégés of Laplace could hardly have been a coincidence. Apart from the honour, each post carried a salary of 4,000 francs. In the case of Poisson, however, who was elected when there were already three *adjoints*, the Minister of the Interior decided that this was an additional post and at the beginning he was unpaid for reasons of economy. Further evidence of Laplace's patronage of Arago is provided by the minutes of the meetings of the *Bureau*. On 25 January 1805 Laplace proposed Arago for the post of secretary-librarian of the Observatory. He was elected unanimously and given a room at the Observatory occupied previously by Bouvard. Arago took up the post the following month at a salary of 1,800 francs, not a large salary, but it should be remembered that he was just at the beginning of his career. On becoming *adjoint* in 1807 his salary increased to 4,000 francs. This was supplemented in 1813 by a further appointment at the Observatory. At one time Lalande had given a general course of lectures on astronomy. At the meeting of the *Bureau* on 11 November 1812 Laplace made a speech about the advantage of a course of practical astronomy at the Observatory for young men. He suggested that this course should be given to Arago at an (additional) salary of 1,500 francs. It is obvious that to have Laplace as one's patron could be rewarding financially as well as stimulating intellectually.

The *Bureau des Longitudes* sometimes functioned as a scientific society, and it was considered appropriate to announce discoveries at its meetings. This was all the more natural after the active functioning of the Society of Arcueil had come to an end and when the members of the *Bureau* included Laplace, Biot, Arago and Poisson. When Arago discovered that an electric current could bring about the magnetization of soft iron, he announced this at a meeting of the *Bureau* on 20 September 1820. It was only the following Monday, 25 September, that he reported his discovery at a meeting of the *Académie des Sciences*. On 22 August the following year Arago read a report on the interference of light at a meeting of the *Bureau*. He demonstrated the cancelling-out effect of two rays by their failure to act on a film of silver chloride.[1]

[1] Arago, *Oeuvres, Mémoires Scientifiques*, vol. i, pp. 484–5.

The 'Collège de France'

A famous educational establishment which had on its staff
members of the Arcueil circle was the venerable *Collège de France*
(founded in 1530 as the *Collège Royal*). During the eighteenth
century science had come increasingly to be represented in what
had once been an institution devoted exclusively to a Renaissance concept of classical education. In 1769 the old chair of
Greek and Latin philosophy was transformed into a chair of
physics. This was given to the mathematician, Cousin, and the
mathematical bias of the chair was emphasized by the foundation
of a chair of experimental physics in 1786. A chair of 'chemistry
and natural history' was founded in 1774. From 1800 these two
disciplines were separated and Cuvier was given the teaching
of natural history and Vauquelin the teaching of chemistry.

On Cousin's death in 1800, it fell to Chaptal as Minister of
the Interior to nominate his successor. The historian of the
Collège de France states that Chaptal's choice of Biot was
prompted by a large number of letters in his support from members of the Institute headed by Laplace. Sometimes the preference of the staff of the *Collège* itself was the deciding factor in
making a new appointment. This was the case with Vauquelin,
who was also supported by a letter from Berthollet to Chaptal.
In 1804 Vauquelin resigned his appointment when he took up
a chair at the *Muséum d'Histoire Naturelle* and Thenard was
appointed as his successor. Thenard held this post for forty
years and was able to boast in his old age of the numbers of
students who had sat before him. The record of longevity in the
teaching at the *Collège de France* was, however, held by Biot, who
took up his duties in 1801 and occupied the chair of general
physics and mathematics until his death in 1862.

The 'École des Mines'

The *École des Mines* had been founded in Paris in 1783. By 1788
it was in a state of decline, but in 1794 it was re-established by
the Committee of Public Safety at the Hotel de Mouchy, Rue
de l'Université.[1] Descotils had been one of the original pupils
in 1794. One of his professors was Haüy, but it was to Vauquelin,

[1] I.e. in the immediate vicinity of the Palais Bourbon which was the site
of the *École Polytechnique* until 1806.

professor of assaying, that he became particularly attached. Vauquelin resigned from his post at the *École des Mines* in June 1801 and Descotils was appointed to succeed him.

Teaching for the year 1801–2 began on 8 December. The course of chemistry applied to mining given by Descotils (just back from Egypt) was described as follows:

> He will make known the methods used to obtain the reagents necessary for assaying and the methods used to estimate the purity of minerals and to purify them in cases where they contain foreign matter. He will then expound the chemical properties of several metals and the means of assaying their ores; he will also discuss the analysis of mineral combustible substances. He will then indicate the principal properties of mineral salts and will endeavour to find means of obtaining under the eyes of the pupils results similar to the corresponding operations on a large scale. He will end his course with the analysis of stones and mineral waters.[1]

Descotils was also given the post of curator of chemicals for the *Conseil des Mines* and director of the laboratory. These non-teaching appointments are particularly significant in the life of Descotils since, when, on the orders of Chaptal, the school was moved to the Mont-Blanc department in 1802, on the principle that it should work in closer contact with mining practice, Descotils alone of the staff of the *École des Mines* was allowed to stay permanently in Paris as director of the laboratory. He was thus able to play his full part in the Society of Arcueil. In 1806 Descotils was given Berthier as one of two assistants. Berthier's analysis of barium sulphate was carefully checked by Berthollet and Thenard at Arcueil, as this was a fundamental datum in gravimetric analysis.[2]

Under the Restoration the *École des Mines* was re-established in Paris. On 1 August 1814 Descotils was appointed provisional director of the school. (There was no permanent director until 1848.) The school was then housed in the Petit Luxembourg but in August 1815 it was transferred to its present site in what was then the Rue d'Enfer. Descotils was prevented by illness from attending the new session beginning in November 1815

---

[1] 'Programme des cours de l'École des mines pour l'an 10', *Journal des mines*, xi (1801–2), 270–1.

[2] 'M. Descotils nous apporta à Arcueil de la même barite qu'avait employé M. Berthier', *M.S.A.*, ii (1809), 46.

and he died in December. Descotils' teaching commitments, being confined to the years 1801–2 and 1814–15, were much less than most of his colleagues at Arcueil. Although he was fortunate in having a laboratory, he had a heavy programme of analysis throughout the period of the Empire and he carried out some of his own research at Arcueil.

The Faculty of Science

Napoleon's establishment of a 'University' in 1808 was an attempt at a completely centralized and integrated system of education from primary school to university level. University teaching was divided into Faculties (medicine, law, theology, arts and science) and these were established at various centres in the provinces as well as in Paris. Altogether fifteen Faculties of Science were established in the French Empire, which now included Brussels, Geneva, Pisa and Turin as well as Strasbourg, Dijon, Toulouse, etc.

The Faculty of Science in Paris was formally constituted in 1808 as a board consisting of two professors from each of the leading institutions catering for higher scientific education as well as two mathematics teachers from the *lycées*. Two basic courses were to be given, one in 'mathematics' (calculus, astronomy, mechanics, physics) and one in science (physics, chemistry, mineralogy and geology, botany, zoology and physiology). The physics course was therefore a common course. It consisted of a study of the general properties of matter, statics, dynamics and hydrostatics, heat, magnetism, electricity and light as well as a special study of air and water. The professor of chemistry was expected to deal with affinities, combustion, salts, bases, animal and vegetable chemistry; the principles of chemical industry were also on the syllabus.

The courses given in the Faculties of Science and Arts were supposed to be a continuation of courses given in the *lycées*. At the beginning there was some overlap and it was decreed that a particular subject should not be taught at the same time in a *lycée* and in the Faculty, so that senior pupils could attend both classes. There was often a duplication of teaching staff between the *lycées* and the Faculties, particularly in the provinces. In theory, there were four professors in each Faculty, but the

Faculty of Science in Paris was wider in scope. Established in the old *Collège du Plessis*, it consisted of two professors from the *Collège de France* (astronomy: Biot, chemistry: Thenard), two from the *Muséum d'Histoire Naturelle* (mineralogy: Haüy, botany: Desfontaines), two from the *École Polytechnique* (mechanics: Poisson, physics: Gay-Lussac) and two teachers from *lycées*. From the names given, the predominant role of the Arcueil group is obvious. Biot, although officially holding the chair of astronomy, had become an authority in physics and in the period 1816 to 1826 the lectures on light, sound and magnetism were given by him.

The provision of funds for apparatus was very limited. In the years 1813 to 1819 the total expenditure on apparatus for the physics laboratory was 4,565 francs and this was spent entirely on optical apparatus.[1] There is a record that the supplier bought back some apparatus which he had originally sold to the Faculty, this apparatus consisting of objects which a man like Biot could be expected to provide himself, so that the very limited funds could be used to the best advantage.

The usual pay for Faculty professors in Paris was 4,000 francs with small additional sums for examination duties. A professor could obtain leave of absence for a period up to a year if necessary but the person taking the professor's place would not be paid except by the professor himself. The teaching duties in the Faculty of Science in Paris were limited to three hours a week. In 1811, for example, Biot together with an assistant had a class for astronomy on Mondays and Fridays from 11.30 to 1.0. Poisson, as professor of mechanics, taught on Mondays and Fridays from 8.30 to 10.0. Gay-Lussac, as professor of physics, gave his class on Tuesdays and Thursdays from 8.30 to 10.0, aided by Hachette. Thenard's class on chemistry took place on Wednesdays and Fridays from 2.30 to 4.0.

The Faculty of Science in Paris did not immediately become the focus of higher education in science in France or even in Paris. Whereas students of medicine in Paris had no choice but to study at the Faculty of Medicine, in science there were several possibilities and the prestige of the *École Polytechnique* continued to attract the cream of young men of mathematical ability desiring a higher education in science. Published versions

[1] J. Lecompte, 'Quelques documents inédits sur Gay-Lussac. Remarques sur son oeuvre scientifique', *87e Congrès des Sociétés savantes*, 1962, 141–5.

of lectures delivered in the Faculty demonstrate that topics were hardly explored much beyond an elementary level and in physics lectures mathematics was excluded![1]

The Reconstitution of the 'École Normale' under Napoleon

In the *École Normale* established by the Convention in the republican year III (1794–5) formal lectures were given by experts in their subjects, men such as Laplace and Berthollet, on the mistaken assumption that students would already be familiar with the principles of these subjects. The failure of this first attempt to provide teachers for the whole of France had not really proved that the idea of a national college was unworkable. In 1808 the *École Normale* was reconstituted as a kind of superior training college for students of both arts and sciences. The students were given board and lodging in addition to their instruction and in return they had to undertake to teach in French *lycées* for at least ten years. The annual budget of the school, including the keep of the three hundred students, the salaries of the teaching staff and the running expenses of the school, was 300,000 francs. The course was at first a two-year one with the students taking the *baccalauréat* after one year and a *licence* at the end of two years. Also at first students were expected to attend the lectures appropriate to their subject given at the *Collège de France*, the *École Polytechnique* and the *Muséum d'Histoire Naturelle*. This was purely a temporary measure until suitable staff was recruited for the *École Normale*.

It was not until 1815 that the school could be entirely independent of other courses given in Paris. At the same time the course was extended from two to three years, the first year being common to all. In the second year for those studying science there were weekly lectures on elementary astronomy, calculus, mineralogy, botany and physics. In the third year the science students had six lectures a week divided between mechanics, chemistry, anatomy and zoology. There was also practical work once a week. The *École Normale* continued on these lines until 1822 when it was suppressed. The official reason given was the undesirability of forming in Paris an élite of the French teaching

[1] See, e.g. Biot, *Précis élémentaire de physique expérimentale*, 1817, vol. i, Avant Propos.

profession, but the real reason for the suppression was the consistent liberal tendencies of this large group of young men. (There is an obvious parallel in the *École Polytechnique*.)

The *École Normale* is only of marginal interest to a study of the Arcueil group. It provided a livelihood for Dulong during the period 1811 to 1822 when he taught chemistry there. The teaching problems of Dulong will be considered later in this chapter, but it may be convenient to mention here a further educational institution with which Dulong was connected, the veterinary school at Alfort.

The '*École Vétérinaire d'Alfort*'

It was in a veterinary school that Dulong obtained the first appointment which provided him with some laboratory facilities. Later in the nineteenth century the Dutch chemist van't Hoff was also to make a living by teaching at a veterinary school, a post which his critics were able to scoff at as being of little distinction. Dulong's veterinary school was the one at Alfort, near Charenton, a few miles to the east of Paris, where the Marne meets the Seine. Candolle too had been connected with the school, being examiner in botany from 1805 to 1807. When the school was reorganized in 1813, provision was made for an establishment of seven professors, each with a salary of 4,000 francs. The new constitution established instruction at two levels and the higher level included the teaching of 'physics and chemistry applied to the ailments of animals'. It was to this post that Dulong was appointed by a decree of 24 July 1813.

When he took up his post in the following October Dulong found that although some instruction had previously been given in chemistry, the chemistry laboratory there had been taken over for other purposes and there was no apparatus or reagents. Nor was there any physics apparatus, let alone a physics laboratory. For the first year Dulong had to manage as best he could, but in December 1814 he received a grant of 4,000 francs which enabled him to make some provision for practical instruction. It was under Dulong's direction that the large chemistry laboratory was divided by a partition, enabling half to be used for practical purposes and the other half as a lecture theatre for about 70 to 80 students. Dulong's post at the veterinary school was only provisional and it did not become established until 1824. He was provided with an assistant, who at one time was Lassaigne, best known perhaps for his method of organic analysis using sodium metal. From 1825 Dulong's poor health prevented him giving all his lectures and he was given several periods of leave of absence, during which Lassaigne deputized for him. Eventually in 1827, after Dulong's resignation, Lassaigne was appointed as his successor.

Quite apart from his other functions as *maître de conférences* at the *École Normale* from 1811 to 1822 and his position as temporary examiner (1813–20) and then professor of physics (1820–30) at the *École Polytechnique*, Dulong worked hard at the veterinary school. Until 1825 there were no regular holidays. Dulong, however, had obtained the unique privilege for a member of staff of not being required to live at the school. He was even given an allowance for his lodgings in Paris. Although this meant a large amount of travelling, living in Paris enabled Dulong to fulfil his other teaching duties and it also kept him more closely in touch with scientific work in Paris.

The 'Athénée de Paris'

Another teaching institution was the *Athénée*. This had been founded in the Rue de Valois before the Revolution and called the *Lycée*. After 1802 it was known as the *Athénée de Paris*. It should not be confused with the *Athénée des Arts*, which has been described in Chapter Three. Lectures were given in scientific subjects as part of a general education. It was not intended to educate specialists and consequently the level of the teaching was fairly elementary. Nevertheless the teaching staff included various well-known figures in the scientific world. Fourcroy was particularly active and Cuvier lectured there until 1810.

Fourcroy was assisted by Thenard. The minute book of the *Comité d'Administration* of the *Athénée* contains some interesting information on Thenard's salary.[1] In May 1800 Thenard (officially Fourcroy's 'pupil') asked for payment for his services and the following year he was paid 300 francs (in comparison with 1,200 francs received by Fourcroy). He continued to be

---

[1] For this reference I am indebted to Dr W. A. Smeaton (private communication).

paid as a demonstrator until December 1806, when he asked for his salary to be brought up to the same level as that of Fourcroy. This request was granted. When Thenard succeeded Fourcroy as professor of chemistry in 1808 his salary was increased to 1,500 francs. Thenard continued to lecture at the *Athénée* till 1817. He was succeeded by several young men in turn including Chevreul and Robiquet and in 1823 Dumas was given the post. Biot lectured at the *Athénée* on physics from 1803 to 1806 and it is possible that Biot helped to draw Thenard away from Fourcroy towards the Arcueil group.

A sample of the teaching programme of the *Athénée* is provided by the *Moniteur* of 5 February 1806: Thenard had been speaking about combustible bodies and this led him on to carbonic acid and other acids. Biot had been concerned with the evaporation of liquids and had then given a general account of meteorology. Biot's next lecture was devoted to radiant heat.

The '*Muséum d'Histoire Naturelle*'

A major teaching and research establishment which cannot be ignored, despite its peripheral relevance to Arcueil, is the *Muséum d'Histoire Naturelle*. In a way it represents the opposite pole to Arcueil, so that when considering French science in the early nineteenth century, one can distinguish clearly at least two main groups, those who were associated with Arcueil and those who gravitated towards the *Muséum*. In a way this was a natural division between the physical sciences at Arcueil and natural history and allied sciences at the *Muséum*. There was some overlap in the subject of chemistry, however, and we shall see later that the Arcueil group was sometimes concerned with the life sciences.

The *Muséum* was all the more suited to be a centre of scientific activity because of its residential character. In the reorganization of the *Jardin du Roi* as the *Muséum d'Histoire Naturelle* in 1793 it was decreed that all professors had the right to living quarters at the *Muséum* so as to be more in touch with their work. Administration, moreover, was, on true republican principles, to be the duty of all professors. This necessitated regular meetings of the teaching staff and increased the community spirit of the *Muséum*. The *Muséum* was helped by several donations.

Q

Bonaparte himself gave some specimens, although the greatest gift was probably Humboldt's herbarium—a collection of 4,600 species of plants from Central America, mostly unknown before his journey. Immediately after the Revolution the *Muséum* and its library benefited from confiscated goods. Sometimes direct government aid was available, as for the reconstruction of 1808–10. Extensions became increasingly necessary as more specimens were collected.

In 1802 the teaching staff consisted of thirteen professors. There were professors of mineralogy (the abbé Haüy) and geology (Faujas de Saint-Fond), two professors of chemistry (Fourcroy and Brongniart), three professors of botany (including Jussieu), three professors of zoology (Geoffroy Saint-Hilaire, Lacépède and Lamarck), three professors of anatomy (including Cuvier as assistant professor) and one professor of drawing and painting. At the foundation of the *Muséum* each professor had a salary of 2,500 livres. In the early nineteenth century this was raised to 5,000 francs.

It is clear that the *Muséum* was only concerned with a limited range of scientific subjects. The inclusion of chemistry might appear to be a concession towards a wider scope than the life sciences alone might provide. Yet the chemistry taught had a definite orientation towards other studies in the *Muséum*, namely towards mineralogy and 'vegetable and animal analyses which might throw some light on the nature of organized bodies'. This was the responsibility of the professor of 'general chemistry' but there was also a professor of applied chemistry (*arts chimiques*). The first chair was held successively by Fourcroy (1793), Laugier (1810) and Gay-Lussac (1832). The second chair was held by A. L. Brongniart (1793), Vauquelin (1804) and Chevreul (1830).

In this list of names the inclusion of Gay-Lussac seems anomalous. He is the only one to have no link with the natural history tradition. A clue is provided by the fact that he did not take up this post until he was in his fifties. The truth that he exchanged his appointment as professor of physics at the *Faculté des Sciences* for the lighter duties of professor of general chemistry at the *Muséum*. In contrast to the rigid officialdom of the *Faculté*, Gay-Lussac was able at the *Muséum* to devise his own syllabus and there were no examinations. Gay-Lussac resigned his chair at the *École Polytechnique* in 1840 but he continued to hold the chair of general chemistry at the *Muséum* until his death in 1850.[1] Two of the most influential professors at the *Muséum d'Histoire Naturelle* were Fourcroy and Cuvier. Fourcroy, aided by Vauquelin (who also lived at the *Muséum* from 1804 onwards), carried out investigations of a large number of organic substances and one of their achievements was the isolation of urea. He was also the inspiration behind the publication of a new journal, the *Annales du Muséum d'Histoire Naturelle*, intended to serve as a medium for publication of the research of the professors of the *Muséum*. His influence at the *Muséum* enabled him to exercise some patronage, his most notable protégé being Vauquelin. When Vauquelin had come to Paris from Normandy as a youth, he had been taken on by Fourcroy as a junior laboratory assistant. He was provided by Fourcroy with board, lodging and pocket money and it was through his influence that he was appointed to the vacant chair at the *Muséum* in 1804.

Fourcroy died in 1809, but even before his death he had begun to be surpassed by the brilliant young zoologist J. L. N. F. Cuvier (1769–1832). In 1803 Cuvier had been appointed one of the two permanent secretaries of the First Class of the Institute, a key position in the official body of French science. In 1804 Cuvier married. After the restoration of the Bourbons, Madame Cuvier became quite a prominent hostess at their house at the *Muséum*. A *salon* was held on Saturdays. Nearly everyone with interests in natural history visited Cuvier at some time or other. The occasion was primarily a social one, although when it was less crowded it was possible to discuss scientific news. Cuvier's closest friends were received in his study. There were several points in common with the more informal of the meetings at Arcueil. One lesson that can be learned both from Arcueil and the *Muséum* is that much of the everyday work of French science (and not least the transmission of scientific intelligence) could be carried out completely independently of the Institute.

The Teaching Duties of the Members of the Arcueil Group

It would create an illusion if the world of Arcueil was treated in isolation, as if the men who worked and talked there had the

---

[1] After 1843 the actual lectures were given by Frémy by private arrangement (Grimaux and Gerhardt, *Charles Gerhardt*, 1900, p. 175).

leisure to pursue scientific research in rural bliss. In the previous chapter we saw that membership of the Institute imposed certain obligations such as attendance at meetings, sitting on committees and drawing up reports. Much more onerous, however, were teaching duties. If Humboldt with his independent income could devote himself to his publications, if Senators Berthollet and Laplace were free from the duties of teaching and demonstrating, most of the more junior members of the Arcueil group were not.

In describing the teaching duties of the majority of the Arcueil circle, we find that there was no simple one-to-one correlation of persons and positions. On the contrary, although teaching posts sometimes provided oportunities for research, they were often so inadequately paid that a family man might only earn enough to keep a wife and children if he had an accumulation of teaching or examining posts. Family responsibilities played a large part in driving men to take on more and more paid work. Also with little money available for apparatus, it was quite common for a man to buy his own apparatus for research. It may be convenient to consider in roughly chronological order the various teaching duties of Biot, Arago and Dulong and see if these had any adverse effect on their research. The question of holding several major teaching posts is probably best discussed in relation to Gay-Lussac and Thenard, and this brings us to the middle of the nineteenth century.

Biot's heavy teaching commitments in 1803 were described by his colleague Delambre, who in the following passage is excusing him for not immediately devoting his time to a memoir for which he was a member of a committee appointed by the Institute.

> Biot is particularly busy. At present he is giving two different courses [at the *Collège de France*], that of mathematical physics, for which he has replaced Cousin who has died, and the course of experimental physics in place of Lefèvre-Gineau, who has been appointed Inspector-General of Studies. Besides this he is teaching at the *Athénée* and on top of all this he is employed in writing an elementary book for the *lycées*.[1]

---

[1] *Correspondance du Grand Ampère*, ed. L. de Launay, Paris, 1936, 43, p. 271. For futher information on Biot's teaching see: Aulard, *Paris sous le Consulat*, vol. ii, p. 622, vol. iii, p. 401, vol. iv, p. 419.

Biot was also involved in the examinations of the *École Polytechnique*, first as a travelling examiner to conduct the annual entrance examination in different parts of France and later as a passing out examiner. This is a useful reminder that the men of Arcueil often lived intensely active lives with only a minority of their time available for their own scientific work. Such a situation can readily be appreciated by the university scientist of today.

The lack of time for research was particularly distressing when a young man felt that he had found a line of investigation which promised to bring far-reaching results. Such a situation arose for Arago. The position was described by Delambre, writing in his capacity as one of the secretaries of the First Class of the Institute, an impartial summary of work carried out by its members in 1812. Biot had written a major memoir on the passage of light through crystals (interpreted in terms of the oscillation of particles of light) which had taken up an entire volume of the *Mémoires* of the Institute. Delambre then turned to the work of Arago:

> We should also have liked to have given an equally detailed account of the several memoirs in which M. Arago described to the Class his new researches on light. These would have included experiments which are no less interesting and theories which before publication require further experiments which M. Arago has conceived and planned. But as he was only able to devote himself to this work in the brief moments of leisure which his duties as astronomer at the Royal Observatory allow, he has only been able to communicate his observations and ideas to the Class in so far as to draft them in separate accounts . . .[1]

In August 1811 when Arago read his first memoir on optics to the Institute he explained that he had been prompted to publish before he had fully completed the work because others (i.e. Biot) were working in the same field.[2] Biot for his part could hardly avoid mentioning Arago's work when he presented his next memoir on light.[3] It must have been doubly frustrating for Arago to see work which he regarded as his own done by his rival. Arago was here suffering from his junior position compared with Biot, who was twelve years his senior. Biot too had duties at

[1] Histoire pendant l'année 1812. *Mém. Inst.*, 1812, Part 2, xi.
[2] *Mém. Inst.*, 1811, Part 1, 1–2n. [3] *Ibid.*, 135–6.

the Observatory but these were mainly on the theoretical side whereas Arago was employed on the necessary but tedious and time-consuming observations made regularly night after night. Eight or nine years previously Biot had been overloaded with work; now it was the turn of Arago. It was in 1810 that Arago had been called upon to give Monge's lectures at the *École Polytechnique*. Although his success did him credit and was a useful additional source of income,[1] it was not obtained without the sacrifice of time which could have been devoted to optical research.

More striking is the case of Dulong. From his correspondence we know how strongly he felt about the burden of his teaching duties which, together with his bad health, often prevented him from doing any research. Dulong was successively *maître de conférences* at the *École Normale*, professor of chemistry at the *École Vétérinaire d'Alfort* and then at the *Faculté des Sciences*.

In 1819 Dulong was appointed *examinateur de sortie* at the *École Polytechnique*. When his friend Petit was dying of tuberculosis and was no longer able to lecture, Dulong and Arago arranged to give his lectures so that he should not forfeit any of his salary. Petit died in June 1820. A year later Dulong confided to Berzelius:

> Through a weakness of character for which I reproach myself incessantly, I have consented to accept the professorship of physics at the *École Polytechnique*, which the death of my unfortunate friend has left vacant. Even with good health the duties of this post would have left me with little free time, so judge how much of this I have had, sick as I have been for the past eighteen months.[2]

Dulong explained to Berzelius that it was his family responsibilities which made him accept such onerous teaching duties:

> If I were free from all the cares which come from bringing up a family, I would quickly get rid of three-quarters of the burden that is weighing me down, so that I could devote myself entirely to the advancement of science.[3]

---

[1] In the session 1811–12 Arago was given the title of assistant professor with a salary of 3,000 f. (i.e. half of Monge's salary).

[2] Letter of 21 August 1821, Berzelius, *Bref*, vol. 2, Part iv, p. 29 (21 August 1821).

[3] *Ibid.*, p. 36 (8 January 1822).

In 1828 when Dulong's health gave way under the strain of his work, Gay-Lussac took over his lectures on chemistry. Dulong told Berzelius that Gay-Lussac was hoping to use these lectures as the basis of a treatise of several volumes on chemistry:

> In this country an elementary text written by a university professor is a way to make a considerable sum of money, and I believe that this consideration enters largely into his decision. If I were free, I would prefer a thousand times to devote my leisure to research, but we have been ordered by the *École Polytechnique* to publish our lectures.[1]

In 1831 Arago succeeded in relieving Dulong of his teaching duties by getting him appointed to the administrative post of director of the *École Polytechnique*. Dulong's health improved but he considered that he had paid too dearly in having to abandon his research:

> I have bought this relief at a high price, since I am obliged to give up my work in science. I am weighed down by a multitude of administrative details which leaves me not one moment of my own. Besides, the rooms which I shall be obliged to occupy will not allow me to have a laboratory. I have almost decided to give up this new position, if, as I hope, my chair of physics becomes vacant again. Unfortunately, if I begin to teach again, it is only too likely that I shall fall back into my former condition.[2]

The position of Dulong might seem an extreme one, as his difficulties were magnified by his bad health. Nevertheless, we are fortunate in having access to the personal letters in which he set out the difficulties of doing research. The alternative sources of income provided by teaching, examining, administration and the writing of elementary text-books are set out here with a certain moving clarity. In his teaching Dulong was respected but he was never popular. He in turn never regarded teaching as much more than a useful source of income. He considered his business in life was to carry out the research at which he excelled. It was a tragedy that Dulong had to spend so much of his time doing work which to him was sheer drudgery.

With his many public duties, all of which were paid, it might have been expected that he would have left a reasonable legacy

---

[1] Berzelius, *Bref*, vol. 2, Part iv, p. 75 (10 August 1828).
[2] *Ibid.*, p. 101 (20 June 1831).

to his family when he died in 1838 at the age of fifty-three. It was a shock to his friends to discover that he had left nothing. Arago described how he had only learned the true state of the financial affairs of his friend on his death.[1] Dulong had spent all his spare money on costly scientific apparatus, and for his wife and children there was little more than the memory of his valuable scientific work. Fortunately Dulong had friends in influential circles, notably Arago, who was able to convince the Minister of Public instruction that Dulong's dependents deserved a state pension.

Another chemist, who had several teaching appointments but in rather happier circumstances, was Gay-Lussac. To his posts at the *École Polytechnique* and the *Faculté des Sciences* in chemistry and physics respectively he added one in technology at the *École d'application des Élèves Ingénieurs des Manufactures de l'État*. This provided training for state industries, notably the processing of tobacco and was known for short as *les Tabacs*. Gay-Lussac's post there involved no more than one lecture a week with practical work and carried a salary of 3,000 francs. For Gay-Lussac, however, teaching was only one of the possibilities available to earn a comfortable living. He found industrial chemistry more lucrative than teaching, perhaps to the envy of some of his academic colleagues. He was following the example of Berthollet in not confining his work to pure science. In 1805 he had been appointed a member of the consultative committee of arts and manufactures. In 1818 he obtained a post in the administration of the state gunpowder factory, a post which provided him with a laboratory at the Arsenal. He later had an interest in a glass factory which proved profitable.

Gay-Lussac's most important work in the 1820's and 1830's was in the field of industrial chemistry and this will be briefly described below. It may be worth first making a fairly obvious point. Teaching at an elementary level was not very congenial to most of the individual members of the Arcueil group with the possible exception of Arago, who saw the communication of the technicalities of science to a general audience as one of the duties and responsibilities of the scientist. Teaching at a more advanced level was also a matter of a job. It provided a regular salary. Yet it was not necessarily at variance with research. Indeed

[1] Discours funéraire, Arago, *Notices Biographiques*, vol. iii, p. 583.

advanced teaching could provide training for valuable collaborators in research. Gay-Lussac's critics felt that by investigating practical problems he had effectively abandoned a profession dedicated to the investigation of nature and the pushing back of the frontiers of knowledge. How little justification there was for this criticism may be apparent from what follows. In 1821 Gay-Lussac had been appointed to study physical means of estimating alcohol in wines. His work amounted to a complete investigation of all possible hydrometers and the laborious construction over a period of more than six months of tables, providing data of permanent value on the correlation of density and alcoholic content. If it was seen by the government as no more than a means of standardizing wines, it led nevertheless to a rather greater achievement, the invention of an alcoholometer.[1] Further, Gay-Lussac in collaborating with Welter developed exact methods of determining the strengths of alkalis, an important item of commerce.[2] This work was one of the bases of volumetric analysis, a branch of science which owes to Gay-Lussac not only some of its techniques but also some of its terminology, e.g. 'titre', 'normal acid', 'burette'. One of his most lucrative appointments was that of chief assayer at the Mint (10,000 francs), to which he was appointed in 1829. Newton had considered it an honour in his more mature years to be appointed Master of the Mint in London. Gay-Lussac's post was less on the administrative side and more on the technical side. Here he developed a method of analysis of copper-silver alloys based on the solution of the metal in nitric acid and the precipitation of the silver as silver chloride.[3] Gay-Lussac's methods replaced the time-honoured but hardly accurate method of cupellation and it is still widely used today.

Finally a word must be said about the French system by which one person occupied simultaneously a number of salaried teaching posts—the system known as *le cumul*. There was no real parallel in other countries, since in the early nineteenth century it was only in Paris that there existed a complex system of higher education in science. Nearly all education was

[1] *Instructions sur l'usage de l'alcoolomètre centesimal*, Paris, 1824.
[2] *Ann. chim. phys.*, xiii (1820), 212.
[3] *Instructions sur l'essai des matières d'argent par la voie humide*, Paris, 1832.

controlled by government departments and professors had salaries comparable perhaps with middle-grade civil servants. Although a single man in his mid-twenties would have been happy with the salary of a professor, when he had made his name and perhaps acquired family responsibilities, he might reasonably seek to supplement his fixed income by accepting other posts. In England, what little organized scientific education was available, was not centralized and it would have been physically impossible, for example, for Davy at the Royal Institution in London to have taken over the duties of professor of chemistry at either of the two English universities of Oxford or Cambridge. Nor need Davy ever have worried about supplementing his income; he was paid handsomely by the Royal Institution.

In France the system of *cumul* had no advantages apart from financial gain to the teacher, and this could have been achieved equally well by increasing the salaries of individual chairs. The most serious consequence for the advancement of scientific research was that many of the most able men spent an unnecessarily large part of their time on a multiplicity of teaching duties. The most serious injustice of the system was that teaching posts in higher education became the monopoly of men who had made a reputation for themselves. Thus young men of high potential were deprived of a means of livelihood.

Obviously there is a limit to the number of teaching and administrative posts that one man can occupy efficiently. This was a point put strongly by Arago when the post of permanent secretary of the *Académie des Sciences* fell vacant on the death of Delambre in 1822. Arago argued that the several teaching and administrative posts that he held made it quite impossible for him to accept an additional onerous post. He used this argument not only for himself but also against Biot's candidature and this was one of the reasons why Fourier was elected. On Fourier's death in 1830 Arago was the most obvious successor but in conformity with his previous declaration, he resigned from his chair at the *École Polytechnique* so as to have the necessary time to fulfil properly the duties of permanent secretary of the *Académie des Sciences*.

There was continual controversy in France over the system of *cumul* and in 1848 Gerhardt launched a public attack. It was largely as a result of the system that he had been unable to obtain a post in Paris. Gerhardt was well qualified to teach chemistry but when a vacancy arose in the capital, a man already holding a teaching post in Paris and having a few influential friends had a far better chance than an outsider like himself.

Significantly it was Thenard who strongly defended the system[1] and we cannot help noticing that he had done rather well out of it. To his posts already mentioned at the *Collège de France*, the *École Polytechnique* and the *Faculté des Sciences*, we must add his salaried membership of the *Comité Consultatif des Arts et Manufactures* and of the *Conseil Royal de l'Instruction publique*. The combined salaries of these posts together with his membership of the Institute came to nearly 30,000 francs. In fairness to Thenard it must be pointed out that this salary was received only at the height of his career and for no longer than six years. He later resigned from several of these appointments. Also Thenard had not stretched the system to the limit, as can be seen by comparing him with the mathematician Charles Dupin (1784–1873) sometimes called the prince of *cumulards* on account of the dozen salaried posts which he held simultaneously.

Thenard's defence of the system emphasized the insufficiency of the salaries of 3,000–5,000 francs for a single chair. Men at the top of their profession, who were to lecture to large audiences including students attracted from many foreign countries, deserved a higher reward than this, especially as a second grade administrator could earn 15,000 to 18,000 francs. Nor were the theoretically high salaries obtainable by *cumul* excessive if viewed over a lifetime. The process of *cumul* would not begin until a man was in his middle thirties and in his fifties he would begin abandoning some of his posts, the process described as *décumuler*. The pension obtained at the end of thirty years service was half of any one salary, that is to say, a maximum of 2,500 francs.

Thus the pursuit of science, begun as an ideal by young men who were prepared to subsist on bread and water in a garret, may seem to have developed in middle age into the greed for money and position. This would be too superficial an analysis of the later history of the young men of Arcueil. Chapter Nine will show whether the spark was still there and, if so, where and how it kindled into a flame. Meanwhile we must retrace our steps to the very beginning of the history of the Arcueil circle.

[1] *Un grand français. Le chimiste Thenard,* chap. xxix.

CHAPTER FIVE

The Origins of the Society of Arcueil

Before the Revolution

THE SOCIETY of Arcueil was unique in its combination of informality with concentrated talent. At a time when membership of the Royal Society was still granted to men of rank without the least scientific pretensions and when in France the First Class of the Institute had a severely restricted membership, and vacancies, when they occurred, were often filled on grounds of seniority and influence rather than on training and potential, it is refreshing to find a small group of able men all actively dedicated to the pursuit of science. The essence of the Society of Arcueil was the rich association of the experience and patronage of men like Berthollet and Laplace with the enthusiasm and talent of young men of science. The Society had no need to be disturbed by the French saying: 'Si jeunesse savait, si veillesse pouvait!'[1] since both the enthusiasm of youth and the practical experience of mature years were at hand and were complementary in constructing a unique edifice in the history of science.

Although the first volume of the *Mémoires de la Société physique et chimique d'Arcueil* did not appear until 1807, important collective scientific work had been done at Arcueil several years previously and in this chapter it is proposed to discuss the work of the Arcueil circle, which developed in 1807 into a definite Society with its own journal. Perhaps it would be appropriate to start around September 1801, when Berthollet had just moved into his country house at Arcueil. Even this, however, would not be early enough if we are to appreciate how the various men who later figured at Arcueil came to be associated with each other. The aspect of personal friendship is particularly important in a small and unofficial group.

The most vital friendship in the whole group was that be-

---

[1] Henri Estienne, *Les Prémices*, 1594, Epigramme cxci.

tween Berthollet and Laplace. Perhaps a small chemical society, founded by Berthollet, might have had a limited success, but the whole strength of the Arcueil circle was based on its dual approach to scientific problems through physics and chemistry and it was Laplace who provided the physico-mathematical stimulus. Laplace is known today primarily for his mathematics and theoretical astronomy and to understand his later interest in physics and chemistry it is necessary to go back to the time before the French Revolution.

It was in 1782 that Laplace was persuaded to turn his attention from mathematics to physical science and it was Lavoisier who invited Laplace to take this important step.[1] In July of that year they began an historic investigation of the measurement of heat, and by the following summer their results were ready to be presented to the *Académie des Sciences*. An important piece of apparatus used in this work, the ice-calorimeter, was probably designed by Laplace.[2]

The memoir on heat led to further collaboration. On 24 June 1783 they carried out the experiment of burning hydrogen and oxygen in a closed vessel and collecting the water formed. Blagden, shortly to become secretary of the Royal Society and then on a visit to Paris, had told them of a similar experiment which had been carried out in England by Cavendish, and Blagden was a witness of the French synthesis of water. Laplace was by no means an idle partner in this collaboration; Lavoisier testified to his frequent help. Laplace, writing to Lavoisier in September 1783,[3] suggested that the inflammable air (hydrogen) which is evolved by the action of a dilute acid on a metal is not, as Cavendish had claimed, phlogiston, but a result of the decomposition of the water. He gave a detailed explanation of this reaction, which had puzzled Lavoisier and was one of the last strong arguments of the supporters of the phlogiston theory. Laplace not only provided a plausible alternative explanation, his letter also stimulated Lavoisier to carry out further experiments on the decomposition of water. In this way Laplace

---

[1] R. Hahn and D. Duveen, 'Deux lettres de Laplace à Lavoisier', *Revue d'Histoire des Sciences*, xi (1958), 337–42. M. P. Crosland, 'The development of chemistry in the 18th century', *Studies on Voltaire and the eighteenth century*, xxiv (1963), 388–9.

[2] 'Mémoire sur la chaleur', *Mém. Acad.*, 1780, 355–408. Partington, *History of Chemistry*, vol. iii, p. 426.   [3] *Mém. Acad.*, 1781, 476–7.

helped Lavoisier to establish the composition of water both by analysis and synthesis.

We must now turn back for a moment to Berthollet's association with Lavoisier in the *Académie des Sciences*. Lavoisier had been elected to the *Académie* in 1768 and in February 1780 when Berthollet diffidently presented three short memoirs on the caustic nature of some salts to the *Académie*, Lavoisier was a member of some standing and reputation. The commissioners appointed to examine the memoirs of the young doctor of medicine (Berthollet was thirty-two and Lavoisier five years his senior) were Lavoisier and Macquer. Berthollet had studied under Macquer but Lavoisier's favour was more in doubt. Berthollet's ideas at that time were certainly different from those of Lavoisier but his referees did not hold this against him. Lavoisier concluded the report in the following gracious manner:

> . . . Although it is possible to provide a full explanation according to another system . . . the three memoirs of M. Berthollet have, nevertheless, the merit of presenting a large collection of new facts, very fine observations and a theory which, if not proven, is at least made probable and established on a basis of a coherent and well presented body of facts. These memoirs can only add to the reputation which the author has already justly acquired by the several memoirs which he has presented to the Academy.[1]

A week later, on 21 April, Berthollet was successful in his candidature for the place of *adjoint chimiste* at the *Académie*, a place which had become vacant by the early death of Lavoisier's friend and collaborator, Bucquet.

Yet Berthollet could not sincerely show his gratitude by embracing the new theory of Lavoisier. On the contrary, in the years 1780–3 he felt compelled to criticize some of Lavoisier's ideas.[2] In 1784 when Lavoisier was appointed to examine the claims of Mesmer on animal magnetism, Berthollet helped his colleagues by attending Mesmer's course and testifying that it was a fraud.[3] This exposed him to the danger of assault from

---

[1] Lavoisier, *Oeuvres*, vol. iv, p. 349. See *ibid.*, pp. 379–87, for a favourable report drawn up by Lavoisier in 1781 on a book which Berthollet proposed to publish.
[2] *Mém. Acad.*, 1780, 467; 1781, 234–42.
[3] Lavoisier, *Oeuvres*, vol. iii, pp. 505–6.

Mesmer's supporters but it probably brought him closer to Lavoisier. Finally in April 1785 Berthollet admitted that the phlogiston theory had outlived its usefulness and his position as a disciple of Lavoisier dates from that time.[1] The following year Fourcroy was completely converted and Guyton de Morveau accepted Lavoisier's theory early in 1787. One of the few chemists of note left in France was Chaptal and he adopted the new theory in his lectures at Montpellier shortly afterwards.

In March 1785 Berthollet in a letter to Blagden, in which he described Lavoisier's latest quantitative experiments, also mentioned Laplace's chemical opinions.[2] In a memoir which he read to the *Académie* in June of the same year, Berthollet referred to his collaboration with Laplace in experiments on the composition of ammonia.[3] His important 'Memoir on dephlogisticated marine acid' (the name for chlorine before 1787) began with a tribute to Laplace for his work on the composition of water and the final overthrow of the phlogiston theory.[4] It seems, therefore, that Berthollet's active collaboration with Laplace dates from 1785, three years after Laplace had begun to collaborate with Lavoisier.

Berthollet and Laplace were included in the four intimate Parisian scientific friends of Lavoisier, who were in the habit of witnessing his experiments and discussing them with him. As Lavoisier put it:

> If at any time I have adopted, without acknowledgement, the experiments or the opinions of M. Berthollet, M. Fourcroy, M. de la Place, M. Monge, or, in general, of any of those whose principles are the same as my own, it is owing to the circumstance that frequent intercourse and the habit of communicating our ideas, our observations and our ways of thinking to each other has established between us a sort of community of opinions in which it is often difficult for everyone to know his own.[5]

It is difficult not to make a comparison between the informal meetings at the Arsenal of Lavoisier with his colleagues and a

---

[1] *Mém. Acad.*, 1785, 276. Partington, *Chymia*, v (1959), 130–7.
[2] Partington, *History of Chemistry*, vol. iii, p. 450.
[3] *Mém. Acad.*, 1785, 319.
[4] *Ibid.*, 276 (published 1788). Lavoisier's name is not included in this tribute.
[5] *Traité élémentaire de chimie*, 1789, trans. Kerr, Edinburgh, 1790, pp. xxxiii–xxxiv.

few chosen young men and the later meetings at Arcueil. Lavoisier devoted one day a week to experiments in his laboratory.[1] As Madame Lavoisier later described these meetings:

> It was for him a day of happiness; some enlightened friends and a few young persons proud of being allowed the honour of co-operating in his experiments, gathered in the morning in the laboratory; there they had lunch and there they held forth and it was there that arose that theory of oxygen which has immortalized its author.

Apart from Lavoisier's friends mentioned above, there were other members of the *Académie des Sciences*, drawn mainly from the sections of chemistry and mathematics, who made a habit of meeting at the Arsenal. He also welcomed many younger men with some talent in physics or chemistry and gave them introductions which helped them to pursue a career in science; among these were his laboratory assistants, Gengembre,[2] Hassenfratz and Adet.[3] When Lavoisier was appointed to a committee to draw up a report on matters of scientific or public interest, he would often invite his fellow members of the committee to the Arsenal and, if he had a new experiment to demonstrate, several of his friends from the nobility as well as scientific colleagues would be invited. Foreign visitors were often honoured with invitations and from England and Scotland came Joseph Priestley, Arthur Young, James Watt, Smithson Tennant, and Sir Charles Blagden, secretary of the Royal Society. The last two named were later to be visitors to Arcueil.

At the beginning of the nineteenth century the Arsenal was the scene of a salon held by Madame de Genlis[4] but by now the 'salon' that mattered most to science was no longer there, nor was it at the home of Lavoisier's widow. The scene had now moved to Arcueil.

Before leaving Lavoisier we must first mention work on

---

[1] A full description of the meetings in the laboratory of the Arsenal is given in Grimaux, *Lavoisier, 1743–1794*, Paris, 1888, pp. 44–50.

[2] Known as the discoverer of the spontaneously inflammable gas (impure) phosphine. Gengembre later gave some assistance to Berthollet at the École Polytechnique (*Ann. chim.*, xxxix (1801), 17).

[3] Hassenfratz and Adet drew up a new set of chemical symbols when Lavoisier and his colleagues revised chemical nomenclature in 1787. See: M. P. Crosland, *Historical Studies in the Language of Chemistry*, 1962, pp. 245 ff.

[4] Junot duchesse d'Abrantès, *Histoire des Salons de Paris*, vol. iii, p. 107.

chemical affinity, which was to become one of the main spheres of Berthollet's interests and the subject of his *Statique chimique*. In his collaboration with Lavoisier, Laplace had been particularly interested in the problems of chemical affinity and he had even led Lavoisier to hope that it would be possible to measure chemical affinity exactly:

> Perhaps one day the precision of the data may be brought to such perfection that the mathematician in his study would be able to calculate any phenomenon of chemical combination in the same way, so to speak, as he calculates the movement of the heavenly bodies. The views of M. Laplace on this subject and the experiments which we have planned according to his ideas to express by numbers the force of the affinities of different bodies, allow us to regard this hope as not completely fantastic.[1]

Yet Lavoisier soon realized that he had been led to hope for the impossible. There were far more variables involved in chemical reactions than in the gravitational attraction operating in the solar system which was familiar to Laplace.

Lavoisier died in 1794 and a few years later Berthollet introduced some new and important concepts into the theory of affinities. It is not surprising that Laplace was keenly interested in Berthollet's work and contributed some notes to his book on the subject. Berthollet for his part was glad to have the advice and support of the great mathematician and astronomer.

After the Revolution

We should now turn to examine briefly to what extent Berthollet's involvement in scientific societies, educational establishments, and expeditions may be regarded as foreshadowing his later associations at Arcueil. In a sense the previous chapters have already provided the necessary background. Here we may first mention the relevance of the *École Polytechnique* and then take a closer look at the Institute of Egypt.

In the first months of the *École Polytechnique* Berthollet had as his assistant Chaptal and their work together consolidated their friendship. Later Welter, one of three *instructeurs-chimistes*, acted partly as Berthollet's assistant. In 1796 Berthollet paid generous tribute to Welter for his help in important research on

[1] *Mém. Acad.*, 1782, 534–5.

R

hydrogen sulphide.[1] Another of the *instructeurs-chimistes* was Bonjour, who had previously been Berthollet's assistant and whom Berthollet later helped to find employment. The cases of Welter and Bonjour are of interest in providing early examples of Berthollet's patronage of young men. A third example was Champy, who assisted Berthollet in Egypt. None of these names, however, is famous in the annals of science. The man for whom Berthollet had been searching proved to be Gay-Lussac, but the role played by Gay-Lussac at Arcueil will be dealt with presently. If we are to follow a chronological order, we must first examine the expedition to Egypt. What might at first seem to be no more than an adventure and a diversion from Berthollet's scientific work may then appear in a different light as in some respects an anticipation of Arcueil.

Bonaparte entrusted the selection of scientific personnel for the expedition to Egypt to Berthollet. Berthollet was not permitted to reveal to his recruits their destination, so that the men who agreed to go must have had great personal confidence in him. The *savants* on the expedition included Descotils and Malus, both later to become members of the Society of Arcueil, although Malus went to Egypt in his military capacity as a captain in the corps of engineers. Descotils, who had chosen the life of a scientist in preference to the navy, was later able to look back to a career no less adventurous.

In August 1798 the Institute of Egypt was founded by Bonaparte largely on the model of the Institute of France. There were to be four Classes: mathematics, 'physics' (including chemistry and natural history), political economy, and literature and art. Each Class was nominally composed of twelve members but only the Class of mathematics was completely filled. This Class included Bonaparte himself, Monge, Malus and Fourier. Among the colleagues of Berthollet and Descotils in the physics section were the physician Desgenettes and the zoologist, Geoffroy Saint-Hilaire. The last two wrote memoirs of their experiences in Egypt.

The actual establishment of the Institute in a suburb of Cairo was a task entrusted to Berthollet, Monge and General Caffarelli.

---

[1] 'Annoncer que j'ai eu Welter pour coopérateur, c'est déclarer qu'il a beaucoup contribué aux observations que je présente'.—*Ann. chim.*, xxv (1798), 233.

They were to choose a suitably large house and establish there a printing works, a chemistry laboratory, a physics laboratory, a library and, if possible, an observatory. There was also to be a suitable room for the actual meetings.[1] When Berthollet established himself with laboratories and a library three years later at Arcueil he must have thought back to his previous experience of equipping a scientific institution.

The Institute of Egypt was to meet every five days but, unlike the Paris Institute, the Classes did not meet separately. The first meeting was held on 23 August at 7 in the morning. The time of day was obviously more suitable in that climate and it did not interfere with the other work of the expedition. Monge was elected president and Bonaparte immediately showed his colleagues what he expected of them by presenting them with a number of practical problems. One of these was an enquiry into the natural resources of Egypt for the manufacture of gunpowder. Berthollet and Malus were among those appointed to consider this question. Malus was later associated with Descotils in an expedition to dig wells in the desert outside Cairo.[2] Berthollet himself presented memoirs to the Institute on new sources of ammonia, the analysis of a sample of gunpowder, the local cultivation of indigo and the dyeing properties of safflower. In collaboration with Descotils he served on several committees concerned with problems such as the examination of mineral specimens, the analysis of Nile water, the dyeing properties of henna and the establishment of a pharmacy in Cairo (the latter in conjunction with Desgenettes).

Apart from his research on various dyestuffs, Berthollet's most important chemical work in Egypt was on eudiometry and, above all, chemical affinity. Berthollet's analysis of the air was carried out in the chemistry laboratory which he had had constructed in the comfortable quarters of the Institute in Cairo. He was helped by a younger member of the Institute, J. Nicolas Champy, who had studied at the *École Polytechnique*. Berthollet spoke highly of Champy,[3] who unfortunately was one of many who died on the expedition.

[1] Napoléon, *Correspondance*, vol. iv, no. 2938.
[2] *Ibid.*, vol. v, no. 3459.
[3] 'Champy, le fils, très exacte observateur' (*Ann. chim.*, xxxv (1800), 30) and 'un jeune chimiste qui donne les plus grandes espérances' (*Ibid.*, xxxix (1801), 4). See also *ibid.*, xxxiv (1800), 82.

Berthollet had an opportunity to see the great trona deposits when he accompanied General Andréossy on a tour in January 1799. Describing his visit later, Berthollet spoke of the lakes as 'a vast laboratory where nature prepares an immense quantity of soda'.[1] Bonaparte did not fail to be impressed by Berthollet's report and he described the commercial importance of the discovery in his next letter to the Directorate in Paris.[2] The difficult military situation and the eventual evacuation of the French force prevented the commercial exploitation of these rich deposits. What impressed Berthollet about the trona deposits was not any possible financial gain but a fundamental aspect of theoretical chemistry. He saw that, contrary to the current theory of affinity, it was possible to reverse a chemical reaction, given sufficient quantities of reactants and the correct physical conditions.[3] With this evidence he was able to work out a completely original approach to chemical affinity which he presented to the Institute of Egypt in the summer of 1799 just before his departure.

On 17 September 1798 Berthollet read to the Institute a letter from Laplace, who recommended that observations should be made of the occultation of stars by the moon. The clear night sky of Egypt was obviously admirably suited to astronomical observation but if we look for any major advance of knowledge made by the Institute it is not to astronomy or even chemistry that we must turn but to Egyptology and geography.

In December 1798 Bonaparte was elected president of the Institute of Egypt and six months later it was Berthollet's turn to receive this honour. Thus when Bonaparte left Egypt hurriedly on 18 August 1799, taking Monge and Berthollet with him, the expedition lost its military leader and the Institute its president. Descotils was among the group of members of the Institute who, less fortunate than Bonaparte's two favourites, arrived back in France in October 1801. He was put in charge of the laboratory of the *École des Mines*. At the end of September 1803 he presented an important memoir to the First Class which

---

[1] *Journal de physique*, li (1800), 5; see also *ibid.*, l (1800), 405–20.
[2] Napoléon, *Correspondance*, vol. v, no. 3952.
[3] The trona (sodium carbonate) had been formed together with the deliquescent calcium chloride from the enormous quantities of naturally occurring sodium chloride (common salt) and calcium carbonate (chalk).

foreshadowed the discovery of the metal iridium,[1] and from January 1804 his name reappeared as one of the editors of the *Annales de chimie*. Malus' military duties had given him less opportunity for scientific work, although while on an expedition in Upper Egypt he found time to draft a memorandum on light. He too arrived back in France in the autumn of 1801 but in the next few years he was posted to various parts of the provinces and it was only in 1809 that he managed to establish himself permanently in Paris. It is for this reason that, unlike Descotils, he was not included in the first list of the Society of Arcueil drawn up in 1807.

Despite Berthollet's personal association with other men of science in the preparations for the expedition to Egypt, despite his personal contacts with Malus and particularly Descotils, despite his role as one of the leading figures in the Institute of Egypt, where he had a small circle of colleagues with interests in the physical sciences, and the part he had played in the selection of these men, this does not take us quite to the development of a private scientific club as was established later at Arcueil. It does, however, contain the seeds of later developments and, on the negative side, it did something equally important. Berthollet's absence of eighteen months from the scientific scene in Paris, following so shortly after his long absence in Italy tended to separate him further from his former colleagues, men such as Guyton and Fourcroy who had stayed at home. To be sure his absence was honourable and it established the vital link with the general who, shortly after his return from Egypt, was to become the effective master of France. Yet in a scientific career an absence of three years is not easily passed over. The only scientific news from Europe that had reached Berthollet in Egypt had been a few of the *Bulletins* of the Philomatic Society.[2] For his part, when he had been on both the Italian and Egyptian expeditions, he had made a point of writing to colleagues in the First Class including Laplace on matters of scientific and medical interest[3] but he could not have helped feeling out of touch.

Berthollet had taken a leading part in the early work of the First Class. As Thomson remarked, 'Of the committees to which all original memoirs are in the first place referred, we

[1] *Ann. chim.*, xlvii (1804), 153–76.   [2] *Ibid.*, xxxix (1801), 3.
[3] *P.V. Inst.*, vol. i, pp. 127, 162, 163, 387.

find Berthollet oftener than any other person a member and his signature to the report of each work stands generally first.'[1] By his absence from the Institute, Berthollet had not lost his seniority but his fellow members of the section of chemistry had not been idle in his absence. This applies not only to scientific research but also to organization. For example, after a lapse of three years in the publication of the *Annales de chimie*, at a meeting held on 27 December 1796 it was decided to publish the *Annales* again from the following month. The senior members of the editorial board who took the decision were Guyton and Fourcroy; Vauquelin and Pelletier were also present. There is the notable absence of Berthollet who was in Italy and also other members of the editorial board who were out of Paris on various government missions. Although Berthollet was back in Paris by the end of November 1797 and rejoined the meetings of the editorial board, Guyton seems to have acted as editor-in-chief and Fourcroy was also prominent. In other words, although the *Annales* was still in the hands of Lavoisier's former associates, it was in no sense Berthollet's journal. If Berthollet had the ambition to produce his own journal, this ambition was only realized in 1807 with the publication of the *Mémoires* of the Society of Arcueil.

For many men in the position of Berthollet, returning to France after the age of fifty with adequate financial means, retirement to the country would have been an obvious choice.[2] It is Berthollet's claim to greatness that, after his return from Egypt he was to begin a new life, or rather a new chapter of the old one, in which the two most important events were the writing of the *Statique chimique* and the founding of the Society of Arcueil. If Berthollet's purchase of a house just outside Paris constituted retirement, there can have been few retirements which have proved more fruitful.

It should not be thought that after 1801 the expedition to Egypt became a thing of the past. In Egypt the Institute had published its own *Mémoires* and one might say that these were continued in the monumental publication called *Description de*

---

[1] *History of Chemistry*, 1830, 31, vol. ii, p. 146.
[2] Berthollet did not buy his country house immediately on his return to France. From 23 September 1800 to 22 March 1801 he was president of the First Class.

l'Égypte which was published over the period 1808 to 1825. This included nine folio volumes of text and fourteen volumes of plates, of which three were of 'atlantic' size—1 metre 20 cm. in length! The text was divided into four parts, concerned respectively with ancient Egyptian civilization, monuments, modern Egypt and natural history. Among scores of contributions it included a memoir by Malus on the branches of the Nile and another by Descotils on the manufacture of sal ammoniac.

The publication of such a work demanded considerable organization. The First Consul by a decree of 6 February 1802 nominated members of a commission who were to assemble together all memoirs, charts, drawings, and observations and materials relating to the arts and sciences in Egypt so that it could be consolidated into one comprehensive work. Berthollet was appointed chairman of the commission of eight members.[1] Different members of the commission were responsible for different parts of the work, which was then edited to ensure uniformity. A secretary was appointed to be responsible for general correspondence, revision of the printed matter, etc. Publication of the work was delayed by the death of the first two secretaries in 1805 and 1807. The post of secretary was then filled by the military engineer, Jomard. It was Jomard who wrote an obituary of Berthollet intended for inclusion in one of the final volumes of the *Description de l'Égypte*. Because of his close association with Bonaparte in Egypt, Berthollet appeared to the government of Louis XVIII to be an undesirable subject for an article in a government-sponsored publication and it was another twenty years before Jomard's obituary of Berthollet was finally published.

The first volume of the *Description de l'Égypte* to be published appeared in two parts in January 1808 and March 1810. This consisted of 1,300 pages of folio text and a large number of plates. The mathematician Fourier, who had been a member of the expedition and was now the prefect of the department of Isère, was chosen to write the preface. One finds in the preface some fulsome references to Napoleon as the patron of science and it is said that the proofs of this part of the work were carefully read by Napoleon before publication.

Two things are clear about the publication of the *Description*

[1] *Correspondance de l'École Polytechnique*, iii (1814–16), 85.

de l'Égypte. The first is that Napoleon took a personal interest in the progress of the work, regarding it as a monument to his own achievement. In 1809 he declined to accept the profits of the work for the state. The money was to be shared between institutions such as the Institute and the *Bibliothèque Nationale* and those authors of the work who had themselves been members of the expedition to Egypt.[1] The second fact to emerge that is relevant to the theme of this book is the central place of Berthollet in the publication. Publication of the work continued under the Restoration and in July 1816 Berthollet, still president of the publication committee, could write feelingly: 'J'ai à coeur de finir ce grand travail.'[2] Berthollet was not merely the chairman of the publication committee meeting occasionally in Paris. His experiences in Egypt had made a profound impression on him and he had deliberately furnished his study at Arcueil in such a way as to be a constant reminder of his experiences in Egypt.

The most detailed account of Berthollet's cultivation of the Egyptian style is given by Jomard,[3] who reports that the curtains and hangings of Berthollet's study were decorated with lotus leaves and other designs copied from the tombs of the pharaohs. The walls were decorated with views of the ruins of Thebes and of Dendera in Upper Egypt. Berthollet's armchair was an exact replica of one portrayed in tomb paintings. Finally he possessed a desk specially made to hold the massive volumes of the *Description de l'Égypte*.[4] This large piece of furniture was in the form of an Egyptian temple, thus completing the striking decorations of the room. We should not be surprised to find Berthollet reminiscing with Malus and Descotils on their common experiences in Egypt and, when visitors came, the conversation would often turn to the same subject. Even Thenard, who had no direct experience of Egypt, found himself drawn into the history of the famous expedition when he married the granddaughter of the inventor Conté, who had been one of the towers of strength among the civilians on the expedition.

[1] Napoléon, *Correspondance*, vol. xx, no. 15974.
[2] Bibliothèque Nationale, MS. Fr. 11275, f. 232v.
[3] *Notice sur . . . Berthollet*, Annecy, 1844, pp. 38, 52–3.
[4] A Paris cabinet-maker was willing to supply such a desk, fully ornamented, for 1,500 francs.—*Revue des Études Napoléoniennes*, xxxvii (1933), 174–6.

Berthollet's 'Statique chimique'

The book, *Essai de statique chimique*, published in June 1803, may be considered to be one of the first productions of Arcueil. Berthollet's *Recherches sur les lois de l'affinité* had been published in 1801 and he spent the major part of the years 1801–3 in enlarging his work. What began as an essay ended as a treatise and it was undoubtedly the solitude and atmosphere of his new house in the country which gave Berthollet the opportunity to write the major part of his book in 1802—his first year at Arcueil. The book belongs to Arcueil in a personal as well as a topographical sense. The name of Arcueil was going to have in scientific circles connotations of co-operative effort. Similarly the *Statique chimique* reflects already the advantages of the association of a group.

Laplace figured quite prominently in the book. On the subject of heat, the 1783 memoir of Lavoisier and Laplace was quoted by Berthollet as his principal source for his remarks on calorimetry.[1] Laplace was referred to again for his work on chemical affinity,[2] but of course Berthollet made references to the work of many other scientists too. Laplace was, however, asked to contribute an extended note or appendix where he dealt with his theory of gases.[3] Another note or appendix was written by Gay-Lussac, whose co-operation was frequently referred to in the course of the book.[4] Finally the *Statique chimique* revealed itself as a precursor of the Society of Arcueil by the opportunity it provided for the publication of work by Berthollet's son, Amédée. He had read a memoir on the precipitates obtained from solutions of metals at meetings of the First Class earlier that year and, as the work had some relevance to the problem of chemical composition and affinity, Berthollet found an opportunity of including it as an appendix in his book, where it occupied some thirty-six pages of small type.[5]

Dumas, writing in 1836, considered the *Statique chimique* to be one of the greatest works of French chemistry but he had to admit that it was rather obscure in places and that the exposi-

[1] *Essai de statique chimique*, 1803, vol. i, pp. 147 ff.
[2] *Ibid.*, vol. i, p. 532.
[3] Note V, *ibid.*, vol. i, pp. 245–7 and Note XVIII, pp. 522–3.
[4] E.g. *ibid.*, vol. i, pp. 157 ff., 260, 279; vol. ii, p. 438.
[5] Note XXII, *ibid.*, vol. ii, pp. 447–81.

tion was not as clear and methodical as might be wished.[1] Dumas said very significantly that there were many passages in the book that could only be understood by referring to the writings of his pupils. We will accept Dumas' judgement. But not only does the work of Gay-Lussac, for example, throw light on the ideas of his master; Berthollet's ideas illuminate the work of his pupils, so that it is impossible to understand the work of the one without turning to the work of the other.

In the following outline of some of Berthollet's ideas on affinity expressed in his *Statique chimique*, one or two specific examples will be given in preference to a generalization. Berthollet, after all, insisted that ideas about affinity should be based on practical experience of chemical reactions.

Berthollet began his book by relating gravitational attraction and chemical attraction. In other words he broke away from the tradition that preferred to speak of chemical affinity (Geoffroy) and returned to the Newtonian concept of attraction acting according to the laws of mechanics.[2] Attraction in mechanics was governed by the masses of the bodies concerned, and it seemed logical to Berthollet that the mass of reactants should affect the course of a chemical reaction. Berthollet actually introduced the term 'chemical mass' but in a rather curious sense. He considered that the quantities of acids and alkalis required to saturate each other were a measure of their affinity. If an alkali were added to a mixture of several acids, the result would not be, as Bergman would have said, that the alkali combined with the strongest acid present. Rather the alkali would combine with each of the acids present in a proportion depending on two factors: (1) the 'capacity of saturation' of the acid (a factor proportional to its affinity) and (2) the quantity of acid present. Berthollet denoted the product of these two factors the 'chemical mass'.

Chemical attraction was sometimes modified by the force of cohesion, a concept on which Berthollet placed some emphasis. When oxalic acid was added to a solution of 'acetate of lime', the whole of the 'lime' (calcium) was precipitated as the oxa-

[1] *Leçons sur la philosophie chimique*, Paris, 1837, pp. 378–9.
[2] The Newtonian concept of attraction applied to chemistry had been accepted by several eighteenth-century chemists but they failed to draw the important conclusions seen by Berthollet.

late, leaving acetic acid in solution. This might appear inconsistent with the reaction of acids and alkalis described above, but it was explained by Berthollet in terms of the superior force of cohesion of the constituents of oxalate of lime.

Sometimes a reaction between two substances could follow quite different paths according to circumstances. Thus, to use modern terms, calcium sulphate and ammonium carbonate would react in solution to produce a precipitate of calcium carbonate and a solution of ammonium sulphate. Yet if the latter two salts were heated together, the former two salts would be produced. Berthollet explained the first reaction in terms of the insolubility of one of the products and the second reaction in terms of the volatility of one of the products. There was then not only a force of cohesion but a force of elasticity. Cohesion was a force present in solids and to a lesser degree in liquids and least in gases. There was the opposing force of elasticity related to heat which brought substances to the gaseous state. In this state they were least affected by attractive forces between the particles.

This is a brief summary of some of Berthollet's ideas which, read in full, would appear less arbitrary than they might seem from this account. Gay-Lussac, writing an historical article on affinity many years later, says that Berthollet was preoccupied with two ideas: the influence of the force of cohesion on chemical phenomena and the measurement of affinities as given by the weights of bodies which combined together.[1] If these began as Berthollet's problems, they continued in the work of his pupils.

The *Statique chimique* may claim to be the first book to contain a table of equivalents.[2] The combining weights of acids and alkalis published had not been determined by Berthollet but were taken over from a note by the German physicist Fischer based on Richter's work. Berthollet was interested in the light that combining weights could throw on problems of affinity and the inclusion of this table in his book gave wide publicity to this early table of equivalents.

Most important of all, the *Statique chimique* reveals Berthollet as a man with a programme of research. This was no tidy synthesis or text-book in which the facts were neatly arranged and tied up in bundles. The book marked the beginning rather

---

[1] *Ann. chim. phys.*, lxx (1839), 414. [2] *Op. cit.*, vol. i, p. 136.

than the end of an era. Its importance lay less in the answers that it gave, than in the questions that it asked. In a review of his own book, Berthollet said that he was submitting his work to the discussion of chemists in the hope that it might contribute to the progress of chemical theory.[1] In the light of the work of his associates and pupils we can interpret this statement as something more than a conventional formula.

The Encouragement of Young Men

Arcueil was essentially a focal point for the encouragement of the scientific talents of young men. There were a few institutions at which a young man embarking on a scientific career could learn the elements of physics and chemistry but not even at the *École Polytechnique* was there any formal 'post-graduate' work in these subjects. At the other end of the scale there was the First Class of the Institute, to membership of which every ambitious scientist aspired. To become a member of the First Class it was necessary to have published work on the appropriate branch of science and to have some personal support among members. Both these qualifications could be and were acquired at Arcueil. In this way Berthollet and Laplace can be seen to have fostered an informal association in which promising young men were helped to do research on which their own reputations were built up. At the bottom end of the scale no one (except perhaps Bérard) came to Arcueil to learn elementary science. All had followed courses of instruction elsewhere, notably at the *École Polytechnique*. Once recognized and elected as members of the First Class, these men never considered it beneath their dignity to frequent Arcueil—how could they when they were in the homes of men who were among France's greatest men of science and whose social position under the Empire was as high as their scientific reputation.

Berthollet was an essentially generous man. With his money he was careless to the point of improvidence and with his advice and encouragement to younger men his generosity was equally well-known. We have seen how, when working with Welter at the *École Polytechnique*, and later with Champy in Egypt, he went out of his way to mention the high quality of the

[1] *Ann. chim.*, xlvi (1803), 293.

work of his young collaborators. It comes as no surprise therefore to read in one of Berthollet's memoirs published in the
Annales de chimie in May 1801 the acknowledgement:

> I owe this observation to citizen Gay[-Lussac], a young chemist
> from the *École Polytechnique*, who combines great insight with
> abundant zeal.[1]

However important may have been Berthollet's patronage of
Gay-Lussac and other bright young men, we must not overlook
someone to whom Berthollet was even more attached. If he
treated the younger members of the Arcueil group almost as
adopted sons, we must not forget that he had a son of his own,
Amédée. This was his only child. He had entered the *École
Polytechnique* in December 1796 but had withdrawn two years
later without qualifying. Through his father he had become
interested in chemical industry and in about 1801 we find him at
the textiles factory at Jouy, near Versailles, working on dyestuffs
used in the industry.[2] He worked in a small chemistry laboratory belonging to Samuel Widmer, a nephew of Oberkampf,
the owner of the factory. Oberkampf's fifteen-year-old son
Émile and several other local people became interested in
chemistry. An elementary course of lectures by Gay-Lussac on
physics and chemistry was arranged. The lectures were given
once a week, the first course being in the autumn of 1802, and a
second was given in the following spring. Amédée Berthollet
continued to work in the laboratory at Jouy until 1805.
      As a result of his practical experience of dyeing, Amédée
Berthollet was in a position to collaborate with his father when
the latter brought out a second edition of his *Éléments de l'art de
la teinture* in 1804. In 1803 Berthollet introduced his son to the
Institute. On 14 March, after Berthollet senior had spoken at a
meeting of the First Class, the son rose to present a memoir
entitled 'Observations on the precipitates of solutions of metals'.
The two chemists appointed by the First Class to examine his
memoir were Guyton and Vauquelin. Several weeks later
Amédée Berthollet presented another memoir on the same subject. He took it upon himself to criticize some aspects of the
work of Fourcroy and Proust and was clearly guided by his

[1] *Ann. chim.*, xxxviii (1801), 119.
[2] A. Labouchère, *Oberkampf (1738–1815)*, 1866, pp. 135–40.

father's ideas on variable proportions. His several appreciative comments of the then unknown Gay-Lussac suggest a close acquaintance under his father's roof at Arcueil. Although the son's work had stemmed from Berthollet's work on affinities, the decision of the latter to publish in full Amédée's long memoir as an appendix to his *Statique chimique* is more easily understood as the pride of a father in the first scientific work of his son rather than as a completely relevant and necessary contribution to the subject of the book.

If the basis of the Society of Arcueil was the encouragement and support of young men, and this began with Berthollet's own son, Gay-Lussac too may be considered as one of the first to benefit from Berthollet's patronage. But although it was Berthollet who selected him from the *École Polytechnique* as a student of great promise with a keen interest in the physical sciences, Gay-Lussac did not work only for Berthollet. Laplace and Humboldt in turn appreciated his talents and asked for his assistance. Similarly, although Biot was a protégé of Laplace, he was a visitor at Arcueil from the very beginning of Berthollet's residence there and he was soon acknowledging the help he had received in discussions with Berthollet.

Berthollet and Gay-Lussac

Arago gives the following account of Berthollet's selection of Gay-Lussac:

> Berthollet, who had returned from Egypt with general Bonaparte, asked in 1800 for a student from the *École Polytechnique* to be his assistant in his laboratory. This privileged student was Gay-Lussac. Berthollet suggested to him a piece of research, the results of which were diametrically opposed to those expected by the illustrious chemist. I dare not state that Berthollet was not a little put out to see himself contradicted in his expectations, but contrary to the attitude of so many other scientists I could name, after his initial unfavourable reaction, the frankness of the young experimenter only increased the esteem of [Berthollet] . . . 'Young man', he said, 'your destiny is to make discoveries; henceforth you will be my table companion. I would like in scientific matters to be like a father to you and this is a title that I am sure I shall one day be proud of.'[1]

---

[1] Arago, *Oeuvres, Notices biographiques*, vol. iii, p. 7.

In 1800 while Gay-Lussac was still a student at the *École Polytechnique* he worked under Berthollet's direction in the chemistry laboratory of the school on the treatment of flax with 'oxymuriatic acid' (chlorine).[1]

Berthollet's first published acknowledgement of Gay-Lussac's assistance dates from May 1801 and in July he was again acknowledging help from Gay-Lussac in his experiments on eudiometry.[2] In 1802 Berthollet arranged for Gay-Lussac to work with the obliging physicist Charles, who possessed the necessary electrical apparatus to test his theories on the similarity of caloric and electricity.[3] Berthollet tried to explain the heat generated by a powerful electric current in a platinum wire in terms of the movement of molecules of the metal. At a meeting of the First Class in December 1803 Berthollet commented on certain criticisms of his *Statique chimique* that had been made by the German chemist Schnaubert. Berthollet defended his theory, giving specific examples of experiments involving precipitation and concluded:

> The experiments, which citizen Gay-Lussac will communicate, throw a great deal of light on the causes of the mutual precipitation of oxides and on the order of their precipitation by alkalis and they have interesting consequences for analysis and the practice of several arts.[4]

Gay-Lussac's memoir, which was his first on a purely chemical subject, shows strongly the influence of Berthollet.

Gay-Lussac's first major research, his work on the thermal expansion of gases, was presented at a meeting of the First Class on 31 January 1802. In the published memoir which appeared in August 1802[5] Gay-Lussac is described as 'Élève ingénieur de l'École nationale des Ponts et Chaussées', although he had in fact left this school the previous year. This memoir must be regarded as one of the first permanent contributions to knowledge to be produced by the Arcueil circle. Gay-Lussac is quite explicit in his acknowledgement of the background of his research:

---

[1] *Journal de l'École Polytechnique*, iv (cahier 11, 1802), 319.
[2] *Ann. chim.*, xxxix (1801), 12.
[3] *Statique chimique*, 1803, vol. i, pp. 260–4.
[4] *Ann. chim.*, xlix (1804), 19–20. Gay-Lussac's memoir: *ibid.*, 21–35.
[5] *Ibid.*, xliii (1802), 137–75.

The difficulty of the research would have prevented me from undertaking it if I had not been strongly urged to do it by citizen Berthollet, whose pupil I have the honour to be. I owe to him the means necessary to carry out this work and I have frequently been guided by his advice and also by that of citizen Laplace; such great authorities will increase the confidence with which my work may be received.

The most recent similar work in France to that of Gay-Lussac had been sponsored by Guyton. In 1788 and 1789 Guyton had had the idea of investigating the expansion of gases caused by heat, but being engaged on the formidable undertaking of compiling a large scale encyclopedia of chemistry, he had been glad to accept an offer of help from Prieur Duvernois, an officer in the *Corps de Génie* with a scientific bent. Guyton had turned over his own laboratory to Prieur, who had worked there for two months to obtain results that Guyton claimed to be very accurate.[1] Guyton himself was hoping to improve on earlier work, including an estimate by Lavoisier and Laplace in their research on heat[2] and experiments carried out in 1786 by Vandermonde, Berthollet and Monge.[3] The latter group had been concerned to compare the proportions of iron in various samples of iron and steel and had adopted the method of comparing the volumes of 'inflammable air' (hydrogen) obtained when standard samples of each were treated with excess of dilute acid. Berthollet and his colleagues wished to make this method more precise by correcting the volume of gas to standard conditions of temperature and pressure. To do this it was necessary to carry out a preliminary quantitative study of the effect of temperature on the volume of a gas.

The above reconstruction of the previous work on the thermal expansion of gases provides at least one reason why Berthollet and Laplace should have encouraged Gay-Lussac to pursue this particular subject. The results which they themselves had obtained earlier in their careers had been called in question by Guyton. Also it was not clear whether different gases expanded by different amounts when subjected to the same rise in temperature. Vandermonde, Berthollet and Monge had found a

[1] 'des résultats exempts d'erreurs et [avec] toute la précision que l'on pouvait espérer', *Ann. chim.*, i (1789), 265.
[2] *Mém. Acad.*, 1780, 369.   [3] *Ibid.*, 1786, 164–6.

slight difference between the coefficient of expansion of air and that of hydrogen but Guyton had been convinced that gases with very different chemical properties could not be similar in their thermal expansion, and the results obtained by him and Prieur showed a wide discrepancy between different gases.

Gay-Lussac presented a detailed criticism of the work of Guyton and Prieur and he was also obliged to point out a defect in the design of the apparatus that had been used by Charles, who had compared the thermal expansion of different gases in about 1787 but had neglected to publish his results. Gay-Lussac said that it was by the 'merest chance' that he had come to know of Charles' work. The most serious error in previous work, however, and this applied particularly to Guyton's research, was that the gases used had not been dry.

One of the merits of Gay-Lussac's work in 1801–2 was the precautions he took to exclude water vapour from his apparatus and the gases under examination. This concern was repeated in 1804 in his analysis of atmospheric air and it is probable that Berthollet was responsible for pointing out the effects of humidity. Already in 1800 Berthollet had commented that a slight apparent difference in the proportion of oxygen in the air in Cairo and in Paris was probably due to a slight expansion caused by a difference in humidity[1] and in 1802 he was again much concerned with the problem of humidity.[2]

Gay-Lussac concluded from experiments, each repeated several times, that equal volumes of all gases expand equally under the same increase of temperature. He also examined the expansion of ether vapour and compared its expansion with that of air. This experiment, which was witnessed by Berthollet, showed no difference between the two. The expansion of gases over the whole range of temperature from that of melting ice to that of boiling water was $1/266.66$ per degree Centigrade.[3] Gay-Lussac referred to experiments he intended to carry out to check thermometric scales.

Gay-Lussac's work on thermometric scales was not com-

[1] *Ann. chim.*, xxxiv (1800), 83–4n.

[2] See Crosland, *Annals of Science*, xvii (1961), 4.

[3] Dalton carried out similar experiments on the expansion of gases independently of Gay-Lussac, but his results were less accurate, as is pointed out by Partington (*History of Chemistry*, vol. iii, p. 770).

s

pleted in time to be included in his memoir read at the Institute in January 1802 and, as it was never published *by Gay-Lussac*, it has often been overlooked. Yet as an alternative to appearing as a small memoir in a scientific periodical it may have a greater claim to immortality by its inclusion in Laplace's monumental *Mécanique céleste*.[1] This was appropriate in so far as it was with the encouragement of Laplace that Gay-Lussac had undertaken the research and full credit is given to the younger man.

Laplace was particularly concerned with atmospheric refraction, as it greatly affected the apparent position of stars low on the horizon. The effect of pressure on a given volume of gas was well-known; the effect of temperature had just been established by Gay-Lussac and independently by Dalton. To complete this research it was necessary to know the exact correlation between a mercury thermometer and an air thermometer, a result also of interest to the theory of heat. Gay-Lussac carried out some twenty comparative experiments, from which he concluded that from 0° to 100°C air and mercury expand uniformly and therefore the two thermometers were equivalent. This problem was to be re-examined later by members of the Arcueil group.

Gay-Lussac also carried out a large number of experiments in 1802 on the effect of pressure on volumes of a gas to test an idea of Laplace on the forces existing between the particles of a gas. Laplace at first concluded that the supposed repulsive force between two molecules of a gas depended only on the temperature but he soon modified this conclusion on theoretical grounds and said that at greater pressures proportionally more heat would be stored in a given volume of gas.[2]

Laplace and Biot

Biot in his old age told the story of how he came to be associated with Laplace.[3] On graduating from the *École Polytechnique*, Biot was appointed as professor of mathematics at Beauvais but this

---

[1] *Op. cit.*, vol. iv, 1805, pp. xxi–xxii.

[2] Berthollet, *Statique chimique*, 1803, vol. i, Note V, pp. 245–7, Note XVIII, pp. 522–3.

[3] 'Une anecdote relative à Laplace' Lue à l'Académie Française le 5 février 1850, *Mélanges*, 1858, vol. i, pp. 1–10.

did not satisfy his ambitions. In the autumn of 1799 he wrote to Laplace, asking if he might be allowed to undertake the task of reading the proofs of the *Mécanique céleste*, of which the first volume had just appeared. Laplace declined, saying that he did not wish his work to be presented to the public until it was complete so that it might be judged as a whole. Biot replied that it was not as a critic but as a humble student that he wished to co-operate. By working through the calculations he could at the same time learn some more mathematics and discover any printing errors. This letter won Laplace over and his reply, in contrast to the formal refusal of the previous letter, was friendly and full of encouragement for the younger man. Biot travelled regularly to Paris to present his corrected proofs personally to Laplace. He was able to discuss his difficulties with the author and tried to elicit explanations of parts of the calculations that had been presented as obvious.

It was during one of these meetings in October 1799 that Biot presented Laplace with the solution of a problem on differential equations. Laplace discussed the work with him, advised him on its presentation and suggested that he should read it at a meeting of the First Class which was to be held the following day, 23 October. The meeting was to begin at 5.30 but Biot deliberately arrived early in order to have the opportunity to write his formulae on the blackboard before the meeting. The minutes record that after he had presented his memoir 'Citizens Laplace, Bonaparte and Lacroix' were nominated to form a committee to report on it. Biot was flattered by the inclusion of the victorious general in this committee but little could he have guessed that by the time the report was presented three weeks later, General Bonaparte would have taken the decisive step[1] which was to make him master of France.

The meeting was adjourned at 7.30 and Biot returned with Laplace to his house in the Rue Christine for dinner. For Bonaparte the first day of the republican month of brumaire had no great significance but for Biot it marked the beginning of a career which during the next sixty years saw the appearance of over three hundred separate publications. Biot's list of publications in the Royal Society Catalogue of Scientific Papers is headed by 'Considerations sur les équations aux différences

[1] The *coup d'état* of 18 brumaire.

mélées', which Biot's commissioners recommended for publication in the *Mémoires des Savans Étrangers*.[1]

Biot's memoir was followed by another on 31 January 1800[2] and again Laplace was one of the commissioners appointed to examine it. Biot's appearances at the Institute and above all his acquisition of Laplace as a patron won him a place in the First Class. Yet when he was elected on 25 May 1800 it was as a non-resident associate in the section of mathematics, since his post at Beauvais prevented him from living permanently in Paris. On 25 November 1800 he was nominated by Chaptal to be the new professor of mathematics at the *Collège de France*. He was thus able to return permanently to the capital, and when the next vacancy occurred in the First Class, he was elected a full member of the mathematics section on 11 April 1803.

Biot's interests, like those of Laplace twenty years previously, had so far been confined exclusively to mathematics, but he could not remain in close touch with Laplace for long without being infected by Laplace's new interests in experimental science. After the visit to Paris by Volta in 1801 with all its attendant publicity, the study of electricity reached the peak of its popularity in France. Laplace carried out some experiments in the laboratory of the *École de Médecine* in which he proved that there was an attraction between the two ends of the voltaic pile. He also considered that at each extremity of the pile 'the molecules of the galvanic fluid mutually repelled each other'. In the summer of 1801 Biot read two papers to the First Class on electricity and he began one of them by stating that Laplace's two discoveries were the basis of his research.[3] Biot considered that the electric fluid moved according to laws depending on the repulsive property of its constituent molecules. Any pupil of Laplace would be likely to analyse phenomena in terms of the attraction or repulsion of particles and this approach was to recur in other studies of the Arcueil group, particularly in connection with capillarity and light.

It was appropriate that the review and summary of Laplace's *Mécanique céleste* compiled for the *École Normale* in 1801 should

---

[1] *Op. cit.*, i (1805), 296–327.

[2] 'Recherches sur l'intégration des équations différentielles partielles et sur les vibrations des surfaces', *Mém. Inst.*, iv (1802), 21–111.

[3] *Journal de physique*, liii (1801), 264–74.

have been by Biot,[1] and Biot again appears as the exponent of Laplace when the latter published two supplements to the *Mécanique céleste* dealing with capillary action.[2] He pointed out the advantages that mathematics could bring to 'la physique vulgaire' and he paid tribute to Laplace as a second Newton. Although a man in Biot's position might be suspected of sycophancy, there is no doubt that Laplace was one of the geniuses of his age and if Biot's words were flattery, his own work gave evidence of flattery in its most sincere form—imitation. In Biot's memoir on heat, which he read to the First Class on 21 May 1804 he again acknowledged the support of Laplace.[3]

In March 1805 Biot read a note to the First Class on the formation of water by compression alone of hydrogen and oxygen, as opposed to the usual method of passing an electric spark through a mixture of the gases. The latter method had recently come into prominence again through the work of Gay-Lussac and Humboldt. Berthollet too had considered the combination of hydrogen and oxygen by heat.[4] This appeared to be an anomaly since one of the properties of caloric was supposed to be to separate molecules, not bring them together to effect combination. Gay-Lussac and Humboldt had argued against Berthollet's simple mechanical explanation that the combination was due to a compression, which brought the molecules together.[5] When Berthollet came to review their memoir for the First Class he again raised this question,[6] which was therefore very topical in the Arcueil circle in the years 1804–5.

Biot's opening remarks illustrate that in the Arcueil group there was no narrow preoccupation with one particular branch of science:

> It was some time ago that, in conversation with M. Berthollet on the nature and properties of heat, I communicated to him the persuasion I had, that the combination of oxygen and hydrogen gases might be determined without the aid of electricity, and merely by a very rapid compression. This appeared to me a consequence so immediately following the observations already made on the heat disengaged from air by compression, that I thought it needless to ascertain it in any other manner. But having since

---

[1] *Séances des Écoles Normales*, 2nd edn., vol. vii, 1801.
[2] *Journal de physique*, lxv (1807), 88–95.
[3] *Journal des mines*, xvii (1805), 203–4.   [4] *Op. cit.*, vol. i, pp. 304–7.
[5] *Journal de physique*, lx (1805), 139–45.   [6] *Ann. chim.*, liii (1805), 244–6.

conversed with M. Laplace, he appeared so interested as to urge me strongly to a verification. I therefore made the experiment, which completely succeeded.[1]

Biot had carried out his experiments in the laboratory of the *École Polytechnique* with the help of Hassenfratz. In the course of the experiments they broke the glass apparatus used to compress the gases, but the First Class agreed to refund the cost. They found that mechanical compression produced sufficient heat to bring about combination of hydrogen and oxygen independently of external heat or the electric spark. Following a remark in Berthollet's *Statique chimique*, Biot concluded that when electricity brings about the combination of gases, this is a purely mechanical effect.

The publication of Biot's paper had several repercussions, including further research by Davy. But perhaps the most interesting consequence was due to its publication in England in Nicholson's *Journal*. A London reader, Thomas Northmore, who had considered that the affinities of gases could be changed under pressure, had tried to combine several mixtures including hydrogen and oxygen. His results, published in 1805 and 1806, include the announcement of the liquefaction of sulphur dioxide and chlorine.[2] The liquefaction of chlorine was rediscovered by Faraday in 1823.

Another piece of research carried out by Biot before 1807 was a study of the refractive indices of different gases. This was also work inspired by Laplace and Berthollet. The refraction of light through gases was a subject of common interest to astronomers, physicists and chemists. Borda had worked on atmospheric refraction but had died in 1799 before his work was finished and his results were lost. Laplace had proposed to the First Class of the Institute that Biot should take up this work and extend it to all gases. Biot asked Arago to help him with the large number of careful but rather tedious observations required and all the experiments and calculations were their joint work. Biot in the report of their experiments made a point of acknowledging the help of two people, Berthollet and Laplace:

[1] *Ann. chim.*, liii (1805), 244–6; trans. Nicholson's *Journal*, xii (1805), 212. *P.V. Inst.*, vol. iii, p. 197.

[2] Nicholson's *Journal*, xii (1805), 368–73, xiii (1806), 233–6. A.C.R. No. 12, pp. 69–79.

The subject of all our research was indicated in their work; their conversation and their advice have provided us with the means of pursuing our research and concluding it.[1]

Laplace's interest in the subject was in the first place the natural concern of an astronomer and a leading figure in the *Bureau des Longitudes*. But Laplace's concern went much deeper than this. The very title of the memoir by Biot and Arago gives a hint of this: 'Memoir on the affinities of bodies for light and particularly on the refractive forces of different gases'. This was pure Newtonian research. As Biot expressed it:

Newton has proved [*sic*] that refraction is the result of an attraction which bodies exercise on particles of light, an attraction which is only sensible at very small distances and in this respect completely similar to chemical affinities. Gases exhibit this refractive force like other bodies, but it is not so sensible on account of their low density . . .[2]

Biot makes repeated fulsome acknowledgements to Laplace and Berthollet. Laplace especially is referred to not only in general but as having suggested particular details of experiments, a method of measuring the refracting angle of a prism, for example. Laplace's treatment of refraction in Book 4 of the *Mécanique céleste* is used. To compare the densities of gases, Biot and Arago had used a sample of distilled mercury supplied by Berthollet. Despite the acknowledgements to Berthollet, one might easily have the impression that this was a subject outside Berthollet's real field of interest. This was not so, as may be confirmed by turning to Berthollet's book on dyeing. In this he refers to Newton's speculation that the high refractive index of diamond indicated that it contained an inflammable substance, and other speculations which had subsequently been shown to contain more than a grain of truth. Berthollet continued:

There still remain interesting observations for those who would like to follow in the footsteps of the great Newton and compare the refractive forces of different gases and different substances of which the constituent principles are now known.[3]

Seldom has a programme of research been more clearly stated.

---

[1] *Mém. Inst.*, 1806, Part 1, 304.   [2] *Ibid.*, 302.
[3] *Élémens de l'art de la teinture*, 1791, vol. i, p. 6.

Capillarity

Another subject which was investigated by the Arcueil group before 1807 was capillary action. This was a subject which had interested several investigators in the Newtonian tradition in the eighteenth century but they had made little progress and the classic source at the end of the century was still the Queries at the end of Newton's *Opticks*. Laplace, whose main claim to fame was perhaps his virtual re-writing of Newton's *Principia*, was also interested in a problem which appeared to be one of attraction on a small scale.

Laplace's interest in capillary action dates back at least to the period of his association with Lavoisier.[1] They had given some attention to the question of standardizing barometers and they had found that by boiling the mercury for a long time they could make a great difference to the meniscus; the addition of a drop of water was sufficient to restore the capillary action of the mercury. The well-known effect of a trace of grease in destroying capillarity led Laplace to conclude that a glass tube could exert no attractive force on a liquid at a small but finite distance and therefore capillary action was a force exerted only at an infinitely small distance.

Laplace was convinced that this was a field which, by the application of the sharp tool of analysis, could be made to yield a rich harvest, and in 1805 he expressed the rise of a liquid in a capillary tube by means of an equation consisting of two terms. The first and greatest term represented the mass of the liquid in the tube up to a point terminated by an imaginary plane surface; this term, Laplace considered, described equally the refracting power of transparent bodies, cohesion and chemical affinities in general. The second term in the equation represented the surface of the liquid, whether concave or convex, and it was this second term that was the distinctive feature of capillary action as opposed to chemical affinity.

Data to test Laplace's differential equation had already been furnished by Newton for parallel glass plates placed close to-

---

[1] Lavoisier, *Oeuvres*, vol. iii, pp. 753–64. Laplace, 'Extrait d'un Mémoire sur la théorie des tubes capillaires', *Journal de physique*, lxii (1806), 120–8.

gether, i.e. mathematically a cylinder of infinite radius. To test his equation at the other limit—for tubes of very small diameter —Laplace asked the abbé Haüy to carry out the necessary experiments and these were found to confirm the theory. At Laplace's request Haüy also carried out several other experiments on capillarity.

Laplace read his first memoir on capillary action at a meeting of the First Class on 23 December 1805. He continued to study various aspects of the subject in memoirs which he presented to the Institute in the latter part of 1806, and more fundamental work which he published at the end of the current volume of the *Mécanique céleste* as a supplement to his previous study.[1] This time he was assisted by Gay-Lussac, who had been away from Paris until the spring of 1806. Laplace intended to extend his original theory, test it by further experiments and show more clearly the identity of the forces that were responsible for capillary action and chemical affinity.

Gay-Lussac made a careful examination of the angle of contact and was able to estimate with extreme accuracy the internal diameters of capillary tubes by a method that has since become standard, that of weighing the tube with an enclosed column of mercury of measured length. Up to this time there had been no agreement about the measurement of the rise of water in a capillary tube of given diameter, estimates varying by as much as 100 per cent. Gay-Lussac used carefully calibrated tubes under standard conditions, noting also the temperature of the liquid since this affected its density. Laplace remarked that Gay-Lussac's measurements had 'the precision of astronomical observations'. From Laplace no higher praise was possible. Not only did Gay-Lussac measure the rise of water, alcohol and mercury in capillary tubes and the dimensions of large drops of mercury, but he also measured the force required to separate a glass disc from the surface of various liquids.[2] This method was reintroduced with refinements in the twentieth century by Noüy.

---

[1] *Op. cit.*, vol. iv, 1805. In the first supplement see especially pp. 3–6; second supplement, pp. 1, 30, 52–9, 66 ff. The second supplement was reviewed by Biot in July 1807 (*Journal de physique*, lxv (1807), 88–95).

[2] The experiment originated with Brook Taylor (*Phil. Trans.* xxxi (1720–1), 267–8). Guyton de Morveau compared affinities by measuring the force required to separate metal discs of standard size from a dish of mercury.

Laplace, however, had not been the only scientist interested in capillary action in 1805. In that year a similar memoir by Thomas Young appeared in the *Philosophical Transactions of the Royal Society*. There is no question here of plagiarism. It is merely one more instance in the history of science of simultaneous independent development. If the value of Laplace's work was lessened by the contributions of others, it was not because of Young so much as John Leslie who had given a satisfactory and much simpler explanation of the rise of liquids in capillary tubes in 1802.[1] It is a pity that greater publicity was not given to Leslie's work at the time since no-one in France seems to have known of it.

Laplace's work on capillarity cannot claim more than a minor place in the history of science yet it is worth mentioning here, if for no other reason than as an illustration of the type of collaboration between mathematician and physical scientist which was one of the pillars of the Arcueil group. It also demonstrated once more the talents of the young Gay-Lussac as a scientist working on the frontiers of physics and chemistry and making measurements of fundamental importance with great accuracy.

The Balloon Ascent

We must now go back slightly to the summer of 1804 when Biot and Gay-Lussac shared a scientific adventure which brought them more into the public eye than their previous laboratory experiments. At ten o'clock on the morning of Friday 24 August 1804 they made a balloon ascent from the garden of the *Conservatoire des Arts et Métiers*, watched by a small group of friends. The expedition obviously required some planning, and the position of Chaptal as Minister of the Interior[2] enabled official sanction to be readily obtained. This official encouragement, says Biot, was obtained through the good offices of Berthollet and Laplace, who had their own interests in the result of this project.[3]

[1] 'On Capillary Action', *Phil. Mag.*, xiv (1802), 193–205. This memoir was not published in any other journal.

[2] Chaptal had been replaced as Minister of the Interior on 5 August but permission had almost certainly been obtained well in advance.

[3] *Journal de physique*, lix (1804), 314–20. Hachette (*Correspondance sur*

The primary object of the ascent was to see if the magnetic intensity at the earth's surface decreased with altitude. De Saussure had reported an appreciable decrease but, by observing the period of oscillation of a magnetized needle, Biot and Gay-Lussac were unable to find any change and concluded that it was constant up to 4,000 metres. The balloonists calculated their altitude from the barometer reading making use of a formula worked out by Laplace.[1] They also carried long wires to test the electricity of different parts of the atmosphere. The third object of their ascent was to collect a sample of air from a high altitude to compare its composition with that of ordinary air. Berthollet in his previous studies of the composition of the air had concluded that its composition was approximately the same in different parts of the globe but he admitted that the question of the composition of the air at high altitudes had not been settled.[2] An opportunity was now provided to answer the question by direct experiment. Yet, in their first ascent, Biot and Gay-Lussac were so preoccupied with reading their barometer, thermometer and hygrometer that they did not have time to collect any air. They had also hoped to measure declination but this too was put off for another ascent, which Gay-Lussac was to make on his own in order to lessen the weight of the balloon and thus reach a greater height.

Gay-Lussac made the second ascent on 16 September 1804.[3] He was able to repeat observations of pressure, temperature and humidity and also make magnetic measurements. He had to abandon an attempt to measure declination because the graduated scale of his instrument was distorted by the dry atmosphere and the needle could no longer move freely. He had taken two evacuated flasks and when over 6,000 metres he opened each in turn to collect a sample of air. He was able to reach a calculated height of 7,016 metres above sea level, a record altitude not equalled for another half-century. Gay-Lussac recorded the effect of the high altitude on his pulse and respiration. He took half an hour to descend and landed in a field on the far side of

---

l'École Polytechnique, i (1804–8), 2nd edn., 1813, 16) says the idea originated with Berthollet and Laplace.

[1] *Mécanique céleste*, vol. iv, 1805, pp. 289–93.
[2] *Ann. chim.*, xxxiv (1800), 85.
[3] *Journal de physique*, lix (1804), 454–62.

Rouen. As soon as he arrived back in Paris, he hastened to analyse the samples of air he had collected in the laboratory of the *École Polytechnique* in the presence of his colleague Thenard and found that the proportion of oxygen was identical with that of ordinary Paris air.

Humboldt and Gay-Lussac

Humboldt had arrived in Paris the week-end before the balloon ascent of Biot and Gay-Lussac and he did not fail to be impressed by the combination of physical courage and scientific curiosity which these two young men had displayed. Not only were these qualities which he shared but he happened to be particularly interested in the subjects of investigation of Biot and Gay-Lussac, magnetic variation and the composition of the atmosphere.

Biot and Humboldt, having a common interest in magnetism, agreed to collaborate in the preparation of a memoir on 'the variation of terrestrial magnetism in different latitudes', which Biot read at a meeting of the First Class on 17 December 1804. Biot referred to the collaboration in the following terms:

> The friendship which M. Humboldt has shown towards me since his return has put me in a position to communicate to him several experiments of this kind which I made this summer in the Alps; he immediately offered to combine them with his own in the memoir which we are presenting today.[1]

Biot, it should be explained, was not having a holiday in the Alps. As one of the entrance examiners of the *École Polytechnique* required to go every autumn to the principal cities of the French Empire to examine candidates, he had been assigned the south-east region. Biot's collaboration with Humboldt took place in November 1804 shortly after his return to Paris. Their estimate of magnetic intensity in different places was based on the number of oscillations made by a magnetic needle in a given time. By combining more than three hundred observations made by Humboldt in various parts of North, Central and South America with the few observations just made by Biot at Turin,

---

[1] *Journal de physique*, lix (1804), 430. The whole memoir occupies pp. 429–450.

Geneva, Grenoble, Besançon, Lyons and Dijon, they reached the general conclusion that magnetic intensity increases from the equator to the poles. They were the first to infer the position of the magnetic equator from direct observation, but they did not appreciate the significance of slight local variations.

Humboldt's collaboration with Gay-Lussac was to be of greater consequence and it was appropriate that their meeting in the autumn of 1804 should have taken place at Arcueil. He relates that he met Gay-Lussac there a few weeks after the latter's balloon ascent.[1] Humboldt had made an inaccurate estimate of the proportion of oxygen in the air when working in Vauquelin's laboratory at the *École des Mines* in 1798. His experiments had been carefully repeated by Berthollet with some help from Gay-Lussac and a courteous criticism of his work was published by Berthollet in 1801.[2] A more severe criticism had been made by N. T. De Saussure.[3] Humboldt readily acknowledged the faults of his earlier work and was glad to have an opportunity of rectifying it by collaborating with Gay-Lussac in further research. Although Humboldt after his celebrated journey to the American continent was becoming a figure of international fame and Gay-Lussac at the age of twenty-five had only just received his first junior appointment, that of demonstrator at the *École Polytechnique*, yet Humboldt had many things in common with the younger man. He was able to benefit from the training that Gay-Lussac had received at the *École Polytechnique* and from Berthollet and he later acknowledged that Gay-Lussac 'exerted a great and kindly influence over my education and the direction of my work'.[4]

Although Humboldt's main task was now the publication of his travels, he made time to join Gay-Lussac in the laboratory of the *École Polytechnique* to compare the various methods of estimating the proportion of oxygen in the air.[5] Their recorded experiments extended from 17 November to 22 December. They

---

[1] See the autobiographical 'Note sur le voyage de Humboldt et Gay-Lussac en Italie' in *Lettres americaines d'Alexandre de Humboldt*, ed. E. T. Hamy, 1905, pp. 244–5. The other major source for the personal aspect of the collaboration of Humboldt and Gay-Lussac is Arago, *Oeuvres, Notices biographiques*, vol. iii. [2] *Ann. chim.*, xxxix (1801), 12.
[3] *Journal de physique*, xlvii (1798), 470–1.
[4] Hamy, *loc. cit.*
[5] *Journal de physique*, lx (1805), 129–68.

paid particular attention to Volta's eudiometer, which Gay-Lussac had used earlier in the analysis of air collected at a high altitude. This was a piece of apparatus in which the gas under test (which had to contain oxygen) was sparked with hydrogen to form water vapour, which condensed. The resulting contraction gave an estimate of the proportion of oxygen in the sample. Obviously this method presupposed a knowledge of the relative proportions by volume in which hydrogen and oxygen combine to form water and one of the principal objects of the work of Gay-Lussac and Humboldt was to determine the proportion with the greatest possible accuracy. After carrying out a large number of experiments with excess of first one gas and then the other, they calculated that, making allowance for a slight impurity in the test oxygen, 100 parts by volume of oxygen combined with 199·89 parts of hydrogen or, they said, in round numbers, 200 parts. This was a more accurate experiment than that carried out in the previous decade by Fourcroy and his associates.[1] Gay-Lussac clearly expressed his preference for volumes, pointing out that the presence of moisture, which would be difficult to estimate gravimetrically, did not alter the volumetric ratio.

This memoir has always been recognized as a precursor of Gay-Lussac's famous research on the combining volumes of gases. The fact that it was not until four years later that the second memoir was written has, however, been generally ignored. Gay-Lussac's law of combining volumes of gases belongs to the period when the Society of Arcueil had been formally established and to arrive at it its author made use of work done by several members of the Society. It will therefore be considered in a later chapter.

Already in January 1805 Humboldt was planning a European tour which was to end in his native Berlin. His close association with Gay-Lussac led him to ask the latter to accompany him, and Berthollet arranged that Gay-Lussac should have a year's leave of absence on full pay from his post of demonstrator at the *École Polytechnique*. While he was away, his duties at the school were carried out by Thenard.[2] Humboldt

---

[1] *Ann. chim.*, ix (1791), 37–41.
[2] *École Polytechnique*, Archives, *Procès-Verbaux du Conseil de Perfectionnement*, vol. ii, f. 23.

and Gay-Lussac left Paris on 12 March for Italy. They passed through Lyons and Chambéry and crossed the Alps by way of Mount Cenis, where they analysed the mountain air, and eventually arrived in Rome on 5 July. Here they stayed with Humboldt's ambassador brother, Wilhelm. The Italian chemist, Morichini, immediately placed a chemical laboratory at the disposal of Gay-Lussac and the two chemists collaborated on an analysis of the famous alum of Tolfa. Gay-Lussac discovered that on strong heating the sulphur trioxide from the alum decomposed into sulphur dioxide and oxygen. He had not time then to carry this research further but he did so later in a memoir that he read at Arcueil.[1] The work that Gay-Lussac had carried out in Rome was reported to Berthollet in a letter which was published in the *Annales de chimie*.[2]

Humboldt and Gay-Lussac went on to Naples and Gay-Lussac was overjoyed at the spectacle of an earthquake on 26 July. They stayed in the region long enough to see an eruption of Vesuvius on 12 August and then left again for Rome. On 2 September Humboldt wrote to Berthollet describing experiments that he and Gay-Lussac had carried out on the torpedo (*Roja torpeda*).[3] They had found many large and powerful electric fish during their stay in Naples. Humboldt was able to compare the shock of the torpedo with the more powerful shock of the gymnotus, which he had studied in Central America.

They finally left Rome on 17 September, this time taking the mountain road for Florence in order to visit the celebrated baths of Nocera. Morichini had claimed that this water contained 40 per cent of oxygen but this was not confirmed by Gay-Lussac, who was interested to find that the water was so pure that no chemical reagent would give a precipitate. When Humboldt and Gay-Lussac arrived in Milan on 1 October they sought out Volta. They left Italy by the St. Gothard pass into Switzerland and thence to the German states; they passed through the university towns of Tübingen, Heidelberg and Göttingen before arriving in Berlin on 16 November. Gay-Lussac spent the entire winter in Berlin, where he had frequent contacts with the chemist Klaproth and the physicist Erman.

[1] *M.S.A.*, i (1807), 215–51. [2] *Ann. chim.*, lv (1805), 258–75.
[3] *Ibid.*, lvi (1805), 15–23.

Apart from widening his scientific horizons, the visit had the effect of making Gay-Lussac reasonably proficient in German. This qualification was later to be of use to his friend Thenard[1] but particularly to Gay-Lussac himself in his editorial duties for the *Annales de chimie et de physique*. When later Liebig[2] criticized the knowledge of foreign languages of French scientists, he made an explicit exception of Gay-Lussac, Arago and Dulong.

The principal scientific task which Humboldt and Gay-Lussac had set themselves had been to measure the magnetic elements at different points on their route. It is evidence of the continuity between the Arcueil group of 1801–6 and the Society of Arcueil that when the latter published its first volume of *Mémoires* in 1807, pride of place was given to the joint work on terrestrial magnetism carried out by Humboldt and Gay-Lussac.

The Difficulties of Publishing Scientific Memoirs

When the *Mémoires* of the Society of Arcueil were first published in 1807, it was not as an extravagant advertisement of the work of the members of the Society but merely a means offered to young men of the Arcueil circle to have their work published reasonably promptly and in full. The decision to publish a journal was the main feature of the transition from the informal gatherings at Arcueil into the slightly more formal Society of Arcueil. It is therefore worth considering the purpose served by the *Mémoires* and indeed the whole question of publication of scientific work in the first decade of the nineteenth century. The lack of facilities for the work of capable young men in most of the scientific periodicals constituted a powerful *raison d'être* for a new journal.

The most distinguished scientific society in France was, of course, the First Class of the Institute. One of its duties was to publish the work of its members and the first volume of its *Mémoires* appeared in July 1798. Subsequent volumes were published at approximately two-yearly intervals up to the publication of volume five in August 1804 and volume six in January 1806. By then, however, it had been realized that the frequency

---

[1] See Chapter Seven, p. 375.
[2] *Annalen der Pharmacie*, ii (1832), 20.

13. Laplace's letter to Napoleon (dated 6 February 1807), asking him to lend Berthollet 150,000 francs.

Sire

je jouissais du bonheur que je devais à votre
Majesté; mais mon imprévoyante tranquillité m'avait
plongé dans des embarras qui ne me laissaient pour
Long tems qu'amertume et inquiétude: votre Majesté
daigne les dissiper; je la Supplie de me permettre
de déposer au pied de son trône le témoignage
de la plus vive gratitude et d'un entier dévouement
à son Auguste personne

je Suis avec un profond respect,

Sire

De votre Majesté,

le très humble et très obéissant
Serviteur et Sujet
Berthollet

14 mai 1807

14. Berthollet's letter of thanks to Napoleon.

15a. Berthollet's house at Arcueil (after a mid-nineteenth-century engraving).

15b. Laplace's house at Arcueil.

16a. The *Palais de Luxembourg*, the meeting place of the Senate.

16b. The *Collège des Quatre Nations*, the meeting place of the Institute from 1806.

of publication was far from satisfactory and it was decided to try to publish the *Mémoires* in half volumes every six months, thus following the practice of the Royal Society with its *Philosophical Transactions*. The first part of volume seven was accordingly published in November 1806 and the second part followed in January 1807. The latter contained memoirs read to the First Class between 1802 and 1806. It was obviously still trying to cope with the backlog of unpublished work.[1] This was the last volume to appear before the decision was taken at Arcueil to publish their own *Mémoires*.

Yet even with an improvement in the position of the *Mémoires* of the First Class, there was little consolation for the great majority of young scientists who had not been recognized by the official body of French science, since publication of research in the *Mémoires* of the First Class was a privilege reserved for members. Young talent was, however, not deprived completely of the patronage of the Institute. Non-members who submitted memoirs to the First Class might have them approved for publication in the *Mémoires des Savans Étrangers*.[2] There is in fact in the first volume of the ordinary *Mémoires* of the First Class a list of papers judged worthy to be published in the *Mémoires des Savans Étrangers*. Yet, despite agitation from within the First Class,[3] this was not published until December 1805, although it included, for example, astronomical observations made by Laplace's young friend and calculator Bouvard in the year 1796! A similar delay occurred in the publication of Biot's first mathematical memoir, a paper that almost deserves a place in political history in view of its associations with Bonaparte. The preface to this volume of the *Mémoires des Savans Étrangers* explains apologetically that not all the memoirs that had been

[1] Similar difficulties in the publication of memoirs had occurred in the *Académie des Sciences* in the 1780's.
[2] The correct title at this period is: *Mémoires présentés à l'Institut des Sciences, Lettres et Arts par Divers Savans et lus dans ses Assemblées*.
[3] See *P.V. Inst.*, vol. ii, p. 49. (6 Frimaire an 8: 'Sur la proposition d'un Membre, la Classe arrête que la commission d'impression s'occupera de faire incessament imprimer le 1er volume de *Mémoires de Savans Étrangers*'.) Also *ibid.*, p. 385. (6 Fructidor an 9: 'La proposition d'imprimer un volume des Mémoires présentés par des savans qui ne sont point Membres de l'Institut, est renvoyé aux Commissions d'impression et des fonds, réunies pour déterminer, chacune en ce qui la concerne, le mode de cette impression.')

T

announced previously were to be found in this volume, since uncertainty about publication had influenced some of the authors to find other means of publishing their work. By the time Biot's first memoir to be accepted for publication had appeared in the *Mémoires des Savans Étrangers*, twenty of his subsequent memoirs had already appeared in print elsewhere.

A second volume of the *Mémoires des Savans Étrangers* was published in January 1811. The majority of the papers contained in it had been read to the First Class about three or four years previously, including a mathematical discussion of the theory of optics by Malus, read on 20 April 1807.

At the Institute the general delay in publication became so notorious that men who had presented their memoirs to the First Class made a habit of publishing them elsewhere, notably in the *Journal de physique* (which greatly benefited) and the *Annales de chimie*. This revolt reached such proportions that in April 1805 the Class of mathematical and physical sciences decreed that henceforth any memoir which had been published elsewhere would not be admissible for inclusion in the *Mémoires* of the First Class.[1] The only exceptions were cases where no more than a summary of the contents of a memoir had appeared or if the authors had made significant changes in the memoir.

Another scientific journal in early nineteenth-century France was the *Bulletin* of the Philomatic Society, which had begun publication in April 1797. This appeared regularly at monthly intervals. It provided summaries of memoirs which had been read either at the First Class or at its own meetings. Within the limits of its small size (usually about eight pages) it fulfilled an important function both as a means of disseminating the scientific news of Paris and as a source of encouragement to its members. The publication of the *Bulletin* ceased abruptly with the number published in February 1805 and it was not resumed again until October 1807 when the first number of the *Nouveau Bulletin* appeared. These dates are relevant to an understanding of the place of the Arcueil *Mémoires*, the first volume of which was published in July 1807. The publication met a demand which was then at a peak and there was no question of duplicating the *Bulletin* of the Philomatic Society.

Another institution which cannot long be left in the back-

[1] *P.V. Inst.*, vol. iii, p. 200.

ground in any discussion on Arcueil is the *École Polytechnique*, which had its own journal. Numbers eleven to fourteen of this journal appeared at two-yearly intervals between 1802 and 1808, although numbers nine and ten were only published in 1808 and 1810 respectively. This was hardly a situation to inspire confidence in potential contributors, who in any case were limited to members of the *École*. It had been planned to issue four to six numbers every year but, in fact, only fifteen numbers were published in the thirty years from 1798 to 1828. The numbers published before 1807 contained several memoirs by Laplace as well as occasional memoirs by Berthollet, Biot, Thenard and Poisson, all to become eventually members of the Society of Arcueil.

We have not yet dealt with two important publications, the *Annales de chimie* and the *Journal de physique*, and it must be admitted that these had neither of the faults of being too selective or having long delays in publication. Berthollet and Chaptal were on the editorial board of the *Annales* and were joined by Descotils in 1804. The control of the *Annales* was never in the hands of the Arcueil group, however, although Berthollet was a loyal contributor, particularly at the beginning of the decade. It could be said that the subject matter of the *Annales de chimie* was necessarily limited, as it was supposed to be a 'collection of memoirs concerning chemistry and the arts related to it', yet this objection could not be applied to the *Journal de physique*, which welcomed contributions on all branches of the physical and biological sciences. In 1806 no less than four memoirs by Laplace were published in it.

To sum up, whilst it would be an exaggeration to say that the situation regarding publication of memoirs was desperate, it was not always easy for men who had not achieved recognition. It would be misleading to present the *Mémoires* of the Society of Arcueil simply as the main solution to the problem of reasonably prompt publication for young scientists, although this was largely true for the first volume.

Early Foreign Visitors to Arcueil

Another characteristic of Berthollet's residence at Arcueil was the hospitality extended to men of science from other countries who visited Paris. The first distinguished foreign visitor to Arcueil was Volta, who spent more than two months in Paris in the late autumn of 1801. He went regularly to the meetings of the First Class and made the acquaintance of the leading men of French science, including Laplace and Berthollet. Fortunately there exists a published transcript of a diary kept by Volta's companion, Brugnatelli, who was professor of chemistry at the University of Pavia and who had contributed to the dissemination of the new chemistry in Italy. Volta's own letters of the period also tell us much about his reception.

The two Italians arrived in Paris on the evening of 26 September 1801. On 30 September they were invited by Berthollet to dinner at Arcueil. The conversation on this occasion included a discussion on the state of water-vapour in the air and, of course, electricity. On 21 October they again visited Arcueil. This time there was more company, which included not only Laplace but Fourcroy and Vauquelin. Volta was invited a third time on 4 November, but as Brugnatelli did not accompany him this time there is less information about this visit. We do know, however, that this was an evening engagement and Volta stayed the night and returned to Paris the following morning.

Apart from these visits to Arcueil, Volta met Berthollet frequently in Paris, whether at a dinner with Laplace, at a reception given by Chaptal as Minister of the Interior or at the ordinary meetings of the First Class. An Italian scholar has suggested that Gay-Lussac's work on the expansion of gases, read at the Institute in the following February, was the development of an idea which Volta passed on to Berthollet during his Paris visit. Berthollet even refers in his *Statique chimique* to some of Volta's ideas on the expansion of gases which, he says, he 'had gathered from his conversation'.[1] It seems that Volta mentioned to Berthollet data which he had published in Brugnatelli's *Annali* in 1793, namely that the rates of thermal expansion of air and of water-vapour are equal. This may possibly have been the origin of Gay-Lussac's demonstration of the equal expansion of a variety of gases. We cannot be certain but the possible connection here serves to remind us that visits to Arcueil were seldom purely social.

In 1802 the prospects of visiting Paris were completely

[1] *Op. cit.*, 1803, vol. i, p. 475.

changed by a temporary halt in the Napoleonic Wars. This affected particularly the communications between France and England and in the fourteen months between the signing of the Peace of Amiens and the resumption of the war in May 1803, many thousands of visitors from Great Britain visited France.[1] The Peace of Amiens was not signed until 25 March 1802, but a number of British travellers, including Sir Charles Blagden, left England before this date, arriving at Calais on 18 March. Blagden reached Paris on 22 March, where he was immediately welcomed by Berthollet.[2]

Sir Charles Blagden (1748–1820) had studied medicine at Edinburgh, where one of his professors was Joseph Black. In 1772 Blagden became a Fellow of the Royal Society and in 1784 he was elected Secretary of that body, a post which he held until 1797. He became Cavendish's assistant in 1782 or early 1783 and, when he visited Paris in June 1783, he was able to tell Lavoisier and his colleagues about Cavendish's experiments on the production of water from the gases now called hydrogen and oxygen. This information was crucial to the final elucidation of Lavoisier's theory of chemistry. Blagden's correspondence with Berthollet began when he returned to England later in 1783 and continued up to his death nearly forty years later. In September 1784 Blagden was officially appointed to the *Académie des Sciences* as Berthollet's correspondent. He visited France again in 1787 and 1792 but the war between Britain and France prevented him from returning to Paris before 1802.

During his stay in Paris in 1802–3 Blagden saw Berthollet repeatedly. Berthollet would often call on him at his house, No. 153, Rue d'Enfer (not far from Berthollet's own town house) either on his way in to Paris or on his way back to Arcueil, for example after a meeting of the First Class. Also Blagden would often visit Berthollet at Arcueil. Blagden's first visit was on 31 March 1802.[3] He remarked on the air of poverty of the village, which he described as 'ill-paved'. At this time Arcueil had just over a thousand inhabitants. In Berthollet's laboratory Blagden found working 'a Mr Gai, who seems a fine

---

[1] In September 1802 it was estimated that there were 10,000–12,000 British visitors in Paris, Sir John Carr, *Les Anglais en France après la paix d'Amiens*, trans., 1898, p. 4.
[2] Royal Society, *Blagden Diary*, vol. iv, f. 3. [3] *Ibid.*, f. 8.

young man. Berthollet gives a great character of him.' Blagden was shown the apparatus with which the experiments on the expansion of gases had been carried out. Blagden described Berthollet's laboratory as 'small'. Certainly the amenities at Arcueil were improved in succeeding years and in 1807 Berthollet wrote to Blagden that his retreat at Arcueil was much improved on what Blagden had seen in 1802.[1] For example, by 1807 the physics laboratory had been extended to several rooms of the house.[2]

Blagden had become quite wealthy as a result of his medical practice and he decided to buy a carriage for his convenience during his stay in Paris. From his diary we see that he was in the habit of lending the carriage to the Berthollet family and in particular to Madame Berthollet. Blagden described Berthollet's wife as 'very fond of plants, knows a little botany'[3] and on his return to England he despatched packets of seeds for her garden. As late as 1819 he was sending strawberry plants to the two French ladies he most admired, Madame Lavoisier (Rumford) and Madame Berthollet.

Blagden returned to England on 5 May 1803, just two weeks before the resumption of the war. Even during the Peace, however, his position in France was not without some embarrassment.[4] Laplace told him that Bonaparte was convinced that he was a spy for the British government. Blagden complained to Sir Joseph Banks, President of the Royal Society, that Laplace's relations with him had consequently changed from extreme 'civility' to 'coldness'. Despite Bonaparte's attitude, Berthollet continued on the friendliest terms and took every opportunity to defend Blagden against the suspicion of spying. Blagden's letters to Banks reveal how disturbed he was by this accusation even many months after his safe return to England.

Another man of science who took advantage of the Peace of Amiens to visit Paris in 1802 was the astronomer Sir William Herschel. Laplace and Herschel had been in correspondence since at least 1793.[5] In May 1802 Herschel had sent Laplace

[1] Royal Society, *Blagden Letters*, B.128 (27 September 1807).
[2] *M.S.A.*, ii (1809), 101.
[3] Royal Society, *Blagden Diary*, vol. iv, f. 29 (30 April 1802).
[4] *The Banks Letters*, ed. W. R. Dawson, 1958, pp. 93–4.
[5] The information in this paragraph is based on letters in the possession of the Royal Astronomical Society, London.

an account of his discovery of the asteroids Ceres and Pallas. Laplace replied on 17 June that he was very curious to know how Herschel had succeeded in measuring such small diameters and overcoming the effect of irradiation. Herschel had told him of his proposed visit to Paris and Laplace welcomed the prospect:

> I shall be delighted and honoured to know you personally and to be able to express by word of mouth the sentiments of esteem for you, which your discoveries have long inspired in me.

The summer of 1802 was a particularly appropriate time for Herschel to visit Paris as he had been nominated for a vacancy as *associé étranger* of the First Class of the Institute and was elected on 24 August.

Herschel arrived in Paris on 24 July 1802 and four days later there is a record of his dining at Laplace's house in Paris, Chaptal, Berthollet and Blagden also being present.[1] This meeting of the greatest theoretical astronomer of the age with the greatest observational astronomer must have been a memorable occasion. It was also a friendly one. Herschel was invited back by Laplace on several occasions for breakfast or dinner. One discussion which Herschel records on one of these visits was on the possibility of three or more stars revolving about a common centre. On 1 August Herschel was invited by Berthollet to Arcueil for dinner, where he met other French scientists. Herschel refers appreciatively to his host and to the pleasant situation of his country house.

Another of the foreign visitors to Arcueil in these early years was the Danish physicist Oersted. Still in his twenties, Oersted had yet to find fame for his discovery of the effect of an electric current on a magnetized needle. Unlike Volta and Herschel, therefore, his first visit to Paris in 1802–3 was not that of a distinguished guest but rather an interesting young man who had made the acquaintance of several men of science in Germany. He was, for example, able to tell the Philomatic Society about Ritter's experiments with the voltaic pile, and Biot told Oersted that he should write to Ritter, telling him to publish his work. As Oersted's command of the French language improved, he got to know more of the Parisian scientists. In March 1803 he mentioned in his letters home that he had gone to hear

---

[1] *The Scientific Papers of Sir William Herschel*, 1912, vol. i, pp. lx–lxii.

Berthollet lecture at the *École Polytechnique* and on 1 June in the company of Friedländer[1] he visited Berthollet at Arcueil. Oersted was obviously impressed by his contact with Berthollet since he refers to him frequently in his subsequent publications, particularly in connection with his ideas on affinity.

At the end of 1812 Oersted again visited Paris and received an offer for the translation of a work of his into French. It appeared under the title: *Recherches sur l'identité des forces électriques et chimiques* and was dedicated to Berthollet. Oersted wrote in the preface:

> The author is honoured that the translation of his work is dedicated to this illustrious man of science, and all the more so because he takes pleasure in acknowledging the great influence which the profound ideas, with which this man has enriched science, have had on his thought.

Whether Berthollet had any reservations on the association of his name with the more general speculations of the young *Naturphilosoph* and man of science is not known. However, if Berthollet had lived a few more months, he would have been proud to see Oersted on his third visit to Paris in 1823 honoured and fêted as the discoverer of electro-magnetism. Oersted came to know better the younger generation of French scientists, including the former members of the Arcueil circle, and it was Gay-Lussac who wrote to him on 10 June 1823 telling him that he had just been elected a correspondent of the Institute.

[1] Michael Friedländer (1769–1824), a German physician who had been living in Paris since 1800 and who was interested in all branches of science.

CHAPTER SIX

The Activities of the Society of Arcueil

The Significance of 1807

THE INTRODUCTION by Berthollet to the first volume of the *Mémoires* of the Society of Arcueil explained the functioning and membership of the Society; it was dated 9 July 1807. This happens to be one of the important dates in the history of Napoleon's military aspirations. It was on 7 July 1807 that he had signed a treaty with Russia and it was on 9 July at Tilsit that Napoleon imposed the terms of a treaty with Prussia which constituted a bitter humiliation to the latter. By establishing peace instead of war with Russia and ensuring the subjection of Germany, Napoleon had reached the peak of a career of an almost unbroken succession of military and political victories accompanied by a growth of the French Empire. Although the territorial expansion continued after 1807 it was accompanied by a loss in strength. It might be thought appropriate that the peace of the summer of 1807 should be accompanied by a renewal at home of the arts and sciences and the foundation of a society whose members were headed by two of the Emperor's favourites.

Yet the slowness of communications in the early nineteenth century may at first seem to reduce this parallel on the military and scientific fronts to little more than a beautiful coincidence. It was on 19 June that emissaries from Czar Alexander I had come to Napoleon to ask for peace but even the news of this armistice did not reach Paris until 10 July, when Parisians came out in their thousands to celebrate the good news. The formation of the Society of Arcueil cannot therefore be related so directly to the Peace of Tilsit. If the Society would hardly have been formed at a time of national crisis as in 1813, for the immediate circumstances favouring its formation we must consider Berthollet's prosperity rather than Napoleon's victories, for financial support was necessary if the Arcueil circle was to

277

develop into a society and undertake the expense of producing a journal. Yet here as before Berthollet's good fortune was linked with Napoleon. Earlier in 1807 Berthollet, despite his large income, had sunk heavily into debt[1] and Laplace informed the Emperor, then with the army in Prussia. This hitherto unknown letter to Napoleon written by Laplace, but also signed by Monge (Plate 13), recalled the Emperor's particular esteem for Berthollet and explained that the chemist, in order to devote himself completely to his scientific work, had handed over full responsibility for his financial affairs to his wife. He had now suddenly found that his affairs had been mismanaged and he was in debt to the extent of 150,000 francs. His friends feared that this situation was likely to have a serious effect on his health. They suggested that Napoleon pay this sum to settle Berthollet's debts, but delicately proposed that this need only be a loan. The Emperor wrote Berthollet the following letter on 1 May 1807 from his camp at Finkenstein, near the Vistula:

> To Senator Berthollet, member of the Institute.
>   I learn that you are trying to borrow 100 to 150,000 francs. I am giving an order to my treasurer to put this sum at your disposal. I am very glad to have this opportunity of giving you a proof of my esteem and to be of service to you.[2]

Berthollet's letter of thanks to Napoleon is reproduced in Plate 14.

In this context it is easier to understand the way in which Berthollet concluded the Introduction to the first volume of the Arcueil *Mémoires*. After speaking of the utility of science, he more or less dedicated the work of the Society to Napoleon:

> With these considerations, may the zeal of the Society of Arcueil merit the approval of the distinguished head of our government!

He continued in the same vein, revealing incidentally the general feeling of a desire for peace. Although news of Tilsit

---

[1] Berthollet's poor financial state is indicated by entries in the treasurer of the Senate's account book for the end of 1806 and the beginning of 1807 which reveal that he drew his salary several days in advance of the other members of the Senate (*Archives du Sénat*).

[2] Napoléon, *Correspondance*, vol. xv, no. 12502.

was not yet available, such news was obviously anticipated in France:

> May the peace, which has long been desired in the heart of the triumphant hero, allow his genius to extend his fertile influence to the arts and sciences. These alone might have made his fame if the destiny of the world had not been confided to him.

The treaty of Tilsit was to prove of more than indirect relevance to the fortunes of Berthollet and in this respect constitutes additional evidence of the high place he continued to hold in the Emperor's esteem. By the treaty the kingdom of Westphalia was established and this provided extra funds for the French exchequer. Documents in the *Archives Nationales* reveal that Berthollet was one of four people chosen by the Emperor in 1808 to receive an additional pension of 10,000 francs annually, the revenue being derived from property in Westphalia.[1] Thus Napoleon not only resolved Berthollet's debts, he provided him with a means of continuing to live grandly in his country mansion and pursue his scientific work free from financial worries. If we add to the income from Westphalia Berthollet's double Senatorial income together with such considerations as the 5,000 francs per annum which he (and Laplace) received as a Grand Officer of the Legion of Honour, we will appreciate not only how wealthy Berthollet was but how much he owed to Napoleon's friendship.

The summer of 1807 was a time of general relief and joy in France at the news of peace. It was also a time of prosperity, particularly in the Paris region:

> The presence of Napoleon at Paris had already exercised its usual influence. French bustle prevailed everywhere. Money was plentiful. Those on whom Napoleon had just conferred wealth were building elegant hotels, and bespeaking costly furniture to adorn them. Their wives spent money in handfuls on the dealers in articles of luxury . . .[2]

The date July 9 1807 found at the beginning of the first

[1] Archives nationales, A.F. IV, 301, pl. 2154, no. 21 (19 March 1808). *Minutes des Decrets*, A.F. IV, 2409 (16 September 1808). The other three beneficiaries were Monge, Bigot-Préameneu (minister of religious affairs) and Fontanes (president of the Legislative Body).

[2] L. A. Thiers, *History of the Consulate and the Empire of France under Napoleon*, trans., 1893, vol. v, p. 87.

volume of the *Mémoires* of Arcueil should not be regarded as of any crucial importance. It did not mark the beginning of regular meetings of the Society, which had been taking place as early as February of that year. When the first volume of its *Mémoires* was published the Society had been meeting regularly for several months, so their publication could contain memoirs read in February, April and June as well as other memoirs, some of them already presented to the Institute by members of the group.

The Meetings of the Society

Berthollet's patronage and encouragement of young men interested in science had been centred at Arcueil since he bought his house there in the late summer of 1801. If the following years constitute the prologue, by 1806, when Laplace bought the house adjacent to that of Berthollet at Arcueil, the stage was set for the first act of the Society of Arcueil. Informal associations were now to be succeeded by meetings arranged in advance and held fairly regularly. The Society was to study physics and chemistry in particular but this was never considered as a restriction, so botany, zoology and geography were also included. If chemistry and physics represented the spheres of interest of Berthollet and Laplace respectively, it would seem that the extension was not unconnected with the interests of Humboldt. From the beginning it was laid down that there should be only a small number of members, and after starting with nine there were never more than twelve; even then it must have been the exception for all to be present at any particular meeting. Yet what was (deliberately) lacking in quantity was made up in quality.

It must be pointed out that, in contrast to other scientific societies, notably the First Class of the Institute, the meetings were not primarily occasions for the formal presentation of memoirs.[1] Memoirs were of course read and many of these were of sufficiently high quality to merit publication. These constitute an invaluable by-product of the Society of Arcueil, the

---

[1] For example, from the evidence contained in letters, we know that the Society of Arcueil met in 1807 on Sunday 30 August and Friday 9 October although there is no record of memoirs read at these meetings.

primary function of which was, however, to promote experiment and discussion of scientific topics. This is clear from Berthollet's Introduction to the first volume of the *Mémoires* of the Society:

> The day on which meetings take place is devoted to repeating new experiments, which seem to justify repetition either by their brilliance or by a need for verification; also to carry out experiments suggested by members of the Society, particularly when they require special apparatus or when the originator wishes to have help, witnesses or advice . . .
>
> Each member undertakes to read one or more journals and newly-published books on the science in which he is particularly interested. A report on them is read at the meeting.

According to Thenard's son[1] the Society met on Thursdays. It is true that it was on a Thursday (9 July 1807) that the papers of members were brought together by Berthollet for the first published volume of *Mémoires*, but a study of the days on which the other memoirs later published were *read* shows that they were usually presented at meetings on Fridays, Saturdays or Sundays, Sunday being the favourite day. We must bear in mind the circumstances of the meetings. It was not only that the week-end was the obvious time to meet in Berthollet's country house. Every one of the members of the Society was either a member of the Institute or aspired to membership. The First Class of the Institute met on Monday evenings. Not only was it unthinkable that the junior Society of Arcueil should meet on the same day. As everyone at Arcueil was deeply concerned with the Institute (whatever its obvious defects), they would at their week-end meetings discuss the memoirs which they were to present on the following Monday. Through Berthollet's international scientific correspondence they would often hear scientific news in advance of their colleagues in the First Class and there was probably more than a little discussion of the internal politics of the Institute.

As regards the regularity of the meetings, Berthollet stated in 1807 that they were held fortnightly, that is from the spring to the autumn. In practice this was probably only the average length of time between meetings. It would certainly have been

---

[1] Paul Thenard, *Le chimiste Thenard*, Dijon, 1950, chap. 5, pp. 94–7, 'Laplace et la Société d'Arcueil'.

rather optimistic to have expected the small number of members to produce worthwhile memoirs every fortnight. Sometimes, on the other hand, circumstances would dictate meetings more frequently, as in August 1813 when Biot wished to add something to a memoir he had read the previous Sunday; or perhaps when eminent visitors were being entertained, the flexibility of a small and informal society would show its advantages.

If the full meetings were held only at intervals of several weeks, there is another aspect of the situation at Arcueil which should not be overlooked. In so far as Berthollet and Laplace and a succession of junior workers lived at Arcueil and the house was provided with a chemistry laboratory, rooms of physical instruments and a library, there is a sense in which the Society of Arcueil was in permanent session. Also Berthollet's house was certainly large enough to accommodate in comfort a number of guests. Although the young men would usually walk back to Paris, Humboldt stayed at least one Sunday night at Arcueil after a meeting.[1]

According to Paul Thenard,[2] on the day of a meeting at Arcueil the members would arrive at about two in the afternoon and at three o'clock the meeting was formally opened. Berthollet and Laplace took turns to preside. After the reading of memoirs and correspondence and the subsequent discussion the meeting adjourned at half past four. The ladies, notably Madame Berthollet and Madame Laplace, would arrive to tell the *savants* that it was time to bring their business to an end. They would then play the game of prisoners' base, Laplace and Berthollet keeping the score. After the game they had dinner and by nine o'clock everyone was gone.

This charming little summary would hardly suggest the serious pursuit of science. Yet of the scientific achievement there can be no doubt—the games and the social interests of the ladies are no more than a backcloth. Nor could Berthollet have sent his guests back to Paris hungry! From Candolle we have a first-hand account of a day at Arcueil.[3] After pointing out the usefulness of the contacts he made there both to his

[1] E. T. Hamy, ed., *Lettres americaines d'A. de Humboldt*, 1905, p. 250.
[2] *Loc. cit.*
[3] *Mémoires et Souvenirs de A.-P. de Candolle*, 1862, pp. 165–6.

career and to his scientific work, Candolle too does not neglect to mention the social aspect of the gatherings. Not least they provided agreeable opportunities for conversation. The younger members of the Society, Biot, Gay-Lussac, Descotils, Candolle and sometimes others would meet at Thenard's rooms at the *Collège de France* and they would walk together to Arcueil, happy to have exchanged the bustle of Paris for the freedom of a country walk. Finally they would arrive at Arcueil in the valley of which ran the Bièvre and they would see in the background the aqueduct spanning the valley, as it still does today. They would walk round Berthollet's house and also stroll in the gardens, the delightful situation of which has been described by several of Berthollet's visitors.

All this should not distract our attention from the value of the laboratory facilities at Arcueil, especially to young men who may not have had access to any other laboratory. From the first year of Berthollet's residence there Gay-Lussac had made full use of the laboratory facilities and in 1806 he continued to acknowledge his debt to Berthollet for his use of his private laboratories.[1] In 1807 Biot carried out most of his experiments on the transmission of sound in vapours at Arcueil.[2] Amédée Berthollet's varied experiments were all carried out there. In 1810 Bérard was carrying out experiments on the chemical effects of different parts of the spectrum.[3] This work, some of which continued into 1811 and 1812, was carried out at Arcueil as was his work in collaboration with Delaroche on the specific heats of gases. The last chemist to learn his subject at Berthollet's side was Dulong, who in 1811 and 1812 did valuable work there on reversible reactions in solution and discovered nitrogen trichloride. After 1813 the laboratories at Arcueil were little used. The young men to whom they had laid open the possibilities of research now had laboratories attached to their teaching posts.

One of the privileges of Berthollet's associates at Arcueil was to have the use of apparatus, often specially constructed by the most famous maker of precision instruments of the time, Nicolas Fortin (1750–1831). Fortin had made apparatus for Lavoisier but it is in the Fortin barometer that his name has been

[1] *M.S.A.*, i (1807), 182.   [2] *M.S.A.*, ii (1809), 98.
[3] *M.S.A.*, iii (1817), 35; see also *ibid.*, pp. 15, 23.

immortalized. It was he who constructed a special aperture for Gay-Lussac's research on the free expansion of gases[1] and the manometer invented by Berthollet was also executed by Fortin.[2] He was perhaps best known to his contemporaries for his delicate balances and the one which he made for Gay-Lussac and Thenard in 1808 was the most sensitive in existence at that time.[3] Biot and Thenard were proud to publicize their use of a Fortin balance.[4] Finally we should mention various pieces of optical apparatus which Berthollet had made for the use of Malus at Arcueil,[5] including the reflecting goniometer.[6]

The Arcueil 'Season'

The Society of Arcueil did not meet regularly at Berthollet's country house in all weathers throughout the year. A point which has been hitherto overlooked is the lack of meetings in the depth of winter. Looking through the list of dates on which the most important meetings were held at Arcueil, that is meetings at which memoirs were read which were later published, none was held after the first week in November[7] or before the second week in February. It seems then that Arcueil was shut up for the winter, at least for the months of December and January. It was not uncommon for owners of country houses in the Paris region to spend the winter in the capital. Also as far as getting to Arcueil is concerned, we must appreciate that the attractions of walking a few miles out into the country are considerably less at this time of the year.

The reality of the 'season' is confirmed by a letter written by Berthollet in October 1811, in which he says that he will be staying at Arcueil only till 13 December and would not be

---

[1] *M.S.A.*, i (1807), 194.   [2] *Ibid.*, 303.

[3] M. Daumas, *Les instruments scientifiques au XVIIe et XVIIIe siècles*, 1953, p. 366 n.

[4] *M.S.A.*, ii (1809), 202–3.

[5] Berthollet wrote to Blagden on 19 April 1809: '. . . Je lui [i.e. Malus] fais préparer des appareils très commodes pour suivre des recherches d'optique dans ma retraite d'Arcueil.' (Royal Society, *Blagden Letters*, B.134).

[6] 'Cet instrument a été construit par M. Fortin avec l'exactitude qu'il apporte dans tous les ouvrages qu'il entreprend.' *M.S.A.*, iii (1817), 127.

[7] It might seem that the first week of November was rather late to come within the season but it may be recalled that the old *Académie des Sciences* started their summer vacation in September and did not return until St Martin's day (11 November).

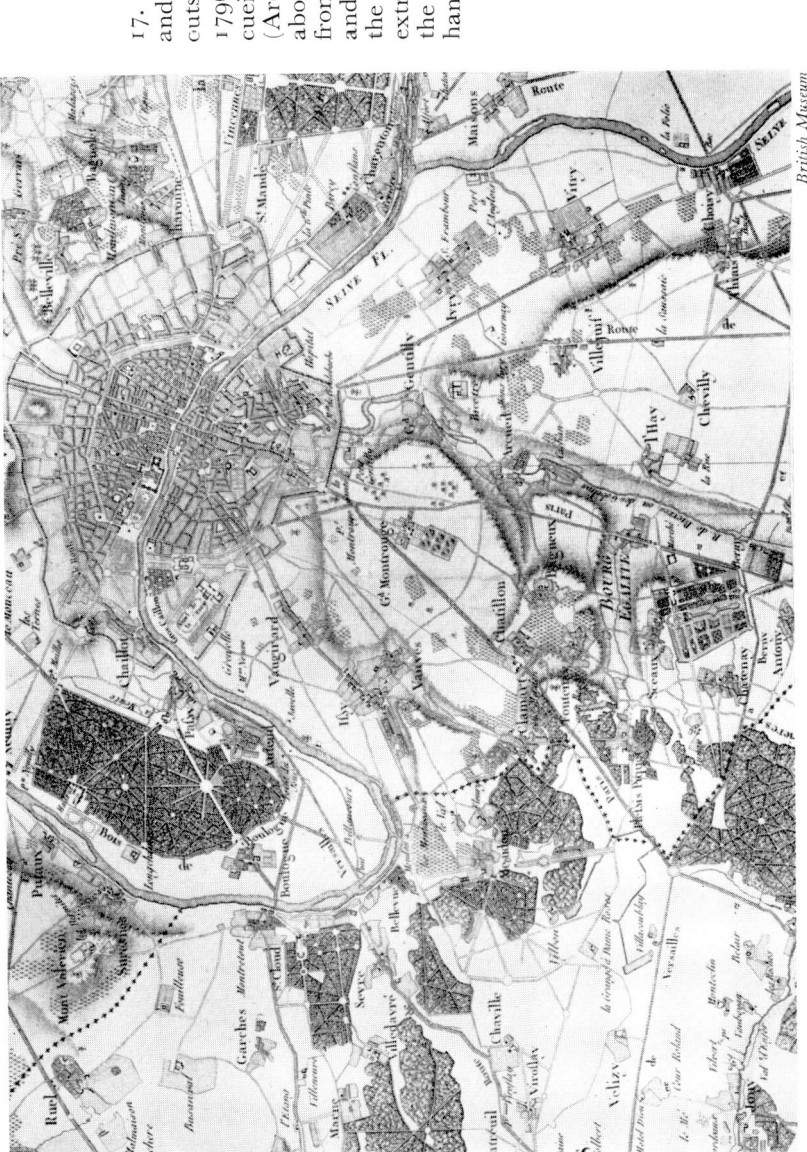

17. Map of Paris and the southern outskirts (Roussel, 1796), showing Arcueil and Jouy. (Arcueil appears about 1½ inches from the bottom and 2 inches from the right on this extract. Jouy is in the bottom left hand corner.)

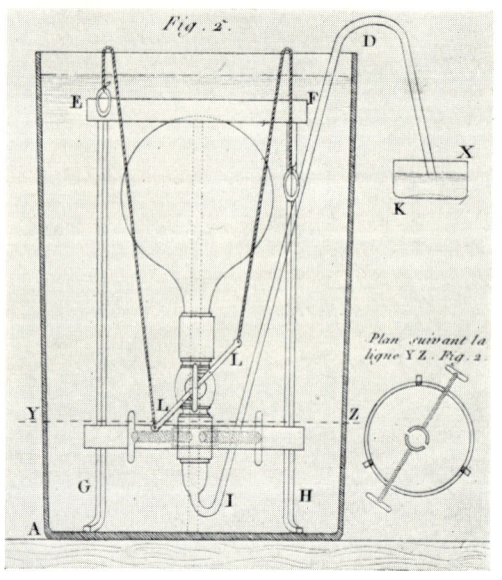

a. The flask containing the gas under test was clamped in the vessel AD filled with water. The flask was fitted with a tap operated by a lever, LL. The curved tube ID leads to a trap KX filled with mercury. The expansion of the gas was measured indirectly by weighing the water drawn into the flask on cooling after each experiment.

18. Gay-Lussac's apparatus for investigating the thermal expansion of gases (from *Ann. chim.*, xliii, 1802).

b. For gases soluble in water Gay-Lussac used two identical graduated tubes over mercury. Air was introduced into one tube and the gas under test into the other. On heating the gases, no difference in their expansion could be detected.

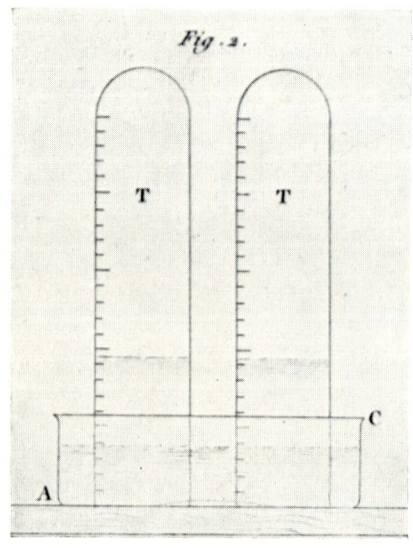

MÉMOIRES

DE PHYSIQUE

ET DE CHIMIE,

DE LA SOCIÉTÉ D'ARCUEIL.

Hommage de la société D'arcueil à la société Royale

19. The Royal Society copy of the first volume of Arcueil *Mémoires*. Note the inscription in Berthollet's handwriting.

20a. Thenard in his full academic robes. He is now a Baron and Vice-President of the Council of Public Instruction.

20b. Biot, now the doyen of the *Académie des Sciences*, photographed by Regnault in his laboratory at the *Collège de France*.

returning till early February.[1] Quite a few of Gay-Lussac's memoirs were read in February, presumably at the start of the new year's activities, and at the meeting of Sunday 3 November 1811 we find him presenting two memoirs on quite different topics as if to take the opportunity of the last full meeting of the season to present his work at Arcueil. For the historian of Arcueil it is a matter of disappointment that two of the most historic contributions by members to the *Mémoires* of the Society of Arcueil, Malus' discovery of polarization and Gay-Lussac's discovery of the simple ratio of combining volumes of gases, were both made in December 1808, or at least were not ready for presentation until that month, so they were formally presented elsewhere.

Gay-Lussac's Memoirs Read at Arcueil in 1807

In 1807, judging by the memoirs he read to the Society of Arcueil, Gay-Lussac appears to have been the most active member of the group. The first memoir recorded as having been read to the Society was by Gay-Lussac on Thursday 26 February 1807. It is doubtful if this was the first meeting of the Society in anything but a formal sense. A 'first' meeting in the bleak month of February in the country lends support to the notion of the gradual development of the informal meetings of 1804, 1805 and 1806 into a Society. The Society was formally constituted in the summer of 1807 and memoirs read to the Arcueil circle earlier that year were retrospectively included in the activities of the Society and published in its *Mémoires*.

Gay-Lussac's first memoir was concerned with vaporization.[2] He attempted to apply his ideas on vaporization to the distillation of a mixture of two liquids, e.g. alcohol and water. He argued that the distillate would contain a higher proportion of the more volatile constituent, alcohol, if the distillation was carried out under reduced pressure. Gay-Lussac was not making here a profound contribution to science. He was using the meeting of the Society as an occasion to throw up some ideas supported by experimental evidence. His paper, taking about ten minutes to read, would be a suitable subject for general discussion. If this was not science of the highest quality, it was at

[1] Berzelius, *Bref*, vol. I, Part i, pp. 29–30.   [2] *M.S.A.*, i (1807), 204–14.

U

least the kind of preliminary investigation which might develop into something bigger later.

Gay-Lussac's second memoir, read at Arcueil on Saturday 11 April 1807, was concerned with the decomposition of sulphates by heat.[1] This was a development of his earlier work on the thermal decomposition of alum of Tolfa, experiments he had carried out in Italy in the course of his journey with Humboldt in 1805. When Gay-Lussac heated the sulphates of metals he found that the corresponding oxides were usually obtained, although in the cases of mercury and silver the final product was the metal itself. Under suitable oxidizing conditions Gay-Lussac succeeded in obtaining the sulphates of zinc and iron, starting from the sulphides. At a higher temperature the decomposition of the sulphate took place. Gay-Lussac was illustrating the effect of temperature on the course of a chemical reaction. His detailed discussion of the relation of sulphides to sulphates was a significant contribution to metallurgy.

As if this were not enough for one memoir, the author went on to make an analysis of sulphur trioxide (*acide sulfurique*) which, as we shall see below, he found to consist approximately of two volumes of sulphur dioxide and one volume of oxygen. He derived this result from experiments on sulphates and on sulphuric acid. His experiment on the thermal decomposition of sulphuric acid in a porcelain tube was carried out at Arcueil with the assistance of Amédée Berthollet and the results were witnessed by Berthollet senior. This memoir also contains a discussion of the optimum temperature for the production of sulphuric acid by the lead chamber process, a branch of chemical industry to which Gay-Lussac was later to make an important contribution, which is commemorated in the 'Gay-Lussac tower'. Among the points made in his conclusion was that sulphur trioxide is composed of 100 parts by volume of sulphur dioxide and 47·79 parts of oxygen. Gay-Lussac was going to return to this ratio in the following year when he discovered his law of combining volumes of gases. This memoir made a major contribution to several branches of chemistry. It was immediately translated into German and it also appeared later in English.

Finally we must mention a brief note[2] read by Gay-Lussac

[1] *M.S.A.*, i (1807), 215–51.   [2] *M.S.A.*, i (1807), 379.

to the Society on Friday 12 June 1807 when most of the first volume of the Arcueil *Mémoires* was already in the press. Berthollet had been interested in equivalent quantities of acids and bases since he considered that these provided a direct measure of their affinities. Gay-Lussac had taken up this investigation of the 'capacity of saturation' of bodies and made the hasty generalization that these were inversely proportional to their specific gravities. He produced some evidence for this and for another generalization but admitted that before going any further he would require to carry out further experiments; this he did the following year.[1]

The Inactivity of the Society in 1808

There have been many societies that have ceased to function after the initial enthusiasm of the first few meetings has evaporated. This might well have been the fate of the Society of Arcueil in 1808. Indeed if one were to estimate the activity of the Society on the basis of the number of meetings held at which memoirs were read which were later published, one would say that after a good start in 1807 the Society went into a decline, since no important meetings were held in 1808. This was partly related to the absence of several members from Paris. There was the temporary absence of Biot from October 1807 to March 1808. It was also in 1808 that Amédée Berthollet left to run a chemical factory in the Carmargue and the household at Arcueil must have felt this loss particularly deeply. Candolle too left for the south of France in 1808, having been elected on 7 December 1807 by the First Class of the Institute to the chair of botany at Montpellier. He accepted this post with some reluctance since it meant leaving his circle of close friends in Paris and also abandoning his claim to the next vacancy in the appropriate section of the First Class of the Institute. Candolle remained in Paris during that winter and in February 1808 he presented a final memoir to the Institute. Yet neither Arcueil nor the Institute had seen the last of this young man. Although officially resident at Montpellier, for the remaining period of the Empire he was able to make regular visits to Paris. There is

---

[1] His memoir was read to the First Class on 5 December 1808 (*M.S.A.*, ii (1809), 159).

evidence that morale at Arcueil was not at its highest in 1808. Thinking perhaps of the unsuccessful experiments of Chenevix (see p. 144), Berthollet wrote on 20 June 1808:

> We continue to follow the occupations dear to us at Arcueil, but the harvest becomes more and more difficult.[1]

For Gay-Lussac, whose active co-operation with Thenard had just begun, the year 1808 was an extraordinarily active and fertile period. Having heard in December 1807 of Davy's isolation of potassium and sodium, they had succeeded in repeating the experiment. During that winter they tried to obtain larger quantities of the two metals and by the beginning of March they were able to announce to the Institute that they had obtained the metals by reduction. Meanwhile the giant Voltaic pile was under construction at the *École Polytechnique* and this was ready by the end of July. Gay-Lussac had all this time been working on potassium and on 3 June he was temporarily blinded by an explosion involving this metal. It was a full five weeks before he was well enough to attend the meetings of the Institute. Gay-Lussac and Thenard were also working on boracic acid and hydrofluoric acid. They presented memoirs on these respective subjects at the Institute on 14 November 1808 and 23 January 1809.

Not least important was Gay-Lussac's work in 1808 on the combining volumes of gases, which he had completed in time to read to the Philomatic Society on the last day of the year. It may seem strange that the most active young member of the Society of Arcueil should present this important memoir to a society in Paris to which he was much less strongly attached. The reason is provided by the timing of Gay-Lussac's great discovery. When his memoir was finished it was already December. To call an extraordinary meeting at Arcueil, with the house shut up for the winter, was out of the question. To wait till the following spring would have been too much to expect of anyone, least of all this impetuous young man with his avowed programme of discovering laws of nature by careful observation and measurement. Gay-Lussac did the sensible thing—he read his memoir at the next meeting of the Philomatic Society, which was on 31 December 1808. By this means he was

---

[1] Royal Society, *Blagden Letters*, B.132.

also able, by the space of a few hours, to claim his work as dating from 1808. By the time the Philomatic Society was able to publish a summary of his work, he had read it to the Institute (23 January 1809). There was no occasion to read it again at Arcueil.

As if all this was not enough for one year, Gay-Lussac was also appointed as a member of half a dozen different committees of the First Class and he was involved in drawing up reports on work submitted to the First Class by non-members. In four of these committees he was appointed together with Berthollet. It is hard to resist the conclusion that with a report which requires discussion and possibly experimental verification,[1] use was not made of the facilities of Arcueil. When the First Class of the Institute appointed committees drawn from a cross-section of its active membership and these turned out to be a selection of the Arcueil group, there seems to have been one obvious place to meet.

While there is no record of any meeting of the Society of major importance in 1808, the 1809 'season' began promisingly at the end of February with a memoir on 'oxymuriatic acid gas' by Gay-Lussac and Thenard. Gay-Lussac presented another memoir at Arcueil later that year.[2] In 1810 experimental work continued at Arcueil but there were few meetings distinguished by the presentation of memoirs. Generally speaking the years 1808 to 1810 may be regarded as the lean years of the Society after the promising year of 1807. The years 1811 to 1813 were more active and it is possible that the Society would have continued to meet later if the political situation had been more stable. Yet even without the collapse of the Napoleonic Empire the Society of Arcueil would probably have gradually run down just as it had been built up gradually. From the point of view of experimental research the Society had, as we shall see, made its own modest contribution, but the goal was always in the future. From the personal aspect, however, the Society had done its work. The young men of promise had been set on the paths of their careers. Berthollet became markedly less active

[1] E.g. in March 1811 a method of quick freezing of water reported to the Institute was confirmed experimentally at Arcueil (*P.V. Inst.*, vol. iv, p. 461).
[2] Gay-Lussac's paper read at Arcueil in November 1809 was published in *Journal de physique*, lxx (1810), 104–5.

after the end of 1813 and, since his patronage was the essence of the Society of Arcueil, it came to an end.

The Influence of Berthollet

A question which naturally arises in the study of a private scientific society is concerned with the influence of the sponsor(s). Berthollet would have qualified as the patron of the Society of Arcueil if he had been content to hand over his laboratory and library for the use of his younger friends. It was also a privilege for them to have access to a man with an international scientific correspondence who could provide news not perhaps available even at the meetings of the First Class of the Institute. Berthollet, however, was not content merely to provide hospitality and gossip, he had to provide ideas. In the final analysis it may even be concluded that he contributed too much. Not content with starting lines of enquiry, he brought his prejudices to bear on the interpretation of evidence and influenced younger men who would have been able to evaluate the evidence more objectively without outside pressure. Yet if this judgement is just in one or two notable instances, in general Berthollet must command our admiration for his constant encouragement of scientific work of all kinds. As Berthollet said in the Introduction to the first volume of Arcueil *Mémoires*, he hoped by forming the Society to make a more effective contribution to the progress of science than by continuing his own experimental work in isolation.

In a sense Berthollet and Laplace provided a programme of research for some of France's ablest young men of science at the beginning of the nineteenth century. In every generation it is important to understand what were the problems which exercised men of science and what approaches they considered useful to solve these problems. At Arcueil both the problems and ideas about methods were provided by Berthollet and Laplace. Problems were probably more important than methods. Often methods suggested by Berthollet proved inadequate and his younger contemporaries were able to improve on them. There are several examples of this: eudiometry and organic analysis come to mind.

Yet the programme provided by Berthollet was very little

more than his own lifetime's work. In his mature years he had not forgotten his work as a young man, although the young chemists of the nineteenth century did not have to rely on Berthollet's memory. His memoirs were available for all to read in the standard scientific literature and there is abundant evidence that they were read by Biot and Gay-Lussac, by Thenard and Dulong as well as by many others who perhaps were not fortunate enough to know personally this veteran of French science. As a teacher Berthollet was never a success but as an adviser to advanced students he could communicate his ideas more profitably. The difficulties of Berthollet's treatise, the *Essai de statique chimique*, have already been mentioned. Because of the abstruse nature of much of the book, it was much more likely to inspire the reader if he had personal contact with the author. It was only the exceptional scholar like J. B. Dumas who would read and re-read the book in isolation until he had mastered its principles.

Berthollet's scientific life may conveniently be divided into two halves separated by his journey to Egypt in 1798-9. Before the Egyptian expedition he had published work on a wide variety of chemical topics but none perhaps was better known than his memoirs on 'oxymuriatic acid' (chlorine). The investigation of the reactions of chlorine was taken further by Gay-Lussac and Thenard and later by Dulong. The substance which Berthollet had discovered by the action of chlorine on caustic potash (potassium chlorate) was used by Gay-Lussac and Thenard in their method of organic analysis. It was Berthollet who had established the composition of ammonia and it was his son who had repeated the volumetric analysis carefully at Arcueil. Berthollet's analyses of hydracids—hydrogen sulphide in 1778 and prussic acid in 1787—provided evidence to undermine one of the weakest parts of Lavoisier's theory, his oxygen theory of acids. It was surely more than a coincidence that it was Berthollet's pupil, Gay-Lussac, who developed this criticism into a general theory of hydracids. Berthollet's interest in eudiometry too was taken up by Gay-Lussac. One of the topics to which Berthollet devoted a lecture at the *École Polytechnique* was the chemical effects of light, a subject of interest to the Arcueil group.

Yet Berthollet's advice was not of the kind given today by the veteran retired sports professional. After his return from Egypt he gave considerable thought to the implications of his discovery of the dependence of the course of a reaction on the quantities of reactants and products. Berthollet's publications on affinity cover the period 1800–6 but as late as 1815 he was planning to publish a second edition of his *Statique chimique*. The problems of Berthollet which rubbed off onto his associates were very much live problems. The implications of Berthollet's discoveries were far reaching. In the first place they allowed compounds to be formed in variable proportions and the investigation of the composition of a large number of compounds was undertaken. If the analyses of Proust are best known, we should not forget the work of Thenard, Gay-Lussac, Bérard and Dulong.

Berthollet's influence stands out very clearly in the early research memoirs of his assistants. The early work of Gay-Lussac belongs to the period before the foundation of the Society of Arcueil and has already been discussed in Chapter Five. The early work of Berthollet's next two protégés, Bérard and Dulong, comes within the period of the active life of the Society and the research described here seems to have been carried out entirely in Berthollet's laboratory at Arcueil.

Three of Bérard's early memoirs are concerned with the analysis of salts.[1] This work was published in 1809 and 1810. In his first paper Bérard says:

> The accurate determination of the component parts of saline substances is of the more importance, because it is employed as the basis of other chemical analyses. Berthollet, who has sought to determine some of these in his late papers, was desirous that they should be carried to the highest degree of accuracy and invited me to resume the subject, reiterating the experiments, varying the methods and taking the greatest care to avoid every source of error.[2]

Bérard's experiments were carried out with a Fortin balance which with a load of one kilogram was sensitive to one milligram. In another paper he described his analysis of various oxalates and superoxalates—experiments which had been published by Thomson as convincing evidence of multiple proportions. Bérard was particularly interested in problems of

---

[1] *Ann. chim.*, lxxi (1809), 41–69; lxxii (1809), 96–101; lxxiii (1810), 263–289.   [2] Trans. from Nicholson's *Journal*, xxvi (1810), 206–7.

solubility and he interpreted the large number of insoluble salts formed by oxalic acid in terms of 'force of cohesion' of the acid, a concept taken from Berthollet.

Bérard's analytical work was largely routine and of little consequence. The same cannot be said of Dulong's first publication, an investigation of the mutual reactions of soluble and 'insoluble' salts.[1] Dulong's memoir, read at a meeting of the Institute on 29 July 1811, was a striking confirmation of Berthollet's thesis that chemical affinities were not fixed and that chemical reactions were, in general, reversible, depending on the conditions. Dulong showed that when barium sulphate, a notoriously 'insoluble' salt, was boiled with a solution containing an equivalent amount of potassium carbonate, it was partly decomposed. In another experiment when 'insoluble' barium carbonate was added to a boiling solution of potassium sulphate, a partial exchange took place. Only a small amount of barium sulphate was formed and Dulong considered that at this point an equilibrium had been reached between the opposing forces in the solution.

When work such as this was done at Arcueil, it does not come as a surprise to find that the first person to show conclusively the reversible nature of the action of steam on red-hot iron was Gay-Lussac.[2] Gay-Lussac and his students did something to develop Berthollet's ideas on chemical equilibrium[3] although it was not until 1866 that the precise formulation of the Law of Mass Action was achieved.

Although the influence of Laplace on the young men of Arcueil was also powerful, it is not seen so clearly during the period of the functioning of the Society as in the period immediately before (e.g. Biot and Gay-Lussac) or immediately after (e.g. Poisson). If one had to single out one instance within the context of the Society of Arcueil of Laplace providing the stimulus for a significant development, one might select Malus' discovery of the law governing the intensity of light polarized by reflection.[4] In general, Laplace continued to encourage the experimental verification of mathematical formulae calculated by himself.

---

[1] *Ann. chim.*, lxxxii (1812), 273–308.   [2] *Ann. chim. phys.*, i (1816), 35–7.
[3] J. R. Partington, *History of Chemistry*, vol. iv, pp. 577–80.
[4] See Chapter Seven, p. 346.

Collaboration and Cross-fertilization

The focus of a study of any scientific society must necessarily be the collaboration and mutual influence of its members. If co-operation was not the complete *raison d'être* of the Society of Arcueil, since it also provided facilities for research and publication, it was a major part of it. In the first place there were research projects in which a senior member of the group provided the basic idea which was then investigated in detail by a junior colleague. Some of the clearest examples of this have already been discussed when considering the origins of the Society of Arcueil. No better example of a junior collaborator can be found than Gay-Lussac who followed up ideas of Laplace as well as Berthollet. A second kind of collaboration was that contributed to equally or at least in a similar way by two people. This can be seen in the famous partnership of Gay-Lussac and Thenard, although it might be misleading to over-emphasize the part of the Society of Arcueil in this collaboration at the expense of the *École Polytechnique*, which was the scene of most of their work. Finally, and not least important, was the collaboration between different disciplines. The Society of Arcueil claimed to be both physical and chemical. Whilst these were the two main lines of investigation, they could not in this small informal group become stratified. The one science was brought to the aid of the other and to physics and chemistry were added botany, plant and animal physiology and physical geography.

By the beginning of the nineteenth century the study of nature had become specialized enough for the 'natural philosopher' to have become an anachronism. Anyone like Humboldt, who tried to grasp the whole of science, laid himself open to the charge of superficiality. There were now physicists, chemists, botanists, etc., and no longer could any single person claim to have mastered the details of all these branches of science. This inevitable specialization had been accepted and codified in the structure of the old *Académie des Sciences* for over a century and was perpetuated in the Institute, the First Class of which was divided into ten sections. It was part of the achievement of the Society of Arcueil to break down this specialization without going to the other extreme of dealing only in vague generalities. It was able to do this for two reasons. In the first place it did not attempt to concern itself with all branches of science from astronomy to medicine, from mineralogy to mechanics. It concentrated on problems of experimental science relating to physics and chemistry. Without excluding biological science entirely, it continued and extended a movement so successfully put into practice by Lavoisier, the union of physics and chemistry. Secondly, the approach by the Society of Arcueil to problems was dominated by men who, whilst having achieved eminence in a particular field, were always prepared to look beyond their own specialities. Laplace, since the days of his collaboration with Lavoisier, had become increasingly interested in physical and chemical problems. Though he always remained a brilliant mathematician, Laplace came to encourage physical research either for its own sake or as a confirmation of his calculations. Berthollet approached science from the other direction. As an experimental scientist and chemist he was interested in many physical problems. There is a story told by Candolle of an argument between Laplace and Berthollet. Laplace insisting that a particular thing was so because it was mathematically true, whereas Berthollet supported it only because it was experimentally true.[1]

To the influence of Berthollet and Laplace we must add that of Humboldt. When Humboldt joined the Arcueil circle he had already acquired fame as a great explorer. His contributions to the work of the Arcueil group included eudiometry, magnetism and botany and he perhaps more than any other person in Paris at the time, tried to be a universal man of science. As Chaptal reported to Napoleon, when Humboldt went on an expedition, it was as if the whole Academy of Science was there, so universal were his interests. His enemies could accuse him of superficiality but in company he was invaluable as a catalyst, asking questions and proposing solutions, never too proud to collaborate with his juniors.

One of the most remarkable features of the Society of Arcueil was the way in which it combined smallness of numbers with breadth of interest. Arcueil could easily have been one of the first chemical societies. It could have developed into a group like the Amsterdam chemists: Bondt, Dieman, Van Troostwyck

---

[1] Candolle, *Mémoires*, pp. 166–7.

and Lauwerenburg, who discovered the 'oil of Dutch chemists'.[1]
With Berthollet at its head and the chemical talents of such
younger men as Gay-Lussac, Thenard and Dulong this would
have constituted quite a respectable chemical group. But this is
to reckon without the important part that the joint study of
physics and chemistry played in the outlook of both Berthollet
and Laplace. Berthollet believed that, quite apart from its own
value, the study of physics was an indispensable aid to chemistry[2] and he looked forward to the time when physics and
chemistry would be more closely related.[3] Laplace remarked
that

> Physics and chemistry [are] two sciences which come into contact
> at so many points today that one cannot be studied with any great
> success without having contributed to the other.[4]

We find early evidence of the happy juxtaposition of several
interests in the balloon ascent by Gay-Lussac and Biot in 1804.
To advance to 1807, the year of publication of the first volume
of the Arcueil *Mémoires*, we find Gay-Lussac's joint work with
Humboldt on magnetism,[5] which demonstrates how misleading
it would be to label Gay-Lussac simply as a chemist. Biot too
had collaborated with Humboldt on magnetism[6] and therefore
had interests which overlapped those of Gay-Lussac. Biot and
Arago collaborated on a study of refraction in different gases.[7]
Although this study began from the point of view of astronomy,
it was carried out in a spirit not far removed from physical
chemistry. Berthollet himself collaborated with Malus in an
intensive study of diffraction fringes, carried out in the physics
laboratory at Arcueil.[8] They found that the fringes were independent of the material of the knife edges. An excellent example
of cross-fertilization is to be found in a joint memoir by Biot
and Thenard[9] who made a comparative study of the effect on
light of different forms of calcium carbonate. This was an ideal
field for the joint discussion of a physicist and a chemist. We

---

[1] I.e. ethylene dichloride.   [2] *Ann. chim. phys.*, ii (1816), 56.
[3] *Eleménts de l'art de la teinture*, 2nd edn., 1804, vol. i, p. 53.
[4] *Journal de physique*, lxiii (1806), 417.
[5] *M.S.A.*, i (1807), 1–22.
[6] *Journal de physique*, lix (1804), 429–50.
[7] *Mém. Inst.*, vii (1806), 301–85.
[8] Arago, *Oeuvres*, vol. x, p. 392.   [9] *M.S.A.*, ii (1809), 176–204.

might go so far as to claim that Biot's use of polarized light to investigate chemical constitution—an approach which was a natural outcome of the interests of his colleagues at Arcueil—would alone have justified the existence of the Society.

The General Problems of the Arcueil Group

When we try to see beyond the detailed contributions to knowledge of the Arcueil group and consider what were the broad problems of general interest we find that one of the broad areas of investigation and speculation was the atmosphere. From the chemical point of view it had only been a generation earlier, when Berthollet was a young man, that the air we breathe had been shown to consist principally of the two gases oxygen and nitrogen. But what might at first seem to be simply a chemical question is soon seen to have been of vital importance to the meteorologists. The work of Dalton illustrates the close connection of these two sciences, although De Saussure probably had a more direct influence on the Arcueil group. In 1802 Berthollet and Laplace took part in a dispute with Lamarck at the Institute on the question of humidity in the air and we find the same concern reflected in the work of their younger contemporaries at Arcueil. Berthollet was in a way outlining a programme of research when he wrote:

> All the phenomena of nature take place in the atmosphere, which frequently contributes to produce them by its compression, its temperature or the combination of the parts which compose it; an exact knowledge of the qualities of the atmosphere under these three relations is therefore necessary.[1]

Whereas Berthollet tended to look at the atmosphere with the eyes of a chemist, Laplace saw it from a physical standpoint. He was particularly interested in atmospheric pressure and he worked out a formula connecting altitude with pressure. This was put to valuable use by Humboldt and the 'portable barometer' later constructed by Gay-Lussac[2] might be more properly described as an altimeter. Nor was the atmosphere of

---

[1] *Chemical Statics*, trans. 1804, p. xxix.
[2] *Ann. chim. phys.*, i (1816), 113–19.

less interest to the astronomers. Since Ptolemy had discovered atmospheric refraction, the dependence of all astronomical observations on the air surrounding the earth had been appreciated. When it was discovered that the atmosphere was not a simple substance, it became a matter of concern to discover if its composition might change. Finally, as if the atmosphere were not already of general enough interest, there was its effect on plants and also problems connected with respiration of fish which were not beyond the scope of the Society of Arcueil.

Related to the interest in the composition of the atmosphere was the adoption by the Arcueil group of Volta's eudiometer. It was undoubtedly his concern with eudiometry that brought Gay-Lussac to consider volumes of gases and eventually to arrive at the law of combining volumes of gases. Members of the Arcueil group used the eudiometer not only to confirm the constancy of composition of the atmosphere but also to investigate the air in the swim-bladder of fish and the composition of the air after respiration. With Gay-Lussac it became a fundamental part of organic analysis and we find him using evidence from eudiometry as the main criterion for establishing the composition of prussic acid, for example.

Rivalling the atmosphere for the generality of its interest was the subject of light. Far from being regarded as solely a branch of physics, it interested most members of the Arcueil group from one aspect or another. Berthollet's own interests served to broaden the approach. In 1786 he had written a memoir on the influence of light[1] in which he had described the effect of sunlight on a solution of 'oxymuriatic acid' (chlorine water) and also on concentrated nitric acid. Berthollet was interested too in the effect of light in bleaching. When he came to write his *Statique Chimique* he did not neglect to include light among the factors which might affect the course of a chemical reaction.[2] One of his problems was to decide whether the difference between heat and light in their effect on chemical reactions was one of kind or of degree. The same problem was taken up by Gay-Lussac and Thenard. They were particularly interested in the effect of sunlight in bringing about the reaction between hydrogen and chlorine and this phenomenon was studied in

[1] *Journal de physique*, xxix (1786), 81–5.
[2] *Statique chimique*, 1803, vol. i, pp. 189–206.

turn by Bérard. The discovery by William Herschel of infra-red radiation led several scientists including Malus and Bérard to study both these rays and the so-called 'chemical' (ultra-violet) rays which so quickly turned white silver chloride black.

This territory could be explored profitably by both physicists and chemists, but another aspect of light was of interest to the botanist Candolle. Berthollet had earlier put forward a chemical theory to explain the absence of colour in plants deprived of light. Humboldt too had been interested to observe plants grown underground in the complete absence of light but it was Candolle who made real progress in this field. By using artificial illumination he succeeded in completely altering the waking/sleeping period of flowers. Extending his studies of heliotropism, he offered an explanation of why the shoots of plants tend towards the light. All this of course ignored the fundamental question of the nature of light. Did it consist, as Newton had suggested, of particles, or of waves? Malus' discovery of polarization by reflection could be readily explained on the corpuscular theory. The period around 1810 was a gloomy one for the supporters of the wave theory.

Newtonianism at Arcueil

One of the unifying themes in the work of the Arcueil group was their acceptance of a tradition centred on the achievements of Isaac Newton. Laplace was acknowledged as the Newton of his age, not only in the sense that he was an intellectual giant comparable to the master, but because he took further the Newtonian model of the solar system, reinterpreting Newton's geometrical approach in the language of mathematical analysis. Yet Laplace and his interests and influence represented rather less than half the Society of Arcueil and without Berthollet this would never have become a dominant theme. Berthollet enters the Newtonian tradition in his insistence that chemical affinity was nothing else than attraction. He therefore considered that chemical reactions depended on the mass of the reactants, just as in Newtonian mechanics the force between two bodies was a function of their mass. Chemical attraction had been considered by Newton in his *Opticks* and he is quoted at length on this topic by Berthollet in his *Statique chimique*.[1] If Berthollet ignored Newton's ideas on atoms (extended so fruitfully by Dalton), it was probably because he had worked closely with Lavoisier, who had managed to build a new chemistry without recourse to entities which he had considered as 'metaphysical'.

Yet if one were to avoid the crude mechanism of such an eighteenth-century Newtonian as Freind, it was not easy to apply Newtonian mechanics to specific chemical problems. It was therefore in physics rather than in chemistry that the Newtonian pattern was repeated on all possible fronts. The work of the Arcueil group was to represent almost a renaissance of Newtonianism. Much of this can be traced to the influence of Laplace. It is almost as though Laplace, hearing himself called the Newton of his age, accepted this title so literally and with such enthusiasm, that having successfully described the solar system, he turned to examine the numerous contributions to physics of the Great Man whose portrait hung in his study at Arcueil. There can be no possible doubt as to Laplace's admiration for Newton, and he described the *Principia* and the *Opticks* as 'still the best models which can be proposed in the sciences and in the delicate art of making experiments and submitting them to calculation'.[2] If Newton's best known physical work was in optics, his investigation of the velocity of sound and his studies on capillarity were also followed up by Laplace. Laplace considered that the rise of a liquid in a very narrow tube could be explained in terms of a force of attraction which decreased rapidly with distance.[3] It was in fact this same kind of attraction between particles of matter that had been used to explain chemical affinity.

Newton's work was not accepted blindly and uncritically at Arcueil. This was no Chateau de Cirey where Voltaire had fallen on his knees before a newly-arrived volume of Newton's works. Yet the spirit that went out from Laplace was no less Newtonian for being critical. Where Newton's ideas did not agree with what was now known by calculation or experiment, an adjustment had to be made, but such adjustments were

---

[1] *Op. cit.*, vol. i, pp. 532–5.
[2] *Système du monde*, trans. H. H. Harte, *System of the World*, Dublin, 1830, vol. ii, p. 308.
[3] *Mécanique céleste*, vol. iv, 1805, Supplément au dixième livre.

always within the Newtonian framework of a world of particles governed by forces of attraction. Newton was remembered as the exponent of the corpuscular theory of light. This was the theory accepted and developed by Laplace, Biot and Malus. Arago too thought this way until the evidence of Fresnel and Young won him over to the wave theory. The demonstration by Fresnel of the value of a wave theory marks a natural boundary in the history of science. The majority of the Arcueil group (the 'orthodox' party) are placed firmly on one side of this boundary. Arago, however, was not prevented by the opinion of his colleagues from lending support with increasing confidence to the rival theory.

Yet Arago had begun his career in science as a fully-fledged Newtonian, taking the *Opticks* to Spain and reading and re-reading this one book during many lonely vigils on the island of Formentera.[1] In his first published memoir[2] he began with a reference to this 'immortal treatise of optics', he ended with a reference to Newton, and in fact presented his whole work as an extension of a part of Newton's researches. But if Arago praised the Master, Biot, closer to Laplace, worshipped him. It was appropriately Biot who was commissioned to write a substantial biography of Newton for the *Biographie Universelle*.[3] Biot, attempting to reconcile Newton the mathematical physicist with Newton the theologian, concluded that all the original scientific work was done comparatively early in Newton's life and that he had only become seriously interested in theology after mental illness. This conclusion throws some light on the conception of Newton at Arcueil. Brewster accused Laplace of having encouraged a Swiss professor to obtain further evidence for this anti-religious thesis.

Malus' work on polarization is related to Newton's optical theory and this applies particularly to the term which Malus introduced to describe this phenomenon. Newton in Query 26 of the *Opticks* explained double refraction through a crystal of Iceland spar by suggesting that 'every Ray may be considered

---

[1] The *Catalogue des livres composant la Bibliothèque de M. François Arago* (1854, no. 1564) lists the Coste translation of Newton's *Opticks* as being interleaved and annotated by Arago.

[2] *Mém. Inst.*, 1811, 93–134.

[3] Biot, *Mélanges scientifiques et littéraires*, 1858, vol. i, pp. 123–236. See also review by Biot (1832) of Brewster's life of Newton, *ibid.*, pp. 264–89.

as having four sides'. He compared the sides of the rays to the poles of a magnet and also suggested that the particles of Iceland spar possess some kind of 'polar virtue'.[1] Malus at first described his discovery of 1808 simply as a property of reflected light and then as a property of the repulsive forces which act on light. It was not until March 1811 that he formally introduced the term 'polarization'.[2] Malus developed Newton's idea of the rays of light having four sides which he spoke of as north–south and east–west. Referring to these sides as 'poles' he arrived naturally at the term 'polarization' for the modification which light may undergo, since this was a property explained by followers of Newton in terms of these 'poles' or sides. Malus' discovery was therefore not only a triumph for the supporters of the corpuscular theory of light (since the alternative wave theory had no satisfactory explanation to offer), it was also marked by the embodiment in the language of physics of a term based on the Newtonian theory.[3]

The Velocity of Sound

The Arcueil circle was Newtonian in two ways, in its choice of problems and its method of tackling them. The problems were those of light, heat, sound and capillary action, at first sight a very large part of physics. A closer examination, however, shows that Laplace and his associates were concerned with a limited aspect of each subject, usually the same aspect as Newton, and they began where Newton had ended. Of this there is no better example than the work of the Arcueil group on the velocity of sound. This was a problem which spans almost the whole of the period of this book. It began about 1801 and continued for the next two decades to interest Laplace and to provide problems for his associates. Laplace was brilliant enough to appreciate that the discrepancy between the

[1] Newton, *Opticks*, 4th edn., 1730, Facsimile reprint, Constable, London, 1952, pp. 373, 388.

[2] *Journal de physique*, lxxii (1811), 344.

[3] Our previous remark that the admiration of the Arcueil group for Newton was not uncritical, applies also in the case of Malus. Malus pointed out that the authority of Newton had overshadowed Huygens' work on double refraction and he wished to give Huygens due credit—'Théorie de la double réfraction', *Mém. Sav. Étr.*, ii (1811), 499–505.

theoretical value given by Newton's formula and the actual measurement of the velocity of sound was due to the heat effect of alternate compression and expansion caused by the sound waves. Because of the speed of this process the heat was not dissipated. It raised the local temperature and hence the pressure, which resulted in a greater velocity of sound than that predicted by Newton.

Biot was the first member of the Arcueil group to publish his investigations on the subject. His memoir on sound was read at a meeting of the First Class on 1 April 1802.[1] This memoir, which made a brave attempt to solve one of the problems of eighteenth-century science, began as follows:

> Citizen Laplace proposed that I should examine the influence which the variations of temperature which accompany the expansion and compression of air might have on the velocity of sound, and to try if possible to reconcile in this way experiment and theory.

For a whole century the discrepancy between Newton's formula for the velocity of sound in air and the value obtained by experiment had been a scandal in science. Newton himself had tried to overcome the difficulty by introducing an arbitrary hypothesis about the nature of the particles of air. His ideas on the humidity of the air and those of the eighteenth-century German mathematician Lambert had been disproved.

It was known, said Biot, that a thermometer in the receiver of an air pump showed a decrease in temperature when the vessel was evacuated and an increase when the air was compressed. Now it was Laplace's contention that sound waves which produced successive expansions and compressions produced similar changes in temperature but on a very much smaller scale. This could be confirmed by calculation but it would first be necessary to know exactly how much heat was produced by the compression of a given quantity of air. Biot remarked on the difficulty of determining this directly but considered it reasonable to assume that the change in temperature was directly proportional to the expansion or compression of the air. When Biot did the experiment, he found a discrepancy between the theoretical result and that observed, but he thought he could

[1] *Journal de physique*, lv (1802), 173–82.

explain this. Biot was not able to come to any very definite conclusion except that the problem merited further study.

Two years elapsed before any experiments on sound were initiated by the Arcueil group. In January 1805 Hassenfratz, professor of physics at the *École Polytechnique*, published a memoir on sound.[1] He said that Laplace has asked him eight months previously to carry out experiments on the velocity of sound, particularly through solids. Hassenfratz had struck the wall of a gallery in a stone quarry beneath Paris and had tried to distinguish the sound transmitted along the stone wall from that which passed through the air. He found that he could hear the sound through the stone only up to about 140 paces, although it was still audible through the air up to 400 paces. He continued,

> M. Berthollet, to whom Laplace communicated these results, wished to confirm if the blow of a hammer could really be transmitted through a mass of stone 140 paces thick and he asked M. Gay[-Lussac], with my agreement, if he would help in my experiments.

Laplace's interest in the first series of experiments of Hassenfratz and Gay-Lussac led them to repeat them in other circumstances and they often found that the transmission of sound through a solid body was almost instantaneous. They concluded that the velocity of sound depends on the medium through which it passes, being much greater for solid bodies of high density than for gases.

Biot in 1802 had been confronted with too big a problem to be solved by one man, although in his calculation of the amount that the temperature would have to rise by compression he had been able to use Gay-Lussac's recent research. In 1806 Gay-Lussac's experiments to compare the specific heats of various gases—experiments in which Laplace took a special interest—made a further indirect contribution to the problem of the velocity of sound.[2] In August 1807 Poisson read at the Institute a memoir on the theory of sound in which he calculated that the compression of the volume of a gas by 1/116 would raise the temperature by one degree C.[3] In October of the same year

[1] *Ann. chim.*, liii (1805), 64–75.   [2] *M.S.A.*, i (1807), 182.
[3] *Journal de l'École Polytechnique*, vii (1808), cahier 14, 325.

Biot had completed experiments at Arcueil in which he applied Laplace's theory to the transmission of sound in vapours.[1]

In December 1810 an opportunity presented itself to overcome some of the difficulties involved in the theoretical determination of the velocity of sound. A committee appointed to decide on a subject for the physics prize of the First Class of the Institute for 1812 decided to encourage further research on the specific heats of gases. It may have been more than a coincidence that the most prominent members of the committee appointed to choose the subject of the prize were Berthollet, Gay-Lussac and Cuvier,[2] and the latter was not likely to have any strong feelings on the subject. A further election in 1812 allowed Berthollet and Gay-Lussac together with Thenard to constitute the majority of the judging committee. They awarded the prize to a comparatively well-known joint memoir by Delaroche and Bérard.[3] What has been overlooked is the statement by the authors that all their experiments had been carried out 'in M. Berthollet's laboratory at Arcueil'.

Not surprisingly Delaroche and Bérard referred to Gay-Lussac's experiments of 1807, which they were now able to surpass. They prepared a supply of gas at constant pressure, heated it, and then allowed it to cool while it was flowing through a calorimeter—a method which was only a slight modification of one used earlier by Lavoisier. Most of the experimental work was done in 1811, their results were calculated in the winter of 1811–12 and on 3 February 1812 they deposited a preliminary memoir at the Institute. The memoir was not required by the First Class until the end of 1812 and they were able to carry out further work during that year. Although Delaroche and Bérard themselves did not try to calculate the speed of sound, they did refer to Laplace's ideas, showing that the subject had not been forgotten at Arcueil. The unsuccessful contestants for the prize were Clément and Desormes, whose method of measuring the ratio of specific heat at constant pressure to specific heat at constant volume has become standard. That they did not win the prize may have been due to their failure to comply strictly with the terms

---

[1] *M.S.A.*, ii (1809), 94–103. See Chapter Seven for details.
[2] *P.V. Inst.*, vol. iv, p. 399; vol. v, pp. 105, 130.
[3] *Journal de Physique*, lxxvi (1813), 155–77.

of the award but it is equally probable that it was the powerful Arcueil pressure group in the First Class which decided against them.

It was not until December 1816 that Laplace read a memoir to the *Académie des Sciences*[1] in which he made use of the data of Delaroche and Bérard to solve the problem that had been worrying him for more than fifteen years.[2] They had found in one experiment that if the pressure of air was increased by 36 per cent, the heat given off increased by 24 per cent. Laplace used these figures to correct the Newtonian value for the velocity of sound and arrived at a figure not very different from that obtained by experiment.

We have not considered the details of Laplace's reasoning because the agreement obtained was largely a coincidence. The data of Delaroche and Bérard were faulty but Laplace had used them trustingly to arrive at a value known by experiment. By 1821 Laplace had developed a completely different theory of heat;[3] he still referred to the Arcueil data, but he admitted that it would be desirable to confirm the accuracy of the experiments of Delaroche and Bérard by further experiments.

In 1822 Laplace made use of data just obtained by Gay-Lussac and Welter.[4] Using a temperature range of −20°C to +40°C and a pressure range from 142 mm mercury to 2,300 mm, they measured the change in pressure resulting from the heat produced in compressing air adiabatically and obtained a value of 1·3748 for the ratio of specific heat at constant pressure to specific heat at constant volume. Multiplying the theoretical velocity of sound by the square root of this ratio gave a velocity of 337·144 metres per second. Using Gay-Lussac's hygrometrical data, this value corrected for water vapour in the air became 337·715 metres per second.

In the same year Laplace suggested to the *Bureau des Longitudes* that it should sponsor further experiments on the determination of the velocity of sound.[5] Laplace's theoretical ingenuity in adapting a succession of theories of caloric to bring the

[1] The First Class of the Institute had been reconstituted as the *Académie Royale des Sciences* in 1816 after the Restoration.

[2] *Ann. chim. phys.*, iii (1816), 238–41.

[3] Laplace, *Oeuvres*, vol. xiii, pp. 291–301.

[4] *Ibid.*, p. 304.   [5] *Ann. chim. phys.*, xx (1822), 210–23.

calculated velocity of sound into agreement with the actual value was hampered by the lack of any recent reliable determination of the velocity of sound. Prony, Bouvard, Mathieu and Arago were chosen from the staff of the *Bureau* and Humboldt was seconded in view of his interest in the subject, as was Gay-Lussac on the strength of his recent heat experiments which had been used by Laplace to obtain a theoretical value for the velocity. Laplace's son, now a lieutenant-colonel in the artillery, also gave his active support to the enterprise.

The group obtained permission from the Minister of War and the Minister of the Interior for the firing of cannon in the middle of the night near Paris. They began their observations at 10.30 p.m. on the night of Friday 21 June 1822. Humboldt, Gay-Lussac and Bouvard were stationed at Montlhéry and Prony, Mathieu and Arago about 20 kilometres to the north at Ville-Juif near Arcueil. The time which elapsed between seeing the flash of the cannon at the far station and hearing the report was recorded with chronometers reading to one sixtieth of a second. After allowing for various errors, they calculated a mean value of 337·2 metres per second at 10°C.

Although a further memoir, completely in the Arcueil tradition, was presented to the *Académie des Sciences* by Dulong in 1828,[1] and Poisson also continued to support Laplace's views, many attacks were made on Laplace's theory of sound, particularly in England. By the mid-nineteenth century, however, the merit of Laplace's basic theory, disentangled from his outmoded theories of heat, had been recognized. Although Laplace had provided the stimulus for this work as well as most of the theoretical framework, we should not forget the mathematical work of Biot and Poisson, nor the experiments of Gay-Lussac, Delaroche and Bérard and others of the Arcueil group. The correction of Newton's formula for the velocity of sound was a major co-operative undertaking and a triumph for the mathematicians and physicists of Arcueil.

To include most of the work related to the velocity of sound under one heading has meant a diversion from the task of describing the activities of the *Society* of Arcueil (which held no regular meetings after 1813) as opposed to the Arcueil group (which had a longer existence). It does, however, serve to

[1] *Ibid.*, xli (1829), 113–59.

illustrate that any attempt to separate the two is essentially arbitrary and artificial.

The Relationship between the Society of Arcueil and the First Class of the Institute

An important feature of the Arcueil group was its relationship with the First Class of the Institute. In the first place it should be stated categorically that membership of the Society of Arcueil never served as an alternative to membership of the Institute. The latter was a national honour; it meant official recognition of one's contribution to science. When one was a member of the Institute, one had 'arrived'. The formal duties were slight and there was a pension which would make a considerable difference to a man without other means of support. Membership of the Society of Arcueil was a much more personal affair. It was less a question of honour than of friendship. Membership brought with it not a pension nor any direct financial reward but simply the right to ask for advice and the right to use other facilities at Arcueil including the laboratories. The Society was also a social club and the small number of members guaranteed an intimacy and familiarity which was unthinkable at the Institute. The fact that by the beginning of 1807 Berthollet and Laplace, Gay-Lussac and Biot, the four men who constituted the core of activity of the early Society of Arcueil, were all members of the Institute, makes it clear that Arcueil, unlike some other societies, was never a club for those who could not aspire to membership of the Institute and took refuge in the lower orbit of their own society.

The informal nature of the Society combined with the extremely high level of competence of its members made it a valuable testing ground for new work. Many memoirs presented by members of the Society of Arcueil at meetings of the First Class were previously read in part or at least discussed at Arcueil. On several occasions Gay-Lussac first read a memoir in its entirety at Arcueil and after any necessary revision it was read again at a meeting of the Institute. On Saturday 11 April 1807, for example, he read a memoir at Arcueil on the decomposition of sulphates by heat.[1] Exactly a month

---

[1] *M.S.A.*, i (1807), 215–51; this includes three respectful references to Berthollet (pp. 227, 235, 241).

later Gay-Lussac read the same memoir at a meeting of the
Institute.

A striking example of the procedure of a preliminary reading
at Arcueil is provided by the memoir on 'oxygenated muriatic
acid' (chlorine) and 'muriates' by Gay-Lussac and Thenard,
which was read at the meeting of the Institute on 27 February
1809.[1] This is one of the classic memoirs in the history of
chemistry. In it there appears the following remark:

> Oxygenated muriatic acid is not decomposed by charcoal, and
> it might be supposed from this fact and those which are com-
> municated in this memoir, that this gas is a simple body. The
> phenomena which it presents can be explained well enough on
> this hypothesis; we shall not seek to defend it, however, as it
> appears to us that they are still better explained by regarding
> oxygenated muriatic acid as a compound body.

The explanation of this statement is provided by events at
Arcueil. The First Class met on a Monday. The previous day,
26 February, Gay-Lussac and Thenard had read their memoir
at Arcueil. There was, however, one important difference
between the memoir read on the Sunday and that read in Paris
the following day. In the first reading the authors had suggested that 'oxymuriatic gas' was an element. Yet to Berthollet,
a veteran in the preparation and use of this gas, the idea seemed
so extraordinary that he persuaded them to alter their remarks
to make this no more than a possibility—as in the above
quotation. That 'oxymuriatic gas' contained oxygen was clear
to Berthollet, who would have shown that by dissolving the gas
in water and exposing the solution to sunlight oxygen could
actually be collected. Hindsight now enables us to say that this
was a case where Berthollet's influence was not to the good.
Because of the pressure he exerted on Gay-Lussac and Thenard,
the discovery of the elementary nature of chlorine is usually
attributed to Davy, who announced it in 1810.[2] Davy was particularly impressed by the fact that charcoal even at white heat
could not affect the decomposition of 'oxymuriatic gas', a
result which one would hardly expect in a gaseous oxide. It was
therefore with some regret that Gay-Lussac and Thenard in

---

[1] *M.S.A.*, ii (1809), 339–58, especially pp. 357–8, *The early history of
chlorine*, A.C.R. No. 13, pp. 34–48, especially p. 48.
[2] *Phil. Trans.*, 1810, 232; 1811, 1–35.

1812 mentioned the circumstances in which the priority of discovery had eluded them.[1]

Berthollet later published an account of what had happened in 1809:

> . . . I fought the opinion of MM. Gay-Lussac and Thenard with great force when the former read at our Arcueil meeting the memoir in which were explained their reasons for regarding oxymuriatic gas as a simple body and I urged them only to put forward this opinion with the greatest care; yet M. Gay-Lussac maintained it in his lectures and MM. Ampère and Dulong adopted it from that time on; thus they have every right to claim to have been the first to regard chlorine as a simple body, although Davy was the first to establish this opinion publicly.[2]

If Berthollet appears ultra-conservative in this matter, it should be remembered that many of the leading chemists of the age, including Dalton, Wollaston and Berzelius, for a long time refused to accept Davy's evidence for the elementary nature of chlorine.

Another connection of Arcueil with the First Class—less direct but none the less real—was the later development of experimental work which had started under the auspices of the Arcueil circle. A good example of this was work which made an important contribution to the development of analysis in organic chemistry.

At a meeting of the Society of Arcueil in November 1809, just before the close of the 'season', Gay-Lussac read a memoir on the decomposition of some vegetable and animal substances by the action of heat.[3] He was interested in the fact that when he dry-distilled some vegetable and animal substances, part was decomposed and part came over unchanged. Gay-Lussac was able to explain this in terms of vapour pressure. He also suggested what has since become the standard simple method of purifying certain unstable solids, i.e. heating them to a temperature a little below that at which they would decompose and passing a current of an unreactive gas over them at the same time.

Gay-Lussac's principal interest in this memoir was the development of a theory of vaporization which he had discussed

---

[1] *Mém. Inst.*, 1812, 2me partie, 121.   [2] *M.S.A.*, iii (1817), 604.
[3] *Journal de physique*, lxx (1810), 104–5.

earlier at Arcueil.[1] At the same time at Arcueil Berthollet was trying to develop a method of quantitative analysis of vegetable and animal substances by the action of heat. He thought that he could use the gaseous products discussed by Gay-Lussac to throw light on the constitution of the compound. In a way this was a retrograde step since Lavoisier had already introduced the principle of combustion analysis by suggesting that the substance under investigation be burned in a known volume of oxygen. Yet this method was only applicable to a minority of organic compounds and Berthollet was searching for a more general method. By strongly heating the substance in a retort a residue of charcoal was left. From the hot gases given off water could be separated by condensing in a vessel surrounded by ice and the remaining gases collected for analysis. The volume of carbon dioxide was determined by noticing the contraction with potash and the remaining gas was sparked with oxygen. There were many theoretical and practical difficulties in the detailed execution of this method, but Berthollet considered that he had been successful enough with his trials on a few substances such as sugar and oxalic acid to be able to present his results to the First Class on 26 December 1809.[2]

It is evidence of the freedom of enquiry in the Arcueil group that, when Berthollet was doing his research, Gay-Lussac and Thenard were developing independently another method which involved the complete oxidation of the carbon and hydrogen in the organic compound.[3] On 8 January 1810 they read a preliminary note at the weekly meeting of the First Class in which they proposed the use of potassium chlorate as the oxidizing agent. At the next meeting of the First Class they announced that they had successfully applied the apparatus they had constructed to the analysis of sixteen vegetable and four animal substances.

This paper represents a milestone in the history of organic analysis but the method was not yet good enough. In 1815 Gay-Lussac found that copper oxide was a more satisfactory oxidizing agent.[4] Yet one major limitation of their method was the dependence on the volumetric analysis of mixtures of

[1] *M.S.A.*, i (1807), 204–14. [2] *Ibid.*, iii (1817), 64–76.
[3] *Journal de physique*, lxx (1810), 257–66.
[4] *Ann. chim.*, xcvi (1815), 306.

gases. This was one of the fields in which the Arcueil chemists prided themselves but it was neither as simple nor as accurate as gravimetric analysis. It was an improvement when Berzelius suggested the use of weighed potash bulbs to estimate the carbon dioxide, and the method was made fully gravimetric by Liebig, whose apparatus of 1830 came into standard use. It is fitting that the man who developed the apparatus to analyse simple organic compounds had been a pupil of Thenard and Gay-Lussac.

Gay-Lussac was always looking out for regularities in the diverse phenomena he handled. In his joint memoir of 1810 with Thenard he could not resist announcing three laws governing the composition of vegetable substances. This amounted to a classification of organic compounds based on quantitative composition. When the ratio of oxygen to hydrogen in a vegetable substance was greater than the ratio of these elements in water, the substance was acid; when it was less, the substance was oily, resinous or 'alcoholic'. There was also a third group of compounds like sugar, gum and starch in which the proportion of oxygen to hydrogen was the same as in water. This classification was taken up by Prout who, in a memoir closely following the work of Gay-Lussac and Thenard, referred to this third group of compounds as the 'saccharine class',[1] later called carbohydrates.[2] The work of Gay-Lussac and Thenard in the winter months of 1809–10 thus contributed to the main stream of organic chemistry. This work was stimulated by Berthollet. Had it been carried out in the summer, had it been done before the publication of the second volume of the Arcueil *Mémoires*, it might in the fullest sense of the term be called a product of the Society of Arcueil. As it happened it serves as an interesting episode in the continual interaction between Arcueil and the Institute.

New Members of the Society

The Society of Arcueil had been formally constituted in July 1807 with nine members. There was a clear intention to keep the Society small and informal. Nevertheless, Malus' permanent

[1] *Phil. Trans.*, 1827, 368, 380–1.
[2] C. Schmidt, *Annalen der Chemie*, li (1844), 30.

transfer to Paris in 1809 enabled the Society to extend its membership to him, and later in the same year Arago, on his return to France, was invited to join. By the beginning of 1810 Bérard, already resident at Arcueil as Berthollet's assistant, had published three analytical memoirs and this would have qualified him for full membership. Probably Chaptal's membership also dates from about this time. Chaptal had frequently visited Berthollet at his country house in earlier years, but each summer he had gone to Chanteloup. From 1810, however, he spent an increasing proportion of his time in the Paris region and he attached himself more firmly to the Arcueil group. Thus on 29 March 1810 he wrote to his son: 'I have spent three or four hours at Arcueil every day . . .'[1] Dulong was working in Berthollet's laboratory at Arcueil in the summer of 1811 and his membership cannot date from much later than this. Finally, after the death of Malus early in 1812, Poisson joined the Society. If this provisional chronology is correct, it means that the Society by four additions and two replacements finally rose in 1812 to thirteen—hardly an excessive number.

One of the most valuable acquisitions made by the Society of Arcueil was Malus. Malus, who had won the friendship of Monge while at the *École Polytechnique*, went back to the army, where he was soon promoted to captain and later came to know Berthollet as a fellow member of the Institute of Egypt. When Malus returned to France in October 1801, however, he was given various postings in the provinces. From 1806 to 1808 he was second-in-command of the fortifications at Strasbourg. Yet Malus, who had written a treatise on optics while on active service in Egypt, was not the kind of man to regard the army as filling his whole life. Moreover, his 'exile' in the provinces was not complete, since his connections with the *École Polytechnique* necessitated regular visits to Paris. From 1805 to 1811 he was the examiner in descriptive geometry for students graduating from the *École* and from 1806 he was also appointed examiner in physics. An interesting document in the French military archives[2] reveals that already in September 1804 Malus had applied for three weeks leave of absence to go to Paris, giving as his reason that he wished to visit his family. The application

---

[1] Pigeire, *La vie et l'oeuvre de Chaptal*, 1932, p. 438n.
[2] Service historique de l'Armée, Vincennes. Dossier: Malus.

was rejected. The following year Malus received his appointment as examiner at the *École Polytechnique*, so that he was now able to spend three months of the year regularly in Paris (usually August, September and October). In 1807 this leave was extended up to 1 April of the following year, ostensibly so that Malus could serve as a member of the central committee of the Corps of Engineers in Paris. In 1808 Malus spent no more than a few months at his post in Strasbourg, since his replacement arrived there on 25 July. Malus' visit to Paris in 1808 was to have important consequences for the history of physics.

On 20 April 1807 Malus presented a mathematical treatise on light to the Institute. His memoir was examined by a committee consisting of Lagrange, Laplace, Monge and Lacroix and they recommended publication. On 16 November 1807 he presented another memoir to the Institute. In this he made use of formulae worked out by Laplace in Book X of the *Mécanique céleste* and applied these formulae to data he had obtained for the refractive index of transparent and opaque wax. His results seemed a further proof of the corpuscular theory of light. Laplace's interest in this question and Malus' contributions were undoubtedly important factors which influenced a committee of the First Class to select an optical problem for the mathematics prize to be awarded in January 1810. The subject, announced in December 1807, was:

> To give a mathematical theory, confirmed by experiment, of the double refraction which light undergoes in passing through different crystalline substances.

Malus, making his discovery of the polarization of light by reflection during a visit to Paris in the autumn of 1808, did not wait until the closing date of the competition to announce his discovery. On 12 December 1808 he read his historic memoir on 'A property of light reflected from transparent bodies'. This is discussed in the next chapter. Here we may note that the committee appointed to examine the memoir (a committee which reported in favourable terms the following week) consisted of Laplace, Haüy, Chaptal and Berthollet.

We know that Malus had the opportunity of many informal contacts with members of the Arcueil group before 1809. Biot in his account of experiments on sound read to the First Class on 7 November 1808 recorded[1] that Malus had witnessed many of his experiments. Through the *École Polytechnique* Malus was known to Laplace, Berthollet, Biot and Gay-Lussac, but he was not asked to join the Society of Arcueil until the spring of 1809 when he came to live permanently in Paris, having secured the post of 'sous-directeur du casernement' for the capital. It now seemed that he might be able to participate fully in the scientific life of France. Yet the Institute was closed to him, at least for another year, such places depending on dead men's shoes. It was the Society of Arcueil which opened its doors to the young officer already known to it for his scientific work. In his obituary notice of Malus, Biot pointed out that the Society of Arcueil had been honoured by being the first to be able to benefit from his discoveries.[2] At Arcueil he was doubly welcome, especially to Laplace, as the man who had produced further evidence in favour of the Newtonian corpuscular theory of light.

If Arcueil provided Malus with intellectual stimulus, if he had ample opportunity there in contact with the chemists to correct some of his earlier naïve ideas about chemistry and even optics, he probably contributed much more than he received. Here, after all, was the man who had opened a new chapter in optics by his discovery of polarization. Without Malus much of the work of Biot and Arago would never have been started. Nor was his influence confined to physics. His arrival at Arcueil re-awakened Berthollet's long-standing interest in the chemical effects of light. Light was to constitute one of the major interests and contributions of the members of the Arcueil circle to science and it is significant that there were no papers on light in the Arcueil *Mémoires* before Malus joined the Society.

Arago in his autobiography recalled that on his arrival back in Marseilles in July 1809 after his adventures in Spain and Algeria the first letter he received from Paris

> was full of sympathy and congratulations on the termination of my laborious and perilous adventures; it was from a man already in possession of a European reputation, but whom I had never seen: M. de Humboldt, after what he had heard of my misfortunes, offered me his friendship'[3]

---

[1] *M.S.A.*, ii (1809), 409.
[2] Institut Impérial de France, *Funerailles de M. Malus* le 25 fevrier, 1812, p. 3.   [3] Arago, *Biographies of distinguished scientific men*, 1857, pp. 49-50.

This was the origin of the deep and lasting friendship between Humboldt and Arago. Humboldt obviously saw in Arago a resourceful traveller of considerable scientific attainments and he asked Arago to accompany him on a proposed expedition to Central Asia, a project which had, however, to be abandoned.

A more immediately useful source of patronage for Arago was the *Bureau des Longitudes*; he was, of course, known to Laplace and Biot as a young man of considerable ability, although he undoubtedly antagonized them from time to time by his complete confidence in his own genius. In fact, despite all he owed to Laplace for his positions at the *Bureau des Longitudes*, Arago makes it clear in his autobiography that he found it difficult to forgive Laplace for not having supported him on every possible occasion, e.g. for having suggested that Arago should withdraw as a candidate for the First Class until Poisson, his senior, had been elected. The politics of the Institute do not, however, concern us here. Enough has been said to show that Arago had friends within the Society of Arcueil who recognized his ability.

Arago was in more than one sense a junior member of the Society of Arcueil. When he joined in the late summer of 1809 he was only twenty-three. Moreover, his absence from Paris had prevented him associating in any way with the group in 1807 or 1808. Yet he was not quite in the same position as Malus as regards membership of the Institute, for his rapid election as a member of the First Class on his return to Paris was without precedent. Arago's contributions in a formal sense to the Society of Arcueil were not very numerous. Yet his presence provided another lively, original and critical mind to contribute to the discussions of scientific matters. Probably he would have done more research at Arcueil if he had not been required to carry out regularly his observational duties at the Observatory.

Bérard had come to Paris in 1807 at the age of eighteen to see something of the capital and acquire a scientific education. His father's connection with Chaptal ensured that he did not have to wander aimlessly around Paris. He went to Arcueil as an assistant in Berthollet's laboratory and he was soon doing valuable work. Already in 1808 his experiments on the density of gases were so reliable that Gay-Lussac was able to use his value for the density of nitric oxide in his classic memoir on the combining volumes of gases, a value which, he acknowledged, was 'determined with great care by M. Bérard at Arcueil'.[1] It was also during this year that a translation he made of a German paper was published in the *Annales de chimie*.[2] The following year saw the first publication of research by him. This was a paper on the analysis of salts, which was closely related to Berthollet's interest in combining proportions.[3] In 1810 a second analytical paper by Bérard was published in the *Annales de chimie*[4] and by now it is obvious that he was more than merely a laboratory assistant. He was worthy to be included as a junior member of the Society of Arcueil.

In 1810 Bérard became even more closely integrated into Berthollet's household. He had already been living with the Berthollet family at Arcueil for three years when the news came of the death of Amédée. Bérard, already accepted as one of the family, now came to take the place of the son. There is even a suggestion by one biographer that Berthollet wished to formally adopt him and asked him to change his name to that of Berthollet. However this may be, it seems certain that in the period 1810–13 Bérard lived at Arcueil almost as an adopted son, favoured in a special way by both Berthollet and his wife. In 1821 Madame Berthollet wrote the following letter to Bérard on the occasion of his winning the prize of the Institute for his work on the ripening of fruit:

Here is the crown which I have taken pleasure in making for you, my very dear boy; put it beneath your feet as you should everything of vanity . . . Be assured of the constant attachment of her whom you call your dear mother, who has all the feelings of one and who wishes you the happiest of days.[5]

When Berthollet died in 1822 it was to Bérard that he bequeathed many of his manuscript notes.[6]

Dulong entered the Society of Arcueil with an unusually varied experience of science for a man of his age. After two years of mathematical studies at the *École Polytechnique*, he had

---

[1] *A.C.R.* No. 4, p. 14.   [2] *Ann. chim.*, lxviii (1808), 134–9.
[3] *Ibid.*, lxxi (1809), 41–69.   [4] *Ibid.*, lxxiii (1810), 263–89.
[5] Letter quoted by Béchamp in *L'Union Nationale* [Montpellier], Dimanche 13 juin 1869.
[6] Académie des Sciences. Dossier: Berthollet.

Y

turned to medicine and from medicine to botany. The renown of chemistry eventually attracted him. Returning to Paris in 1807, he set up in his house a course of elementary experimental chemistry. His activities came to the attention of Berthollet, who had also given a private course of chemistry in his younger days.[1] The careers of both Berthollet and Dulong started in medicine and ended in chemistry. It was probably on Berthollet's recommendation that Thenard took on Dulong as his laboratory assistant at the *Collège de France*. This temporary post served to bring Dulong more into contact with chemistry but it was at Arcueil that he really became a chemist.

There was room in Berthollet's laboratory at Arcueil for a young man with Dulong's talents and he soon showed that he could profit from the laboratory facilities. His first serious piece of research on the mutual reaction of soluble and insoluble salts was an extension of Berthollet's own work. When Dulong read this memoir to the First Class in July 1811 it was appropriate that the two men appointed to examine it should be his two patrons, Berthollet and Thenard. In October 1811 he discovered nitrogen trichloride and was seriously injured by the explosion of this dangerous compound. In February 1812 when Berthollet reopened his country house, Dulong carried out further experiments there in consultation with other members of the Arcueil group.

Dulong's fundamental research at Arcueil in 1811 and 1812 entitled him to become formally a member of the Society. The choice of many of his research projects illustrates the influence of the Arcueil group. It was Arcueil which offered him facilities for research when he did not have them elsewhere. He came to rival Gay-Lussac in his achievement and like the latter, whom Berthollet had taken into his laboratory ten years earlier, he combined skill as a chemist with considerable ability in mathematics and physics. We must give due honour to the system of the *École Polytechnique* for the mathematical training which was to stand Gay-Lussac and Dulong in good stead but it was Berthollet who made chemists of them both.

Poisson was probably the person who contributed least to the Society of Arcueil, partly because of the late date of his joining

[1] See *Cours de matière médicale, chimique et pharmacologique, par M. Berthollet. Prospectus*, Paris, 1779.

but also because, as a mathematician devoid of ability in experimental science, he was something of an anomaly. His career, unlike that of Biot, did not pass from mathematics to physics. Yet if he did not follow Laplace completely in the breadth of his interests, he was, nevertheless, a disciple and protégé of Laplace. He studied the same problems and in several instances he was able to take them further. He took pleasure in reducing every physical situation to the action of constituent particles and it was in this way that he treated problems of heat, electricity, magnetism and capillary action. His work on astronomy and capillarity also invites comparison with that of Laplace. After the death of Laplace in 1827 it was Poisson who was recognized as the leading figure in applied mathematics in France.

Yet, despite his great talent, Poisson does not appear to have achieved recognition as rapidly as Biot, Arago and Malus. Biot and Malus were, however, his seniors and it is by comparison with Arago, five years younger than Poisson, that this is most clearly shown. It was Arago who was chosen before Poisson as assistant astronomer at the *Bureau des Longitudes* and when Arago was elected to the Institute in 1809, it was at the expense of Poisson. When Poisson finally obtained a place in the First Class in 1812 it was due to the tragically early death of Malus. Poisson not only succeeded Malus at the Institute but also at Arcueil. The greatest significance of this for the history of science was that it brought him into even closer touch with Laplace. As far as the history of the Society of Arcueil is concerned, his presence had the effect of strengthening the mathematical side and restoring the balance with respect to the predominantly chemical interests of Chaptal, Dulong and Bérard.

Memoirs Read at Later Meetings of the Society

We have considered so far the work of the Society of Arcueil up to about the time of the publication of the second volume of *Mémoires* in 1809. Although the *Mémoires* had been intended as an occasional publication and not as an annual or even biennial series, the delay in the publication of the third volume was exceptionally long. From 1810 onwards, therefore, when there was no immediate prospect of publication of the Arcueil series, we must look further afield for details of the research of the

Society. It was for this reason that we find several memoirs which had been read at Arcueil by Gay-Lussac appearing in 1810, 1811 and 1812 in the *Journal de physique* and more particularly in the *Annales de chimie*. In 1811 and 1812 five of the memoirs by Gay-Lussac which were published in the *Annales de chimie* had their origin at meetings of the Society.

The number of the *Annales de chimie* for February 1811 contained some observations by Gay-Lussac under the heading 'Extract of a memoir on triple salts',[1] the original memoir having been read at Arcueil earlier in the same month. The title is misleading since Gay-Lussac made a number of points, only the first of which was concerned with triple salts. He also dealt with oxides of nitrogen and general problems of chemical decomposition. Equally prompt was the publication in the *Annales de chimie* of another memoir by Gay-Lussac on oxides of iron; this had been read at a meeting of the Society of Arcueil on 3 November 1811.[2] He was concerned with the Arcueil problem of variable proportions, but far from supporting Berthollet's thesis, he correctly concluded that there were not an indefinite number of oxides of iron but only three. In 1811 it might be thought that the question of definite proportions was little more than a domestic problem at Arcueil. Yet in 1816 Gay-Lussac still had to insist on the existence of the third oxide against Berzelius who accepted only two.[3]

A more significant contribution to chemistry was contained in another memoir which Gay-Lussac read at the same meeting, on the precipitation of metals by hydrogen sulphide.[4] This may be seen as a development of earlier work by Berthollet.[5] It was generally thought that it was impossible to precipitate such metals as zinc, manganese, cobalt and nickel by passing hydrogen sulphide through solutions of their salts. Gay-Lussac was able to demonstrate that precipitation was possible if these metals were present in combination with acetic, tartaric or oxalic acids (i.e. weak acids) or, better, if an alkali such as

[1] *Ann. chim.*, lxxvii (1811), 134–6.

[2] *Ibid.*, lxxx (1811), 163–70.

[3] *Ann. chim. phys.*, i (1816), 33. Already in 1805 Thenard had stated that there were *three* oxides of iron—*Ann. chim.*, lvi (1805), 66, 77.

[4] *Ann. chim.*, lxxx (1811), 205–8.

[5] *Ibid.*, xxv (1798), 271; Partington, *History of Chemistry*, vol. iii, p. 512.

ammonia solution was used to prepare the solution. Gay-Lussac's discovery became the standard method of separating these metals in systematic inorganic analysis and it is still used to some extent today.

Arago was another contributor to the memoirs read at Arcueil in 1811. His memoir on the colours of thin films was read to the Institute on 18 February 1811. It was given a preliminary reading at Arcueil which, on the assumption of fortnightly meetings, would have been on Sunday 10 February, the same day as Gay-Lussac had presented some of the work he was doing. Arago's memoir was published only in the Arcueil collection.[1] Unfortunately the second part was destroyed when it was at the printers, and this part of Arago's memoir as it has come down to us is therefore a later revision, as opposed to the first half, which appears to give Arago's actual text at Arcueil in February 1811.[2]

Arago introduced his major study of thin films with the remark that this subject had served as a touch-stone by which theories of light were judged. Newton had devoted a whole book of his *Opticks* to their examination. Arago, however, tempers his adulation of Newton with a description of Hooke's earlier account of the colours of thin films. We have here the first signs of a challenge to the Newtonian orthodoxy. This was not exactly heresy but rather a re-examination of doctrine in the context of the early Fathers.

Arago examined Newton's rings by observing them through a crystal of the doubly refracting substance, calcite. He was able to measure the angle of polarization of light forming rings in different media and obtained results which could not easily be explained by the emission theory. This led to an examination of an alternative wave theory, such as had been proposed by Young in the *Philosophical Transactions of the Royal Society*, in a series of memoirs which encouraged Arago to look for an alternative and which made him the natural ally of Fresnel a few years later.

Passing on to memoirs presented to the Society of Arcueil in 1812, we find that at a meeting in June of that year Gay-Lussac

[1] *M.S.A.*, iii (1817), 323–70.
[2] E.g. Arago says (p. 323) 'Dans le Mémoire que j'ai l'honneur de présenter *à la Société* . . .' (my italics). See Arago, *Oeuvres, Tables*, p. cli.

described to his colleagues experiments he had carried out on the colour changes which took place on heating certain substances such as mercuric oxide and zinc oxide.[1] More vital to the stream of nineteenth-century physical chemistry were two memoirs which Gay-Lussac presented to the Society in May 1812 and October 1813 respectively. The first was on deliquescence.[2] Since Newton's time this had been explained vaguely in terms of the affinity between a salt and the water vapour in the air. Gay-Lussac pointed out that some salts, which had not previously been considered to be deliquescent, could exhibit deliquescence under certain conditions. Also, since affinity varied with temperature, so did the degree of deliquescence. He tried to find a connection between the boiling point of a saturated solution of a salt and its deliquescence. He was unable to find the relationship between vapour pressure of a solution and the weight of solute. This had to wait for Raoult in 1887. Gay-Lussac's second memoir was a study of the conditions under which a solution of sodium sulphate and certain other salts formed crystals.[3] These studies were extended in 1819 into an historic memoir on the solubility of salts in water at different temperatures, in which may be found the first solubility curves.[4]

The year 1813 was a particularly active one for Biot at Arcueil. Yet at this time he was deeply immersed in the preparation of his four-volume *Traité de physique expérimentale*. His mind was therefore fully centred on problems of physics. In the summer during the period of preparation of this book he was in the habit of renting a large country house near Beauvais, and his visitors included Berthollet and his wife. This did not prevent him, however, from frequenting Arcueil.

On Saturday 29 May Biot read a memoir to the Society of Arcueil 'On a way of imitating artificially the phenomena of colours produced by the action of thin films of mica on polarized rays of light'.[5] In this memoir Biot attempted to demonstrate that the polarization produced by mica, calcium sulphate and rock crystal could be explained completely in terms of attract-

---

[1] *Ann. chim.*, lxxxiii (1812), 171–80.
[2] *Ibid.*, lxxxii (1812), 171–7. Berthollet had discussed efflorescence in his *Statique chimique*, vol. i, pp. 403–9.
[3] *Ann. chim.*, lxxxvii (1813), 225–36.
[4] *Ann. chim. phys.*, xi (1819), 296–315 and folding plate.
[5] *M.S.A.*, iii (1817), 106–21.

ive and repulsive forces acting according to certain laws. He had attempted to confirm his theory experimentally. In discussing the colour effects produced by polarized light, Biot was developing a discovery of Arago, a situation which the latter resented. In fact, the next recorded meeting of the Society on Sunday 27 June was the occasion of the signing of an agreed statement aimed at healing a dispute between Biot and Arago. Biot, however, would never agree to abandon his researches on polarized light to leave the field open to Arago. We find him, for example, at one of the last meetings of the Society of Arcueil on Sunday 7 November 1813 reading a memoir on the effects of light of different colours on Iceland spar.[1] This memoir consisted of a development of observations made by Malus. It is not an outstanding contribution to optics and is perhaps of most interest in showing Biot's hesitation in applying the same hypothesis of forces acting on particles to the phenomenon of double refraction as he used for light polarized by reflection. The revival of the wave theory was not far distant.

The meeting at Arcueil on Sunday 7 November is more memorable for having been graced by the visit of Sir Humphry and Lady Davy.[2] This visit is referred to in one of Humboldt's letters.[3] Humboldt made a very favourable impression on Davy, who later described him[4] as 'one of the most agreeable men I have ever known; social, modest, full of intelligence, with facilities of every kind; almost *too fluent* in conversation . . .' Davy later contrasted the manner in which he had been received by Laplace in 1813 with his more graceful reception by Laplace when he again visited Paris in 1820. In November 1813 Laplace had given Davy the impression of arrogance, in particular in his attitude to Dalton's atomic theory. Berthollet impressed Davy less on an intellectual plane than on a moral

---

[1] *Ibid.*, 371–84.

[2] Although Davy's visit to Paris in 1813 caused quite a stir and he was visited by numerous French men of science (including Gay-Lussac, Humboldt, Thenard and Dulong), it is interesting to observe that he received most attention not from the Arcueil group but from men then on the fringe of French science such as Ampère, Clément and Chevreul. Davy had no direct contact with Napoleon during his visit .

[3] Royal Society, *Blagden Letters*, H. 52 (12 November 1813). Davy apparently kept no notes of his visit to Paris (John Davy, *Memoirs of the life of Sir Humphry Davy*, 1836, vol. i, p. 467).

[4] John Davy, *op. cit.*, vol. i, pp. 469–70.

one. Davy's highest admiration in his own field of chemistry was reserved for Gay-Lussac.

In view of controversies which have surrounded the early work on iodine, the precise date of Davy's visit to Arcueil is of some interest since it was only on 23 November that Davy was given a specimen of the new substance.[1] Gay-Lussac obtained some about the same time and was able on 6 December to publish the results of his preliminary experiments. By 11 November Davy reached the provisional conclusion that they were dealing with a new element and on 12 December Gay-Lussac published in *Le Moniteur* a statement drawing attention to its analogy with chlorine. Both Davy and Gay-Lussac continued their independent research in 1814 and discovered various compounds of iodine. Neither was the discoverer of iodine (a title that must go to Courtois) but their simultaneous research provides a classic example of scientific rivalry with the added piquancy of Davy's work on 'enemy' territory. Once more, however, the onset of winter excluded Arcueil as a possible scene of the work. The feverish research carried out in the last week of November and in December 1813 was all done in laboratories in Paris. An interesting sequel is provided by the assistance given to Davy by Bérard in Montpellier (see p. 135).

At the end of the eighteenth century and the beginning of the nineteenth several attempts were made to obtain exact measurements of thermal expansion. The scientists of Arcueil were concerned with this problem which had been one of the subjects of the collaboration of Lavoisier and Laplace a generation earlier. Their work on the expansion of glass and metals had been carried out at the Arsenal in 1781–2, but it had not been published during Lavoisier's lifetime. It was only in 1803 that Lavoisier's widow included it in her husband's *Mémoires de chimie*, a book which was presented on a personal basis to her friends and to several institutions.[2] Biot carefully examined this posthumous work and was fortunate enough to obtain from Madame Lavoisier the unpublished table of results of the experiments on expansion which Lavoisier and Laplace had

---

[1] See Partington, *History of Chemistry*, vol. iv, 1964, pp. 85–90, for a summary of early work on iodine.

[2] Duveen and Klickstein, *A Bibliography of the Works of Lavoisier*, 1954, pp. 200, 205–6. They state that the tables were probably never printed.

calculated thirty years previously. Biot published it in his text-book of physics, together with a major part of the memoir of Lavoisier and Laplace which he quoted *in extenso* as a model of experimental work.[1] This, therefore, provides some of the background to Biot's presentation to the Society of Arcueil on Sunday 8 August 1813 of a long and detailed memoir on the thermal expansion of liquids.[2] He attempted to represent the expansion of all liquids by the equation

$$\delta_t = at + bt^2 + ct^3$$

where t is the temperature and a, b and c are constants for any particular liquid. In the ensuing discussion, Berthollet had referred Biot to Dalton's work on the subject, published in his *New System of Chemical Philosophy*. Accordingly, when the Society of Arcueil met again on the following Friday, 13 August, Biot was able to present a comparison of his own work with that of Dalton.[3] Laplace too had contributed to the discussion by suggesting that Biot might be able to eliminate the term containing the cube in the above equation by using instead of a mercury thermometer the temperature of an ideal thermometer related to the latter. Biot, however, found himself unable to arrive at a simpler formula. This was not Biot's most brilliant work. Yet this memoir added to the variety of solid achievement accomplished by the Society of Arcueil and illustrates the valuable critical role which senior members were able to play at meetings of the Society.

Biot's publication of the Lavoisier and Laplace manuscript in 1816 led Gay-Lussac and Arago as editors of the *Annales de chimie et de physique* to reproduce the table in their journal together with other data on the expansion of solids, liquids and gases.[4] Gay-Lussac himself was prompted to study the expansion of liquids.[5] He tried to find a basis for the comparison of the coefficients of expansion of water, alcohol, carbon disulphide and ether by relating them to their respective boiling points. He also asked his assistant Despretz to check Biot's formula against the observed expansion of these liquids. Gay-Lussac was

[1] *Traité de physique*, 1816, vol. i, pp. 146–58.
[2] *M.S.A.*, iii (1817), 191–248; see especially p. 224n.
[3] *Ibid.*, 249–61.   [4] *Ann. chim. phys.*, i (1816), 101–10.
[5] *Ibid.*, ii (1816), 130–6.

disappointed in his attempt to derive a general law for the expansion of liquids. His work is of interest to us mainly as providing further evidence of work by members of the Arcueil group which was inspired by the earlier collaboration of Lavoisier and Laplace. The work of Dulong and Petit which was awarded the physics prize of the *Académie des Sciences* for 1818 was also in the same tradition.[1]

Books by Members of the Society

The members of the Society of Arcueil were to make a significant contribution to learning by their personal example, influence and teaching but they reached an even wider audience by means of the printed word. The output of papers of the Arcueil group during the life span of its members was prodigious and merely to list these contributions would fill up a large part of a book. If one turns over the pages of the *Mémoires* of the Institute, the *Annales de chimie*, the *Journal de physique* or the *Journal des mines* published in the early nineteenth century, one finds the names of the members of the Arcueil group time and time again. Anyone who is interested in this testimony to their activity may turn to the *Royal Society Catalogue of Scientific Papers*, where he will find three hundred entries under the name of Biot alone and half that number for Gay-Lussac, if one omits publications involving collaboration with another person. To limit the scope of this book we must necessarily concentrate on memoirs which were actually read at Arcueil or which were published in the *Mémoires* of the Society, the most tangible monument to the endeavours of its members.

Yet to look only at the memoirs written by members of the Arcueil group would be to ignore an even more solid contribution to nineteenth-century science, the many books which they wrote. A large proportion of these were not simply the work of one man but were related to the work of other members of the Arcueil group. Books by Berthollet, Laplace, Humboldt, Gay-Lussac and Thenard certainly come in this category. Another example is Biot's *Traité de physique*, published in 1816 in four volumes. The dedication was to Berthollet. Their relationship

---

[1] *Ann. chim.*, vii (1817), 113–54; see especially pp. 138–9, 154.

was no longer that between a young man and an elder statesman. Biot begins:

My dear and respected friend,
  A work which is intended to set out the true principles of
physics and to establish its different branches on a permanent
foundation cannot be alien to your interests nor to your work;
you have shown too well the connection of this science with
[chemistry] . . . not to approve of efforts to bring them even
closer together . . .

As regards the method of physics, one should first define all the
circumstances that determine a particular phenomenon and
then treat each characteristic numerically. This was the method
of Newton, although perhaps it had been too little followed; it
was also, said Biot, the method which Laplace had used in his
Mécanique céleste. There are further extensive references to
Laplace on such topics as capillarity and thermal expansion.
Particularly numerous are references to work by Gay-Lussac,
and Dulong is also quoted. The published and unpublished
work of Biot's colleagues formed a valuable store on which he
could draw. By the time Biot in volume four comes to give a
detailed account of Bérard's experiments on ultra-violet light,
we realize how the author's friendships at Arcueil had made
the former mathematician competent to write a comprehensive
treatise on physics.

The catalogue of original works written after 1800 by members of the Arcueil circle is a formidable one, not only as
regards quantity but quality. The two most important works
were undoubtedly those produced by the two leaders of the
Society—Laplace's *Mécanique céleste* (Volumes 3 and 4, 1804–5)
and Berthollet's *Statique chimique*, largely composed at Arcueil
and published in 1803. Both these works are classics in the
history of science, the first completing Newton's celestial
mechanics and showing that the irregularity found in the
motion of the planets by Newton was self-correcting. In the
second work Berthollet, extending the Newtonian concept of
gravitation to the micro-scale, had insisted on the importance
of mass on the course of chemical reactions. Both these works,
moreover, belong to the Arcueil tradition in their inclusion of
work by other members of the group.

Laplace had written two works on astronomy, the first his

popular cosmology, the *Exposition du Système du Monde* (1796), which was followed by his highly technical *Mécanique céleste* (1799–1825). Similarly his interest in statistics led him to write two quite different works on the subject. This time it was the technical treatise which preceded the popularization. The *Théorie analytique des probabilités* (1812) was followed by his more readable *Essai philosophique sur les probabilités* in 1814.

If Laplace's genius was not limited to one book or one type of book, nor was that of Berthollet. He had already published his *Éléments de l'art de la teinture* in 1791, but the development of the subject of dyeing to which he himself had contributed, as well as the experience of his son at Oberkampf's factory at Jouy, provided the occasion for a second edition published jointly by the father and son in 1804. The most notable additions from the practical point of view were a long and detailed section describing bleaching by 'oxymuriatic acid' and a chapter on dyeing with Turkey red. The latter dye had recently been introduced from the east and its successful application was a matter of some difficulty. The subject was taken up again three years later by Chaptal, whose book on the art of dyeing cotton red was dedicated to Berthollet. Berthollet's book also included a new section 'Of Dyeing Operations in General' and a revised discussion of the theory of dyeing in the Introduction.

Chaptal, who had made his scientific work the excuse for his resignation from a key position in Napoleon's government, soon produced a succession of books which bear witness to his industry. Most valuable was his general survey of applied chemistry, which was published as *La chimie appliquée aux arts* in four volumes in 1806. This was followed by his *Art de la teinture du coton en rouge* in 1807 and his *Art des principes chimiques du teinturier dégraisseur* in 1808.

As industrious as Chaptal, although in a different field, was Candolle who was, moreover, an enthusiastic member of the Arcueil circle at a time when Chaptal was only the occasional guest of Berthollet. Most of Candolle's work consisted of memoirs published in the periodical literature. He did, however, write the text of volumes 1–4 of *Les Lilaciées* (1802–16) by P. J. Redouté. When Candolle left Paris for Montpellier in 1808 the task was continued by Humboldt's collaborator, Provençal. Candolle's major work was the publication of a new edition of Lamarck's *Flore Française*, substantially altered and enlarged by Candolle. This appeared in five volumes between 1805 and 1815. In a related field, Humboldt was busy with the publication of his travels in Central and South America. This was published in twenty volumes, of which the first fourteen were devoted to botany, five were concerned with physical geography, geognosy and astronomy and one to the geography of plants. Strictly speaking this had no connection with the Society of Arcueil, although Humboldt made full use of his contact with members of the Arcueil circle, notably Laplace, Biot and Gay-Lussac, to develop the observations which he had accumulated.

Finally as an example of original research published in book form, there was the *Recherches physico-chimiques* of Gay-Lussac and Thenard. It is not unlikely that these two volumes published in 1811 were intended for submission for the next of Napoleon's *prix décennaux*. In 1810 the jury appointed to judge scientific books had commented that Gay-Lussac's experiments were all published in the periodical literature and not being in a separate publication did not come within their terms of reference.[1] The *Recherches physico-chimiques* was an edited version of memoirs which the authors had read earlier at meetings of the First Class. The book was divided into four parts, the first of which was concerned with the investigation of the effects of the electric pile. Part Two dealt with potassium and sodium and Part Three with hydrofluoric acid, chlorine, etc. The final part of the book contains the authors' important contribution to the quantitative analysis of organic compounds.

Among the books associated with the Society of Arcueil we must not neglect to mention the French translation of Thomas Thomson's *System of Chemistry*. A letter written in December 1809 by Faujas de St Fond in Paris to Banks in London announced that Berthollet was about to publish a new 'chemical philosophy' which was said to be greatly superior to that of Fourcroy.[2] This was in fact the French translation of the third edition of Thomson's *System of Chemistry*. This *Système de chimie* appeared in a translation by Riffault in nine volumes. Each

[1] *Rapports et Discussions . . . sur les ouvrages admis au Concours pour les Prix décennaux*, 1810, p. 15.
[2] British Museum Add. MS. no. 8100, pp. 54–5.

volume carried on its title page the information that this work
was preceded by an introduction written by Berthollet. This
occupies 170 pages and provides an interesting summary of
contemporary chemistry. Not the least interesting feature is
Berthollet's strictures on Dalton's atomic theory which he described as not only 'speculative' but 'seductive'.[1] It had been
Berthollet who had recommended the publication of a French
edition of this work and he had taken an active part in its production, ensuring that the translator had each of the English
volumes straight from the printers and also undertaking to
revise the translation if necessary. Thomson's *Système de chimie*
was often referred to by the Arcueil chemists as an authoritative
work as indeed it was. It was, however, largely superseded within
a few years by Thenard's text-book of chemistry.

The younger members of the Arcueil circle made a major
contribution to the writing of scientific text-books, some of
which continued in use up to the middle of the nineteenth century. In this respect the most indefatigable of the authors was
Biot. His *Traité analytique des courbes et des surfaces du second degré*
first appeared in 1802. It was obviously considered to be a
standard mathematical treatise since it went through eight
editions, the last being in 1834. An English translation designed
for use in colleges in the United States appeared in 1840.
Under the influence of Laplace, Biot published his *Traité
élémentaire d'astronomie physique*, which first appeared in two
volumes in 1805. By the time it had reached its third edition
(1844–7) it had been expanded to four volumes. Under the
stimulus of the Arcueil circle Biot turned from pure mathematics and astronomy to experimental science. His *Traité de
physique*, published in four volumes in 1816, has already been
mentioned. It was soon followed by a *Précis élémentaire de physique
expérimentale* (2 vols, 1817; 3rd edn, 1824). It says much for Biot
as an author that several parts of his books were translated into
English and published separately in the 1820's.

Gay-Lussac also appears as the author of text-books, albeit
unwillingly. The *Leçons de physique* and *Cours de chimie* published
under his name in 1828 were pirated editions based on his lectures. The standard text-book of chemistry in France for nearly
a quarter of a century was Thenard's *Traité de chimie élémen-*

[1] *Op. cit.*, see especially pp. 20–1, 25, 27.

taire. This first appeared in four volumes in 1813–16 at the rate of one per year. Twenty years later it had reached a sixth edition. Thenard's book appeared in German, Italian and Spanish translations.

As if to provide evidence of the universality of interest and competence within the whole range of the sciences, the list of achievements of the Arcueil group does not end with mathematics, astronomy, physics and chemistry. Not only is there Poisson's *Traité de mécanique* (2 vols., 1811) based on his course of lectures at the *École Polytechnique,* but also Candolle's *Traité élémentaire de la botanique,* which first appeared in 1813; a third edition came out in 1844. Candolle's book contains his famous doctrine of symmetry and his natural classification based on the relative number and position of the floral organs, a classification which he developed in later works and which acquired considerable repute.

Finally there were the popularizations. If any major scientific work of the period required an explanatory commentary it was surely Laplace's *Mécanique céleste.* Biot brought out in 1801 his *Analyse du 'Traité de mécanique céleste',* which in a way marked a stage in his apprenticeship to Laplace. Biot also wrote a short history of science since the time of the Revolution, which was published in 1803. Arago had been giving public lectures at the Observatory since 1813. Yet his *Astronomie populaire* was only published posthumously in 1854–7. Like several other of the works listed above it was translated into English. Finally there were Humboldt's popularizations by which he sought to interest the educated classes in scientific investigations by depicting the wonders of nature encountered in his travels. His *Aspects of Nature* and *Cosmos* fired the imagination of many a young man but, as the connection of these books with the activities of the Society of Arcueil is remote, they will not be insisted upon here.

Rivalry and Enmity within the Society

The members of the Arcueil group collaborated with each other and with other scientific colleagues with general harmony over several decades. Within the Society of Arcueil there was, however, one particular note of discord which, if it did not strike as harshly as the famous acrimonious dispute between

Newton and Hooke in the Royal Society, was, like the earlier instance, inspired by rivalry. In its logical conclusion after the dissolution of the Society of Arcueil the dispute was to herald a new era in the history of physics. It seems that Biot had the occasional habit of claiming the works of others as his own or at least in omitting to acknowledge his full indebtedness to others. As more than once the other person involved was the excitable young Arago, the matter was never passed over quietly. The comment of Goethe[1] seems appropriate:

> Questions of science are very often career questions. A single discovery may make a man famous and lay the foundations of his worldly fortunes . . . Every newly observed phenomenon is a discovery. Touch a man's property and his passions are immediately aroused.

For all the co-operative effort at Arcueil, the young ambitious man of science was eager to grasp for himself the prizes to be won at the frontiers of knowledge.

The first incident was trivial enough. On 25 January 1805 Arago was nominated secretary of the Observatory. The very next day Biot asked him to collaborate in an extensive piece of research on the refractive indices of gases. When this was eventually completed it was presented to the First Class in March 1806. Naturally it was Biot who read the memoir, because he was not only the senior partner but also a member of the First Class. The memoir was presented as their joint work but Biot tried to have it published under his name only with, however, reference to help from Arago.[2] The latter was furious, and when he told his story to his friends Poisson and Thenard, they advised him to moderate the language of his original letter of protest. His remonstrance had the desired effect and when the paper appeared in the *Mémoires* of the First Class later that year the authors were given as Biot and Arago. At the very outset of his career to be nearly robbed of his claim to joint authorship of his first scientific memoir left an unfortunate impression with Arago. Nevertheless, the dispute did not prevent a further collaboration between Biot and Arago on the measurement of the arc of the meridian in Spain in 1806–8.

---

[1] Eckermann, *Gespräche mit Goethe*, 30 December 1823.
[2] Arago, *Oeuvres, Mémoires Scientifiques*, vol. ii, pp. 702–3.

Another dispute arose in the full publicity of a meeting of the First Class on 11 March 1811, when Malus read a memoir in which he announced that, following his previous discovery of polarization by reflection, he had found that when light is incident on a plane of glass at an angle of 35° 25′ the refracted ray is also partly polarized.[1] Biot then rose to claim that he had made a similar discovery and had in fact come to the meeting with a memoir containing a description of the relevant experiments. Humboldt says[2] that Biot only knew about polarization by refraction because Malus had previously described his discovery to Laplace in the presence of Biot. Laplace, realizing the source of Biot's knowledge, was indignant at this blatant dishonesty and saw to it that an acknowledgement of Malus' priority was made.[3]

Such a context helps us to understand the circumstances of Arago's first individual memoir read to the Institute in August 1811. Arago stated that he had decided to publish the first part of his researches instead of waiting until they were complete because 'several people had recently undertaken the same research'. This was a clear reference to Biot, but perhaps Malus was also included. A further dispute arose at a meeting of the First Class on 30 March 1812 when Biot read a memoir on certain phenomena connected with polarization. Arago immediately stood up and told the assembly that he had previously made some of the same observations and as confirmation of his claim he invited representatives of the First Class to inspect his laboratory records at the Observatory.[4] This was done immediately after the meeting adjourned and Arago's claim was completely vindicated.

The use of the signature of one of the secretaries of the First Class as a guarantee of the priority of a piece of research was a procedure usually reserved for major discoveries, although Lavoisier in his time had made quite frequent use of this facility. In 1812, however, Biot suggested that Arago, who

---

[1] *Mém. Inst.*, 1810, Part 2 (1814), 105–11.
[2] Letter from Humboldt to Pictet, Paris, 17 April 1811 (*Mémoires de la Société de Géographie de Genève*, vii (1868), 194–5).
[3] *Nouveau Bulletin des Sciences par la Société Philomatique*, ii (No. 42, March 1811), 252.
[4] *P.V. Inst.*, vol. v, p. 41.

appeared to him unduly sensitive about questions of priority, should have the date of his work verified officially:

> When I wished to study [polarization] I invited M. Arago in the presence of the *Bureau des Longitudes* to have his memoirs initialled by the permanent secretaries of the Institute in order to decide definitely what facts or theories he had discovered at that time. This request seemed no more than just and M. Arago himself appeared to accept it; but since then he has neglected to follow this formality.[1]

On 21 June 1813 the First Class met in secret session to hear Arago's protest at a note inserted by Biot at the beginning of one of his publications,[2] which had just appeared in the *Mémoires* of the First Class. Biot was absent and the dispute was settled not at the Institute but at Arcueil on the following Sunday when the following letter[3] was drawn up in time for the next meeting of the First Class:

> The note which was inserted at the foot of the first page of my memoir having given rise to a protest by M. Arago, we have both agreed to suppress both the note and the protest, so that no trace of them should remain in the *Mémoires*.
> Consequently we beg the members of the Class to return to the secretary the volumes which have been distributed to them in order that a page may be substituted in which this note is omitted.
> At Arcueil 27 June 1813.
>
> (Signed) Arago and Biot.

It is because of this action that copies of the *Mémoires* of the First Class which we have consulted give no indication of this particular dispute.

The incidents mentioned above relate to the period of functioning of the Society of Arcueil. They may suggest a fundamental split in the group, but it would probably put the matter in better perspective to see in these disputes a deeply felt rivalry among colleagues. This rivalry, which provided a stimulus both to research and publication, was one of the features of the Society of Arcueil and it is significant that both Arago and Biot presented memoirs at meetings of the Society in the years 1811–13.

[1] Arago, *Oeuvres*, *Tables*, p. clv.   [2] *Mém. Inst.*, 1811, Part 1, 135.
[3] *P.V. Inst.*, vol. v, p. 224.

A further trivial incident adds to the evidence that Biot was largely at fault. At the end of March 1821 Ampère heard by chance that Biot was preparing to read a memoir at the Institute describing recent progress in electromagnetism but minimizing the part of Ampère and Arago.[1] Ampère decided to correct this by reading a summary of the work of Arago and himself at the same meeting. There is a touch of irony in the protest made by Biot that he had had no notice of this memoir.

Although Biot and Arago often found themselves in a position of rivalry, which was due to differences of temperament, differences in the scientific theories they upheld and even to differences in politics, they did not spend their entire lives at loggerheads. In 1817 a reconciliation of the two men was effected through their wives, but unfortunately the election of a secretary of the *Académie des Sciences* in 1822 reopened the old wounds and a final reconciliation had to wait until 1840.

[1] L. de Launay, *Le grand Ampère*, 1925, p. 200.

CHAPTER SEVEN

The 'Mémoires' of the Society of Arcueil

Introduction

TO SPEAK of the 'Arcueil memoirs' is rather ambiguous. This phrase might refer to memoirs which were given a formal reading at Arcueil; but most of these have already been mentioned in the previous chapter. Alternatively the reference might be to memoirs, the contents of which were discussed at Arcueil before formal presentation elsewhere, notably at the Institute. Unfortunately we shall never know exactly how many fall into this category. Again, there were the memoirs presented to the Institute, but based on experimental work done at Arcueil. Finally there is the definite class of memoirs written by members of the Society which were published in the three volumes of *Mémoires* of the Society of Arcueil. It is with this publication that we shall be concerned in the present chapter.

The three volumes entitled *Mémoires de Physique et de Chimie de la Société d'Arcueil* were published in 1807, 1809 and 1817 respectively. The *Mémoires* were intended to be no more than an occasional series and although the delay in publication of the third volume may suggest a decline, we do not find, as with some new journals, a falling away of the quantity or quality of the material. As regards size, the first volume had rather less than four hundred octavo pages, the second volume nearly five hundred and the third volume more than six hundred. The balance of the memoirs, which were supposed to be both physical and chemical, also improved. The first volume was rather dominated by a succession of memoirs on organic chemistry by Thenard and chemical topics occupied nearly three-quarters of the total bulk. Notable physical topics were a memoir by Gay-Lussac and Humboldt on the earth's magnetism, and Gay-Lussac's important work on the heat changes which take place in the expansion of gases.

In the second volume there were a number of interesting

memoirs on all branches of chemistry, but there were also three memoirs on light as a witness of the stimulus to the Arcueil group of Malus' discovery of polarization by reflection. Heat and sound were also represented and there were memoirs on respiration, of both animals and fish. Light featured even more prominently in the third volume with six different papers, of which three were by Biot and the others by Malus, Bérard and Arago respectively. As if to illustrate the range of interests of the members of the Arcueil group, this volume also contained significant contributions to such apparently diverse fields as physical geography and botany.

The Delay in Publication of Volume Three

The third volume of the Arcueil *Mémoires* was due to be published in 1811. This at least was the intention of the Society in February of that year.[1] But the recent death by suicide of his only son weighed too heavily on Berthollet's mind, and in his despair he did not pursue the editorial task of bringing out a further volume. Yet Berthollet found some slight consolation in his return to scientific studies and there is a record of a further meeting of the Society of Arcueil on 3 November of that year. The Society revived in 1812 and 1813 and in the latter year pages were made ready for the press. Indeed the number of the *Annales de chimie* which appeared in September 1813 included a paper by Gay-Lussac which was said to be 'taken from Volume III of the *Mémoires* of Arcueil (October 1813)'.[2] There is in fact in the Bibliothèque nationale in Paris a copy of volume three of the Arcueil *Mémoires* which is identical with other copies in all respects except the title page, which bears the date 1813. By mistake this title page was used when the *Mémoires* were published in 1817. It provides further evidence that volume three was actually in the press in 1813 when bankruptcy prevented the completion of the publication.

The year 1813 was a year of crisis for the Napoleonic regime. Yet one might think that the military crisis of the period, when Napoleon was trying to keep back the allies against increasing odds, need not have affected the publication of a scientific

[1] *Ann. chim.*, lxxvii (1811), 134n.
[2] *Ibid.*, lxxxvii (1813), 225.

journal. If the primary cause was the bankruptcy of the publisher Klostermann, this was followed in 1814 by the arrival of
the allies in Paris. During their advance some of the printed
sheets intended for volume three were burned. After the political upheavals of 1815 Berthollet took some time to adjust
himself to the new scene. There was therefore a further delay
before he resumed his active interest in the publication of the
work of the Arcueil group and it was not until 1817 that volume
three finally appeared. A special case where publication was
urgent was Dulong's memoir on 'a new detonating substance'
(nitrogen trichloride). This was read at a meeting of the First
Class on 7 January 1813 and an extract was immediately published in the *Annales de chimie*.[1] Four years later when it appeared
in the third volume of the *Mémoires* of Arcueil, Dulong inserted a
foot-note, excusing his 'betrayal' by previous publications on
the grounds of the dangerous nature of his discovery.

Again in the summer of 1816 the third volume was said to be
going to appear without delay.[2] In fact Berthollet wrote a note
dated 20 May 1816[3] on the reactions of insoluble salts, which was
a reply to a misunderstanding by the English chemist Richard
Phillips of his principle of the effect of mass on chemical
reactions. In view of the imminent publication, Berthollet wrote
another note dated 10 April 1816[4] to serve as a postscript to a
previous memoir of his printed earlier in the same volume.[5] In
the first memoir, read at the Institute in March 1811, he had
discussed the composition of 'oxymuriatic acid', considering it
as a compound body. He was now prepared to admit his mistake and he divulged that it was his intervention which had prevented Gay-Lussac from publishing this as an established fact
in 1809.

When the volume finally appeared in 1817, Berthollet
pointed out in the preface that this delay had had the one advantage that it had enabled him to include Humboldt's memoir
on isothermals. Humboldt had read this in four parts on successive Mondays at the *Académie des Sciences* from 26 May to 16
June 1817. At the very next meeting on 23 June the *Académie*
acknowledged receipt of the third volume of the *Mémoires* of

[1] *Ann. chim.*, lxxxvi (1813), 37–43.
[2] *Ann. chim. phys.*, ii (1816), 141n.   [3] *M.S.A.*, iii, 453–61.
[4] *Ibid.*, 603–11.   [5] *Ibid.*, 171–9.

Arcueil containing the full text of 140 pages of Humboldt's memoir. It was in every way a 'scoop' for Arcueil. The *Annales de chimie et de physique*, despite its sympathies, was only able to give ten pages to a summary of the paper and one British journal had to present it split into five sections.[1] The printing of the third volume was poor and shows every sign of hasty publication without proper proof-reading. There are mistakes in the pagination and a large number of printing errors, although many of these are corrected in two Errata sheets bound at the end of the volume. It is clear that by 1817 Arcueil as a Society was no more. The Society had done its work. . . .

A word must be said about the provenance of the contents of the three volumes. In volumes one and three a fair number of memoirs are presented as having been read at Arcueil at specific meetings of the Society. The second volume, however, published in the summer of 1809, came after the comparative passivity at Arcueil in 1808. Yet if the meetings at Arcueil in 1808 were neither so frequent nor so fruitful as in 1807, it was because the members of the Society were active elsewhere. The publication of the second volume of the Arcueil *Mémoires* is a witness to the contributions to science of the members of the Society, even if the work had been presented on the national stage of the Institute rather than informally at Arcueil. Rather more than half the memoirs had been read at the Institute. These include Laplace's memoir on the theory of light, which was later published in the *Mémoires* of the First Class. The memoirs by Descotils and Provençal and Humboldt were also published elsewhere *after* they had appeared in the Arcueil collection. Of the eighteen full memoirs, those by Berthollet (two), Candolle, Descotils and Malus appear to have been written specially for publication in the Arcueil *Mémoires*. The last part of the volume also contained a miscellaneous collection of notes written mainly by Berthollet but also by Biot and Thenard and these belong exclusively to this collection.

To sum up we may say that the *Mémoires* of Arcueil represent a genuine collection of the scientific work of the men who belonged to the Society. The Arcueil journal provided a means of publication to circumvent the inefficient machinery of the Institute.

[1] *Edinburgh Philosophical Journal*, iii (1820)–v (1821).

As an alternative to the method of summarizing the contents
of the *Mémoires* volume by volume in the order in which they
were printed, it may be preferable to consider the *Mémoires* as a
whole, treating the contents subject by subject. In this way it
may be easier to assess the contribution of these three volumes to
early nineteenth-century science. We shall accordingly begin
with a survey of the memoirs on physical subjects, properties of
matter, magnetism, heat, sound and light before considering
the chemical work. Finally there are a number of papers on
other sciences which deserve to be mentioned. Where possible,
the various memoirs by one author are discussed together and
throughout some attempt has been made at a chronological
sequence.

The Free Expansion of Gases

In September 1806 Gay-Lussac read his historic memoir on the
temperature changes undergone by gases when compressed or
allowed to expand. Gay-Lussac had become interested in the
specific heats of gases in the course of his experiments with
Humboldt on the combining volumes of hydrogen and oxygen.
It had occurred to Gay-Lussac as a rather obscure deduction
from his experiments, that all gases might have the same capacity for heat. This was one of the generalizations which inspired
Gay-Lussac's early scientific work. Yet he was not able to put it
to the test immediately, owing to his travels through Europe
with Humboldt. Returning to Paris in the spring of 1806, he
says he was impatient to begin experiments to test his conjectures:

> I communicated my plan to M. Berthollet, who encouraged me
> to carry it out and he himself together with M. Laplace has taken
> the greatest interest in it. If it is flattering for me to be able to cite
> these two illustrious scientists, who honour me by their esteem,
> I must at the same time state that I owe much to their enlightened
> advice. It was at Arcueil in the physics laboratory of M. Berthollet
> that my experiments were performed. As regards the heat capacity
> of gases, my experiments have led me to unexpected results, con-
> trary to those which I had anticipated, and they have revealed
> to me several new phenomena which seem to be very important
> for the theory of heat.[1]

[1] *M.S.A.*, i (1807), 182.

Starting from the premises that all gases expand equally when heated and that their volumes are inversely proportional to their pressures, he set up the following apparatus in which differences of change of temperature would be attributable to differences in the values of the specific heats of the gases under test.

He took two flasks, each of 12 litres capacity and each with a double neck. To one neck a tap was fitted and to the other a sensitive alcohol thermometer. Each flask contained anhydrous calcium chloride to absorb all moisture. One of the flasks was then evacuated and the other filled with the gas under test. The flasks were then connected with a lead pipe, the taps opened and the readings of the thermometers carefully noted. It was known that compression of gases was accompanied by evolution of heat and expansion by absorption of heat. Gay-Lussac, however, wished to discover the relationship between heat absorbed and heat evolved in his two flasks. From his experiments he concluded that these were equal within the limits of experimental error. The change of temperature was, moreover, directly proportional to the change of pressure. This he found by connecting the flasks, equalizing the pressures by opening the tap (i.e. reducing the pressure to half, since the volumes were equal) then evacuating the second flask and repeating until the temperature change was so slight as to make accurate measurement impossible. For hydrogen, the difference of temperature was much greater than that for air, an effect which was explained by the rates of effusion being inversely proportional to the square root of the densities of the gases. Even when allowance was made for this by altering the orifice by means of a regulating device constructed by Fortin, the temperature difference was still greater for hydrogen than for air. Yet it was greater for air than for oxygen and greater for oxygen than for carbon dioxide, the time of effusion in all cases being made the same by regulating the size of the orifice. Obviously the specific heats of the gases were by no means equal as Gay-Lussac had originally conjectured. From his experiments he concluded that their specific heats were in some way inversely proportional to their densities. He emphasized that this conclusion was a provisional one and he was hoping to develop his experiments later.

Gay-Lussac's experiment with two connecting vessels was repeated nearly forty years later by Joule,[1] who apparently knew nothing of Gay-Lussac's work, although he was glad to note that his results agreed with

> the discovery of Dulong that equal volumes of all elastic fluids taken at the same temperature and under the same pressure, when suddenly compressed or dilated to the same fraction of their volume, disengage or absorb the same absolute quantity of heat.

Joule gave the reference to Dulong's memoir on the specific heats of gases, published in the *Annales de chimie et de physique*,[2] in which Dulong, not unnaturally, referred to Gay-Lussac's work of 1807. It therefore seems that, although Joule was working in complete ignorance of Gay-Lussac's earlier achievement, had he pursued the sources one stage further he would have found that in one aspect of his crucial work on heat he had been anticipated by Gay-Lussac.

The Polarization of Light

One of the claims to fame of the Arcueil *Mémoires* must be that it published Malus' memoir[3] describing a new property of reflected light, which he later called polarization. In 1807 Malus had already read two memoirs on optics at the Institute. It was probably the second of these memoirs which decided a commission of the First Class to select double refraction in crystals as the subject of the next prize in mathematics. Contestants were required to submit a mathematical theory but it was stipulated that the theory had to be confirmed by experiment. This explains why Malus happened to be turning over a crystal of calcite in his hand during his stay in Paris in the autumn of 1808. The story of how the discovery of polarization took place was first described by Biot.[4] It was repeated by Arago and it is Arago's description which is given here:

> One day, in his house in the Rue d'Enfer, Malus happened to examine, through a doubly refracting crystal, the rays of the sun

[1] *Phil. Mag.*, [3], xxvi (1845), 369; Joule, *Scientific Papers*, London, 1884, 172–89.
[2] *Op. cit.*, xli (1829), 113–59; see especially pp. 156, 121n.
[3] *M.S.A.*, ii (1809), 143–58.
[4] *Biographie universelle*, 1820. Biot, *Mélanges*, vol. iii, p. 112.

reflected by the glass panes of the windows of the Luxembourg Palace. Instead of the two bright images which he expected to see, he perceived only one, the ordinary or the extraordinary, according to the position which the crystal occupied before his eye. This singular phenomenon greatly impressed him: he tried to explain it by supposing some particular modifications which the solar light might undergo in traversing the atmosphere. But when night came, he caused the light of a taper to fall on the surface of water at an angle of 36°, and found, by the test of a doubly refracting crystal, that the light reflected from the water was also polarized, just as if it had emerged from a crystal of calcite.[1]

Malus did not wait for the closing date of the prize of the Institute to communicate his discovery. He read an account of it at the meeting of 12 December 1808, but there was no question of this being published in the *Mémoires* of the First Class, since he was not a member. Malus had discovered that reflected light could, under certain circumstances, behave exactly like one of the rays of light emerging from a doubly-refracting crystal, or, as Malus expressed it in the language of Newtonian mechanics:

> The cause of this partial reflection, which has hitherto escaped the researches of natural philosophers, seems in several circumstances to have some analogy with the forces that produce double refraction.

In his memoir Malus described this 'new property of reflected light'. He had investigated the phenomenon with a variety of substances and in each case noted the polarizing angle. He had studied the effect of reflection from transparent bodies such as water and glass and also from opaque polished bodies including marble and ebony. If received by reflection at an angle rather less or greater than the polarizing angle, the light was found to be more or less modified as it would be emerging from two crystals of calcite, the axes of which were not exactly parallel or perpendicular. The polarizing angle (90° minus the angle quoted by Arago) for water was found by Malus to be 52° 45′. For glass it was 56° 30′.

Malus found that he could use his discovery to obtain a ray

---

[1] Arago, *Notices Biographiques*, trans.: *Biographies of Distinguished Scientific Men*, London, 1857, p. 387.

of light not subject to the usual partial reflection which occurs when light is incident on a transparent substance. He suggested that this should be used to obtain an accurate measurement of the quantity of light absorbed by transparent substances, a datum almost impossible to obtain previously because of partial reflection.

In a second memoir published in the 1809 volume of the Arcueil *Mémoires*,[1] Malus described further experiments he had carried out and considered their implications for optical theory. He had found that light polarized by reflection at a mirror behaved on further reflection differently from ordinary light reflected at the same angle of incidence. Whereas the intensity of ordinary light on reflection *increases* with increasing angle of incidence, that of light reflected at a second mirror after polarization at a first with its plane of incidence perpendicular to that of the second, *decreases* with increasing angle of incidence at the second mirror, giving a minimum intensity at the polarizing angle before increasing again. The interesting thing about this experiment was that whereas most optical phenomena could be explained either on Newton's corpuscular theory of light or on Huygens' wave theory, these experiments could *not* be explained by the wave theory, according to Malus, since they showed,

> not only that light is a substance obedient to the forces that set other bodies in action, but also that the form and arrangement of its particles have great influence on the phenomena.

To explain the results of his experiments, Malus supposed each particle of light to have three axes mutually at right angles. The intensity of the reflected light would then depend on the relation between these axes and the planes of the mirrors. Malus elaborated this theory to arrive at the law that if light is reflected at the polarizing angle successively from two mirrors with the planes of incidence inclined at an angle α, the intensity of the final reflected light is to that of the incident light as $\cos^2\alpha : 1$. An interesting aspect of this law is that it holds equally for two crystals of calcite, the planes of which are inclined at an angle α. Malus' theory had the merit of connecting a series of phenomena previously unrelated. He concluded his memoir:

[1] *M.S.A.*, ii (1809), 254–67; trans. Nicholson's *Journal*, xxx (1812), 161–8.

I do not pretend to point out the cause of this general property of the repulsive powers that act on light; I merely exhibit the means of connecting the phenomena with each other, of ascertaining them beforehand by calculation, and of measuring them with accuracy; at the same time in referring the figures of the luminous particles to three rectangular axes, as those of an octahedron would be, I anticipate nothing respecting the real figure of these particles; but I present the result as a consequence of the calculation to which I have been led by the analysis of the phenomena that I have observed.

Malus' memoir was entitled 'On a property of the repulsive forces which act on light' and in it he was concerned to explain polarization in terms of the forces acting on particles. To understand the background to this memoir, it is necessary to turn to another contribution published in the same volume of the Arcueil *Mémoires*, the memoir by Laplace 'On the movement of light in transparent media'.[1] This was read at a meeting of the Institute in January 1808 and published by the Society of Arcueil in 1809 and in the *Mémoires* of the First Class the following year with a long technical appendix.

Laplace mentioned that Wollaston in England and Malus in France had confirmed the application of Huygens' wave theory to doubly-refracting substances. Yet the intensity of the ordinary and the extraordinary rays emerging from such a substance presented an anomaly that was inexplicable by Hugyens' theory. Laplace remarked that it would be a matter of considerable interest to discover the law governing the intensity of these rays of light. Also:

> It would be very interesting to relate Huygens' law to attractive and repulsive forces, as Newton did with regard to the law of ordinary refraction; indeed it is very probable that it depends on similar forces.

The remainder of Laplace's memoir is concerned with deriving a mathematical theory to express this idea, based on the principle of least action. According to this principle, a particle of light in its passage between two given points, one outside and one inside the crystal, must describe such a path that the distance traced before it enters the crystal multiplied by its velocity, and the distance traced after its entrance multiplied by the

---

[1] *M.S.A.*, ii (1809), 111–42.

corresponding velocity, should together give a sum which is a *minimum*. Laplace hence derived two differential equations in which the internal velocity was an indeterminate function of the angle which the refracted ray made with the shorter axis of the rhomboid crystal. He then examined two cases in which these equations were modified. Laplace's mathematical analysis occupies about a dozen pages of the memoir.

This memoir by Laplace has a very obvious connection with Malus' work. Laplace made several references to the numerous experiments which Malus had carried out on doubly refracting crystals, but more important still in the connection with Malus' future work. Once Malus had discovered that polarization was a general property of light, not confined to light passing through a few crystalline substances, he was able to pursue his investigations along the lines clearly suggested by Laplace. In particular he analysed the phenomenon of polarization in terms of forces acting on particles and, stimulated by Laplace's suggestion, he formulated the law describing the intensity of light polarized by reflection. It is not merely a coincidence that in the Arcueil *Mémoires* Laplace's paper is followed immediately by Malus' contribution: 'On a property of repulsive forces which act on light'.

A third memoir by Malus was only published posthumously in the Arcueil collection.[1] This was a description of a goniometer, an instrument for measuring with great accuracy the angles of crystals and the angles of refraction of light passing through crystals. Malus' instrument had been constructed in 1810 independently of a goniometer made by Wollaston the previous year.[2] Previously the angles of crystals had been measured by reflection of light from two faces. The angles were measured with a graduated circular scale not connected in any way with the crystal, so that after taking readings they had to be repeated to check that the crystal had not moved. The goniometer enabled the angle to be read off more quickly and accurately. Malus' goniometer, constructed by Fortin, was not as simple as Wollaston's but Malus claimed that his instrument was better adapted for dealing with very small crystals; also it was capable of much finer measurement and more general application. Malus presented his instrument as a contribution to

[1] *M.S.A.*, iii (1817), 122–31.   [2] *Phil. Trans.*, 1809, 253–8.

greater precision in crystallography. This was very much needed at this time, as the current theory of Haüy was tenable only so long as there was uncertainty about the precise angles of crystals.[1] Malus concluded his memoir with data he had obtained by it for the elements of barium sulphate and calcium carbonate. His value of 105° 5′ for calcite was conceded by Wollaston to be more accurate than his own estimate of 105°.[2]

Sound

The second volume of the Arcueil *Mémoires* contains two papers by Biot on sound. It will be remembered that in 1801–2, at the request of Laplace, he had undertaken some research on the velocity of sound. In 1807 he took up further work on sound, extending his investigations to the transmission of sound in vapours.[3] According to theoretical considerations it might seem that sound should not travel at all through vapours. For the vibration of a sonorous body would cause condensation of vapour to liquid on one side when there was compression, and on the other side rarefaction would cause the formation of an additional amount of vapour. These condensations and rarefactions would take place in the immediate vicinity of the vibrating body but would not be produced beyond it. If, however, the compression of vapour produced a certain finite quantity of heat, the heat evolved would increase the elasticity and the compressed vapour would remain a vapour; similarly rarefaction would cause a decrease in elasticity and the situation in vapours would be completely analogous to that in permanent gases. An investigation of the transmission of sound in vapours would therefore decide the question whether heat is really evolved by the emission of sound in a vapour:

> Thus we may subject to decisive proof the ingenious idea of M. Laplace, by which he has found means of reconciling the mathematical theory of transmission of sound in air with the results of experience, taking into account the heat evolved; for if

---

[1] I am indebted to Dr D. Goodman for this point.
[2] *Phil. Trans.*, 1812, 161.
[3] *M.S.A.*, ii (1809), 94–103; trans. Nicholson's *Journal*, xxx (1812), 169–73.

the effect he supposes does not take place, the vibrations of sonorous bodies in vapour should not produce any sound; and if they do produce sound, it can be only in consequence of the evolution of heat.

Induced by these motives, I made some experiments on the subject, which completely succeeded. I then repeated them in a more perfect manner in the physical laboratory at Arcueil, with my friend, Amédée Berthollet. M. Berthollet and M. Laplace were present at these experiments, and themselves verified the facts I am going to relate.

The experiments were carried out with a bell suspended in a glass globe of 36 litres capacity. When the globe was evacuated, no sound could be heard, but when water vapour (but not air) was introduced, the sound became perceptible and even quite loud when the quantity of vapour was increased by heating. When the experiment was repeated with alcohol vapour, which has a greater density than water vapour, the sound was much clearer, so that 'it was heard from one extremity to the other of the rooms that form the physical laboratory [at Arcueil]'.

Thus, even though it was impossible to measure the tiny momentary heat changes involved in the transmission of sound in vapours, Biot was able to demonstrate that they existed. This memoir was probably in the fullest sense a memoir of the Society of Arcueil since a meeting was held on 9 October,[1] the Friday before the memoir was presented at the Institute. Considering the contents of Biot's memoir, it is most unlikely that he did not first favour his colleagues at Arcueil with it. Soon after presenting this memoir at the Institute, Biot left Paris to return to the Balearic islands and he was therefore unable to do any further work on sound until the next year.

Biot's second memoir on sound was one he had read at a meeting of the First Class in November 1808. It was entitled, 'Experiments on the transmission of sound through solid bodies, and through air in very long tubes'.[2] Chladni's visit to Paris and the fact that much tunnelling was going on round Paris for the construction of aqueducts and conduits gave Biot incentives to carry out experiments on the transmission of sound through

[1] Royal Society, *Blagden Letters*, B.129.
[2] *M.S.A.*, ii (1809), 405–23; trans. Nicholson's *Journal*, xxx (1812), 103–13.

these pipes. Biot was helped by Bouvard, his colleague at the Observatory, and Malus too participated in many experiments. They compared the time taken for sound to travel along a series of cast iron pipes varying in length from about 200 metres to 1,000 metres. One experimenter would strike the pipe with a hammer when the second hand of his watch was exactly on $0''$ or $30''$ and the other would record the reading of the second hand of his watch when the sound reached him (a) through the pipe, (b) through the air. Biot concluded that the velocity of sound is about 10·5 times as great in iron as in air.

Magnetism

It was perhaps appropriate that the first volume of Arcueil *Mémoires* should open with the joint paper by Humboldt and Gay-Lussac on terrestrial magnetism.[1] Not only did it precede many of the other memoirs in time, having been read at the Institute on 8 September 1806, but it showed clearly the intention of the Society to take physics seriously as well as chemistry. The memoir was an example of collaboration between two men who had been associated with Arcueil for several years.

Humboldt's interest in terrestrial magnetism was, of course, connected with his voyages of exploration. A few not very systematic observations made during his American travels could now be supplemented by a regular series of readings of the magnetic elements in western Europe. The journey planned by Humboldt was to take him through France to Italy, where he would see his brother in Rome. He would then return to Prussia by way of Switzerland. Berthollet persuaded Fourcroy to release Gay-Lussac from his duties as *répétiteur* at the *École Polytechnique* so that he would be able to accompany Humboldt. A general account of the journey has already been given in Chapter Five. It remains to describe the magnetic observations made by the Prussian and his young French friend.

The compass needle used to determine the angle of dip was one which had been made for Borda by the instrument maker Lenoir and had been lent to them by the co-operation of the Minister of the Navy. Gay-Lussac and Humboldt devised a method of compensating for any inaccuracy that might arise

[1] *M.S.A.*, i (1807), 1–22.

A A

due to the possibility that the centre of gravity of the needle might be slightly off the magnetic axis. A further suggestion by Laplace on the theory of determining the angle of dip was found not to be practicable.

To obtain the magnetic intensity the period of oscillation of the magnetized needle was determined. It was suspended by a silk thread in a box to prevent disturbance from draughts. The magnetic intensity was then proportional to the square of the number of oscillations made by the needle, displaced slightly from the magnetic meridian, in a given time. In practice the mean time was recorded for sixty oscillations. Their results were recorded in a table giving the name of the place where observations were made, the latitude and longitude, the declination, the period of oscillation of the horizontal needle and the magnetic intensity calculated from it. These intensities were compared with the intensity at [a point on] the magnetic equator, which had been determined by Humboldt. From his observations it appeared that a needle that performed 245 oscillations in a given time in Paris would only make 211 in the same time on the magnetic equator.

In making the observations, they had taken note of the nature of the nearby ground in case this had any effect on the needle. Gay-Lussac had already discovered in his balloon ascent with Biot that altitude had no appreciable effect on the magnetic intensity and this was therefore not recorded. All observations were made between 15 March 1805 and 1 May 1806. They did not think that magnetic intensity in any one place changed with time since, for example, on taking readings at Milan on entering and leaving Italy at an interval of six months, they found no difference. As regards diurnal variation, a series of prolonged experiments both on Mount Cenis and in Rome had not revealed any difference at different hours of the day and night. As regards the general accuracy of their readings, it had to be admitted that many were made under conditions which were far from ideal but they estimated that the greatest discrepancy between their angular readings could not have been more than 10 minutes of arc. They had been particularly interested to discover if the Alps would have any effect on the general variation of the magnetic elements and they had not been able to discover any appreciable effect.

Their general conclusion was that the horizontal component of the Earth's magnetic intensity increased from north (Berlin) to south (Naples) but the total intensity decreased on approaching the equator. Humboldt thus confirmed in Europe what he had observed in his previous travels. Declination also varied fairly regularly. One of the difficulties of drawing exact quantitative conclusions from these observations was that they depended on an assumption about the position of the magnetic equator deduced by Biot from the previous observations by La Peyrouse and Humboldt in America.

Magnetic research did not form a major part of the activities of the Arcueil circle, although in 1809 Gay-Lussac was again taking readings of declination both at the Observatory and at Arcueil, from which he concluded that the angle of declination in Paris was decreasing at the rate of five minutes per annum.[1] In 1813 Poisson was developing the powerful theory of potential[2] and some ten years later he applied this to magnetism. The active but less mathematically-inclined Humboldt continued his interest in magnetism after his return to Prussia by founding a Magnetic Union together with Gauss and Weber. The early work of Humboldt and Gay-Lussac may look amateurish compared with the later brilliant mathematical advance made in terrestrial magnetism by Poisson, Weber and Gauss. Yet a link between all this research is to be found in the person of Humboldt.

Optics and Chemistry

The memoir on the comparison of aragonite and calcite by Thenard and Biot[3] provides a good example of the cross-fertilization which took place within the Society of Arcueil. The fact that Biot was a physicist who had begun as a mathematician and that Thenard's own work was always strictly within the field of chemistry makes this collaboration all the more striking. What is more, their work was completed at the end of the summer of 1807, the first year of the existence of the Arcueil circle as a Society.

In the first place, if there was any difference in chemical

---

[1] *P.V. Inst.*, vol. iv, p. 241 (21 August 1809).
[2] *Nouveau Bulletin de la Société Philomatique*, iii (1813), 388.
[3] *M.S.A.*, ii (1809), 176–206.

composition between rhombic aragonite (density 2·92) and hexagonal calcite (density 2·71), it must have been very slight. Thenard himself had previously proved that each contained exactly the same quantity of base. Yet none of the experiments previously carried out on these substances could be considered to have proved exhaustively that they were identical. This was now done first by chemical means. They strongly heated equal weights of the two substances and then determined the weight of a given acid required to combine with the residue. Using what we now call hydrochloric acid in the last experiment provided two solutions of calcium chloride and these specimens were shown to be identical by enclosing them in a hollow prism and determining the angle of refraction under standard conditions. The carbon dioxide evolved from each on treatment with acid was then subjected to a series of physical tests, including the refraction of light under known conditions of temperature and pressure. The mean of twenty observations was taken and the final conclusion was that aragonite and calcite were absolutely identical chemically.

Thenard and Biot determined the respective refractive indices in a laboratory at the *École de Médecine*. The mean value for aragonite was $\mu = 1·67904$ and for calcite $\mu = 1·64959$, although they admitted that these figures were not as accurate as they would have liked, owing to the impossibility of obtaining a perfect crystal of aragonite. They then calculated, following Newton, the 'refractive force' of each by dividing the refractive index by the density and obtained two values differing by 2·7 per cent. This was a disappointment to Biot in particular, since it meant that, even allowing for differences of density, the action of light was not exactly the same for two chemically identical substances. A few years were still to elapse before Biot discovered that when ordinary light failed, *polarized* light provided evidence relating to the chemical constitution of substances through which it was passed. From their work in 1807 Thenard and Biot concluded that the same chemical principles combined in the same proportions could form physically different bodies, probably because of the different arrangement of their molecules. Their investigation of calcite and aragonite constitute one of the earliest proofs of the existence of what was later called 'dimorphism'.

Further work by Malus in collaboration with Bérard at Arcueil was not completed before Malus' death and was published (with an explanation of its origins) by Bérard in the third volume of the Arcueil *Mémoires*.[1] This was a critical examination of Herschel's discovery of infra-red rays, published in 1800. There had been some dispute about the reality of these invisible rays beyond the red end of the spectrum[2] and when Malus made a heliostat[3] for Berthollet's physical laboratory, Berthollet suggested that he and Bérard should use it to confirm Herschel's work.

They suspended five thermometers in a straight line. The bulb of each thermometer was blackened and insulated from its neighbour by a small screen. The line of thermometers was placed in the spectrum of light from the sun, the heliostat (as its name implied) ensuring that the spectrum remained stationary as the sun progressively changed its position. By this means readings could be repeated any number of times without touching the prism or the thermometers, a circumstance which made for greater accuracy; it facilitated, for example, the reading of the exact distance between the red edge of the visible spectrum and the point where the maximum heating effect was obtained. They confirmed the existence of Herschel's 'invisible rays of solar heat' but they disagreed with him about the exact position of the maximum heating effect. Bérard himself showed that these invisible rays could be polarized by reflection, like visible rays. He showed, moreover, in a large number of experiments witnessed by Berthollet and Dulong, that the heat radiated from hot bodies was also subject to polarization.

In the second part of the memoir Bérard turned his attention to the invisible rays at the other end of the spectrum. Scheele had been the first to notice that violet rays of light blackened silver chloride more quickly than other rays and Wollaston had shown that the effect was more marked for rays beyond the violet. Bérard now wished to examine the effect of different parts of the spectrum on chemical reactions in general. He

---

[1] *M.S.A.*, iii (1817), 5–47.
[2] E.g. Laplace had earlier asked the First Class for confirmation of the properties which Herschel had attributed to infra-red rays (*P.V. Inst.*, vol. ii, p. 588).
[3] The construction of this instrument is described by Hachette in: *Nouveau Bulletin de la Société Philomatique*, i (1809), 390–1.

began by mixing equal volumes of hydrogen and chlorine in tiny flasks and exposing them to different rays. He found that the ultra-violet rays had the greatest effect. Exposing paper impregnated with silver chloride to the whole spectrum produced darkening from the green part of the visible spectrum, through the blue to 40 mm beyond the violet. Examining further the properties of these 'chemical rays', Bérard found that they passed through glass and could be focused by a lens and even undergo polarization by reflection.

One of the problems that continually exercised the Arcueil circle and many of their contemporaries was the precise difference between heat and light. Gay-Lussac and Thenard had produced evidence[1] that light from the sun had the same effects as heat. Bérard was able to show that the red, orange and yellow part of the spectrum which had the greatest heating effect had the least effect on blackening silver chloride. The different effects of light therefore merited further investigation.

Gay-Lussac's Law of Combining Volumes of Gases

If one had to select from the Arcueil collection two or three memoirs that had the greatest impact on the development of science in the nineteenth century, there would be little hesitation about choosing Gay-Lussac's memoir in which he announced that gases combine together in volumes which bear a simple ratio to each other. Joule later described this work as 'one of the most important discoveries ever made in physical science'.[2]

Gay-Lussac began[3] by pointing out the unique character of the gaseous state. For solids and liquids a particular increase in pressure would produce a change different in each case; it was only matter in the gaseous state that increased equally in volume for a given increase of pressure. This important law had been discovered by Gay-Lussac and one could hardly over-emphasize the importance of this success to him and the fact that it applied to gases. Gay-Lussac as a young man was inspired by the desire to discover laws of nature. Eight years later he wrote the following sentences:

---

[1] *Recherches physico-chimiques*, 1811, vol. ii, pp. 186–206.

[2] J. P. Joule, *Scientific Papers*, vol. ii, 1887, p. 11. I owe this reference to G. Talbot and A. J. Pacey.

[3] *M.S.A.*, ii (1809), 207–34; trans. A.C.R. No. 4, pp. 8–24.

I devoted myself to research on the expansion of liquids, trying to discover some law . . . Laws are necessarily derived from the observation of a large number of facts; but *if one were not animated with the desire to discover laws*, they would often escape the most enlightened attention.[1]

This passionate search for laws of nature is revealed by a study of some of Gay-Lussac's earlier work. After the discovery of the equal expansion of gases in 1802, there was the balloon ascent of 1804, in which he had tried to derive a law relating temperature and altitude. Two years later he announced a generalization about the relation of the specific heats of gases to their densities and in 1808 he announced a general principle relating the weights of acid in a salt with the weight of oxygen in the corresponding metal oxide. This latter principle was sometimes called the 'law' of Gay-Lussac, although today anyone mentioning 'Gay-Lussac's law' would probably be understood to mean the law of combining volumes of gases.

Gay-Lussac did not state the law of combining volumes of gases quite as clearly as it is stated in any modern elementary text-book of chemistry. The nearest we can get to this in his own words is:

. . . gases combine in very simple proportions . . . and . . . the apparent contraction in volume which they experience on combination has also a simple relation to the volume of the gases, or at least to one of them.[2]

He gives the following examples of the simple ratios of combining volumes of gases (modern symbols are used for brevity):

Combinations	$O : H$	$= 1 : 2$
	$HCl : NH_3$	$= 1 : 1$
	$BF_3 : NH_3$	$= 1 : 1$ and $1 : 2$
	$CO_2 : NH_3$	$= 1 : 1$ and $1 : 2$
	$CO : O_2$	$= 2 : 1$
Analyses	NH_3:— $N : H$	$= 1 : 3$
	SO_3:— $SO_2 : O_2$	$= 2 : 1$
	N_2O:— $N : O$	$= 2 : 1$
	NO:— $N : O$	$= 1 : 1$
	NO_2:— $N : O$	$= 1 : 2$

---

[1] *Ann. chim. phys.*, ii (1816), 130 (my italics).
[2] A.C.R. No. 4, p. 15.

It would be tedious to reproduce Gay-Lussac's actual experimental results. We must note, however, that he inferred his law from a few fairly clear cases (particularly the first few listed above) and glossed over discrepancies in some of the others. The simple reaction between hydrogen and chlorine, which is often used today as an elementary illustration of the law, was not discovered until 1809 and is only included as a footnote in this memoir.

Gay-Lussac presented his law of combining volumes of gases as a natural consequence of his collaboration with Humboldt when they had found that 100 parts by volume of oxygen combines with almost exactly 200 parts of hydrogen. That his work of January 1805 with Humboldt led naturally to the law of combining volumes may be *logically* true but *historically* the connection is less direct. One has to explain the interval of nearly four years between obtaining the first data and the announcement of the law. It is true that immediately after presenting their work at the Institute in 1805 Gay-Lussac and Humboldt had left Paris but Gay-Lussac on his return the following year showed no interest in combining volumes of gases. On the contrary, he immediately began an investigation of the specific heats of gases, a piece of research which, he said, he was eager to begin and which was a consequence of one aspect of his joint memoir with Humboldt. Nor was the young Gay-Lussac the sort of man who would patiently collect evidence over a number of years and publish it only after the most critical examination. Moreover, the year 1808, on the last day of which he read his memoir to a meeting of the Philomatic Society, was a particularly busy one for him. It seems reasonable to conclude that something had happened earlier in 1808 which made Gay-Lussac turn his attention back to his earlier work and realize that the value he had obtained for the combining volumes of hydrogen and oxygen was more than a coincidence and was in fact only one example of a general phenomenon. The full context of Gay-Lussac's own words may provide a key to the mystery:

Suspecting, from the exact ratio of 100 of oxygen to 200 of hydrogen, which M. Humboldt and I had determined for the proportions of water, that other gases might also combine in simple ratios, I have made the following experiments. I prepared fluoboric [boron trifluoride], muriatic and carbonic gases and made them combine successively with ammonia gas. 100 parts of muriatic gas saturate precisely 100 parts of ammonia gas, and the salt which is formed from them is perfectly neutral, whether one or other of the gases is in excess. Fluoboric gas, on the contrary, unites in two proportions with ammonia gas.

The importance attached to 'fluoboric gas' in this passage is striking. In the summer of 1808 Gay-Lussac and Thenard had been investigating 'fluoric' and 'boracic' acids. The first part of their research was published in November 1808, but it was only in their paper read at the Institute on 23 January 1809 that they announced the discovery of 'fluoboric gas'. This discovery, therefore, probably took place in November or early December 1808.[1] Moreover we know that they were particularly impressed by one of the properties of this new gas, the dense fumes produced when it came into contact with the air and *they compared these fumes with the fumes produced by the reaction of muriatic acid gas and ammonia.*[2] It seems likely that Gay-Lussac, struck by the reaction of boron trifluoride with moist air, tried its reaction with other gases including ammonia. An obvious reaction for comparison would be the one which they mentioned, that between hydrochloric acid gas and ammonia. These experiments, carried out with attention to volume changes, give us the main contents of the paragraph quoted above.

One of the points of strength of the memoir was that it took data from a wide variety of reputable sources. This was no suspect generalization based on the biased experimental work of its author. On the other hand the data had not, of course, been all conveniently assembled for Gay-Lussac to publish. In many cases the analyses that had appeared in the chemical literature had only given the gravimetric composition and Gay-Lussac, taking reliable data for the density, had to convert this to a volumetric ratio. The density of muriatic acid gas (hydrogen chloride) was determined jointly by Biot and Gay-Lussac. For the densities of carbonic acid gas and ammonia Gay-Lussac used

---

[1] Since some of its reactions are described in Gay-Lussac's paper read on 31 December 1808.

[2] *Ann. chim.*, lxix (1809), 204–24; Gay-Lussac and Thenard, *Recherches physico-chimiques*, Paris, 1811, vol. ii, p. 74.

the data of Biot and Arago, and further data on nitric oxide were obtained by Bérard at Arcueil. When we add to this the data on the volumetric composition of ammonia obtained by Amédée Berthollet, Gay-Lussac's own data on the composition of sulphur dioxide published in the first volume of the Arcueil *Mémoires* and the data on the combining volumes of hydrogen and oxygen obtained by himself and Humboldt, we begin to appreciate this memoir as a by-product of Arcueil. One thing is certain—it was not the work of an individual working in isolation.

There is no doubt that the greatest influence on Gay-Lussac was that of Berthollet. This can be readily seen on reading the memoir. Before Gay-Lussac presented his data, he referred to the conflict of opinions on variable proportions and mentioned Berthollet's view that compounds were always formed in variable proportions except in special circumstances and at the end of the memoir he said:

> I shall conclude this memoir by examining whether compounds are formed in constant or variable proportions, as the experiments of which I have given an account lead me to the discussion of these two opinions.

He then presented successively the opinions of Dalton, Thomson and Wollaston on definite and multiple proportions and the opinion of Berthollet on variable proportions. He reconciled these as follows:

> We must first of all admit with M. Berthollet that chemical action is exercised indefinitely in a continuous manner between the molecules of substances, whatever their number and ratio may be, and that in general we can obtain compounds with very variable proportions. But then we must admit at the same time that—apart from insolubility, cohesion and elasticity, which tend to produce compounds in fixed proportions—chemical action is exerted more powerfully when the elements are in simple ratios or in multiple proportions among themselves, and that compounds are thus produced which separate out more easily. In this way we reconcile the two opinions, and maintain the great chemical law, that whenever two substances are in the presence of each other, they act in their sphere of activity according to their masses, and give rise in general to compounds with very variable proportions, unless these proportions are determined by special circumstances.

This is powerful support for Berthollet's opinions, but if it is remembered that these words were to be published in what was, after all, Berthollet's house journal, they might be interpreted as no more than good diplomacy. Yet Gay-Lussac's work was influenced by Berthollet in a much deeper sense than could be inferred from the above passage. This was written when all the experimental work was done. More vital is what led Gay-Lussac to carry out the experimental work in the first place. Most of the problems that led him towards his work on combining volumes of gases were problems set by Berthollet—the state of water vapour in gases, eudiometry, the theory of chemical affinity and the special case of the gaseous state and equivalent proportions.

In June 1807 Gay-Lussac had been looking for a general principle governing the 'capacity of saturation' of bodies and thought that he had found it in their specific gravities. Eighteen months later he discovered that if one considered volumes and not weights, there was a very simple relationship. In his concluding paragraph he observes:

> It is remarkable to see that ammonia gas neutralises exactly its own volume of gaseous acids; and it is probable that if all acids and alkalies were in the elastic state, they would all combine in equal volumes to produce neutral salts. The capacity of saturation of acids and alkalies measured by volume would then be the same, and this perhaps might be the true manner of determining it.

This brings us to an important difference between the ideas of Gay-Lussac and Dalton. Dalton considered that matter consisted of atoms characterized by weight. For Gay-Lussac weight or mass was not so fundamental a property as volume since volumes had led him to a regularity of nature where weights showed none:

> It is very important to observe that in considering weights there is no simple and definite relation between the elements of any one compound.

Gay-Lussac therefore tended to speak the language of volumes whereas Dalton spoke a different language. This conceptual difference had far more influence in preventing each having a proper appreciation of the other's work than their national or linguistic differences.

The Collaboration of Gay-Lussac and Thenard

One of the longest and most interesting of the chemical memoirs in the Arcueil collection is that published by Gay-Lussac and Thenard in the second volume.[1] It is, in fact, a summary of eight different memoirs, which they had presented jointly at meetings of the First Class between 7 March 1808 and 27 February 1809. These twelve months had been most fertile, and if their hard work in their Paris laboratories had led Gay-Lussac and Thenard to forsake Arcueil temporarily, they were to some extent making amends by reviewing their previous work and writing a special summary of it for the Arcueil *Mémoires*. Most of their joint work had been published at the first available opportunity in the *Annales de chimie*, but some, such as their description of the properties of potassium and sodium now appeared for the first time.

In their first memoir (read at the Institute on 7 March 1808) Gay-Lussac and Thenard announced that they had prepared potassium and sodium in *large* quantities and in a pure state by chemical means. It was in October 1807 that Davy, working at the Royal Institution in London, had isolated potassium and sodium by electrolysis of caustic potash and caustic soda respectively. A letter from Marcet, written on 23 November, made Davy's discovery known to the Arcueil circle and by 8 December Gay-Lussac and Thenard had succeeded in repeating Davy's experiments. The chief practical disadvantage of Davy's method of electrolysis was the tiny amount of metal produced. Feeling that this was unsatisfactory and inspired by the knowledge that the metals actually existed, Gay-Lussac and Thenard turned to other methods. It was not by chance that these young associates of Berthollet made use of a method based on reasoning about the variability of chemical affinity. Thinking that the action of strong heat might reverse the usual affinities of oxygen with iron and the alkali metals, they fused the alkalis with iron filings heated to a bright red heat in a bent iron gun-barrel coated outside with clay and sand. The vapour of the metal was

[1] *M.S.A.*, ii (1809), 295–358.

condensed in a receiver luted to the gun-barrel. In this way batches of about 25 grams of each metal were prepared at a comparatively low cost. Even Davy agreed[1] that from the practical point of view the chemical process for making potassium was more satisfactory than his own electrolytic process.

Although the name of Davy is generally associated with potassium and sodium and the work of Gay-Lussac and Thenard is often overlooked, the fact that the French chemists were the first to prepare reasonable quantities of the two metals had two important consequences. Gay-Lussac and Thenard were better able to determine the properties of these metals and also they were able to use them as reagents to make further discoveries.

Their second memoir was concerned with the properties of potassium. They found its specific gravity to be 0·874, whereas Davy had earlier but incorrectly given the figure as 0·6.[2] Gay-Lussac and Thenard later discovered the alloy of potassium and sodium which has the peculiar property of being a liquid at room temperature.[3] They recorded other properties of potassium, such as its violent reaction with water, and they measured the volume of hydrogen evolved, but what struck them most was the reactions between potassium and different gases, a topic not investigated by Davy. They discovered that when potassium is strongly heated in hydrogen, it combines with it to form a grey solid (potassium hydride) which is decomposed by water. They proposed the use of heated potassium as a means of performing an accurate volumetric analysis of nitrous and nitric oxides. The results obtained in this way by Gay-Lussac about the composition of nitric oxide were used by him later in the year as evidence for his law of combining volumes of gases. They found that heated potassium metal decomposed muriatic acid gas, forming muriate of potash and hydrogen. Unfortunately they were prevented from arriving at the true composition of muriatic (i.e. hydrochloric) acid by the conviction that the reaction was really due to water vapour in the gas, the presence of which had been demonstrated by Henry and Berthollet.

In a third memoir Gay-Lussac and Thenard described an experiment in which potassium was heated in dry ammonia,

[1] Nicholson's *Journal*, xxii (1809), 150.
[2] The modern value is 0·859 at 0°C.   [3] *M.S.A.*, ii (1809), 338.

forming a solid and liberating hydrogen. When this solid (KNH_2) was heated strongly, part of the original ammonia was regenerated, leaving a solid residue (K_3N). When this was treated with water more ammonia was obtained, so that the total was now equal to the original ammonia absorbed. Not realizing that some of the ammonia in the last stage came from the hydrogen in the water, they explained the excess hydrogen as having come from the potassium. Potassium, therefore, was not an element at all but a hydride. It would be profitless to discuss the details of their controversy with Davy on the composition of the alkali metals. We may note, however, that the views of Gay-Lussac and Thenard on this matter were shared by Dalton. Despite their mistaken conclusions the French chemists deserve credit for their discovery of a new class of compounds, the amides or metals.

In their next memoir Gay-Lussac and Thenard made further use of potassium as a reagent, this time to decompose 'boracic' (i.e. boric) acid. They were not, however, alone in this field, since in the early summer of 1808 Davy turned his attention to their method. In a memoir read to the Royal Society on 30 June 1808 he described in a footnote how, by igniting boracic acid and heating the product with potassium in a gold tube, he was left with a black substance.[1] He did not identify this but it was later recognized to be boron. It was not until Davy's fourth Bakerian lecture, read on 15 December 1808, that he made any claim to the discovery of a new substance.[2] The experimental work reported here shows signs of haste and the standard of his work was not as high as usual. He admitted that he had had a report that Gay-Lussac and Thenard were investigating the decomposition of boracic acid by potassium. This was in the summer of 1808 and he had no reports of their success but there is no doubt that he feared anticipation. In December 1808 Davy had prepared larger quantities of potassium by the method of Gay-Lussac and Thenard and had used this to decompose boracic acid. For the first time he was able to describe the properties of this 'peculiar inflammable substance' although he was doubtful whether it was a 'simple body'.

Gay-Lussac and Thenard's discovery of boron was first an-

[1] *Phil. Trans.*, 1808, 343n.
[2] *Ibid.*, 1809, 39–104; see especially pp. 41–2, 76, 83.

nounced in November 1808.[1] The memoir published in the Arcueil collection is a summary of two memoirs read to the First Class in June and November 1808. On 20 June they mentioned an olive-grey substance obtained by the action of potassium on fused boracic acid but it was not until 14 November that they claimed to have isolated a new element and discovered its properties. They described the preparation of boron as follows:

> To decompose boracic acid, place equal parts of the metal [potassium] and very pure vitreous boracic acid in a copper tube to which a bent glass tube is attached. Place the copper tube in a small furnace with the end of the glass tube in a flask of mercury. When the apparatus is ready, heat the copper tube gradually until it becomes faintly red; keep it in this condition for several minutes; then the operation being ended allow it to cool and take out the material. This is what is seen in this experiment:
>
> When the temperature is about 150 degrees, the mixture suddenly glows strongly, which appears in a striking manner if a glass tube is used. So much heat is produced that the glass tube melts slightly and sometimes breaks and the air is almost always driven out of the vessel with force . . . The metal [potassium] is used up decomposing part of the boracic acid; and these two substances are converted by their mutual reaction into an olive grey material which is a mixture of potassium, potassium borate and the radical of boracic acid. Extract this mixture in a tube by pouring water into it and heating slowly, and separate the boracic radical by washing with cold or hot water. That which does not dissolve is the radical itself.[2]

They proposed the name *bore* for the 'boracic radical' and noted the similarity of its properties to those of carbon, phosphorus and sulphur; boron would form borides similar to carbides, etc.

Their success in decomposing boracic acid and isolating its 'radical' led Gay-Lussac and Thenard to apply their reagent, potassium, sometimes as we have seen, described simply as 'the metal' to try to isolate other radicals. Although the natural limitations of their method prevented them achieving their immediate objective, they made a number of interesting discoveries. In the course of these experiments they tried to prepare

[1] *Ann. chim.*, lxix (1809), 204–20.
[2] *M.S.A.*, ii (1809), 311–16; trans. M. E. Weeks, *Discovery of the Elements*, 5th ed., 1948, pp. 339–40.

pure 'fluoric acid' by heating together a mixture of calcium fluoride and vitrified boracic acid.[1] Investigating the properties of their 'fluoric' acid, they found it did not possess the well-known property of hydrofluoric acid of attacking glass and they reasoned correctly that this must be because it was already combined with an element similar to the basis of silica, namely the boron from the acid used in its preparation. They therefore named the gas 'fluoboric gas' (boron trifluoride).

They were now ready to prepare true hydrofluoric acid and attempt its decomposition with potassium. They were able to prepare nearly anhydrous acid by distilling calcium fluoride with concentrated sulphuric acid in a lead retort. Their first trial resulted in an explosion and from the detailed description of the dreadful effect of the acid on the skin, it is clear that they had not escaped unscathed. Repeating the experiment with great care they obtained potassium fluoride, hydrogen and water. After further experiments they concluded that the fluoride radical was so reactive that it could only be studied in combination. It was not until 1886 that Moissan finally overcame all the difficulties involved in the isolation of fluorine.

After an unsuccessful attempt to isolate the muriatic radical by the action of heated potassium on muriates (chlorides) of metals, they turned their attention to oxymuriatic acid (chlorine), hoping to decompose it by removing its supposed oxygen. Potassium was useless, but they were even more surprised when they found that even strongly heated carbon would not decompose the gas. This was all the more unexpected since sunlight decomposed it so easily. This led them to carry out further experiments on the effect of light on chemical reactions. They prepared two mixtures of chlorine and hydrogen and one was placed in darkness and the other in feeble sunlight. The first mixture was still greenish-yellow in colour after several days but the second had reacted completely by the end of a quarter of an hour, to judge by its colour. The experiment was repeated with olefiant gas (ethylene) and oxymuriatic acid gas which were mixed and left for two days in perfect darkness. As soon as they were exposed to bright sunlight there was a violent explosion. This confirmed their hypothesis that the speed of

[1] Boric acid was used as a substitute for concentrated sulphuric acid because they suspected that the latter always contained traces of water.

the reaction was proportional to the intensity of the light. These studies on the effect of time on chemical reactions are elementary but are interesting as a further illustration of the influence of Berthollet's ideas.[1] We shall see presently how Thenard introduced the time factor into his study of organic reactions. A further point of interest in this part of the memoir, which in other ways is rather disappointing, is the authors' remarks on the necessity of the presence of water for certain reactions to take place, for example, the combination of sulphur dioxide and oxygen to form sulphur trioxide.

Other Memoirs on General and Inorganic Chemistry

In another memoir[2] Gay-Lussac made a quantitative study of the precipitation of metals from solutions of salts. Salts were at this time considered as compounds of metallic oxides with acid anhydrides, although the latter were always described as 'acids'. Gay-Lussac stated that the weight of acid in the salt of a metal is directly proportional to the oxygen in their oxides. If there were two metals A and B, and A to form its oxide combined with twice as much oxygen as the same weight of B, in a precipitation reaction twice as much of B as of A would dissolve in order to neutralize the same quantity of acid. Such a principle might have been deduced from Dalton's atomic theory but Gay-Lussac's approach was purely empirical.

An important use of this principle was to determine the composition of all the salts of metals. The analysis of *insoluble* salts was comparatively straightforward but there was little agreement about the composition of the majority of salts, those which were *soluble* and could not therefore be weighed as precipitates. For example, insoluble lead sulphate had been found by analysis to consist of: lead 100·00, oxygen 7·29, acid 37·71. Knowing the proportions of oxygen in the corresponding oxides of lead and copper, soluble copper sulphate must therefore contain 'oxygen' and 'acid' in the same proportions as lead sulphate: copper 100·00, oxygen 24·57, acid 127·09, which was in fairly close agreement with the value obtained experimentally by Proust. An extension of Gay-Lussac's principle

---

[1] Berthollet, *Statique chimique*, vol. i, Section V, chap. 4, pp. 409 ff.: 'De la propagation de l'action chimique'.   [2] *M.S.A.*, ii (1809), 159-75.

could be used to determine the composition of sulphites indirectly. Direct determination presented practical difficulties because sulphites are easily oxidized by the atmosphere to sulphates. The principle could be used in reverse if the composition of the salt was known and the weight of oxygen which would combine with a given weight of the metal was required. This was applicable to the newly isolated barium.

The preoccupation at Arcueil with combining proportions, long after the dispute appeared to most chemists to have been settled in favour of Proust, may appear to be one of the major weaknesses of the association. In a way it was, but it was equally a source of strength, since it directed the attention of the younger chemists, Gay-Lussac, Dulong and Bérard, to particular problems which were far from settled and even led to several valuable discoveries.

Gay-Lussac's memoir[1] on the oxides of nitrogen was in this tradition. He pointed to the wide discrepancies between the values that had been obtained for the ratio of combining volumes of nitric oxide and oxygen. Starting with data from his memoir on combining volumes of gases, he did an experiment from which he concluded that 200 parts by volume of nitric oxide combine with 100 parts by volume of oxygen to form 'nitric acid' (nitrogen dioxide). This only happened, however, if the oxygen was in excess. If the nitric oxide was in excess, 300 parts by volume of nitric oxide combined with 100 parts of oxygen to form 'nitrous acid' and he cited an experiment of Thenard which seemed to confirm this. Unfortunately the oxides of nitrogen presented a more complex field of study than Gay-Lussac realized in 1809 and not only his conclusions but his experimental data were at fault. The memoir is of interest because in it Gay-Lussac concluded that nitrous vapour and nitrous acid were not, as was often said, of variable composition, but 'compounds always the same, always constant in their proportions'. As regards the history of the Arcueil circle it is of interest because, convinced that nitric oxide combined with oxygen in a definite known ratio, Gay-Lussac considered that it could still be used as a method of estimating the proportion of oxygen in a sample of air and he collaborated with Humboldt in a further series of experiments to confirm this.

[1] *M.S.A.*, ii (1809), 235–53.

Yet, however wrong Gay-Lussac's data on oxides of nitrogen had been, he made a definite contribution to the history of the subject. Gay-Lussac had criticized Dalton and Dalton in turn criticized Gay-Lussac.[1] When Davy too was prompted to carry out further experiments in the subject[2] which gave different results again, Gay-Lussac felt that he must re-examine the whole question with great care. This he did in 1816 with outstanding success.[3] He analysed the reasons for previous discrepancies in experimental evidence—diameter of the tube, speed of mixture, which reactant was in excess. This time he mixed the gases both dry and over caustic potash instead of water. He recognized five oxides of nitrogen which he listed as follows:

	Vols. of nitrogen	Vols. of oxygen	Modern formula
Oxide d'azote	100	50	N_2O
Gaz nitreux	100	100	NO
Acide pernitreux	100	150	N_2O_3
Acide nitreux	100	200	NO_2
Acide nitrique	100	250	N_2O_5

Gay-Lussac's second memoir on oxides of nitrogen illustrates that error is not necessarily fatal for the progress of science. The work of one man provides a stimulus to the next and in this case Gay-Lussac showed a willingness, which does him credit, to revise earlier work.

At the end of the second volume of the Arcueil *Mémoires* Berthollet contributed a paper on combining proportions.[4] He had previously crystallized a succession of acid sulphates of potash of different composition. He now attempted to produce evidence of a similar variation in composition of carbonates and bicarbonates of potash and soda. Perhaps the chief interest of this memoir is in the comment it contains on the law established by Gay-Lussac for the combining volumes of gases, an obvious example of *definite* proportions:

It may be concluded from the facts which I have just presented that there are substances which are disposed to form with others

[1] *A New System of Chemical Philosophy*, vol. i, part 2, 1810, pp. 555 ff.
[2] *Elements of Chemical Philosophy*, 1812, vol. i, p. 263.
[3] 'Sur les combinaisons de l'azote avec l'oxigène', *Ann. chim. phys.*, i (1816), 394–410.   [4] *M.S.A.*, ii (1809), 470–84.

compounds in simple or multiple proportions . . . that in these proportions a compound is more stable; nevertheless it can form intermediate compounds in the liquid or solid state; for the observations which Gay-Lussac has made in this volume seem to prove that these intermediate combinations do not take place for simple gaseous substances . . . but if the immense number of combinations recorded by chemists are considered, it seems that there are a very large number either not subject to this law or not in a way perceived by us.

Berthollet then was careful to point out that Gay-Lussac's law applied only to gases and did not affect the majority of known compounds. Yet it might seem ironical that Berthollet accepted the law of combining volumes of gases while it was rejected by Dalton. In the history of science our heroes are not always to be found on the same side of a dispute as we might expect to find them.

The Arcueil collection also contains two memoirs by Berthollet on gaseous hydrocarbons. This was the continuation of a research interest that he had had before the Revolution. He was now using some of his leisure at Arcueil to revise his earlier work and extend it in the light of more recent research by William Cruickshank, de Saussure, Thomson and others.[1] His previous analyses of hydrocarbons by sparking them with oxygen had been carried out over water and had been inaccurate in other ways. He had now obtained the assistance of Bérard, who had carried out each analysis several times in a well-constructed eudiometer over mercury.

By the time Berthollet published his second memoir,[2] Dalton had published the second part of his *New System*. In this he gave considerable attention to the two hydrocarbons olefiant gas and marsh gas, which he considered as compounds of one atom of carbon and one of hydrogen, and one atom of carbon and two atoms of hydrogen respectively. To examine this hypothesis Berthollet had asked Dulong and Bérard to carry out a number of experiments on the decomposition of these hydrocarbons. Dalton had claimed that the passage of electric sparks would decompose both gases completely into their elements but after passing sparks for eight hours the Arcueil group concluded that

[1] *M.S.A.*, ii (1809), 68–93.   [2] *Ibid.*, iii (1817), 148–64.

this was a supposition of Dalton rather than an experimental observation. The influence of Berthollet can hardly be seen more strongly than in the work of his son. Amédée Berthollet's memoir, 'Research on the reciprocal action of sulphur and carbon',[1] consisted of a critical examination of the discovery by Clément and Desormes of carbon disulphide. It is perhaps relevant to mention that they had made this discovery accidentally when seeking to disprove a theory held by Berthollet that carbon contained hydrogen.[2] Berthollet *fils* therefore had a personal interest in this question as relating to an attack on his father's ideas. The subject, moreover, seemed a promising one as an example of indefinite proportions, as Clément and Desormes had reported the formation not only of the liquid 'carburetted sulphur' but also of a solid and a gas, all of which appeared to be compounds of carbon and sulphur formed under different conditions. Amédée Berthollet stressed in particular the influence of the relative proportions of the reactants and the temperature and gave references to his father's *Statique chimique* in support. Most of his experimental work does him credit, but the memoir suffers from the author's readiness to interpret his results as a confirmation of his father's theory of the presence of hydrogen in carbon.

Amédée Berthollet was prompted to undertake an analysis of ammonia in the early spring of 1808,[3] when he heard a report that Davy had discovered oxygen in it.[4] For Amédée Berthollet research on this subject had a double interest. Not only did it seem to provide an opportunity to challenge the work of a well-known foreign chemist, but it was also an occasion to continue work which his father had started. It was in the *Mémoires de l'Académie Royale des Sciences* for 1785 that Berthollet senior had published the composition of ammonia, which he gave as 2·9 volumes of hydrogen to 1·1 of nitrogen. Using both chemical and physical tests, Berthollet junior confirmed that ammonia

[1] *Ibid.*, i (1807), 304–32.
[2] A sample of charcoal might well contain adsorbed hydrogen and other gases.   [3] *M.S.A.*, ii (1809), 268–94.
[4] *Phil. Trans.*, 1808, 35 ff. At the time no copy of Davy's paper was available in France and this information had come to Amédée Berthollet through the Geneva periodical *Bibliothèque britannique*. In England Davy's analysis was not disproved till May/June 1809 (*Phil. Trans.*, 1809, 430).

contained no oxygen. He gave its volumetric composition as hydrogen : nitrogen = 755 : 245, which is significantly nearer to the true ratio of 3 : 1 than his father had obtained some twenty years previously. Amédée Berthollet's ratio was eagerly seized upon by Gay-Lussac later in 1808 as further evidence confirming his hypothesis about combining volumes of gases. Amédée Berthollet himself had not been negligent in using the work of other members of the Society of Arcueil. In his memoir read to the First Class he made use of the work of Biot and Arago and he concluded with observations on accuracy in eudiometry, taking the joint publication of Gay-Lussac and Humboldt as a model.

Descotils contributed two memoirs to the Arcueil collection. In the first he suggested an alternative method of preparing pure platinum, in which the first stage was the solution of the crude metal in molten zinc.[1] His second contribution was a study of the action of gases on metallic sulphides with particular reference to the gases evolved in the reduction of sulphide ores.[2] Descotils paid particular attention to the behaviour of galena (lead sulphide) on heating. He tried successively the effects of sulphur dioxide, water vapour, hydrogen and air. The latter was particularly important, since this was the method used to oxidize the galena to obtain lead. Descotils observed that all gases when passed over heated galena favoured its partial sublimation, which confirmed a general principle pointed out by Gay-Lussac in the previous volume of Arcueil *Mémoires*.[3] The practical consequence of this was the waste that must occur in the ordinary production of lead. Descotils suggested that lead could be extracted more economically if a method were found of absorbing the combined sulphur in the galena, which normally combined with the air to form sulphur dioxide.

Dulong's Discovery of Nitrogen Trichloride

Dulong was in many ways a second Gay-Lussac. Like Gay-Lussac he owed his training in chemical research to Berthollet and, like Gay-Lussac, much of his work entitles him to be considered as a chemist of the first rank. Two of his memoirs, both

[1] *M.S.A.*, i (1807), 370–8. [2] *Ibid.*, ii (1809), 424–40.
[3] *Ibid.*, i (1807), 204.

important in the history of chemistry, were published in the Arcueil collection. They presented the discovery of interesting new compounds, nitrogen trichloride and hypophosphorous acid.[1]

The history of nitrogen trichloride is usually presented as an example of an 'accidental' discovery. As in the cases of many other discoveries so described, however, there is room to discuss how wide an interpretation one can give to such a term.

The history of chlorine is inseparable from the history of the Arcueil group since, quite apart from the work of Gay-Lussac and Thenard, a substantial part of Berthollet's fame in early nineteenth-century France rested on his studies of 'oxymuriatic acid' and its application to bleaching. Another substance he had investigated quite independently was ammonia. We shall see the connection between these two substances. In 1790 the German chemist Westrumb carried out a series of experiments on what he preferred to call 'dephlogisticated muriatic acid'. Although his studies of this gas (chlorine) had originally been prompted by its use in bleaching, he published his work as an attack on the oxygen theory and this was printed in the *Annales de chimie*.[2] Berthollet wrote a reply defending the oxygen theory. With the details of the reply we are not concerned here. It will be enough to quote a passage referring to a detail in Westrumb's experimental work:

> M. Westrumb claims that when ammonia is mixed with oxy-muriatic acid, an oil is formed which is slowly precipitated; I affirm on the contrary that when oxymuriatic acid is mixed with pure ammonia no oil is formed nor is there any precipitate. Let this simple experiment be tried and then it will be possible to judge between us.[3]

To take up the story twenty years later might seem to involve the lapse of an incredibly long period of time for there to be any connection between the events. There may or may not be a connection. In his published memoir Dulong does not mention one. The impossibility only becomes less plausible when we find other early ideas of Berthollet, ideas of even before the French

---

[1] Dulong's work on the acids of phosphorus (published in *M.S.A.*, iii (1817), 405–52) is described in Chapter Eight.
[2] *Ann. chim.*, vi (1790), 240–65.   [3] *Ibid.*, xi (1791), 11.

Revolution, tried out at Arcueil a generation later. Whereas an older man can generally claim to be richer in experience, his powers of original thought are usually less. It is not so surprising to find that Berthollet in his sixties went back over some of his earlier ideas or encouraged others to do so. To take only one example, in his paper on the quantitative analysis of nitric acid published in the last volume of the Arcueil *Mémoires*,[1] Berthollet used a method depending on the decomposition of potassium nitrate which, as he remarked, was one of the first experiments he had carried out in chemistry.

In 1809 Gay-Lussac and Thenard had carried out an important study of chlorine. One experiment they did was to react it with ammonia, although they interpreted the result as an estimate of the oxygen in the 'oxymuriatic acid'. A more fundamental experiment was the attempted decomposition of the gas; they found that even carbon heated to the highest temperature of the forge did not react with it. Dulong began his research on chlorine two years later. At the beginning of his memoir[2] he pointed out that only three elements were apparently unable to combine with 'oxymuriatic acid': nitrogen, carbon and boron. He presented his work as an attempt to make 'oxymuriatic acid' combine with nitrogen. Dulong considered that there was no theoretical reason why such a combination should be impossible, the only problem was to find suitable practical conditions. Although the two gases could not be made to combine directly, Dulong was more successful when he passed a current of chlorine through a fairly concentrated solution of ammonium chloride. After the reaction had been going for two hours at a temperature of between 7 and 8°C a yellow oil began to form.

In attempting the preparation of this new compound (nitrogen trichloride) Dulong was exposing himself to considerable danger. He had first prepared a small quantity of the substance in October 1811. Not realizing the danger involved, he took no precautions, and he was seriously injured, losing a finger and the sight of one eye.[3] On 11 November he sent a sealed note to

[1] *M.S.A.*, iii (1817), 165–70.

[2] *Ibid.*, 48–63.

[3] Letter from Ampère to Davy: 26 August 1812, *Correspondance du Grand Ampère*, ed. L. de Launay, vol. i, 1936, pp. 416–17; see also Davy's reply: 6 March 1813, *ibid.*, pp. 430–1. For details of Dulong's accidents see also

the Institute, claiming priority for the discovery of a new substance and explaining that he was recovering from injuries
received in its investigation. It was not until February 1812 that
he was sufficiently recovered from his injuries to proceed
further with his investigations. He discussed his work with the
other chemists at Arcueil and began with care to repeat his
work. Finding that the impure product exploded violently
above about 30°C, he realized that it was impossible for him to
continue safely during the summer months. He took up his
research for a third time in October 1812 but, despite the precautions he took, he was again seriously injured. Berthollet had
little difficulty in persuading him to abandon further research
on this particularly dangerous substance. Fortunately Dulong
had succeeded at least in determining the qualitative composition of the compound. When he allowed it to come into
contact with copper, the only products were copper chloride and
nitrogen. Dulong presented his research to the First Class on
11 January 1813. Meanwhile Davy had been informed by
Ampère of the discovery of an explosive oil, which his French
informant told him was a compound of nitrogen and chlorine.
In this further example of rivalry between Davy and the Arcueil
chemists, Davy was successful in preparing the compound but
not without slight personal injury.

Organic Chemistry

In the early nineteenth century the study of animal and
vegetable preparations was slowly developing into the science
of organic chemistry. This transition is illustrated in the work
of Thenard. The Arcueil *Mémoires* contain a generous proportion of such memoirs; there are eight in the first volume and a
further three in the second.

Thenard's two papers on bile had been read to the First
Class in 1805 and 1806. They had been recommended for publication in the collection of *Savans Étrangers*, which amounted in
practice to an indefinite postponement. At Arcueil Thenard
found an alternative medium of publication. In his first
memoir[1] he pointed out the difficulties which confronted the

---

M.S.A., iii (1817), 48n. and Cuvier, *Mém. Inst.*, 1812, 13, 14 (in one volume),
cxxiii–cxxiv.   [1] *M.S.A.*, i (1807), 23–45.

chemist who wished to make an analysis of solid animal matter. For liquids the problems were fewer, and such fluids as blood, urine, and milk had already undergone a successful preliminary investigation. Fourcroy had been prominent in this field. Thenard, convinced that bile must contain a peculiar active principle, tried to extract it by treatment with alcohol, ether and a variety of salt solutions. Using a solution of lead nitrate he was successful in isolating a substance, which, on account of its bitter-sweet taste, he called *picromel* (probably a mixture containing sodium taurocholate[1]) which was a good solvent of fats. His final analysis showed that bile was a mixture consisting principally of water, 'picromel', a resin and a variable quantity of a yellow albuminous matter; there were also present small quantities of various inorganic substances, including the chloride, phosphate and sulphate of soda. Thenard's second memoir on bile[2] included a study of calculi associated with the bile, an extension of work carried out earlier by Fourcroy.

Thenard's work on 'ethers' is of some importance in the history of organic chemistry. The name 'ether' was given to the product formed by the action of acids on alcohol. Whether the acid used was sulphuric, nitric, muriatic (hydrochloric), phosphoric or acetic, the product was generally an inflammable volatile liquid with a characteristic smell. The only one of these five compounds to be studied with any success had been 'sulphuric ether' (diethyl ether), which had been the subject of research by Fourcroy and Vauquelin. Thenard was now hoping to throw light on the composition of the others.

In his first memoir on 'ethers'[3] (i.e. esters) Thenard, after reporting previous work on 'nitric ether' (ethyl nitrite), described his own preparation of the substance. As the crude ester was acid, he treated it with lime. This combined with the acid portion, leaving the ester. The purified ester was examined at Arcueil by Berthollet father and son, and its vapour pressure was found to be 75 cm of mercury at 21 °C. Any slight increase in temperature resulted in its vaporization. In the course of his analysis Thenard had cause to determine the density of a mixture of gases obtained in the decomposition of the ester. For this purpose he borrowed the delicate balance which Biot and

---

[1] Partington, *History of Chemistry*, vol. iv, p. 93.
[2] *M.S.A.*, i (1807), 46–72.   [3] *Ibid.*, 73–114.

Arago had used in their experiments on refraction in gases. This memoir is interesting for a number of reasons, in the first place as an example of preparative organic chemistry (Thenard gave the yield and described the purification). Thenard gave (rather inaccurate) figures for the gravimetric composition of the ester. It thus provides an example of quantitative organic analysis, a field of study which was to be developed jointly by Gay-Lussac and Thenard. Finally this memoir illustrates an important transition in Thenard's career, for we have seen how he passed from the problems of his earlier teacher Fourcroy into the Arcueil circle and made full use of the physical approach and apparatus of the latter.

Thenard's second memoir on esters was concerned with 'muriatic ether' (ethyl chloride).[1] There was some disagreement as to whether there was such a compound or whether, when 'muriatic acid' reacted with alcohol, the result was merely a mixture. Thenard showed that his product had no effect on litmus nor on silver nitrate solution and therefore did not contain any free 'muriatic acid'. He described in detail the conditions necessary to obtain the compound. Its boiling point ($11°C$), freezing point ($-29°C$) and specific gravity ($0·874$) were determined for him by Amédée Berthollet at Arcueil.[2] Thenard had read his memoir at the Institute on 18 February 1807 and the French chemists considered it to be interesting new work. A month later, however, Gay-Lussac happened to be reading Gehlen's chemical journal and found that Gehlen himself had published a memoir on 'muriatic ether' in 1804.[3] Thenard reported:

> As M. Gay-Lussac is a great friend of mine, he wished to see if there was any similarity between the German chemist's memoir and mine; and as he found there was much in common and, as I do not know German, he did me the favour of translating it.

Thenard's third contribution on ethers to the Arcueil *Mémoires*[4] therefore consisted of a comparison of Gehlen's work with his own.

[1] *Ibid.*, 115–34. In this memoir Thenard speculated about the composition of muriatic acid, a topic which he developed later in collaboration with Gay-Lussac.
[2] The modern values are b.pt. = $12·3°C$, f.pt. = $-138°C(?)$, D = $0·90$ at $10°C$.
[3] *Neues allgemeines Journal der Chemie*, ii (1804), 206–27.
[4] *M.S.A.*, i (1807), 135–9.

In his next memoir[1] Thenard investigated the effectiveness of using metal chlorides instead of hydrochloric acid to produce the corresponding ester. He then turned to examine the effect of chlorine on alcohol, a subject which had been studied briefly by Berthollet in 1785. Thenard obtained an oily substance which was very soluble in alcohol but insoluble in water. It had a characteristic smell but quite unlike that of the other 'ethers'. Thenard concluded that it was not an 'ether'. It was probably chloral (CCl_3CHO), usually considered to have been discovered by Liebig exactly a quarter of a century later. Finally Thenard made a careful study of the action of acetic acid on alcohol. His work is notable for its quantitative character and he made a point of referring all quantities of acid to equivalent weights of potash. Distillation of the 'acetic ether' (ethyl acetate) with a solution of caustic potash yielded alcohol and potassium acetate. Thenard therefore proved both by synthesis and analysis that 'acetic ether' was a compound of acetic acid and alcohol—a fundamental step in the understanding of esters.

In a further memoir read to the First Class in 1807 Thenard presented further research on 'muriatic ether'.[2] He began with the details of a painstaking quantitative analysis. There remained the question of how its elements were combined together; were the hydrogen, oxygen and carbon combined in the same way as in alcohol? As regards the muriatic acid, he had already noted that the ester did not form a precipitate with silver nitrate nor did it react with alkalis. He now realized that he had neglected one important factor—time. There is no explicit reference by Thenard to Berthollet here, but it will be remembered that the latter had stressed the influence of time on chemical reactions in his *Statique chimique*. Thenard was now able to report on experiments which he had carried out between 21 February and 19 May. In one experiment he had studied the reaction between the ester and a concentrated solution of caustic potash. After an hour at room temperature there was no action, but after a day the addition of silver nitrate solution indicated traces of free 'muriate' (chloride); after three months at room temperature this amounted to 0·4 gram from 10 grams of ester. For the first fortnight the flask had been shaken

[1] *M.S.A.*, i (1807), 140–60.　　　　[2] *Ibid.*, i (1807), 337–58.

periodically to mix the reagents. In another series of experiments the effect of silver nitrate solution was tried successively on the ester in the vapour and liquid forms. A further experiment in which the state of the reactants affected the result was the action of nitric and sulphuric acids on the ester. At ordinary temperatures there was no effect, but the ester was immediately decomposed when its vapour was passed through the boiling acid.

This memoir shows a new and fertile approach to problems of organic chemistry. Thenard now appreciated the importance of the time factor and the state of the reactants and he turned in a further memoir[1] to apply the same method to the study of 'nitric ether'. This memoir is also notable for its quantitative approach, but Thenard's conclusion that ethyl nitrite is a compound of nitrous acid, acetic acid and alcohol was mistaken. He did not realize that the nitric acid used in its preparation had oxidized nearly all of the alcohol and was itself partly reduced.

A more important memoir by Thenard was contributed to the second volume of the Arcueil *Mémoires*. Having been read at the Institute in November 1807, it had come too late for inclusion in the first volume. In this memoir[2] he described the preparation of the esters of benzoic, oxalic, citric, malic and tartaric acids. Thenard had been successful where others had failed because he added concentrated sulphuric or hydrochloric acids to the reagents. He was, moreover, able to show by hydrolysis of each ester that these mineral acids did not enter into their composition. Thenard also investigated the proportions of acetic acid, alcohol and concentrated sulphuric acid required for the optimum yield of 'acetic ether' (ethyl acetate) and whether sulphuric acid could be replaced by other acids.

In Thenard's last major contribution to organic chemistry published in the Arcueil *Mémoires*[3] he stated that when alcohols combine with a vegetable or mineral acid, the alcohol acts as a 'true salifiable base'. The memoir described various experiments in which Thenard tried to extend his investigation of the action of acids on alcohol to their action on a variety of vegetable and animal substances. One cannot help feeling on

[1] *Ibid.*, 359–69.   [2] *Ibid.*, ii (1809), 5–22.   [3] *Ibid.*, 23–41.

reading it that organic chemistry was still awaiting a major
breakthrough that would establish it among the sciences.
Among those who contributed to this we may mention not only
the names of men associated with influential theories, men such
as Liebig and Dumas, but also Chevreul whose important work
on saponification was to some degree an extension of the
previous work of Fourcroy and Thenard. It was fitting that,
when in a note at the end of the Arcueil *Mémoires*,[1] Thenard
stated that by then (1809) he had broken off his research in
organic chemistry, he mentioned Chevreul among those who
were then active in the field.

Biological and Geographical Memoirs

Among other subjects discussed in the Arcueil collection,
respiration constitutes a recurrent theme. Berthollet's work on
respiration has a definite place in the history of nineteenth-
century physiology.[2] One of the uses which Berthollet suggested
for his manometer was to make an exact study of differences in
pressure and composition of the atmosphere brought about by
the respiration of small animals.[3] Legallois had a similar
manometer made after the description given in the Arcueil
Mémoires and used it in his research on animal heat.[4] By the
mid-century Regnault and Reiset had devised improved and
more complex apparatus for the study of animal respiration.[5]
The work on triangulation carried out by Biot and Arago
in the islands off the coast of Spain enters only marginally into
the story of Arcueil. Yet Biot found time during this expedition
to carry out some quite different experiments on his own
account and these were published in the Arcueil collection.[6] He
made a special study of the air contained in the swim bladders
of fish found off the islands of Iviza and Formentera. One purpose of this organ was to enable fish, by filling up with air, to
decrease their average density and so rise towards the surface
or by expelling air to sink, but it was not clear how the air was

[1] *M.S.A.*, ii (1809), 492–5.
[2] C. Ludwig, *Lehrbuch der Physiologie des Menschen*, 2nd edn., Leipzig and
Heidelberg, 1858, 61, vol. ii, p. 554. I am indebted to Mr F. L. Holmes for
this reference.   [3] *M.S.A.*, i (1807), 282–303; iii (1817), 454–63.
[6] *Ann. chim. phys.*, iv (1817), 15.   [5] *Ibid.*, [3], xxvi (1849), 310.
[4] *M.S.A.*, i (1807), 252–81.

obtained by the fish. Biot had learned of the value of Volta's eudiometer from Gay-Lussac and it was with this instrument that he analysed the air. Biot can claim credit for recording the extremely high proportion of oxygen secreted in the swim bladder of certain fish which live at great depths.[1] He found a maximum of 87 per cent of oxygen, a figure that agrees well with the modern value. Biot compared this high proportion of oxygen with that dissolved in the water at the same depth. The latter he found to be very little different from the proportion contained in water near the surface. Although he remarked on the blood vessels in the walls of the swim bladder and he guessed that they might be connected with respiration, the significance of the swim bladder for the respiratory system of fish is complex, and it is only fairly recently that it has been fully understood.

In another paper on the same subject[2] Biot reported that he had repeated his previous experiments and confirmed most of his conclusions on a second visit to the islands in the company of Delaroche. An interesting extension of his previous work was the idea of lowering a mixture of gases in a container to great depths to see if the pressure resulted in chemical combination. It was found that, even at pressures of 24 and 31 atmospheres, oxygen and nitrogen, hydrogen and oxygen, and hydrogen and nitrogen would not combine, even though they had been mixed in proportions appropriate to the formation of nitrogen dioxide, water and ammonia respectively. Biot's aim was theoretical, not practical, and he drew the conclusion[3] from his experiment that, even when pressure was increased thirty times and consequently the volume was reduced to one thirtieth of the original, the molecules were still too far apart to be in contact and even to exercise their chemical affinity. The distance apart of the molecules of a gas under compression was also an important feature in the theory of sound.

Not unconnected with the work of Biot and Delaroche on the contents of the swim bladder, was a joint memoir by Provençal and Humboldt on the respiration of fish.[4] They confirmed that the air dissolved in water contains a significantly higher percentage of oxygen (31·05 per cent by volume) than atmospheric

[1] *Ibid.*, 258, 275. [2] *Ibid.*, ii (1809), 487–91.
[3] *Traité de physique*, 1816, vol. ii, p. 16.
[4] *M.S.A.*, ii (1809), 359–404.

air. Their memoir also made an important contribution to physiology by their discovery that fish absorb nitrogen from the water, a fact which they related to the surprisingly high proportion of nitrogen in muscular tissue.[1]

Botany too was represented in the Arcueil *Mémoires* by Candolle, who contributed a short but important paper on heliotropism, the tendency of plants to turn towards the light.[2] It was well known that plants grown in the absence of light are white instead of green. Candolle found that if such a plant was exposed to daylight it acquired in the course of two days a green colour similar to that of ordinary plants and if only a part of the plant was exposed to daylight only that part became green. The phenomenon was therefore purely local and temporary. Between the two extremes, the colour of a plant was related to the intensity of the light of its environment. To explain why plants bend towards the light, Candolle considered that the side of the plant exposed to least light was subject to minor etiolation and therefore slightly elongated compared with the side towards the light. This would result in the stem being curved towards the light. To confirm this hypothesis, Candolle was able to demonstrate that the extent of the bending towards the light was proportional to the difference in the intensity of illumination on the two sides of the plant. Also heliotropism only took place on the parts of plants subject to etiolation. Finally those plants which are not coloured by light, such as *cuscuta*, had no tendency to exhibit heliotropism. Although advances in chemical knowledge make Candolle's explanation unacceptable today, he must be given credit for a very plausible hypothesis.

Candolle also contributed a memoir on double flowers to the Arcueil collection.[3] Although such flowers were favoured by the florist for display, botanists had tended to ignore them since Linnaeus, having found difficulty in incorporating them into his classification, had excluded them as brilliant monstrosities. Candolle argued that even if they were abnormal, their study might throw light on the 'normal'. He made a particular study of *Ranunculaceae*. He pointed out that the term 'double flower' was applied to a wide variety of cases and tried to clarify the position by the introduction of new terms. He adduced evidence

---

[1] F. L. Holmes, *Isis*, liv (1963), 63. [2] *Ibid.*, 104–10.
[3] *M.S.A.*, iii (1817), 385–404.

that the form, size, number, direction and colour of all parts
of flowers were very variable while the relative positions of the
parts of flowers was constant. Candolle's memoir may therefore
be considered as a case study within the framework of his insistence on a *natural* method of classification of plants depending
on the relative positions of the floral organs.

Among the claims to fame of the Arcueil group may be
included the study of plant geography, since both Humboldt
and Candolle made important contributions to this field. Indeed
by the publication in 1807 of his influential *Essai sur la géographie
des plantes*, Humboldt may be considered to have established
the subject. Stimulated by Humboldt and the conclusions
drawn from his American travels, Candolle published a memoir
in the Arcueil collection on plant geography in France in which
he related the occurrences of particular plants to the altitude.[1]

Candolle acknowledged the work of Humboldt and pointed
out that he was the first to have prepared a botanical map in
which the growth of particular plants was related to temperature and altitude. Candolle had already published on the subject in 1804 (i.e. before Humboldt's book appeared) but he
admitted that as an associate of Humboldt he knew of his work
before it was published. Since then he had travelled in every
department of the Napoleonic Empire over a period of six years,
inspired by the concept of a geography of plants. Candolle
intended to publish his work more completely at a later date
and in this memoir he was concerned with only one aspect, the
influence of altitude on vegetation. In fact his proposed book
on plant geography never appeared and the Arcueil *Mémoires*
were fortunate in possessing his only paper on this subject.

Altitude could affect plants in various ways, the temperature, the intensity of light from the sun, humidity and the difference of density of the atmosphere. The mean temperature
of a region depended both on latitude and altitude and Candolle attempted to reconcile his own observations in France
with the rather different observations which had been made
by Humboldt near the equator. Some plants could be found
at almost any altitude or latitude but in the case of other plants
which only grew in certain regions depending on the mean

[1] *Ibid.*, 262–322.

c c

temperature, it was found that the limit of the area of their occurrence was a function both of latitude and altitude. The dryness of the mountain air increased the rate of transpiration and consequently the absorption of water by the roots of plants. This factor, together with the intensity of the light, explained the remarkably quick growth of some mountain plants, provided there was a constant supply of water from melting snow. It might be thought that the low amount of oxygen on high mountains would prevent the growth of plants, but this effect would only operate above the snow line. Candolle concluded his memoir with a table of 1,500 species of plants classified according to the altitude range at which they were found. Every attempt had been made to multiply observations of every species, but Candolle admitted that it might be possible to find an odd example of a plant growing at an altitude different from that which he had recorded.

Finally we turn to Humboldt, who, by his concept of isothermal lines inaugurated a comparative study of the climates of different countries. Not only did he suggest the idea but he provided a means of carrying it out. The most interesting aspect of this work is how he carried over a concept and method from one branch of science to a completely different one, a powerful vindication of the broad approach to science for which Humboldt was well known.

A map showing lines of magnetic declination had been published by Halley in 1702 and a map with lines of magnetic dip had appeared in 1768. Although Humboldt had made over a hundred observations of the magnetic elements in his American travels, this was not enough to permit the drawing of exact lines. Instead he drew a map of so-called 'isodynamic' zones where the total magnetic intensity was the same. Deeply interested in this aspect of magnetism, he had coined the terms 'isogonics', 'isoclines' and 'isodynamics' for the lines of equal declination, inclination and intensity respectively. In 1817 he was ready to speak of 'isothermals' and his memoir published in the Arcueil collection was entitled 'On isothermal lines and the distribution of heat over the globe'.[1] In the following passage Humboldt outlines his methodology of science and it is

[1] *M.S.A.*, iii (1817), 462–602; trans. *Edinburgh Philosophical Journal*, iii (1820), 1–20, 256–74, iv (1821), 23–38, 262–81, v (1821), 28–39.

clear that he saw science as a cumulative activity with his own work serving as a possible guide to further improvements:

> Although we may not be able to refer the complex phenomena to a general theory, it will be of considerable importance to fix the numerical relation by which a great number of scattered observations are connected, and to reduce to empirical laws the effects of local and disturbing causes. The study of these laws will point out to travellers the problems to which they should direct their principal attention, and we may entertain the hope that the theory of the distribution of heat will gain in extent and precision in proportion as observations are multiplied and directed to those points, which it is of most importance to illustrate.

Humboldt's precise contribution is summarized in the following words:

> I endeavoured to find, at every 10° of latitude, but under different meridians, a small number of places whose mean temperature had been precisely ascertained and through these, as to many fixed points, passed my *isothermal lines* or *lines of equal heat*. I had recourse, in so far as the materials have been made public, to those observations the results of which have been published.

He was handicapped, however, by the fact that many altitudes were not known and many accepted mean temperatures were inaccurate. Humboldt considered successively the distribution of heat at the surface of the globe, on the sides of mountains, in the oceans and in the 'interior' of the earth, the latter data being derived from observations of springs and in mines. He pointed out that, whereas the climate of Europe had always been taken as the norm, various factors contributed to give it a climate very different from that of other regions of the same latitude. He considered in turn the influence of the seas— 'immense reservoirs of an almost invariable temperature'—the direction of chains of mountains in relation to prevailing winds, the influence of land masses and many other factors which affected temperature and complicated the drawing of any direct conclusions about the distribution of heat. He suggested that the current concept of a 'mean temperature' was inadequate. Finally he attempted to relate isothermal lines to the different systems of climate and he concluded with a large folding table which showed places of comparable mean temperature, their position, altitude and their mean seasonal temperatures.

In the course of this memoir Humboldt made many references to previous work on meteorology, etc. He included observations by Arago at the Observatory, Candolle's work on plant geography, the relation between height and altitude determined by Gay-Lussac in his balloon ascent and the studies of Gay-Lussac and Thenard on the effect of sunlight on mixtures of chlorine and hydrogen. This is enough to establish the right of this monograph to be included in the Arcueil *Mémoires*. It also illustrates that, whereas we might classify this memoir as a contribution to the history of physical geography, for its author there were no sharp divisions between the various branches of science.

Conclusion

The range both of subject and standard of excellence in the Arcueil *Mémoires* may be judged from the above summary. Contributions ranged in length from the monograph of nearly 150 pages by Humboldt to a half-page note by Gay-Lussac. The best memoirs would have been outstanding in any collection, but several others were reports of work in progress rather than polished memoirs in which all the repercussions of a subject were fully discussed.

The published contents of the *Mémoires* were usually edited versions of what had been read at Arcueil or elsewhere. A trivial example is when Humboldt writes that he does not wish to tire 'the reader' with details of calculations.[1] More important are the occasions when Berthollet's comments on a paper caused some change in the manner of presentation or in the conclusions reached. Yet the *Mémoires* is full of acknowledgements to the work and interest of other members of the group. The younger members often proclaim proudly that their experiments have been witnessed by Berthollet or Laplace or by both. Everyone is willing to acknowledge what ancillary help he has received from his colleagues, whether an idea or some experimental data.

Despite the apparent diversity of the contents, the Arcueil

[1] *M.S.A.*, ii (1809), 376.

Mémoires are characterized by a certain unity. This is by no means the work of an isolated community, yet there was continual collaboration and help from other members of the Society, even in the most unlikely cases. Biot said[1] that the primary aim of the Society was one of pleasure and mutual education, but the pleasure was greater for seeing a concrete result for their labours. Whether or not the primary purpose of the Society of Arcueil was internal, by publishing its *Mémoires* it made a significant contribution to early nineteenth-century science.

The Communication and Reception of the 'Mémoires'

However vital some of the contents of the *Mémoires* of the Society of Arcueil may have been, they would have made little contribution to early nineteenth-century science if they had not been circulated and discussed. Whereas it is unlikely that anyone doing serious scientific work at this time would ignore the *Philosophical Transactions of the Royal Society* or the *Mémoires* of the First Class of the Institute, a small and private scientific society could easily find its publications overlooked. The question is in the first place one of publicity. Apart from many copies which Berthollet presented to various men of science all over Europe[2] and to scientific institutions, the memoirs would not have been sought and read if the scientific books and periodicals of the time had not made reference to them. The attitude of the journals was probably of crucial importance. There was never any suggestion that the Arcueil *Mémoires* constituted a rival publication. On the contrary, it provided an additional source of material, especially to the foreign journals, and the best of this material in translation would add distinction to the journal which published it. The less notable contributions to the *Mémoires* could be used to fill up a number in a lean season.

In France advance publicity was given to the Arcueil *Mémoires* by the *Journal des Mines*. At the end of the number of June 1807 under the heading of 'General Announcements' the *Journal des Mines* devoted three pages to a complete list of

---

[1] *Le Moniteur*, 26 August 1809.
[2] E.g. De Saussure, whose copy of volume two is inscribed: 'Donné par M. Berthollet'—Duveen, *Bibliotheca Alchemica et Chemica*, 1949, pp. 26–7.

contents of volume one of the *Mémoires*, the list being introduced
with the remark that the prospective reader would be able to
judge the interest of the publication from the titles of the
memoirs it contained.[1]

The next journal to mention the Arcueil *Mémoires* was the
Annales de chimie.[2] The reviewer (Descotils) remarked that the
contents of the first volume were concerned entirely with physics
and chemistry and would naturally be of interest to readers of
the *Annales*. Instead of attempting an appraisal of the merits of
the new publication, he understandably adopted the easier
course of giving a summary of the contents and this summary
was continued in the next volume of the *Annales*. The *Journal
de physique*, the only other independent scientific journal of
importance in France, was not far behind in publicizing the
Arcueil *Mémoires*. In the issue for August 1807 the editor, La
Metherie, reproduced the introduction to volume one in full
together with a list of members of the Society.[3] He concluded,

> We decided to report this introduction in full; this will enable our
> readers to understand the aims of an association which will con-
> tribute greatly to the progress of natural philosophy. This first
> volume, which we announce, is a sure guarantee of this from the
> interesting memoirs which it contains.

It would be expecting too much to find an equally enthusiastic reception from the Class of mathematical and physical
sciences of the Institute. At the meeting of 3 August 1807 Berthollet, with his tongue in his cheek, concluded his report on
Thenard's memoir on muriatic ether with the usual formula,
that it deserved to be published in the collection of *Savans
Étrangers*. This was said just after it had appeared in the
Mémoires of Arcueil. There is no record in the published minutes
of the First Class of Berthollet's presentation of the first volume
of the *Mémoires* of his Society, but he did present the Institute
with the second and third volumes as they were published.
Official recognition and publicity of another sort was given in

---

[1] *Journal des Mines*, xxi (1807), 486–8. The next number of the *Journal*
contains extracts from two of Gay-Lussac's memoirs taken from the Arcueil
collection.

[2] In the number dated 31 July 1807 it announced the publication of
volume one at a price of 5 francs. The current price of the *Annales* was 4 fr.
50 cent. *Ann. chim.*, lxiii (1807), 330–2; lxiv (1807), 321–36.

[3] *Journal de Physique*, lxv (1807), 157–9.

a two-column review of the *Moniteur* on 26 August 1807. The unique position of the *Moniteur* as the only national newspaper meant that the Society of Arcueil received widespread publicity in France and indeed the whole of Europe.

A further source of publicity in France for the *Mémoires* came, not unnaturally, from the publisher. In August 1807 Bernard circulated a brochure containing the numerous scientific publications of his firm. Apart from the official journal of the *École Polytechnique*, Bernard also published the *Annales de chimie* and many scientific books, including those of Berthollet, Biot and Thomson. With respect to the Arcueil *Mémoires*, he gave a list of its members and said,

> The names of the members of this illustrious gathering are sufficient to give an idea of what it offers and of what it promises to the sciences. But the Society will only publish volumes according to the importance of the experiments carried out with great care in its midst. The progress of science is the only object of its work.[1]

Bernard's comment that the best testimonial of the value of the contents of the *Mémoires* were the names of its members was taken up elsewhere, as in Germany. The German journals were quick to report on the publication of the first volume of the Arcueil collection. The *Journal für die Chemie, Physik und Mineralogie*,[2] edited by Berthollet's friend, Gehlen, gave in full a translation of Berthollet's introduction. There was also a list of contents and later volumes contained translations of selected papers from the *Mémoires*.

L. W. Gilbert's *Annalen der Physik*[3] reported the publication of the first volume of the Arcueil *Mémoires* from the standpoint of its contribution to physics. Gilbert welcomed the activities of the Society of Arcueil and suggested that the standard of his journal would be enhanced by the inclusion of the work of the French scientists:

> The first volume of memoirs of the Society of these excellent physicists appeared some months ago . . . There are in it so many

---

[1] *Notice abrégée des principaux livres de Bernard*, Libraire de l'École Polytechnique et de l'École impériale des Ponts et Chaussées, éditeur des Annales de chimie, quai des Augustins, no. 25. Août 1807, p. 4.
[2] *Op. cit.*, iv (1807), 67–71.   [3] *Op. cit.*, xxvi (1807), 450–3.

instructive studies and real advances in natural science, and in every essay the idea of an exact science seems to be so truly present, that we are justified in holding out the highest hopes for physics from this Society of such outstanding men. It goes without saying that I shall make a point of having all the essays from this Society's memoirs relating to physics and physical chemistry published in the *Annalen der Physik* in a form worthy of them . . . I am making a start in the present issue and the next with the works of Messrs. Biot, Gay-Lussac and von Humboldt. It will be enlightening to find memoirs and studies like these next to those that have previously been published in this journal.

Gilbert gave an equally enthusiastic welcome to the second volume of the Arcueil *Mémoires* when Berthollet sent him a copy.[1]

In Geneva the *Bibliothèque britannique* fulfilled the important function of keeping the continent informed of advances in science in Great Britain. It was not part of its policy to report on French works and it passed over the first volume of the Arcueil *Mémoires* in silence. In August 1809, however, immediately after the publication of the second volume, it could not refrain from referring to the event.[2] Pictet gave a list of members of the Society and continued:

Reading these names one is less surprised by the frequency and richness of the productions of this Society. The Society provides a combination of circumstances which is most favourable to the exercise of talent. We see that it is formed of men distinguished in the exact sciences and in all branches of natural science; the maturity of age is associated with the vigour and activity of youth, the Frenchman with the foreigner; the proximity of a large town keeps thought active and its products germinate at Arcueil. There the peace which a stay in the country brings, the leisure which it leaves, a liberal use of wealth for the profit of science, allow these first ideas to be followed up and brought to fruition at frequent intervals. The depth and scope of the attainments distributed in this Society provide an opportunity to apply for the progress of science the principle of the division of labour which is so fruitful in the mechanical arts both with regard to quantity and quality.

---

[1] *Op. cit.*, xxxiv (1810), 390–1n.
[2] *Bibliothèque britannique*, xli (1809), 395–6n.

Turning to Britain, the Royal Society recorded at its meeting on 3 May 1808 that it had received the first volume of Arcueil *Mémoires*. Volume two was transmitted more rapidly, since it was received by 9 November 1809. As regards the scientific journals, the *Journal of Natural Philosophy, Chemistry and the Arts*, edited by William Nicholson, contains no reference to volume one of the Arcueil collection but a note on the Society appeared in the number for August 1809. It was not until 1811 that Nicholson was able to give translations of the contents of the volume that had appeared two years earlier. The *Philosophical Magazine* also suffered from the difficulty of communications between England and the continent of Europe. In October 1808 the editor, Alexander Tilloch, had had to borrow a French journal from Humphry Davy and was reduced to making an appeal for foreign journals:

> . . . our friends who happen to obtain any of them cannot confer on us a greater favour than by allowing us the use of them for a few days.[1]

Looking through the British scientific journals of this period we find a fair number of the Arcueil *Mémoires* appearing in translation with a delay ranging from two or three months to two or three years. More remarkable than the translation of important scientific memoirs appearing in scientific journals is the fact that two of the leading British literary journals, the *Edinburgh Review* and its rival, the *Quarterly Review*, gave prominence to the Arcueil *Mémoires*. By the time an anonymous review (by John Leslie) of volume one had appeared in the *Edinburgh Review* for October 1809,[2] the second volume of the *Mémoires* was already in the reviewer's hands. Leslie noted this as evidence that the Society of Arcueil was a flourishing group and it probably convinced the editor that this was an important series which merited the attention of his columns. Leslie was full of praise for the Society of Arcueil:

> This volume is the production of a little association, better calcu-
> lated, we conceive, than the older establishments for advancing
> the progress of physical science. The celebrated Berthollet, whose
> labours have so materially contributed to extend the practice and

[1] *Phil. Mag.*, xxxii (1808), 89n.
[2] *Op. cit.*, iii (1809–10), 142–52. The second volume of Arcueil *Mémoires* was reviewed in *ibid.*, 418–41 (January 1810).

improve the theory of chemistry, anxious, amidst the possession of ease and competence, to promote in his declining years the objects of his earliest ambition, has gathered around him a few ingenious and active individuals, who assemble once a fortnight at his country residence near Paris and spend the day in philosophical occupations . . . At their meetings the latest scientific journals are consulted, philosophical papers are read and discussed and new experiments are proposed, repeated, or set on foot. The advantages of such a plan are most obvious. Mistakes may be detected, errors avoided and important lights struck out by the collision of ideas. In the actual state of science no experiments are truly valuable, but those that have been performed with the most scrupulous precision. The art of experimenting itself has now become so refined and attended with such vast expense, as often to lie beyond the reach of individual exertion. We are therefore inclined to augur favourably of a society of this nature which descends to guide and assist the details of enquiry. If our expectations have not been fully answered, we yet discern the germs of more important communications; and we trust that similar associations, furnished with more ample means, will soon be formed at home.

The note of reserve in Leslie's last sentence was largely inspired by his refusal to accept the conclusions of Gay-Lussac's memoir which describes the change in temperature of a gas on expansion.[1] Nearly half of his review was devoted to this subject. Leslie's review of volume two of the *Mémoires* was a more balanced account. He clearly considered this volume of greater importance and dealt at some length with all the major contributions in it.

Thomas Young's review, published in the *Quarterly Review* for May 1810, although marred by personal attacks on Leslie, is of great interest as being one of the more detailed reviews received by the Arcueil *Mémoires*. It occupied some twenty closely printed pages in its survey of the first two volumes, as if to compensate by thoroughness for the lapse in time since the appearance of the work. Young was prompted to write the review for two reasons. In the first place, the intrinsic merit of the work:

The two volumes of the Memoirs of the Society of Arcueil are particularly interesting, as they contain, besides some original

---

[1] Gay-Lussac had criticized Leslie's work in *M.S.A.*, i (1807), 197, 185.

articles of high importance, a summary view of the principal investigations which have, during the last two or three years, employed the most celebrated of the philosophers of France.

There was, however, another motive related to Young's hostility to the influential *Edinburgh Review*, which had published a violent attack by Lord Brougham on Young and his theories of optics. The fact that the review was by Young, one of Britain's most capable men of science of the period, adds considerably to the remarks which began as follows:

> These volumes are composed exclusively of the productions of a select decad of the most celebrated men of science resident at Paris, who meet once a fortnight to pass the day together, in making and discussing philosophical experiments, at the house of the elder Berthollet, now a count of the French empire, situated at Arcueil, in the neighbourhood of a villa which has lately been purchased by Count Laplace. These two gentlemen may be considered as the fathers of the Society . . .
>
> The researches of the Society of Arcueil extend to the most important and interesting of the topics which constitute the occupation of the First Class of the Institute of France . . .
>
> There is not uncommonly a degree of zeal and emulation attending the pursuits of a private association, which cannot always be obtained in an equal degree by any public encouragement held out to science. Thus the stipends of the academicians of the Institute, which are sufficient to induce men of small fortunes and moderate wishes to devote their attention to science, are by no means calculated to call the most brilliant powers into the strongest action; and a society so constituted is more likely to do a great deal tolerably, than a little admirably.

Obviously Young placed the Arcueil group in the latter category. His method of review of the *Mémoires* was to summarize the contents of the two volumes and then concentrate on those memoirs closest to his own interests—Malus' memoirs on polarized light and Biot's memoirs on sound.

From the above remarks by Young, it is clear that in whatever other ways he differed from the *Edinburgh Review*, he agreed with its reviewer in paying the most generous tribute to the Society of Arcueil and this tribute was all the more significant, coming from the man who was Foreign Secretary of the Royal Society. If the Society found no imitators in Britain it was due to the different social conditions and also perhaps to the absence of a patron with scientific training and sympathies. Whilst the immediate reception of the Arcueil *Mémoires* may be judged by reviews in the journals, more vital to the development of science in the early nineteenth century was its impact on a few key figures in the science of the time, men like Dalton, Davy and Berzelius.

Berthollet did not distribute copies of the first volume of the Arcueil *Mémoires* as widely as the subsequent volumes. He had planned to send seven copies of the first volume to his friend Blagden, asking him to distribute copies to the Royal Society, the Manchester Literary and Philosophical Society,[1] Davy, Hatchett, Nicholson, Thomson, and to keep one himself.[2] At the beginning of October it seemed that a means of conveying at least three of these copies had been found, but Hall, the intending traveller, changed his plans at the last moment.[3] The Arcueil *Mémoires* therefore were not sent to England until the following year. Blagden states that he received three copies of volume one on 7 May 1808.[4] Blagden for his part was able to send a copy of Dalton's *New System of Chemistry* (Volume 1, Part 1) to Berthollet, who received it before the end of August 1808.[5]

In the first part of Dalton's *New System* there is no mention of Arcueil, although as proof that Berthollet's views were not a matter of indifference to Dalton there are fifteen pages devoted to criticism of the French chemist's ideas as expressed in the *Statique chimique*. In the late summer of 1809 Dalton received from Berthollet a copy of the second volume of the Arcueil *Mémoires* and as the printing of Part 2 of Dalton's *New System* had only just begun, he was able to make use of the new material. He referred courteously to the 'very important and valuable papers' contained in the Arcueil collection,[6] but its real importance to Dalton may be judged by the number of references (ten in all) he made to this volume. Dalton's interests ranged over several topics but most significant were his comments on Gay-Lussac's law of combining volumes of gases, to which he de-

---

[1] Berthollet had been elected an honorary member on 30 April 1790.
[2] Royal Society, *Blagden Letters*, B. 128 (27 September 1807).
[3] *Ibid.*, B. 129 (9 October 1807).
[4] *Ibid.*, B. 130A (draft reply to Berthollet).
[5] *Ibid.*, B. 133 (Berthollet's acknowledgement, 31 August 1808).
[6] *New System*, vol. i, part 2, 1810, p. 353n.

voted several pages in an appendix.[1] It is curious that, instead of welcoming Gay-Lussac's work as a vindication of his atomic theory, he rejected it as inexact, preferring, for example, his own figures of 1·97 : 1 for the ratio of the combining volumes of hydrogen and oxygen to the figures 2 : 1 of Gay-Lussac. No-one can say here that the course of chemical history would have been different if Gay-Lussac had not published his work in an 'obscure journal'.

It will have been gathered that Berthollet was more fortunate in his despatch of the second volume of the Arcueil *Mémoires* than in the case of the first. In July 1809 Chenevix was travelling from Paris to London and Berthollet entrusted him with seven copies of the *Mémoires*, intended for the Royal Society, Blagden, Thomson, Davy, Wollaston, Hatchett and Dalton.[2] Thomas Thomson, shortly to found the journal *Annals of Philosophy*, was the author of a standard text-book of chemistry which he constantly kept up to date in successive editions. To the fourth edition, then in preparation, he added an appendix which refers to the main chemical contributions of the second volume of Arcueil *Mémoires*.[3]

Berthollet had been particularly anxious to let Davy have a copy of the Arcueil *Mémoires* in gratitude for Davy having sent him copies of his own memoirs.[4] Davy publicly acknowledged his receipt of this volume in his Bakerian lecture of 16 November 1809.[5] He was, of course, particularly interested in the research of Gay-Lussac and Thenard and he had previously made several references in his published work to a copy of the *Moniteur* (27 May 1808) containing a summary of some of their experiments. Davy was now in possession of a more complete account of their work. This volume contained the memoir on oxymuriatic acid in which they had attempted to decompose the gas by passing it over red-hot charcoal. Davy was particularly impressed by this experiment and he was led to the inevitable conclusion that 'oxymuriatic acid' was a simple body, to which he gave the name 'chlorine'. Of Gay-Lussac's paper

[1] *Ibid.*, pp. 555–9.
[2] Royal Society, *Blagden Letters*, B. 135 (9 July 1809).
[3] *System of Chemistry*, 4th edn., Edinburgh, 1810, vol. v, pp. 767 ff.; see also vol. iii, p. 467.
[4] Royal Society, *Blagden Letters*, B. 134 (19 April 1809).
[5] *Phil. Trans.*, 1810, 17–18; see also *ibid.*, 64n., 232.

on the combining volumes of gases Davy said no more than that it was 'very curious'.

Berzelius went further. Berthollet had sent him the two volumes of Arcueil *Mémoires* in 1810 and Berzelius immediately seized on Gay-Lussac's memoir. In thanking Berthollet for the books, Berzelius wrote:

> These memoirs are all the dearer to me because besides all the interesting things contained in them, they have provided me with a more detailed knowledge of the work of Gay-Lussac on the same subjects that I have been working on for several years.[1]

In fact in the memoir which Berzelius enclosed for publication in the *Annales de chimie*[2] he made considerable use of Gay-Lussac's data. Convinced of the validity of Gay-Lussac's law of combining volumes of gases and accepting the general principles of Daltonian atomism whilst being wary of accepting Daltonian atoms, Berzelius sought to effect a synthesis of the two theories by substituting the word 'volume' for 'atom'. For Berzelius one of the difficulties of the atomic theory, in which one is compelled to speak of self-contradictory half-atoms, was resolved by considering half-volumes. Also Berzelius considered that the theory of volumes was based on more experimentally established facts than the theory of atoms.

[1] Berzelius, *Bref*, vol. i, part i, p. 14.
[2] *Ann. chim.*, lxxix (1811), 233–64.

CHAPTER EIGHT

Arcueil – The Last Phase (1814–1822)

The Overthrow of Napoleon and the Allied Occupation of Paris

THE YEAR 1812 witnessed Napoleon's disastrous Russian campaign with its heavy losses. Back in Paris in 1813, Napoleon set the wheels in motion for a ruthless conscription which might provide him with the manpower to overcome the increasing forces of the allies. By the end of the year, however, his enemies were menacing the frontiers of France and meeting with very little opposition from the local inhabitants. Napoleon's armies could not hold for long the combined armies of Prussia, Russia and Austria advancing from the east and the allies finally entered Paris on 31 March 1814. Berthollet, perhaps fearing the worst, had made his will at Arcueil on 2 February 1814.[1]

In 1814 the Senate was the only branch of the legislature still functioning, the Tribunate having been dissolved in 1807 and the Legislative Body having been adjourned at the end of December 1813 because of its open appeals to Napoleon for peace. The Russian Emperor had declared his intention of allowing the French nation through the established bodies of the state to settle the question of who should rule France. On 31 March the allies entered Paris and late in the evening letters were sent to all Senators believed to be in Paris, summoning them to a special session at the Luxembourg the following afternoon. A meeting of the Senate at which half the members were absent would have had no legal powers and Talleyrand's emissaries spent all day on 1 April seeking out more Senators, not an easy task since some had gone into hiding. Others of the 144 Senators, including Chaptal, who was one of those who had been sent to supervise conscription in the provinces, were absent from Paris. Nevertheless, at a second meeting called that same evening sixty-four Senators were present.

[1] Archives de la Seine, Bureau d'Ivry Villejuif, *Mutation par Décès*, 1820–4, f. 125.

The Senate voted in a provisional government. Among the signatures to this document were those of Bonaparte's ex-colleagues during the Consulate, Ducos and Sieyès, also Fontanes (the head of the University) and Berthollet. At a third session on 3 April the Senate resolved that the Monarch existed only from a social compact and this had been broken by Napoleon. This Act of Deposition was also signed by Berthollet. By contrast Laplace had had the foresight to absent himself from Paris during this awkward moment in the nation's history. The registers of the First Class show his absences on 28 March and on 4 and 11 April.

We are fortunate to have Berthollet's own version of the circumstances in which he supported the downfall of his patron. Writing during the Hundred Days to his friend Blagden, Berthollet explained:

> When the foreign troops entered Paris, I retired to Dulong's house, resolved to avoid any act which would be contrary to the obligation which I owed to the Emperor; unfortunately when the Senate was summoned in the name of the Emperor of Russia, I considered that it was my duty as a citizen to comply with this invitation, without knowing what had been done previously; the previous day the deposition [of Napoleon] had been proclaimed. The minutes of this meeting were read and all members present were forced to sign it.[1]

Napoleon was indignant that the Senate, whose members he had favoured with wealth and title, should have turned against him in this way. Later, when exiled at St Helena, he had time to reflect on the crucial events of 1814 and 1815. The following account of an episode at St Helena is due to Las Cases:[2]

> After dinner the Emperor looked at the *Dictionnaire des Girouettes* (Dictionary of Weathercocks[3]) . . . The Emperor read to us several articles from the dictionary . . . he . . . several times . . . burst into a hearty fit of laughter. However, after going through a few pages, he closed the book with an expression of disgust and

---

[1] 'On a obligé tous les membres présents à le signer'—Royal Society, *Blagden Letters*, B. 141 (28 March 1815).
[2] Count Las Cases, *Journal of the Private Life and Conversations of the Emperor Napoleon at Saint Helena*, trans., London, 1824, vol. ii, part 3, pp. 254–5.
[3] A collection of biographies of men whose opinions were said to have changed in conformity with the wind of politics.

regret . . . One article seemed to affect him deeply, namely that on Berthollet, whom he had so loaded with favour, and on whom he said, he had every reason to rely.

Las Cases then mentions that Napoleon had behaved generously to Berthollet, who failed to show his gratitude in the crucial moments of 1814:

His conduct affected Napoleon at the time and he was often heard to exclaim—'What Berthollet! . . . on whom I thought I could rely with such confidence!'

This is how Napoleon is reported to have seen the issue but from the other side there is the question to what length loyalty can be expected to go. Berthollet had been prepared to support Bonaparte when he had contributed to the glory of France. In March 1814 only the most fanatical supporters of Napoleon could hope for any solution which did not involve his deposition.

Two days after the Senate had formally deposed Napoleon, the Institute met and approved its action. They prudently resolved, however, that this should not be recorded in the minutes. At the same time the Institute proposed to form a deputation to thank the allied powers for protecting the monuments of the capital and for this purpose it visited successively the King of Prussia and the Emperors of Austria and Russia. On 21 April the Emperor Alexander and the King of Prussia paid a formal visit to the Institute. In the speech of welcome made by the president, the visit of Peter the Great to the *Académie des Sciences* in the seventeenth century was recalled, nor was the role of Frederick the Great as a patron of science overlooked. The Institute welcomed the respective successors of these two sovereigns as well as their own king. This did not prevent the Institute declaring the following year, after the return of Napoleon, that since 1814 science and the arts had been in mourning.

As regards the military occupation of the Paris region, Humboldt proved a useful intermediary with the Prussian forces and, when a Prussian regiment was about to establish itself at the *Muséum d'Histoire Naturelle*, his intervention led to their being sent elsewhere and hence prevented much possible damage. At Arcueil cuirassiers from a Lichtenstein regiment were stationed, and there still exists a letter written to the authorities on 17 April 1814 by Berthollet, as one of the most influential residents of the village, complaining of the rough treatment which some of the villagers were receiving from the soldiers.[1] In another letter Berthollet recorded that both his town house and particularly his house at Arcueil had been occupied by foreign troops.[2]

Berthollet's Work and Fortunes in the Years 1814–22

On 13 August 1814 Berthollet wrote to his old friend, James Watt:

> I have retired completely to the country and I only go to Paris when I am called there for urgent business. I am beginning to take up my work again.[3]

Berthollet's experimental work at Arcueil had always been of an occasional character. His importance during most of the Arcueil period depends on his influence and on his collaborators rather than on his own actual laboratory work. Nevertheless, even after the collapse of the Napoleonic regime, when regular meetings were no longer held at Arcueil, Berthollet continued to make some use of the laboratory facilities of his country house. Contrary to his usual practice, in the first winter after Napoleon's defeat Berthollet did not move to Paris but kept his house at Arcueil open. It is amusing to find Blagden recording in his diary on 27 January 1815 the complaint that 'Berthollet avoided telling me what he was doing in his laboratory, only that he had succeeded in a course of experiments'.[4] In fact Berthollet was investigating the action of chlorine on organic liquids.[5]

In the winter of 1814–15 Berthollet began working on a new edition of his *Statique chimique* but his concentration on this project was interrupted by the turn of political events in March 1815, when Napoleon returned to power.[6] In October 1815

---

[1] Archives de la Seine, MS. 4, Az. 523.

[2] '. . . C'était un tems ou mon habitation de ville et surtout celle de campagne, étaient encore occupées par les troupes alliées'—Letter to James Watt, Arcueil, 18 February 1815, J. P. Muirhead, *The Origins and Progress of the Mechanical Inventions of James Watt*, 1854, vol. ii, p. 361.

[3] *Ibid.*, p. 360.   [4] Royal Society, *Blagden Diary*, vol. vii, f. 13v.

[5] *Ann. chim. phys.*, i (1816), 426–9.

[6] Royal Society, *Blagden Letters*, B. 140 (23 March 1815).

Berthollet wrote to Proust from Arcueil that he was undertaking a revision of the *Statique chimique* but that this was proving a slow process.[1] Berthollet's manuscript has recently been rediscovered.[2] It reveals that in his old age Berthollet still kept up with the literature but there is little evidence of any new insight or fresh experimental work.

The return of Napoleon in March 1815 did not help Berthollet. In the first place, he had at least in a technical sense, betrayed his patron. Secondly Napoleon had no more use for a Senate. Through the good offices of Monge and Carnot Napoleon agreed to see him. Berthollet writes:

> The Emperor received me as before but there is no longer a Senate and my fortune is reversed for the moment.[3]

Nevertheless, this did not prevent Berthollet from welcoming the return of Napoleon[4] and finding the second Restoration difficult to accept.[5]

The end of the Hundred Days of Napoleon and the Second Restoration brought with them the renewed presence of foreign troops in Paris and this time the armies of Wellington and Blücher were to stay in France for longer than the allies in 1814 and they were to harass the population and requisition their property on a much larger scale.

We should not pass over one fruitful introduction which resulted from the presence of Prussian troops in the French capital. Heinrich Rose, later to achieve an international reputation for his work in chemical analysis, began his career as a pharmacist. He then volunteered for the Prussian army and found himself at the age of twenty together with his brother Gustav in Paris in 1815. He took the opportunity of meeting Biot, Gay-Lussac, Vauquelin and above all Berthollet. In 1807 Berthollet had written to Gehlen in Halle asking for details of the analytical work of Valentine Rose but was told that Rose had just died.[6] Fate was to send his sons to Berthollet and

---

[1] Académie des Sciences, Dossier Proust.

[2] An intensive study of these notes is being undertaken by Madame Sadoun-Goupil, to whom I am indebted for this information.

[3] Royal Society, *Blagden Letters*, B. 141 (28 March 1815).

[4] 'Il est incontestable que la grande majorité voit avec satisfaction le retour de Napoléon', *ibid.*, B 140 (23 March 1815).

[5] *Ibid.*, B 142 (2 October 1815).

[6] *Ann. chim.*, lxv (1808), 316–24.

Berthollet saw much of the young Heinrich Rose and explained to him his conception of chemical reactions.[1] In many of his later publications Rose developed Berthollet's ideas on the influence of mass, etc., on the course of chemical reactions.[2] The months that he spent in contact with Berthollet had a decisive influence on him and he would later recommend students to go to Paris for postgraduate experience, as for example, Bunsen in 1832.[3] Heinrich Rose's younger brother Gustav became a mineralogist and taught in the University of Berlin, numbering Mitscherlich among his early students. Gustav Rose had been favourably impressed by his first visit to Paris, however unusual the circumstances, and returned there later. He came into contact with Humboldt, and when the latter went on an expedition to Siberia in 1829 he took Gustav Rose with him.

We must return to Berthollet and the state of his fortune in the period of the Restoration. In February 1816 he told Blagden that his income had been reduced to 24,000 francs a year, of which he had received payment for one quarter.[4] Although he and his wife were planning to return to Arcueil as the winter ended, he assured Blagden that he had reduced his expenses to a minimum.[5] Evidently his English friend had feared a return to his old extravagance and carelessness in financial matters.

In 1816 Berthollet was doing further work on reversible reactions in solution and his short paper on this subject, published in the final volume of the Arcueil *Mémoires*, is dated 20 May 1816.[6] Yet he was spending less and less time in the laboratory and no more work of note appears to have been done there till the visit by Berzelius in 1819. Even after Berzelius had gone, Berthollet, now over seventy years old, wrote that he had a younger brother of Jacques Étienne Bérard as an assistant and he was getting him to put everything in his laboratory in good

---

[1] *Allgemeine Deutsche Biographie*, Leipzig, vol. xxix, 1889, p. 178.

[2] C. Rammelsberg, 'Gedächtnissrede auf Heinrich Rose', *Abhandlung der königlichen Akademie der Wissenschaften zu Berlin*, 1865, 1–31 (see especially pp. 17–18).

[3] T. Curtius, 'Gedächtnissrede gehalten für R. W. Bunsen', *Journal für praktische Chemie*, N.F., lxi (1900), 381–407, especially p. 385.

[4] Royal Society, *Blagden Letters*, B 143 (3 February 1816).

[5] *Ibid.*, B 144 (14? March 1816).

[6] *M.S.A.*, iii (1817), 453–61.

order with a view to doing further work. A year later, however, Berthollet had to admit that all his enthusiasm for research had now left him.[1]

Berthollet's life, however, had always extended beyond the confines of his laboratory. He continued to go regularly to the meetings of the *Académie des Sciences* and took part in the work of the *Chambre des Pairs*. Berthollet also attended meetings as a member of the *Conseil de Perfectionnement* of the *Conservatoire des Arts et Métiers* and among his colleagues there were Chaptal, Gay-Lussac and Arago. On the death of Guyton de Morveau in 1816 he delivered an oration. Two years later when his friend Monge died, former students of the *École Polytechnique* addressed to Berthollet a letter proposing a subscription for a monument in commemoration. Although Monge had died exiled from the *Académie* as a Bonapartist and the students of the *École Polytechnique* had been prevented by the government from attending his funeral, Berthollet was glad to associate himself with this subscription, which was given publicity by Arago and Gay-Lussac in the *Annales de chimie et de physique*.[2]

Berthollet had now had a long association with the village of Arcueil and in 1820 he was chosen as mayor of the commune.[3] He resigned, however, after a few months, giving poor health as a reason.

The Work of the 'Berthollet School'

Of more consequence than the work actually done by Berthollet in the closing years of his life was the work which he inspired others to do. Despite many of his brilliant insights, the fact remains that on one or two important issues his ideas were disproved. The law of constant composition is an example of this. Yet such questions were to be answered by careful analysis in which Berthollet trained his young collaborators. The analytical skill of Gay-Lussac and Dulong combined with the Arcueil interest in combining proportions could hardly fail to lead to valuable discoveries. Berthollet may have been largely

[1] Berzelius, *Bref*, vol. 1, part i, pp. 70, 73.

[2] *Op cit.*, viii (1818), 428–30.

[3] A letter dated 20 September 1820, and signed by Berthollet in his capacity as mayor of Arcueil, has been found by M. Desguine, who has kindly communicated its contents to me.

mistaken in his belief in elements combining in indefinite proportions, but Gay-Lussac was able to show that the opposite extreme as represented by Berzelius' wish to reduce the oxides of iron to two was not justified in the light of his own analysis of a third oxide.[1]

Oxides of nitrogen seemed to provide an example of two elements combining to produce a large number of possible compounds. No doubt it was the challenge of this problem as well as the traditional use of nitric oxide to estimate oxygen (the method used by Priestley) that interested Gay-Lussac,[2] whose work on this problem was taken further and corrected by Dulong. By heating *dry* crystals of lead nitrate Dulong obtained liquid dinitrogen tetroxide in a tube surrounded by a freezing mixture.[3] He recorded its boiling point at 28°C.[4] He was the first to make a study of the colour changes undergone by this interesting compound over a wide range of temperature from a colourless solid at $-20°C$ to a deep red vapour when heated.

Dulong did some valuable work on the acids of phosphorus. In a memoir which he read at two meetings of the *Académie des Sciences* in July 1816, he explained the origins of this research. His memoir was published in full only in the Arcueil *Mémoires*,[5] the *Annales de chimie*, for example, being unable to give more than a summary of his work.[6] Dulong began by emphasizing the importance of an exact knowledge of combining proportions and pointed to the divergencies in the published analyses of phosphoric acid, mentioning the proportions given by Lavoisier, Thomson, Rose and Davy, among others. Phosphorous acid had been analysed by Thenard, but Gay-Lussac, using the analogy of the oxy-acids of sulphur, had arrived at a quite different result. It was in an attempt to clarify this position that Dulong discovered that there were at least four acids of phosphorus. In addition to the two already mentioned, the composition of which he determined accurately, Dulong confirmed the exist-

---

[1] *Ann. chim. phys.*, i (1816), 32.

[2] *M.S.A.*, ii (1809), 235–53; *Ann. chim. phys.*, i (1816), 394–410.

[3] 'Observations sur quelques combinaisons de l'azote avec l'oxigène', read to *Académie des Sciences* in September 1815, *Ann. chim. phys.*, ii (1816), 317–27.

[4] The modern value for the pure product is 22°C.

[5] *M.S.A.*, iii (1817), 405–52.

[6] *Ann. chim. phys.*, ii (1816), 141–50.

ence of hypophosphoric acid and discovered a further acid which he named hypophosphorous acid. The memoir contains a careful analysis of the new acid and a discussion of its salts. At the end he returns to the question of which elements were most similar to phosphorus. Finding no consistency, he concludes in the best tradition of the *Chemical Statics*:

> It seems, therefore, that the forces which produce combinations must come from another source than those which determine their proportions.

As a final example of an extension of Berthollet's work by one of his followers, we may cite the memoir on prussic acid presented by Gay-Lussac to the *Académie des Sciences* in September 1815.[1] Gay-Lussac began, as indeed anyone of whatever nationality would have done, by referring to Berthollet's work on this acid. In 1787 Berthollet had carried out a careful qualitative analysis of prussic acid from which he concluded that it was a compound of nitrogen, hydrogen and carbon.[2] He did not state categorically that it contained no oxygen, a fact which would have been in direct conflict with Lavoisier's theory of acids. Berthollet made a decisive step towards undermining Lavoisier's theory when he showed in 1796 that hydrogen sulphide had all the properties of an acid and yet contained no oxygen.[3]

In Gay-Lussac's analysis of prussic acid it was characteristic of the man that he should investigate the substance quantitatively in terms of gaseous volumes. Having a volatile acid and taking advantage of hot days in August he carried out his quantitative analysis with a Volta eudiometer. By means of these and other experiments Gay-Lussac showed convincingly that prussic acid contained no oxygen. It was a hydracid in which the carbon and nitrogen together played a role similar to, for example, the iodine in hydriodic acid. He developed the analogy between the hydracids and suggested that prussic acid be called 'hydro-prussic acid'. In the tradition of the French reformers of chemical nomenclature and with the approval of Berthollet and other chemists in Paris, Gay-Lussac proposed a

---

[1] *Ann. chim.*, xcv (1815), 136–231.   [2] *Ibid.*, i (1789), 38.
[3] *Ibid.*, xxv (1798), 237.

new name for the radical of prussic acid—cyanogen, and he was successful in isolating this.

The 'Annales de chimie et de physique'

It was pointed out in Chapter Six that the publications of the members of the Arcueil group were by no means confined to the *Mémoires* of the Society of Arcueil. They contributed to the *Journal de physique*, the *Journal des mines*, the *Mémoires* of the First Class of the Institute and above all to the *Annales de chimie*.

The *Annales de chimie* had first been published in 1789 as the journal of the new chemistry. The editorial board was composed of Guyton de Morveau, Lavoisier, Monge, Berthollet, Fourcroy, the Baron Dietrich, Hassenfratz and Adet. The *Annales* stopped publication after Lavoisier's arrest in 1793 but publication was resumed under the chairmanship of Guyton from 1797. The following years saw the inclusion on the editorial board of several other chemists, including Chaptal (1798), Descotils (1804) and finally Gay-Lussac and Thenard (1814).

The steady course of the *Annales* was suddenly interrupted by the death of its secretary, Descotils, on 6 December 1815. An extraordinary meeting of the society of the *Annales de chimie* was called for 11 December. The obvious business was to elect a new secretary but in fact the meeting agreed to a proposal of much greater consequence. The number of volumes was now approaching a hundred and it seemed appropriate to begin a new series. There was also the feeling that chemistry had become so closely linked with physics that neither could be studied in isolation. A new journal should therefore be founded devoted to both chemistry and physics.

The liberation of chemistry from iatrochemistry was now complete. Lavoisier had preached the union of chemistry and physics but when the *Annales de chimie* was founded it was decided to emphasize in a sub-title not this aspect but the more popular conception of the *utility* of chemistry.[1] In 1799 the incorporation of the *Journal de la Société des Pharmaciens de Paris* with the *Annales* resulted in the inclusion on the editorial committee of Deyeux, Parmentier and Bouillon Lagrange. These

---

[1] *Annales de chimie ou Recueil de Mémoires concernant la chimie et les Arts qui en dépendent.* After 1800 the words *et surtout la pharmacie* were added.

men together with the original membership of Fourcroy, swung the balance of interest of the *Annales* towards pharmacy and from January 1800 the word 'pharmacy' was incorporated into the title of the journal.

On the other hand Berthollet and his associates at Arcueil had developed the links between chemistry and physics and they had proclaimed their interest in the title of their journal—*Mémoires de physique et de chimie de la Société d'Arcueil*. When the regular meetings at Arcueil came to an end the men who formed the group had the opportunity of making their attitude to science even more widely felt. The journal of French chemistry would be replaced by a more comprehensive periodical entitled *Annales de chimie et de physique*. By using smaller type, substantial space could be given to physical topics without sacrificing the chemistry content and without increasing the number of pages in each issue.

Arago was appointed editor for the contributions on physics and Gay-Lussac was editor for the chemical part, although it was appreciated that many contributions would lie on the borderline. On 15 January 1816 Berthollet was appointed president of the society of the *Annales* to succeed Guyton who had died a fortnight before. Finally in March the membership of the editorial board was increased by the inclusion of Biot, Dulong and Chevreul. Not only were the two editors of the *Annales* prominent members of the recently active Society of Arcueil but the majority of the editorial board under the chairmanship of Berthollet had belonged to the Arcueil group. If there is any truth in our claim that the men who met at Arcueil represented an influential cross-section of French science, it is the *Annales de chimie et de physique* which illustrate it.

Gay-Lussac is conspicuous in the early volumes for his frequent contributions of both original research and editorial comments. Not only did younger members of the Arcueil group such as Dulong describe their valuable discoveries in its pages, but older members, notably Laplace and Humboldt, contributed their work and Berthollet did his share by writing reviews of the recently published text-books of chemistry and physics by Thenard and Biot respectively. In so far as the Society of Arcueil had come into existence to provide a means of publication, one might say that the *Annales de chimie* in its new form had rendered this service superfluous. Arcueil had entered into a final period of decline but the men who had once met together at Arcueil continued to be active.

The editors of such a journal were in a powerful position. Although theoretically impartial, in practice the editorial influence can often be seen in the contents. In 1817 they went so far as to criticize the recent election of a foreign associate of the *Académie des Sciences*.[1] One of the candidates had been Sir Humphry Davy and the editors deplored the fact that despite his major contributions to science and the service he had rendered to humanity by the development of the safety lamp, he had been defeated by a relatively unknown anatomist, Scarpa. In 1820 Arago not only brought news of Oersted's discovery of electromagnetism to his colleagues in Paris at the *Académie*, he gave it a wider publicity by immediate insertion in the *Annales* with a personal guarantee of its authenticity.[2] In 1825 when Balard discovered a new element, it was mainly due to Gay-Lussac, both as a member of the *Académie* and as editor of the *Annales*, that the new element was called 'brome' (bromine).[3]

New Alliances

The existence of a circle of associates at Arcueil led to some fruitful collaboration. With the decline of the activities of the Society after 1813, other associations were made and new alliances were formed. The most famous collaboration is probably that between Dulong and Petit, which led to the discovery of the law named after them.[4] Less well known is the collaboration of Arago with Petit. A joint memoir by Arago and Petit on the refractive indices of liquids and their vapours appeared in the first volume of the *Annales de chimie et de physique*. Petit, a brilliant graduate of the *École Polytechnique*, had married Arago's sister and it may well have been through Arago that Petit became acquainted with Dulong.

The first of three joint memoirs by Dulong and Petit was read at the Institute on 29 May 1815.[5] They were concerned

[1] *Ann. chim. phys.*, v (1817), 223n.
[2] *Ibid.*, xiv (1820), 417–25.   [3] *Ibid.*, xxxiii (1826), 222.
[4] Specific heat of an element × atomic weight = approximately constant.
[5] *Ann. chim. phys.*, ii (1816), 240–63.

with a problem of which different aspects had already been studied by Lavoisier and Laplace and by Gay-Lussac, the laws of thermal expansion. Dulong and Petit devised a method of determining the absolute coefficient of expansion directly, using apparatus consisting of two vertical columns of mercury connected at the base, one column being heated while the other remained cold.[1] This method of 'balancing columns', later modified by Regnault, became standard for the direct determination of the absolute coefficient of expansion of a liquid. Dulong and Petit later undertook a complete examination of Newton's law of cooling. This constituted the second part of a memoir that was to win them the prize of the *Académie des Sciences*.[2]

The rift between Biot and Arago led each to seek new co-workers with valuable results in both cases. Biot, for example, pursued his optical researches with the help of Pouillet, *répétiteur* at the *École Normale*, and they published a joint memoir in 1816.[3] Better known is the joint investigation in 1820 of the magnetic force due to a long straight wire carrying an electric current by Biot and Savart. Savart was Biot's junior colleague at the *Collège de France*.

The alliance which was to have the greatest impact on science in the nineteenth century was that between Arago and Fresnel. Augustin Fresnel (1788–1827), a graduate of the *École Polytechnique*, became a civil engineer and spent the final years of the First Empire supervising the construction of roads in the French provinces. It was in 1814 that Fresnel had begun to take an interest in problems connected with light, and on passing through Paris in 1815, he obtained some brief advice from Arago. At the beginning of the Hundred Days Fresnel associated himself with the royalist army and was subsequently placed under police surveillance. He was soon allowed to return to his native village near Caen in Normandy. He now had leisure and he used it to do some optical experiments, although he had no books and only the crudest apparatus. This was the occasion of his first memoirs on light, which he sent to Arago for comment. The restoration of the Bourbons enabled Fresnel to resume his career as a state civil engineer and through

[1] *Ibid.*, vii (1817), 113–54. [2] *Ibid.*, 225–64, 337–67.
[3] 'Sur la diffraction de la lumière', *Bull. Soc. Philomatique*, 1816, 60–1.

Arago's influence he spent several months at the beginning of 1816 in Paris where he had better conditions for research. From this resulted his 'Memoir on diffraction', which Arago published in the *Annales de chimie et de physique*, preceded by his own report to the *Académie* in which he declared that Fresnel's analysis of diffraction fringes seemed to him destined to found a new epoch in the history of optics.[1]

In January 1817 a commission was appointed by the *Académie des Sciences* to choose a subject for the next prize in physics. The members were Laplace, Biot, Berthollet and Charles. Laplace and Biot considered this as an opportunity to sponsor further research, which would strengthen the corpuscular theory of light and, accordingly, on 10 February 1817 we find Biot, on behalf of the commission, proposing the subject of diffraction. Fresnel, of course, entered for the prize.

Fresnel had written from Rennes to Arago in December 1816, asking him if he had shown his experiments in favour of the wave ·theory to Laplace. To have convinced the great mathematician of evidence in favour of the wave theory would have been a great triumph for Fresnel. A month later, however, Arago replied that he had not even had time to check the experiments himself.[2] In the summer of 1818, however, Fresnel had the opportunity of visiting Laplace at Arcueil in the company of Arago. In a letter written on 5 September 1818 Fresnel described the encounter.[3] The conversation apparently turned largely on the value of mathematical analysis in optics, whereas Fresnel would naturally have preferred to have taken Laplace step by step through his experimental evidence. Yet the interview was not without value, since Fresnel considered it worthwhile revising several points of the memoir in the light of his discussion with his venerable opponent.

Meanwhile, as Fresnel was not living in Paris, his uncle, Léonor Mérimé,[4] kept him informed of the scientific news of

---

[1] *Ann. chim. phys.*, i (1816), 199–202, 239–81.
[2] Fresnel, *Oeuvres*, 1866–70, vol. ii, pp. 782–5.
[3] *Ibid.*, vol. ii, pp. 848–9.
[4] Léonor Mérimé taught drawing at the *École Polytechnique*. In 1800 he had collaborated with Thenard in the discovery of 'Thenard's blue' and it was he who, twenty years later, applied Thenard's discovery of hydrogen peroxide to the restoration of oil paintings. *Ann. chim. phys.*, xiv (1820), 221–3.

the capital as well as the internal politics of the *Académie des Sciences*. They were both afraid that the commission to judge the prize would be chosen from among the supporters of Biot ('la secte des Biotistes') headed by Laplace.[1] Their worst fears were not realized, although it is true that the commission of five appointed by the *Académie* on 27 July 1818 contained a majority hostile to the wave theory: Laplace, Biot and Poisson. Arago, however, was also on the commission and the fifth member was Gay-Lussac who, on this question, could be relied upon to be impartial. If any illustration is needed of the power of the Arcueil group within the *Académie* in the first quarter of the nineteenth century, the choice of this commission surely provides it.

While examining Fresnel's memoir, Poisson saw that his formula implied that if an opaque circular screen were placed perpendicular to the incident light, the centre of the shadow would be just as bright in the absence of the screen.[2] This was verified experimentally and was powerful evidence in support of Fresnel's theory. The report by the commission on the memoirs submitted for the prize of the *Académie* was read by Arago on 15 March 1819. There was no great difficulty in deciding that Fresnel's was the best memoir.

Enough has been said to show that Fresnel had a powerful patron in Arago. From the very beginning of his work on light, Arago had given him help and encouragement, provided laboratory facilities for him in Paris and, not least important, had fought as his champion and his collaborator behind the closed doors of the *Académie des Sciences*. The acceptance of the wave theory in France owes as much to Arago's support as it does to Fresnel's experimental insight.

When discussing the new alliances, we should not forget to mention the renewal of the old. In 1823 Dulong and Thenard jointly investigated reports that spongy platinum was able to bring about the combination of hydrogen and oxygen.[3] They found that certain other metals such as palladium and rhodium are equally effective catalysts at room temperature. Thenard's laboratory assistant tells how they would write up their experiments independently at the week-end and then read each

[1] Fresnel, *Oeuvres*, vol. ii, p. 842.   [2] *Ibid.*, vol. i, p. 236.
[3] *Ann. chim. phys.*, xiii (1823), 440; xiv (1823), 380.

other's account on the Monday morning, ready to present the
final memoir in the evening at the meeting of the *Académie des
Sciences*.[1]

At the request of the *Académie des Sciences* (acting in response
to a government appeal) Dulong and Arago in collaboration
undertook a long, tedious and dangerous investigation of high
steam pressures to make safer the operation of boilers. This
work began in 1824 and was continued intermittently for the
next few years, not reaching completion until 1830. Meanwhile
Gay-Lussac, whose period of active collaboration with Thenard
was over, found some common problems with Welter, a former
assistant of Berthollet, and between 1819 and 1821 Gay-Lussac
and Welter published three joint papers. In one of these[2] they
helped to lay the foundations of volumetric analysis.

Visitors to Arcueil

In the two decades of the residence of Berthollet (1801–22) and
Laplace (1806–27) at Arcueil, their houses attracted many
foreign visitors to the French capital although, of course, very
few between 1803 and 1814. To follow a chronological order in
the period of this 'last phase' at Arcueil we might begin with the
visit of the distinguished Scots physicist Sir John Leslie in July
1814.[3] In 1802 after the Peace of Amiens Leslie related that he
spent 'several months very agreeably . . . in that vortex of
pleasure and centre of information' (i.e. Paris). With the temporary end of the Napoleonic wars in 1814 Leslie returned to
the continent for a six-week tour of France and the Netherlands.
In a letter written on 1 August 1814 he recorded that he had
been very well received in Paris and had been drawn, almost
despite himself, into close contact with the scientists of the
French capital. He continued:

> Humboldt has been very kind and attentive to me, and introduces
> me wherever I want. They are much better acquainted with
> what we are doing than I should have imagined. My book on
> Heat is better known than in England. I was even reminded of

[1] F. Dubois, *Éloge de M. Thenard*, 1863, p. 49.

[2] *Ann. chim. phys.*, xiii (1820), 212–21.

[3] *Encyclopaedia Britannica*, 7th edn., vol. xiii, Art.: Leslie, Sir John,
pp. 242–52, especially pp. 245, 248.

some passages in it which in England were considered as fanciful, but which the recent discoveries on the polarity of light have confirmed. Even Laplace has, in consequence of some observations of mine, silently omitted a passage in the last edition of his *Système du Monde*. I paid a visit the other day at Arcueil. Berthollet has a fine chateau seated on a bank amidst gardens, vineyards, etc.; and Laplace has another, little inferior, and adjoining to the grounds. I dine with Laplace next Sunday . . .

In 1817 Paris was visited by that extraordinary self-educated Scotswoman, Mary Somerville, whose popular account of Laplace's *Mécanique céleste* had a great success in the 1830's. Mary Somerville was presented by Arago to Laplace and his wife, who invited her to visit them. To continue in Mrs Somerville's own words:[1]

> We were invited to go early and spend a day with them at Arcueil, where they had a country house. M. Arago had told M. de la Place that I had read the *Mécanique céleste*, so we had a great deal of conversation about astronomy and the calculus and he gave me a copy of his *Système du Monde*, with his inscription, which pleased me exceedingly. I spoke French very badly but I was less at a loss on scientific subjects, because almost all my books on science were in French.
> The party at dinner consisted of MM. Biot, Arago, Bouvard and Poisson. I sat next M. de la Place, who was exceedingly kind and attentive. In such a great assemblage of philosophers I expected a very grave and learned conversation. But not at all! Everyone talked in a gay, animated and loud key, especially M. Poisson,[2] who had all the vivacity of a Frenchman.

Berzelius at Arcueil

In 1810 Berthollet wrote to the Swedish chemist Berzelius, then aged thirty-one, saying that he had heard that he was hoping

---

[1] *Personal recollections from early life to old age of Mary Somerville with selections from her correspondence by her daughter, Martha Somerville*, 1873, pp. 109-10.

[2] Mrs Somerville records that this was near the day of Poisson's marriage. She goes on to describe another dinner party given by Madame Biot at which M. and Mme Arago, M. and Mme Poisson and Humboldt were present. She also refers (p. 111) to the rich furnishings of the Laplace house. Mrs Somerville paid another visit to Arcueil after the death of Laplace (*ibid.*, p. 186).

to come to France and inviting him to stay at Arcueil.[1] Berzelius replied that he was hoping to come to Paris and also to visit Arcueil. He mentioned that he was not wealthy enough to undertake the journey at his own expense but was hoping for aid from the government. Berthollet's invitation was shown to the Crown Prince of Sweden who promised to provide money for the journey.[2] Berthollet wrote tactfully that Berzelius would have no other expenses on his visit to Paris than those necessary for the journey.

At the outbreak of war between France and Sweden Berzelius was advised not to travel to Paris, although Berthollet had obtained a passport for him. Instead he spent the summer in England. It was not until 1818 that the visit to which he had looked forward for so long eventually took place. Meanwhile Berthollet had sent him the *Mémoires* of the Society of Arcueil and he had made full use of their contents, not least the memoir of Gay-Lussac on the combining volumes of gases. In far-away Stockholm, before he had even visited France, Berzelius could therefore refer to Arcueil as 'that place so justly famous in the annals of chemistry'.[3] In 1811 when he managed to obtain a copy of Gay-Lussac and Thenard's *Recherches physico-chimiques*, he wrote to Gay-Lussac telling him that he had made more fine discoveries in two years than many chemists did during their whole lives.[4] It was therefore a great climax in the life of Berzelius when he was able to meet the men with whom he had corresponded and whose chemical work he had studied. France was still at the centre of the chemical world.

Berzelius travelled with the newly-appointed Swedish ambassador to France, Count Löwenhjelm, who invited him to be his guest at the embassy during his stay in Paris. On their arrival on the morning of 24 August Berzelius hastened to seek out Berthollet. His visit to Paris, which lasted until June the following year, was a period which he could later describe with sincerity as the happiest year of his life.[5] It goes without saying that Berzelius visited Arcueil, but his visit amounted to rather more than a pleasant afternoon in the country. During the

[1] Berzelius, *Bref*, 1912–35, vol. 1, part i, p. 9.
[2] Berzelius, *Autobiographical notes*, trans. O. Larsell, Baltimore, 1934, p. 73.   [3] Berzelius, *Bref.*, vol. 1, part i, p. 10.
[4] *Ibid.*, vol. 3, part vii, p. 114.
[5] *Ibid.*, vol. 2, part iv, p. 6.

months of February and March 1819 he stayed permanently at Arcueil. He described his day as follows:

> The residence with Berthollet continued in quite a patriarchal manner. I worked in my room until breakfast, which was served between 8 and 9 o'clock, usually having proofs of my papers to read. After breakfast I worked alone in the laboratory, to which the distinguished old gentleman seldom came, until dinner, which was served at 5 o'clock, and after that we read some non-chemical book in Countess Berthollet's company in front of the fireplace until 9 o'clock, when I retired.[1]

Berzelius therefore used all the daylight hours for his chemical work.

In a letter to his friend Marcet on 8 March 1819 Berzelius wrote:

> I have been at Arcueil for six weeks and I am doing chemical work in M. Berthollet's laboratory from morning to evening. I have not even left the house except on Mondays to go into town to attend the meetings of the *Académie*.[2]

The previous winter, however, Berzelius had made full use of the unique facilities for scientific education which Paris offered. He attended the lecture courses of Gay-Lussac, Vauquelin, Thenard, Haüy and Brongniart. Biot even gave him a special course dealing with his studies on polarized light. Writing in December 1818, he said that he was so busy attending all these lectures that he hardly had time to sleep. Yet there was hardly a lecture at which he did not learn something.[3] Berzelius for his part gave instruction on the use of the blowpipe to a group of Paris mineralogists. We are reminded by this that Berzelius was a distinguished mineralogist as well as an outstanding chemist. Haüy asked him to investigate some minerals and he took the opportunity of his stay at Arcueil to use Berthollet's laboratory for his analyses, which he described at a meeting of the *Académie des Sciences* and which were promptly published in the *Annales de chimie et de physique*.[4] Berzelius had been elected as a corresponding member of the *Académie* in 1816 and during his stay in Paris he made a point of attending the meetings regularly. It was the

[1] *Autobiographical Notes*, p. 183, note 212.
[2] Berzelius, *Bref*, vol I, part iii, p. 185.   [3] *Ibid.*, p. 180.
[4] *Op. cit.*, xii (1819), 12–37.

E E

custom always to sit in the same place and he took his seat between Thenard and Poisson.

Berzelius came into contact with Gay-Lussac in a special way since Gay-Lussac was able to give him practical help with research on gunpowder in his laboratory at the Arsenal and when he visited the powder factory at Essone, it was in the company of Gay-Lussac, now superintendent of the factory. Although Berzelius himself was mainly concerned with pure science, his government was interested in the practical application of science and it was on the understanding that he would study developments in the production of gunpowder abroad that he had been provided with leave of absence and payment of expenses. He records in his autobiography that because of the generosity of Löwenhjlem and Berthollet he was able to use most of the money he had been given to buy instruments and materials in France—apparatus that was later to be used to train a whole generation of German chemists in his own laboratory in Stockholm.

Another of the French scientists with whom Berzelius was particularly friendly was Thenard. He was especially impressed by the frankness of Thenard, who was prepared to discuss openly with Berzelius his current research on hydrogen peroxide and related compounds, whereas many of the other chemists were more guarded in their communications.[1]

Not the least of the achievements of Berzelius when he was in France was the supervision of the translation of one of his works: *Essai sur la théorie des proportions chimiques et sur l'influence chimique de l'electricité . . . traduit . . . sous les yeux de l'auetur.* This was the work of which he received proofs daily at Arcueil. It was not until the beginning of June 1819 that the book finally appeared and Berzelius postponed by a few weeks his departure from Paris to supervise its publication.

Berzelius and Dulong

One of the closest friends that Berzelius made in his visit to Paris was Dulong. Dulong was rather shy and perhaps difficult to get to know from a casual social meeting. Berzelius, writing to a friend in Sweden,[2] said that this was why Berthollet introduced

---

[1] Berzelius, *Bref*, vol. 1, part iii, p. 181.   [2] *Ibid.*, vol. 2, part iv, p. 3.

them to each other at Arcueil, where Dulong gradually blossomed out and Berzelius was able to appreciate fully the young man's scientific talents as well as his personality. Berzelius records his collaboration with Dulong in March 1819 in the following terms:

> The last weeks at Arcueil were used in collaboration with Dulong to determine through accurate experiments the atomic weights of hydrogen, nitrogen and carbon and also the specific gravities of oxygen gas, nitrogen gas and carbonic acid gas. During this investigation I obtained much new knowledge of a kind of research in which previously I had occupied myself but little. I also learned to recognize in Dulong an unusually profound scientist and won in him a steadfast friend.[1]

The central problem in the collaboration of Berzelius and Dulong was the determination of the ratio of the weights of hydrogen and oxygen in water. This was a fundamental datum of chemistry and it was vital that it should be known exactly. Berzelius explains how their collaboration on this particular topic came about:

> I happened one day to mention to Dulong that in the analysis of the oxides of lead and copper I obtained less water than was to be expected from the accepted numbers for the two constituents of water. Dulong answered that he had found that the weight of hydrogen is lighter than the value given by Biot and Arago, and we then determined to repeat our experiments in collaboration. This was done, the most important experiments on the weight of gas being made by Dulong, who was more accustomed than I to handling the instruments for such determinations.[2]

The way in which they proposed to do this depended entirely on the work and methods of the Arcueil group and makes this series of experiments an achievement of Arcueil in the fullest sense.[3] They relied in the first place on the combining volumes of gases. For hydrogen and oxygen this meant using the work of Humboldt and Gay-Lussac of 1804, extended for gases in general by Gay-Lussac in 1808. In the determination of the densities of the gases they intended to improve on the accuracy of the work of Biot and Arago. They were able to determine

[1] *Autobiographical Notes*, p. 103.   [2] *Ibid.*, p. 183, note 214.
[3] *Ann. chim. phys.*, xv (1820), 386–95.

the densities of some fifteen compound gases and calculate their gravimetric composition.

For the gravimetric composition of water they arrived at the ratio of $H : O = 11 \cdot 1 : 88 \cdot 9$, or, as Dumas represented it, $1 : 8 \cdot 008$. Dumas pointed out that this remarkably accurate result was partly due to the cancelling out of errors. It was only in 1842, nearly a quarter of a century after the work of Berzelius and Dulong that Dumas carried out his classic re-determination of this ratio.[1] He was influenced by Prout's idea that atomic weights should be exact whole numbers. There was also the feeling at this time that the authority of Berzelius had influenced chemistry for too long. Dumas was able to carry out a greater number of determinations of the ratio, he worked on a much larger scale and he introduced more corrections. In fact Berzelius and Dulong were working to an accuracy of about $1/60$; Dumas was able to increase this to $1/200$. The work of Dumas, therefore, whilst not producing a result substantially different from that of Berzelius and Dulong, illustrates the increasing precision which characterizes the development of the physical sciences.

The experiments of Dulong and Berzelius were not achieved without complications.[2] There were a large number of accidents and their goal of accurate measurement was handicapped by the limitations of the apparatus available in the declining state of Berthollet's laboratory in 1819. Determinations were repeated several times and many that were not consistent were ignored. Dulong with his onerous teaching duties and personal problems could not find time to do the necessary calculations and it was eighteen months later before their work was published.

This collaboration set the seal of firm friendship between Berzelius and Dulong and when Berzelius left Paris in June 1819, Dulong took leave of his friend with tears in his eyes. After Berthollet's death in 1822 Dulong, of all the French men of science, was the one with whom Berzelius kept up the closest contact, although a regular detailed correspondence between the two men was prevented by Dulong's poor health.

[1] *Comptes Rendus*, xiv (1842), 437–47.
[2] Berzelius, *Bref*, vol. 2, part iv, p. 16.

Blagden's Later Visits to Arcueil

Only the resumption of war between France and Britain in 1803 prevented Blagden from visiting France under the Empire. After the downfall of Napoleon in 1814 he was able to resume his visits to Paris and to his dear friend Berthollet. Blagden was in Paris from the late summer of 1814 and visited Berthollet at Arcueil regularly. He was also in constant touch with Biot and it is Biot who reminds us in the Arcueil *Mémoires*[1] that Blagden was known to them not only as a friend but as the discoverer of 'Blagden's law' relating to the freezing point of solutions.

Blagden left Paris early in March 1815 shortly after the news of the landing of Napoleon from Elba had reached Paris. Already at the end of March Berthollet was writing to Blagden that he could safely return to France.[2] In fact Blagden did not return to France until July 1816, by which time, of course, France had undergone one more political upheaval. This time Blagden stayed until the following spring but in September 1817 he was again in Paris! Thus, for example, on 22 September 1817 he attended the meeting of the *Académie des Sciences* and then took Berthollet back to Arcueil, where they had dinner. In this way Blagden divided his time fairly evenly between London and Paris and this pattern continued until 1820. When Blagden arrived again at Arcueil in March 1820 it was with the intention of spending the summer in Berthollet's house.[3] On this occasion Blagden appeared in his usual good health but on 26 March he had an attack of apoplexy and died at Arcueil within a few hours. An obituary notice[4] tells us of his constant generosity, particularly towards the poor in the village of Arcueil.

Dalton's Visit to Arcueil

The visit of John Dalton to Arcueil in 1822 is an event of considerable interest, not only because of his importance in the history of science but also because of his earlier refusal to accept

---

[1] *M.S.A.*, iii (1817), 200, 206, 234.
[2] Royal Society, *Blagden Letters*, B 141, 28 March 1815.
[3] Berzelius, *Bref*, vol. 1, part i, p. 73.
[4] *Revue Encyclopédique*, vi (1820), 234–6.

Gay-Lussac's law of combining volumes of gases, a product of Arcueil not only in its inspiration but also in its publication. On the other side, the Arcueil group had shown considerable resistance to the acceptance of Daltonian atoms. In 1809 Berthollet had written a preface to the French translation of Thomson's text-book of chemistry and he had taken the opportunity of warning French readers of the extremely hypothetical basis of Dalton's atomic theory. As late as 1816 Berthollet, when reporting on a memoir by Dulong, had gone out of his way to point to some of the difficulties and dangers of the atomic theory. He had even composed a separate memoir on the subject: 'Esquisse de l'état actuel de la doctrine atomistique', which, although read to the *Académie des Sciences* on 21 October 1816, was never published and unfortunately is missing from the archives of the *Académie*. Laplace too was hostile to the atomic theory. Of the others only Dulong was really enthusiastic about atoms. As he confided to Berzelius in a letter written in 1820:

> Despite the objections of M. de Laplace and some others, I am convinced that this theory (i.e. the atomic theory) is the most important concept of the century and in the next twenty years it will bring about an incalculable extension to all parts of the physical sciences.[1]

Dalton had had few connections with the Continent of Europe during the Napoleonic wars. In December 1816, however, he was elected a corresponding member of the Paris *Académie des Sciences*. For the three vacancies he had come second with Wollaston first. In the following year Biot was able to pay a visit to Dalton during his visit to the British Isles on a geodesic expedition. Dalton in a letter to his brother on 30 October 1817 wrote in terms that suggest that Biot had made a favourable impression on him:

> I have just received a visit from M. Biot . . . who has been in the Shetland Isles, making observations on the pendulum, etc.; he has lately written on the expansion of liquids, in reference to my essays . . . He is a very intelligent gentleman and pleasant companion.[2]

---

[1] Berzelius, *Bref*, vol. 2, part iv, p. 12.
[2] W. Henry, *Memoirs of . . . John Dalton*, 1854 p. 163.

In the summer of 1822 Dalton had the opportunity of visiting Paris and fortunately he kept brief notes of his journey.[1] Some of these are reproduced below as they mention Arcueil and also give an impression of the scientific life of the capital:

[July] 7th Sunday [morning attended chapel]. After 4 p.m. took coach with companions for Arcueil, to dine by invitation with the Marquis La Place and Lady. Met Berthollet, Biot and Lady, Fourier, etc., etc. A most agreeable and interesting visit, and a beautiful place.

Monday 8th July, walked to the Arsenal, saw Gay-Lussac for half an hour . . . [visited *Jardin des plantes* and *Institut*—introduced by Biot].

Sunday, 14th, Gay-Lussac and Humboldt called and spent an hour on meteorology, etc.; took coach to Thenard's, breakfasted à la fourchette with him, family and Dr Edwards;[2] went to the laboratory near M. Biot's and saw a full set of experiments on the deutoxide of hydrogen[3] most curious and satisfying.

On 15 July Dalton saw Gay-Lussac and Cuvier. He then went by coach to the *Académie des Sciences*, where he saw and spoke to Biot, Cuvier, Laplace, Berthollet and others.

One notices how the Arcueil circle had come to dominate the scientific life of Paris. Our main interest here, however, is with the details of the events on the afternoon of Sunday 7 July 1822, the time of Dalton's visit to Arcueil. Fortunately a Mr Dockray, one of Dalton's fellow-travellers, was prevailed upon some thirty years later to give a description of this memorable dinner. The details of the extensive grounds,[4] the personalities and the conversation provide an intimate picture of a style of living which it is not easy to imagine but which was as much a part of Arcueil as the laboratory work and the meetings of the former Society:

July 7 1822. At four in the afternoon, by coach with Dalton to Arcueil, La Place's country seat, to dine. Engaged the carriage to wait for our return at nine. On alighting, we were conducted

---

[1] *Ibid.*, pp. 164–8.

[2] Henry Milne Edwards (1800–85) was a zoologist and a naturalized Frenchman. At Arcueil Edwards acted as interpreter, since Dalton could speak little French and few of the French *savants* spoke English.

[3] I.e. hydrogen peroxide, recently discovered by Thenard.

[4] The grounds of Laplace's house, together with the adjoining property of Berthollet, occupied about 27 acres.

through a suite of rooms, where in succession, dinner, dessert, and coffee tables were set out;—and onwards through a large hall, upon a terrace, commanding an extent of gardens and pleasure grounds. There was a sheet of water in front, and a broad spreading current pouring into it from some rocks, where was seen a sculptured figure—an antique—found in the locality, representing the genius of the place. It is in these grounds that there are still remaining the principal Roman works near Paris—the vestiges of Julian's residence as governor of Gaul. Avenues, parterres, and lawns, terraces and broad gravel walks, in long vistas of distance, are bounded by woods and higher grounds.

As yet we had seen no-one, when part of the company came into view at a distance: a gentleman of advanced years and two young men . . . We approached this group, when the elderly gentleman took off his hat and advanced to give his hand to Dalton. It was Berthollet! The two younger were La Place's son and the astronomer royal, Arago. Climbing some steps upon a long avenue, we saw at a distance, La Place walking uncovered with Madame Biot on his arm; and Biot, Fourier and Courtois, father of the Marchioness La Place. At the front of the house this lady and her grand-daughter met us.

At dinner, Dalton was on the right hand of Madame La Place and Berthollet on her left, etc. Conversation on the zodiac of Denderah and Egypt, Berthollet and Fourier having been in Egypt with Napoleon; the different eras of Egyptian sculpture; the fact that so little at Rome—of public buildings—is earlier than Augustine, etc. After dinner again abroad in the beautiful grounds, and along the reservoir and aqueduct of Julian. These ancient works after falling very much into decay, were restored by Mary of Medicis. Dalton, walking with La Place on one side, and Berthollet on the other, I shall never forget.

The Death of Berthollet

Dalton's visit to Arcueil was the last memorable event of the Berthollet-Laplace partnership at Arcueil. Berthollet continued to attend regularly the weekly meetings of the *Académie des Sciences* until mid-October. He was then taken ill and died in his country house on 6 November 1822 at the age of seventy-four. The day before he died, he was visited by Chaptal. Chaptal tried to reassure him about his health but Berthollet was not deceived. He said it was sufficient consolation for him to have the memory of Chaptal's friendship over a period of forty years, a friendship which had never wavered.[1]

The last days of Berthollet at Arcueil were described by the faithful Dulong in a letter to Berzelius.[2] No-one, said Dulong, could have felt more deeply than he the loss of their mutual friend:

> We were present, Gay-Lussac and I, at the last moments of his life. He could have prolonged his career if he had not refused the care necessary to his age. I have never known a man less sensible to physical pain. For a long time he had large abscesses, which must have made him suffer terribly but nobody knew it. Finally, one day when he was dining with Chaptal at Arcueil he felt weak and retired to bed. It was then that we knew that he had an enormous abscess above the thigh. He called a surgeon from a neighbouring village who regarded it only as a local trouble and treated it accordingly. Three days later he was overcome by symptoms of a delirious fever, delirium and after a short period of agony he expired with a smile of goodness on his lips.

Dulong concluded that with the death of Berthollet he still had many acquaintances left in Paris, but no real friends. Leaving personal feelings aside, Dulong foresaw that the death of Berthollet would have a bad effect on the scientific life of Paris. By his open character Berthollet had done much to preserve harmony between rival men of science.

Berthollet was the last of the four great French chemists who had established France as the centre of the new chemistry. The leader of the group, Lavoisier, had been executed in 1794. Fourcroy had died in 1809 and Guyton de Morveau in 1816. Berthollet had seen his friend Monge die two years later and had spoken at his funeral. He had suffered the loss of his only son in 1810 and his widow had no other children to console her in her bereavement. Berthollet's death certificate was signed by Gay-Lussac, Louis-Simon Auger of the *Académie Française*[3] and the mayor of Arcueil.

Auger, as a friend of the Berthollet family, later wrote to the *Académie des Sciences* offering on his own behalf and that of

---

[1] Pariset, 'Éloge de Berthollet', *Histoire des Membres de l'Académie Royale de Médecine*, vol. i, 1850, pp. 206–7.

[2] Berzelius, *Bref*, vol. 2, part iv, pp. 44–5.

[3] Auger wrote an obituary of Berthollet in the *Journal des Débats*, 23 November 1822.

Madame Berthollet a bust of the famous chemist.[1] It fell to Thenard as president in 1823 to accept on behalf of the *Académie*. The bust may be seen today by anyone who visits the Institute. Berzelius in far-off Sweden wrote to Paris asking for a portrait, medallion or some representation of the features of the friend whom he had admired so much. Dulong duly managed to send a bust of Berthollet to him and Berzelius kept this in his room.[2] Thus the leading international figure in chemistry in the 1820's and 1830's chose to pay homage to the doyen of the French chemists of the previous generation.

According to one account,[3] Berthollet was almost bankrupt at the time of his death and his widow, left without resources, was cared for by a servant. Documents in the *Archives de la Seine*,[4] however, reveal that Madame Berthollet, who was the only beneficiary under her husband's will, was left with property worth 38,443 francs. Dulong, writing to Berzelius in November 1823, described her as being comfortably off and continuing to live in the house at Arcueil.[5]

On the morning of 8 November 1822 a funeral procession passed through the streets of Arcueil on its way to the local cemetery. Many of the leading figures in French science were present. It was Chaptal who delivered the first oration at the grave-side. Without exaggeration Chaptal could refer to his old friend as one of the most distinguished men of science of Europe. He spoke of a personal friendship that had extended over forty years and outlined Berthollet's career. Chaptal remarked that Berthollet had first done his duty towards the state and then returned to Arcueil where his research and his friends always awaited him.

Chaptal was followed by Thenard, not only as an old friend but then vice-president of the *Académie des Sciences*. Thenard too stressed the warmth of Berthollet's personality, his strength of character, his courage and his generosity. The honours and titles he had received had never affected his natural simplicity and directness. Berthollet would be missed, not only because of

---

[1] *P.V. Inst.*, vol. vii, p. 468.

[2] Berzelius, *Bref*, vol. 2, part iv, pp. 43, 60.

[3] L. L. Veyssière, *Arcueil et Cachan*, 1947, p. 112.

[4] Bureau d'Ivry Villejuif, *Mutations par Décès* (1820–4), f. 125 and *Tables des Successions Payées* (1820–5).

[5] Berzelius, *Bref*, vol. 2, part iv, p. 45.

his own contribution to science, but also for the part he had
played in helping and protecting those who studied science.
Thenard went on to introduce a personal note when he described Arcueil:

> With what great simplicity and cordiality he received us! We
> shall never forget those meetings that took place in the retreat
> which he had chosen for himself where, when we were still young,
> we discussed profound scientific problems under his auspices and
> in the presence also of some other no less able masters. He
> listened to us with such great interest, he joined so much in the
> new ideas which sprang from the discussion; he encouraged us so
> well and so constantly! From his venerable head he might have
> been taken for a patriarch in the midst of his children, teaching
> them to do well and hoping to relive his life in each of them.
> Yes, we looked upon him like this; he never doubted our grati-
> tude, our devotion, our filial piety and we might go so far as to
> say that, apart from his worthy wife, it was this bond which was
> most important to him in making life worth living.[1]

Gay-Lussac owed even more than Thenard to Berthollet and
in a few sentences he tried to convey the sense of loss which had
overcome him on the death of his master and friend. Finally
Jomard spoke on behalf of the commission concerned with
Egyptian monuments. Having accompanied Berthollet to
Egypt and worked with him in the publication of the giant
Description de l'Égypte, Jomard could speak of his high qualities
from personal experience. Jomard was so impressed with the
life and work of Berthollet that he decided to write his biography. Published as a booklet in 1844 this still remains the
only attempt at a full biography.

The Death of Laplace

With the passing of Berthollet, Arcueil had become a different
place. Nevertheless, Laplace continued to live in his country
house and led an active life in the remaining four years of his
life. On 5 March 1827 he died at the age of seventy-eight. His
contemporaries were not slow to note that the month and the
year were exactly a century after the death of Newton. Laplace
who gloried in the title of the second Newton during his lifetime

---

[1] *Funerailles de . . . Berthollet*, 1822, pp. 8–9.

had followed Newton even in the time of his death. Among those who came to visit Laplace in his last illness was Thenard, now a Baron and an honorary member of many foreign scientific bodies. Leaving his assistant in an adjoining room, he went in to see Laplace. He came out with tears in his eyes:

> Laplace is dying. He will not last the night. Ah, what are people like us beside a man like that?[1]

The next day the most illustrious man of science in Europe was dead.

At the request of Laplace's son it was Biot who made a short speech at the funeral.[2] He praised Laplace not only as a mathematician but as a man who had applied mathematics to physics and chemistry. He had not been a solitary thinker but had been a source of encouragement and help to others. The official *éloge* of Laplace on behalf of the *Académie des Sciences* was given by Fourier in his capacity as secretary[3] and Pastoret delivered the *éloge* on behalf of the *Chambre des Pairs*.[4] Laplace had been elected to the *Académie Française* in 1816 and another *éloge* was read on behalf of this body by Royer-Collard. Nor can we forget the *Bureau des Longitudes*, which was represented by Poisson.[5] Laplace, he said, had served all branches of science. He concluded in a personal vein:

> When I think of the welcome he extended to me as a young man, of the tokens of a warm friendship which he has so often bestowed upon me, to the communication of his ideas, which guided my thinking on so many different subjects, I am only too conscious of my powerlessness to express, in this last farewell, all the affection I had for him and all the gratitude I owe him.

The Fate of the Houses at Arcueil

After the sale of Berthollet's house, it passed into the hands of a group of Dominicans and in 1863 it became a school with the name *École Albert le Grand*. Berthollet's wife was the same age as

[1] F. Dubois, *Éloge de M. Thenard*, 1863, pp. 52-3.
[2] Biot, *Mélanges*, vol. i, pp. 11-13.
[3] *Mém. Acad. Sc. Inst.*, x (1831), lxxxi-cii.
[4] Laplace, *Oeuvres*, 1878-1904, vol. xiv, pp. 388-92.
[5] *Discours prononcé aux obsèques de M. le Marquis de Laplace* par M. Poisson, président du Bureau des longitudes.

her husband and she died in 1828. By contrast Laplace not only had a son alive to succeed him and to inherit the title of marquis but he had married a wife twenty years younger than himself and she lived for over thirty years after his death.

On the death of Laplace, his house at Arcueil continued to be used by his family. An example of its continued use for the entertainment of men of science is provided by an undated note in the Laplace dossier at the *Académie des Sciences*: Laplace's widow invites M. and Mme. Dumas to Arcueil to dinner, the other principal guests being Thenard and his wife. The Marquise de Laplace did not die until 1862 and we know that Laplace's son, now a general, took pleasure in short holidays spent at Arcueil.[1] The house then passed to Laplace's granddaughter, the Marquise de Colbert, who died in 1889. Meanwhile it had come into the news when its contents were badly damaged by a gang of vandals.[2]

The house was then sold to the Dominicans as a preparatory school attached to Berthollet's old house, which was already in use as a secondary school. The name 'Laplace' was kept for the preparatory section. By the law of 1901 many Church schools were closed, including that at Arcueil. The state acquired the property and the grounds were divided up and sold. By the outbreak of the first World War the houses of both Berthollet and Laplace had been demolished. The modern visitor to Arcueil in search of them is therefore disappointed. The property which once witnessed scientific research and lavish entertainment is now occupied by a branch of the French National Savings Bank.

In the mid-nineteenth century Arcueil was connected to Paris by a railway line. The advisability of constructing this line, called the *Ligne de Sceaux*, was examined by a committee which reported to the Chamber of Deputies in 1844. The report was drawn up by Arago,[3] who had previously reported to the *Académie des Sciences* on some of the technical difficulties involved. When the line was constructed it was an appropriate gesture to name the station before Arcueil 'Laplace'. The name of this station is today one of the few reminders to the inhabitants of this suburb of Paris that a place near by was once the

[1] Laplace, *Oeuvres*, 1878–1903, vol. i, p. vii.
[2] *Nature*, iv (1871), 108.   [3] Arago, *Oeuvres*, vol. v, pp. 419–26.

meeting place of some of the most distinguished men of science in the early nineteenth century. The commuter who travels daily the short distance by rail between the stations of Arcueil and Luxembourg seldom gives a thought to Berthollet, whose more leisurely journeys from his country house at Arcueil to the meetings of the Senate in the Luxembourg palace constituted one of the links between science and government in the France of the First Empire.

The Verdict on Arcueil

Before finally leaving Arcueil we might reconsider briefly what the group really meant. The author would argue that the achievement of the Arcueil group can only be properly understood in the light of the next chapter but it is of some interest to see how the friendships of Arcueil appeared later to the men who had in their youth been inspired, flattered and encouraged by the active interest of Berthollet and Laplace.

We may begin with the reminiscences of Candolle. In the following passage he was not referring specifically to Arcueil but to the general scientific life in Paris, which he contrasts with the comparative freedom from pressure which he had found on leaving the capital. We have said much about the value of the stimulus of powerful minds. Here Candolle reminds us of the other side of the coin:

> It cannot be denied that life in Paris offers a multitude of opportunities for learning and encouragement to study; but quite apart from the distractions which are numerous and compelling, there are for a young man of science several disadvantages which I know from experience.
>
> One is too easily involved in a variety of occupations, stimulated by the work of others, to be able to follow one's own research, or at least to be able to undertake it wholeheartedly. One becomes too anxious to read memoirs at learned societies or to publish them in the journals to give oneself always the time to do them well.
>
> One is surrounded to such an extent by people who are seeking or obtain rewards, that one becomes infected by the fever of obtaining positions and this fever turns one away from any major work. As the fever can only be cured by the favour of powerful men, one becomes involved in writing works which will not hurt

others by the criticisms expressed in them rather than works which tend to have a profound effect on the state of science. One aims more to do work which does not lend itself to criticism than to do work which encompasses the really difficult questions of science.[1]

Arago mentioned the Society of Arcueil in the course of his biography of Gay-Lussac, written at the end of his life.[2] He remarked that this 'dismemberment of the First Class of the Institute' gave rise to some critical comments at the time. Yet,

For young men beginning their career in science it was eminently flattering to have as the first judges of their work men of a celebrity that extended throughout Europe, such as Laplace, Berthollet and Humboldt and to receive advice from them. But could one be assured that preconceived ideas, to which the best minds succumb more easily in a group which is, so to speak, intimate, than before a larger public, could not result in stifling the spontaneity of genius and restrain research to a conventional level? On the other hand, the desire to give evidence of ability in the presence of the most celebrated men of science of their age, might surely lead enthusiasts to throw themselves into speculative theories.

It is probable that Arago had the corpuscular theory of light in mind when he made these remarks but with his own support of the wave theory he could hardly claim that his genius had been stifled.

The excessive influence of the patrons of Arcueil—in this case Berthollet—is also hinted at by Biot in the reminiscences of his old age. Speaking of the discovery of the simple nature of 'oxymuriatic acid' by Gay-Lussac and Thenard and their refusal to commit themselves on this point, Biot wrote:

If you consider the great authority of the opinions which were dominant around them, you will agree that it needed considerable strength and independence of judgement to break away from it . . . This can be confirmed by witnesses still living.[3]

In this case Berthollet was clearly at fault.

When one considers the disadvantages of patronage, it might

[1] Candolle, *Mémoires et souvenirs*, 1862, p. 205.
[2] Arago, *Oeuvres, Notices biographiques*, vol. iii, pp. 33–4.
[3] Biot, 'Notice sur Gay-Lussac', *Mélanges*, vol. iii, pp. 135–6.

seem that there is much to be said for the attitude of someone like Spinoza, who valued his independence too much to accept a university position and preferred to earn his living grinding lenses—an occupation which left his mind free for meditation. Yet the scientist is not in the same position as the philosopher. The experimental scientist can do little without access to a laboratory and may sometimes be prepared to sacrifice independence in order to be able to work. As Pasteur expressed it:

> Outside their laboratories the physicist and the chemist are soldiers without arms on the battlefield.[1]

If Arago and Biot both sounded a note of caution, it was because they took the advantages for granted. The reservations by the younger generation of Arcueil about the benefits they received serve to remind us that no society is perfect. If Arcueil overcame many of the disadvantages of the Institute, it was at the expense of other weaknesses. The distance of Arcueil from the centre of Paris made it more suitable for a social occasion on a fine summer's day than as a regular place of work and discussion for men with daily duties in Paris. The closing down of Arcueil in the winter deprived the Society of Arcueil of several major discoveries which would otherwise have been announced at its meetings.[2] In the last analysis Arcueil is justified not as the Society meeting between 1807 and 1813 but as a group of men of central importance in French science for the whole of the first half of the nineteenth century.

[1] *Le budget de la science*, 1868, p. 3.
[2] The fading out of the meetings at Arcueil each winter may be contrasted with the situation in the Philomatic Society in Paris, which had been founded in the winter and kept the anniversary.

The Influence of Former Members of the Society of Arcueil on Nineteenth-century Science

THERE REMAINS one big question: what impact did the men who had once met at Arcueil have on nineteenth-century science? The friendships, the alliances, the collaboration and the patronage which have been described may only be relevant to French science in the first two decades of the nineteenth century. Alternatively it is possible that the men of Arcueil had some significance for the whole of nineteenth-century science, both in France and elsewhere.

In this chapter the emphasis will be on *personal* contact and influence. The teaching and administrative positions held in the second quarter of the nineteenth century by the younger generation of Arcueil enabled them to exercise a powerful influence for good or evil. The men who had been associated with the establishment *became* the establishment. Apart from Bérard at Montpellier and Candolle at Geneva, the ex-members of the Arcueil circle were concentrated in Paris, still in many ways the scientific capital of Europe. In the 1820's, when German science was not yet in the ascendant, young German students of science still came humbly to the French capital, where they came into contact with the men we have described in these pages.

The Influence of Humboldt

In speaking of the influence of members of the Arcueil group, it is not possible for long to avoid the name of Humboldt. Humboldt had been profoundly affected by his long stay in France. By the time he finally returned to Prussia in 1827, he was as much French as German and indeed regarded living in what was technically his native land as a kind of exile from his beloved

Paris. Laplace had died two months before Humboldt left Paris, but he had close ties with other French scientists, notably Arago. Although Humboldt was obliged to return to the Prussian court, he obtained the concession that he might spend four months of the year in Paris. He therefore remained a constant link, fostering good relations between men of science on both sides of the Rhine. We find him encouraging young men such as Mitscherlich in Berlin and Dumas in Geneva to enter the scientific circles of Paris. When he was still resident in France he encouraged the young and unknown Liebig. Humboldt was at once an ambassador and a patron. Humboldt's credit extended to Britain and a letter of recommendation from him did much to secure the appointment of Thomas Graham (the founder of colloid chemistry) as professor of chemistry at University College, London, in 1837.

Back in Berlin Humboldt sponsored the cause of science in various ways. In 1827 he organized one of the first national scientific conferences. His position as chamberlain at the court enabled him to overcome the suspicions of the Prussian government about the possible subversive effects of such a large gathering. The fact that he was organizing the conference also gave it international prestige and such men as Berzelius, Oersted and Gauss came, as well as Babbage from England. Humboldt in his opening address to the conference emphasized the importance of personal contact in the exchange of ideas, a sentiment no doubt inspired by his own experiences in Paris. This Berlin conference was the inspiration of the British Association for the Advancement of Science, which first met in 1831. Humboldt also collaborated with Gauss in the organization of the German Magnetic Union. The aim of this body was to make systematic observations of the magnetic elements (dip, declination and intensity) at particular places. Observations were begun in 1834. This may be viewed as the culmination of Humboldt's long-standing interest in magnetism and an extension of his collaboration with Gay-Lussac in their European travels of 1804–5, an account of which had been published as the first contribution to the new *Mémoires* of Arcueil in 1807.

A recent reviewer of nineteenth-century science[1] has asked

---

[1] Walter F. Cannon, 'History in depth: the early Victorian period', *History of Science*, iii (1964), 27.

why there was a great outburst of enthusiasm for the subject of
terrestrial magnetism in the early nineteenth century. He explains:

> This enthusiasm led to the establishment of a network of magnetic
> observatories throughout Europe and Asia and, once the British
> government became involved, throughout the world. It led to the
> instruments and theoretical work of Gauss relating to magnetism
> and then to the introduction of absolute measurements. It led to
> Ross's great Antarctic expedition of 1838–41. And it led to the
> foundation of modern meteorology through the suggestion that
> the same or similar observatories and the same or similar methods
> of simultaneous observation could be used to put that subject on
> a sound basis. Taken as a whole, this was, to a contemporary
> historian, 'by far the greatest scientific undertaking which the
> world has ever seen'.

The only explanation satisfactory to the writer quoted lies in the
powers of persuasion of Humboldt.

The last fifteen years of Humboldt's life were occupied with
the publication of his *Cosmos*, a work he had dreamed of even
before he had gone to live in Paris. The themes he tackled,
nature, the structure of the universe and man were wide in
scope. To have planned such a work is understandable for a man
in the tradition of German *Naturphilosophie*. Yet Humboldt was
saved from becoming another Oken[1] by his long period of close
contact with the scientists of Paris. His book, therefore, while
general and speculative in conception, also gives an account of
some fundamental scientific observations. Scientific observations
must be guided not by the vague and subjective imagination of
the poet but by experiment and a mathematical approach to
nature. Much of the subject matter prominent in the *Cosmos*
was work with which Humboldt was personally familiar. His
account of astronomy and particularly geomagnetism was
masterly. He did not neglect to draw on the ideas of his former
colleagues of Arcueil, whether of Arago on light, of Laplace on
various aspects of astronomy, or of Poisson on an electrically-
charged layer beyond the atmosphere (an anticipation of the
discovery of the ionosphere). The references to Arago's work
were particularly numerous.

[1] The *Naturphilosoph* Oken was the author of the highly speculative
Elements of Physiophilosophy (first edn. 1810, Eng. trans. 1847).

Humboldt's *Cosmos* was very favourably received. We may be pardoned for quoting *in extenso* part of a eulogistic review by John Herschel. The opinion of one of England's leading scientists in the mid-nineteenth century may serve as a testimonial to Humboldt's contribution to nineteenth-century science:

> Science has produced no man of more rich and varied attainments, more versatile in genius, more indefatigable in application of all kinds of learning, more energetic in action, or more ardent in enquiry; and we may add, more entirely devoted to her cause in every period of a long life. At every epoch of that life he has been constantly before the public, realizing the ideal conception of a perfect traveller; a character which calls for almost as great a variety of excellences as those which go to realize Cicero's idea of a perfect orator. To such a one, science in all its branches must be familiar, since questions of science and its applications occur at every step, and often in their most delicate and recondite forms. The habit of close attention to passing facts, which seizes their specific features, and detects their hidden analogies must join with the broad *coup d'œil* which generalizes all it sees, and stereotypes it in memory in its simplest and most impressive forms. To these must be added a knowledge of man and of his history in all its phases, social and political; a ready insight into human character and feelings, and a quick apprehension of local and national peculiarities.
>
> Above all things is necessary *a genial and kindly temperament, which excites no enmities, but on the contrary finds or makes friends everywhere: in presence of which hearts open, information is volunteered and aid spontaneously offered.* No man in the ranks of science is more distinguished for this last characteristic than Baron von Humboldt. We believe that he has not an enemy. His justice, candour and moderation have preserved him intact in all the vexatious questions of priority and precedence which agitate and harass the scientific world; and have in consequence afforded him *innumerable opportunities of promoting and befriending the cultivators of science, which would never have fallen in the way of a less conciliatory disposition, and of which he has not been slow to avail himself.* The respect of Europe, indeed, has gone along with him to a point which has almost rendered his recommendations rules. It has sufficed that von Humboldt has pointed out lines of useful and available enquiry, to make everyone eager to enter upon them.[1]

---

[1] *Edinburgh Review*, January 1848; reprinted in John Herschel, *Essays*, 1857, pp. 262–3 (the italics are mine).

Finally there can be no stronger testimonial to the influence of Humboldt throughout the civilized world by his writings in their numerous editions and translations than the admission of Charles Darwin. Darwin, who probably as a student derived little benefit from formal instruction in Cambridge, was inspired by reading one of Humboldt's works:

> During my last year at Cambridge, I read with care and profound interest Humboldt's 'Personal Narrative'. This work and Sir J. Herschel's 'Introduction to the Study of Natural Philosophy', stirred up in me a burning zeal to add even the most humble contribution to the noble structure of Natural Science. No one or a dozen other books influenced me nearly so much as these two. I copied out from Humboldt long passages . . .[1]

On another occasion Darwin wrote:

> I shall never forget that my whole course of life is due to having read and re-read as a youth his [i.e. Humboldt's] *Personal Narrative*.[2]

To inspire through the written word was obviously a second gift which Humboldt added to his personal encouragement and patronage of aspirants to the developing world of professional science. Through Darwin Humboldt is linked with the theory of biological evolution.

German Students in Paris

From Humboldt we pass to the generation of German students who drew inspiration from the scientific milieu of Paris in the 1820's. The most famous teacher of chemistry in the whole nineteenth century was Justus von Liebig (1803–73). A German, and a student at Bonn and Erlangen at a time when German science was at a low ebb, Liebig realized that he would have to leave his native land if he was to receive the training which would enable him to make a significant contribution to science. Many of his contemporaries, men like Mitscherlich, Wöhler and Magnus, had gone to Stockholm to study chemistry under Berzelius, that great organizer of the science. Liebig states that he decided to go to Paris instead of Stockholm, because only in Paris would

---

[1] *Autobiography, Life and Letters of Charles Darwin*, 1887, vol. i, p. 55.
[2] Charles Darwin's letter to J. D. Hooker, 10 February 1845, *ibid.*, p. 336.

it be possible for him to receive competent instruction at a high level, not only in chemisty but also in other branches of science such as physics. Liebig was only $17\frac{1}{2}$ years old when he made the most important decision of his life. He was to come under the influence of the leading figures on the Paris stage of science and his youth made him all the more impressionable. His youth and his lack of influential friends made him set a high value on the advice and help offered him by the men whose names are familiar to readers of this book. Liebig in his *Autobiographical Sketch* writes:

> My journey to Paris, the way and manner in which I came in contact with Thenard, Humboldt, Dulong and with Gay-Lussac, and how the boy found favour in the sight of those men borders on the fabulous.

Liebig was most impressed by the lectures of Gay-Lussac, Thenard and Dulong at the Faculty of Science. He praised their use of a mathematical approach to chemistry. He was fascinated by their lecture demonstrations. He was won over by the logical clarity of the French language. Yet when he arrived in Paris in October 1822 he had no letter of introduction and he was no more than one among many students.

In the summer of 1823 Liebig had advanced sufficiently with his work to be able to read a paper on fulminating silver to the *Académie des Sciences*. At the end of the session a gentleman approached him, questioned him closely about his work and eventually asked him to dinner on the following Sunday. The young German accepted but through nervousness and confusion forgot to ask the name of his prospective host. It was only after the date of the invitation that he was told that he had been speaking to Humboldt. Liebig immediately explained his predicament to the latter, who accepted his apology and repeated the invitation to dinner the next Sunday. It was at Humboldt's lodgings that Liebig made the personal acquaintance of Gay-Lussac, who was so impressed by the ability and enthusiasm of the young German chemist that he invited him to work with him in his laboratory. Of the joint work which they did on fulminating compounds in the winter of 1823–4 Liebig wrote proudly:

> Gay-Lussac . . . worked with me as he had formerly worked with Thenard; and I can well say that the foundation of all my later

work and of my whole course was laid in his laboratory in the Arsenal.

The laboratory referred to by Liebig was that acquired by Gay-Lussac on his appointment as superintendent of the State gunpowder factory.

Liebig, in dedicating to Humboldt his book on Chemistry and its applications to Agriculture and Physiology, referred to his first conversation with Humboldt as the corner-stone of his future. The importance to the young Liebig of personal contacts with the leading chemists in Paris is best described in his own words:

> Unknown, without introductions, in a city where the assemblage of so many great men from every quarter of the globe is the greatest hindrance to personal acquaintance with scientific men high in renown, I might, like so many others, have remained unnoticed—perhaps have failed altogether; this danger was now entirely averted. From this day forth I found all doors, all institutes and laboratories open to me. The lively interest [Humboldt] took in me procured me the affection and intimate friendship of my dear teachers, Gay-Lussac, Dulong and Thenard.

From this it might appear that this was no more than a matter of useful contacts, but, as Hofmann pointed out, it made all the difference to the quality of Liebig's work. Liebig had previously done some research on his own on fulminates and if the quality of this is compared with his joint publication with Gay-Lussac one can see 'how much the young German chemist owed to his French teacher, who was soon to become his paternal friend'.

Hofmann goes even further. Not only did Gay-Lussac guide Liebig in his chemical research, but he inspired Liebig to create what he is most renowned for—the great school of chemistry of the nineteenth century:

> It was in Gay-Lussac's laboratory that Liebig conceived the idea of founding in Germany a chemical school, where he hoped to be to his younger fellow-workers what Gay-Lussac had been to him.

It adds to the value of Hofmann's testimony that he was a German chemist speaking about another German chemist to a British audience; he had no conceivable motive for exaggerating the influence of the Paris chemists on Liebig.

Humboldt performed one last great service to Liebig. He provided a strong recommendation to the Grand Duke Ludwig I, who agreed to appoint Liebig as professor extraordinary at the University of Giessen by a decree dated 26 May 1824.

Thus about the time of his twenty-first birthday, Liebig was launched on a career which brought fame and honour to himself, his university and his native land. He was only too willing to share this honour with other men who had been his teachers during the most important formative period in his scientific career—the two years he spent in Paris learning from men who had themselves earlier learned their science at the *École Polytechnique* and at Arcueil. It is one of the lesser ironies of history that as young Liebig arrived in Paris in October 1822, Berthollet lay dying at Arcueil. They never met, but we have shown that, through Berthollet's star pupil, Gay-Lussac, the torch was passed on.

Another German chemist who was in Paris in the winter of 1823–4 was Berzelius' pupil, Mitscherlich. One of his early publications on isomorphism had come to the attention of Humboldt, who wrote him an appreciative letter from Paris in May 1822.[1] In the following summer Humboldt returned to Berlin and took the opportunity of calling on Mitscherlich, who had been appointed assistant professor of chemistry there. Humboldt showed his appreciation of the work of the younger man in a way which was typical of his character. He proposed to the Prussian minister of education that Mitscherlich should be allowed leave of absence to visit Paris and London.[2] Gustav Rose was then on a visit to Paris and the two Prussian chemists shared lodgings in the French capital.

The main source of information of Mitscherlich's visit to Paris in the winter of 1823–4 is a letter written by him to Berzelius from Paris on 16 January 1824.[3] He describes the leading Paris chemists and the reception accorded him by each. He begins with Gay-Lussac, of whom he obviously had high hopes. Gay-Lussac had also studied the growth of crystals of one salt in a

[1] Mitscherlich, *Gesammelte Schriften*, p. 132.
[2] *Ibid.*, p. 62.
[3] *Ibid.*, pp. 22–3. Berzelius, *Bref*, vol. 6, part xiii, pp. 55 ff.

solution of another[1] and he had previously as editor of the *Annales de chimie et de physique* written politely to Mitscherlich, thanking him for a paper for the journal and congratulating him as the successor of the famous Klaproth to the chair in Berlin.[2] Mitscherlich was now frankly disappointed that Gay-Lussac spent so much time on commercial enterprises and was not able to be of any use to him. Mitscherlich goes on, however, to speak of the other *savants* in very different terms. Their names will not be unfamiliar:

> I see Arago frequently. He has offered me everything I could wish and I am very happy to have made his personal acquaintance. Dulong has quite accepted me as your friend; I feel really happy in his company . . . Biot has returned to town some time ago from his country estate; I visited him immediately. He welcomed me very kindly and offered to show me all his optical instruments that I might wish to see . . .

The next passage in the letter refers to a temporary cooling-off in Biot's kindness when he realized that Mitscherlich was also associating closely with Arago and Fresnel. Mitscherlich continues,

> Of the chemists, I see most of Berthier; he is by far the friendliest, if I except Thenard . . . I see Thenard often; he has already rendered me many services and is extraordinarily friendly.

Thenard had shown Mitscherlich over the *École Polytechnique*. Mitscherlich was most impressed by the laboratories and determined to press for similar accommodation for practical work in Berlin. Mitscherlich also collaborated with Dulong on the expansion of crystals,[3] drawing on Dulong's method for the determination of the coefficient of absolute expansion of solids.

Mitscherlich was followed in 1829 by a German student, Henry Gustav Magnus (1802–70), later to become an important physicist and teacher. Magnus was Mitscherlich's pupil at Berlin. After doing post-doctoral research with Berzelius in Stockholm, he went to Paris where he worked in Gay-Lussac's laboratory. Magnus was later to reinvestigate the thermal expansion of gases, using Gay-Lussac's method and was able to show that, contrary to the opinion of his mentor, there was a slight difference between

---

[1] *Ann. chim. phys.*, ii (1816), 176.   [2] Mitscherlich, *op. cit.*, p. 194.
[3] *Ann chim. phys.*, xxxii (1826), 111.

the coefficients of expansion of different gases. Although Magnus' research made a definite contribution to nineteenth-century science, it was as a teacher that Magnus achieved his greatest fame and he exerted a major influence on science in Germany. It was said of him that 'He loved youth and knew how to make himself beloved while imparting a taste for that science to which he had consecrated his life.' Magnus had drawn his inspiration for experimental research from Berzelius and Gay-Lussac. He in turn numbered Helmholtz and Tyndall among his pupils.

In 1834 Magnus returned to Paris in the company of Friedrich Wöhler (1800–82). They spent several weeks in the capital with the object of studying chemical industry. Their principal guide was Gay-Lussac's assistant, Pelouze. Yet there was also a social side to their visit. Wöhler describes their entertainment in enthusiastic terms:

> I vividly remember the many parties and dinners to which we were invited and which were of the greatest interest to us because of the famous names of the guests and their witty conversation; for example, a brilliant dinner at Thenard's house in the company of Ampère, Arago, Chevreul, Dumas and Pelouze; another with Dulong as the host with Lassaigne and others present. There was yet another at Gay-Lussac's house at Chatillon with Arago and Thenard . . .[1]

When they attended a meeting of the *Académie des Sciences*, they sat in the public seats until they were noticed by Gay-Lussac, who invited them to sit with the members of the *Académie*.

Such personal details may not be the primary concern of the historian of science. Yet the social life of Paris was not divorced from the scientific life. An invitation to dinner implied the acceptance of the guest in the circle of *savants* of the capital. When Thomas Graham visited Paris in 1851 a dinner was given by Thenard in his honour. Thenard could boast that his guest could see round his table all the leading French chemists. The absence of two, Gerhardt and Laurent, was more than a coincidence as we shall see shortly.

[1] Wöhler's letter to Hofmann. A. W. von Hofmann, *Zur Erinnerung an Vorangegangene Freunde*, vol. i, p. 57.

Gay-Lussac and Thenard and Their Students

The training given by Gay-Lussac to Liebig in the early 1820's in methods of chemical research would alone justify his position as a teacher in Paris under the Bourbons. However, Gay-Lussac also lectured to large and enthusiastic audiences of students and we have the testimony of Sir Robert Christison, who went to Paris in August 1820, drawn there by the high reputation of the French chemists.[1] He was accompanied by Edward Turner, who was later to become the first professor of chemistry at the newly-founded University of London. Christison wrote:

> Gay-Lussac was perhaps the most persuasive lecturer I ever heard. His figure was slender and handsome, his countenance comely, his expression winning, his voice gentle but firm and clear, his articulation perfect, his diction terse and choice, his manner most attractive; and his lecture was a superlative specimen of continuous unassailable experimental reasoning.

Christison was advised to attend the meetings of the *Académie des Sciences* and here he watched with awe the debates of the leading *savants* of that age. He was impressed by the 'venerable appearance' of Laplace and remarked that he 'usually sat and talked with Berthollet the chemist'.

Christison contrasted Gay-Lussac's method of lecturing with that of his friend Thenard:

> Thenard was a tall powerful man, with the head, front, curls and eyes of a bull and a conformable voice, strong, rough, and commanding. His matter was excellent; and he laid it down with a slap from his tongue and a blow with his fist, which made it irresistible. But the incessant vigour, *sans relache sans repos*, made one long for a little of his friend's no less persuasive quiet occasionally.

As had happened to Boerhaave in the eighteenth century, the popularity of Gay-Lussac's lectures led to the publication in 1828 of a version based on notes taken by shorthand writers. Gay-Lussac repudiated this publication[2] and his plans for his own textbook of chemistry never got beyond the manuscript stage.

---

[1] *The Life of Sir Robert Christison, Bart.*, edited by his sons, vol. i, *Autobiography*, Edinburgh, 1885, pp. 207, 239 ff.

[2] *Ann. chim. phys.*, xxxvii (1828), 441–3.

Among Gay-Lussac's students we may number Robiquet, who carried out successful research in the field of organic chemistry. Despretz began life as Gay-Lussac's laboratory assistant and later became professor of physics at the *École Polytechnique*. The life work of Regnault was based on the fundamental physical experimental investigation of the properties of gases undertaken by Gay-Lussac and other members of the Arcueil group, which Regnault tried to repeat with even greater precision. The geologist Boussingault had some contact with both Thenard and Gay-Lussac and thought highly enough of the latter to name a new mineral after him. Boussingault's real patron, however, was Humboldt.

One of the most interesting of Gay-Lussac's students was Jules Pelouze who, after successfully taking a competitive examination, had entered the government saltpetre factory. He met Gay-Lussac purely by chance, but the older man was impressed by his apparent ability and offered him a position in his own laboratory. Dumas refers to this event as the most decisive step in the career of Pelouze.[1] When there was a vacancy for an assistant lecturer for a course of chemistry at Lille, Pelouze secured the appointment through the good offices of Gay-Lussac. Gay-Lussac's final act of benevolence towards his former student came just before his death in 1850 when he resigned his position of scientific consultant at the glass factory of Saint-Gobain and recommended as his successor Pelouze, who was appointed.

When Pelouze was working as a young student in Paris under Gay-Lussac, he was introduced to Liebig and a firm and lasting friendship developed between the two men. Even after Liebig's return to the other side of the Rhine, they met and communicated their research to each other. Only one memoir was published jointly under both their names, but this is really a collection of several papers on organic chemistry amounting to fifty pages. These were published in 1836 after a visit which Pelouze had made to Giessen to work with his distinguished friend.[2] Their most important joint work was the discovery of the acid which they called oenanthic acid (heptylic acid), which formed an ester responsible for the characteristic smell of wines.

[1] 'Éloge', *Mém. Acad. Sc. Inst.*, xxxviii (1873), xv.
[2] *Ann. chim. phys.*, lxiii (1836), 113–63.

Pelouze also collaborated in research with Gay-Lussac's son, Jules.

Meanwhile Thenard continued to teach at the *Collège de France* and in 1836 he was nominated Director of that venerable establishment for higher education. He resigned three years later on his appointment to the even more important post of vice-president of the Council of Public Instruction. In this capacity he exerted a powerful influence over the whole of the French educational system, particularly on the teaching of science. He had the power to make scientific appointments in schools and universities throughout the whole of France. Without Thenard's patronage, advance was impossible to the young aspirant. Generally speaking, Thenard acted wisely within an over-centralized framework of administration in which politics figured too prominently for the healthy pursuit of science.

The Early Career of Dumas in Paris

Jean-Baptiste Dumas occupies a dominant position in French chemistry in the middle of the nineteenth century. His position can be compared with that of Liebig on the other side of the Rhine and when these two great chemists collaborated in the writing of a memoir in 1837 'On the present state of chemistry' the rest of the civilized world could well feel that this was a manifesto of the great powers.

Dumas was born at Alais in the Department of the Gard in 1800. At the age of fifteen he was apprenticed to an apothecary, but feeling that his ambitions could not be fulfilled if he stayed in his native town, he decided to go to Geneva. Paris would have been an obvious choice but he knew no-one there. In Geneva on the other hand, an international cross roads with a good academic tradition, he had a relative. Through the latter he was introduced to Candolle and Théodore de Saussure, who encouraged him in his studies. He attended lectures on botany by Candolle, who had just been appointed professor of botany at the Academy. He also attended lectures on physics by M. A. Pictet and on chemistry by Gaspard de la Rive.

Hofmann tells us the books that Dumas used in his studies at this time. Biot's *Traité de physique* had just appeared and Dumas found, especially in the first volume, much to direct his attention to experimental work. To learn of the latest developments in science he had access to the volumes of the *Annales de chimie et de physique*, but this would only be of occasional value as a source of reference to the young student. With greater diligence he studied the works of Lavoisier, which he was later to edit for the French nation. He also studied Berthollet's *Statique chimique*. Writing twenty years later, he called himself a most sincere admirer of the work, despite its difficulties.

> It occupied me almost constantly for three or four years; from the ages of seventeen to twenty-one I read it, re-read it and thought about it . . . I read it pen in hand, making extracts, thinking and making a commentary; this work and those efforts, I must confess, have been most useful to me. It is with Berthollet that my formation in the study of chemistry was achieved . . .[1]

Meanwhile Dumas as a student of pharmacy had collaborated with a prominent Geneva physician in a study of the way in which iodine should be administered in the treatment of goitre. More sustained was his collaboration with Prevost on various physiological topics. It is probable that Dumas would have remained largely unknown outside Geneva if it had not been for an interview with a stranger in 1822. Dumas tells his own story in the following words reported by Hofmann.[2] It serves to enlarge our acquaintance with Humboldt as well as illustrating how a young man from the provinces succumbed to the allurement of Paris:

> One day [said Dumas], I was in my study completing some drawings at the microscope, and, it must be added, rather negligently attired, in order to enable me to move more freely. Some one mounted the stairs, stopped on my landing, and gently knocked at the door. 'Come in,' said I, without looking up from my work. On turning round I was surprised to find myself face to face with a gentleman in a bright blue coat with metal buttons, a white waistcoat, nankeen breeches and top boots. This costume which might have been the fashion under the Directory, was then quite out of date. The wearer of it, his head somewhat bent, his eyes deep set but keen, advanced with a pleasant smile, saying 'Monsieur Dumas?' 'The same, sir, but excuse me.' 'Don't disturb yourself. I am M. de Humboldt, and did not wish to pass through

---

[1] Dumas, *Leçons sur la philosophie chimique*, Paris, 1837, p. 379.
[2] Trans. W. A. Tilden, *Famous Chemists*, London, 1921, pp. 207-8.

Geneva without having had the pleasure of seeing you.' Throwing on my coat, I hastily reiterated my apologies. I had only one chair. My visitor was pleased to accept it, whilst I resumed my elevated perch on the drawing stool.

Baron Humboldt had read the papers published by M. Prevost and myself on blood, which had just appeared in the *Bibliothèque universelle* and was anxious to see the preparations I had by me. His wish was soon gratified. 'I am going to the Congress at Verona', said he, 'and I intend to spend some days at Geneva, to see old friends and to make new ones, and more especially to become acquainted with young people who are beginning their career. Will you act as my cicerone? I warn you, however, that my rambles begin early and end late. Now could you be at my disposal from six in the morning till midnight?' This proposal, which was, of course, accepted with alacrity, proved to me a source of unexpected pleasure. Baron Humboldt was fond of talking; he passed from one subject to another without stopping. He obviously liked being listened to and there was no fear of his being interrupted by a young man who for the first time heard Laplace, Berthollet, Gay-Lussac, Arago, Thenard, Cuvier and many others of the Parisian celebrities spoken of with familiarity. I listened with a strange delight; a new horizon began to dawn upon me . . .

What he had told me of life in Paris, of the happy co-operation of the scholars there, of the aids which the metropolis on the Seine placed at the disposal of the disciples of knowledge, had made a lasting impression on me. It began to be obvious to me that Paris was the only place where, under the auspices of the leaders of the physical and chemical sciences with whom (how could I doubt it?) I would immediately come into the closest contact, I could hope to find the counsel and assistance which would enable me to bring to fruition the works over which I had brooded for such a long time. My resolve was soon made. To Paris!

Dumas arrived in Paris in the spring of 1823 and during the course of that summer he presented several memoirs on physiology by Prevost and himself to the *Académie des Sciences*. After one of these meetings he was approached by Laplace, who invited him to come to his house for lunch. Dumas had previously thought of Laplace as the great astronomer of the age but in their conversation Laplace reminded him of his early interest in physiology through his collaboration with Lavoisier.

Dumas was now to receive some of the benefits of a personal

acquaintance with the great *savants* of whom Humboldt had spoken so familiarly. When there was a vacancy for the place of assistant (*répétiteur*) to Thenard at the *École Polytechnique*, Arago proposed Dumas, who was given the appointment. Through friendship with Ampère, Dumas obtained a post giving popular chemical lectures at the Athénée. It was with these appointments that physiological problems began to recede more and more into the background and Dumas began the fundamental work on chemistry which was to bring him lasting fame. With his experimental work and his theories of organic and physical chemistry, however, we are not concerned here. At the age of twenty-four Dumas had been set on the road which was to be his life's work.

To summarize, we find what in a different context might almost appear as a conspiracy. At the beginning of his career Dumas was helped successively by nearly all the leading figures of the Arcueil circle. From Candolle he went to Humboldt, from Humboldt to Arago, Thenard and Laplace. He arrived in Paris just too late to meet Berthollet but with years of study of the *Statique chimique*, Dumas was prepared to acknowledge his debt as a reader of Berthollet as he had been of Biot. There had been, of course, many others who had befriended Dumas as a young man both in Geneva and in Paris, men such as Prevost and Ampère, who were his friends and Adolphe Brongniart, whose sister he married. But if we are asked to name Dumas' teachers and patrons, the answer is clear and the extent of this patronage has been described above.

We might mention, in conclusion, that when in 1832 Gay-Lussac retired from his chair at the Faculty of Science, it was Dumas who replaced him, and three years later, when Thenard retired from teaching at the *École Polytechnique* Dumas, who had started as his *répétiteur*, was appointed to succeed him. In this symbolic way Dumas inherited the mantle of these two great chemists.

Gerhardt and Laurent

The careers of Charles Gerhardt (1816–56) and Auguste Laurent (1807–53) provide a great contrast after considering the meteoric rise to fame of Dumas. In any selective study of

French science in the nineteenth century which attempted to prove a thesis at any price, it might be a temptation to ignore these two *enfants terribles*, the two chemists who appeared to have been ostracized by the Paris clique and who were referred to ominously as *les deux*. Yet if this book is concerned with patronage, and the story is taken up to the mid-nineteenth century, the cases of Gerhardt and Laurent are no less important than their undoubted contributions to organic chemistry.

Gerhardt had studied in 1836–7 under Liebig at Giessen and it was Liebig who suggested that he should go to Paris. He wrote him a letter of recommendation, which obtained him a post as assistant to Dumas. We are able to follow Gerhardt's career in Paris in this period through his correspondence with Liebig. Gerhardt was soon complaining of the difficulty of convincing the Paris chemists of his new ideas on chemistry and Liebig was able to advise him from his own experience of Paris and the *Académie des Sciences*. He warned Gerhardt that to present new theories was to court disaster, since this was the prerogative of the established order. Gerhardt must learn the lesson of tact and his work should be factual rather than speculative. If Gerhardt was treated with some consideration by the Paris chemists, it was largely through his personal contact with Liebig.

In March 1841 a vacancy occurred for a post in the Faculty of Science at Montpellier. The post was offered to Gerhardt largely through the good offices of Dumas, who gave him a letter of recommendation to Bérard, still professor of chemistry at the *École de Pharmacie*. Gerhardt soon became dissatisfied with the social and intellectual life of Montpellier and began to agitate for a position back in the capital. One friend he did make during his stay in the south of France was Bérard, who many years later wrote to him offering advice on the furtherance of his career.[1]

Gerhardt did what little research was possible with the facilities at Montpellier and hurried back to Paris every vacation. In 1848 he left Montpellier for good to join Laurent in Paris. Yet he had meanwhile made an enemy of Dumas and he had little hope of securing an academic appointment in the capital. Dumas must certainly bear much of the blame for the

[1] Grimaux and Gerhardt, *Charles Gerhardt*, Paris, 1900, p. 263.

GG

ostracism of Gerhardt and Laurent, both his former associates. On the other hand Gerhardt was not blameless. He never lacked confidence in the correctness of his own opinions and he antagonized Thenard by his dogmatism. In fact in September 1842 when he called on Thenard to present a memoir containing the blunt statement that a particular opinion was false, Thenard threw him out, saying that not even Lavoisier would have given so little credit to his opponents. Yet seven years later, on 27 February 1849 to be precise, it was Thenard who invited him to a *soirée* at which he asked him to bring out a new edition of his textbook. Gerhardt agreed to undertake the task in collaboration with Laurent, and Thenard was prepared to give over all his rights in the book to the two younger men. The project was abandoned because no publisher could be found, but the incident is worth mentioning as an act of generosity by Thenard towards two men who stood in need of recognition.

It was not until 1856 that Gerhardt, now at Strasbourg, achieved recognition by the *Académie des Sciences*, when he was elected as correspondent in the chemistry section. Thenard, as the senior member of the section, immediately sent him a telegram of congratulation. Gerhardt himself acknowledged that his success here was due to 'le brave père Thenard'.[1] It had been Thenard who had supported Gerhardt's appointment to two chairs at Strasbourg in the Faculty of Science and in the School of Pharmacy. When writing his letter of recommendation to the minister of education, Thenard had said to his protégé:

> M. Gerhardt, when you are old and have power, remember always to protect young active men. It is a way of still being useful to science.[2]

Unfortunately Gerhardt was never in a position to extend the sacred trust passed on to him by Thenard. He died in 1856 at the age of forty. Thenard therefore outlived him and indeed was prompted by his death to found the *Société de secours des amis des sciences*.[3]

[1] Grimaux and Gerhardt, *Charles Gerhardt*, Paris, 1900, p. 563.
[2] *Ibid.*, p. 259.
[3] Thenard founded the society in March 1857. Not content with encouraging others to support this charitable organization, he himself donated 20,000 francs. Thenard died a few months later.

Laurent was more modest than Gerhardt. Obscurity rather than dogmatism was his chief failing. Like Gerhardt, he wanted to reform the theoretical approach to organic chemistry and, like Gerhardt, he failed to win official approval in Paris. From 1839 to 1845 he was professor of chemistry at Bordeaux, but the attractions of Paris were too strong for him and he preferred to starve in a garret in the capital than have a regular salary in the provinces. His letters to Gerhardt mention Gay-Lussac, Arago and Thenard among men of influence who were prepared to support him[1] and *père* Thenard's influence may have been decisive in obtaining for the unfortunate Laurent the very modest appointment of assayer at the Paris mint in 1848. Earlier, Gay-Lussac had repeatedly offered Laurent positions in industrial chemistry, where he would have earned at least 4,000 francs, but Laurent refused such posts, preferring to dedicate his life to pure chemical research.[2]

In 1850 a vacancy occurred for a professor of chemistry at the *Collège de France* and it was the usual practice for the *Académie des Sciences* to make the appointment, taking into consideration the views of the professors of the *Collège*. There were two candidates, Balard, the discoverer of bromine, and Laurent, and Laurent had the support of the majority vote of the *Collège de France*. Biot, who was the senior professor at the *Collège*, saw the possibility that Balard, who already held two chairs, would be appointed rather than the less well known Laurent, who was without any academic appointment. Biot accordingly sent a letter to each member of the chemistry section of the *Académie*.[3] He pointed out the desirability of appointing a man who was active in research, as opposed to a man whose career lay in the past. He had to defend Laurent against the possible objection that, if appointed, he would use his teaching position to propagate his own theoretical views. The whole letter is written on the defensive, as if Biot knew how impossible was the task he had set himself of supporting a suspect outsider against a member of the establishment. If the *Académie* elected Balard, Biot said, they should state their reasons; it was not sufficient to elect

[1] M. Tiffenau (ed.), *Correspondance de Charles Gerhardt*, vol. i, pp. 182, 202, 262.

[2] Letter from Laurent to Dumas (1837?), reproduced by J. Jacques, *Revue d'histoire des sciences*, vi (1953), 336.

[3] Grimaux and Gerhardt, *op. cit.*, pp. 588–91.

him because he was a colleague in the *Académie*. He ended with a plea based on practical considerations:

> For many years M. Balard has been in possession of two large laboratories, where he should have been able to carry out all the work which his zeal might have suggested, while all the work of M. Laurent has been carried out by his own personal effort and at the cost of the most severe sacrifices. To put M. Balard in the *Collège de France* is to add nothing to the instruments of study which he has long held in his hands; but it is to deprive M. Laurent of the means of research which he has always lacked and which we have the opportunity of providing for him.

It was a sad day for French science when the *Académie* ignored this plea. Laurent was broken-hearted, and this probably brought about the onset of an illness of which he died two years later. When Laurent was on his death-bed the entire chemistry section of the *Académie*, as if by way of atonement, presented themselves to the minister of education with a plea for a pension for his widow and two young children. The deputation was headed by Biot, who was now the senior member of the *Académie des Sciences*.

In his last long illness Laurent had forced himself to write his *Méthode de chimie*. It was published after his death by Biot, who also wrote an introduction:

> This work, abounding with new ideas, oftentimes fruitful in their results to the author himself, presents us with the intimate convictions of a man who has enriched science by numerous and unlooked-for discoveries. It is a summary of the thoughts of his whole life.

Biot presented the book as one which deserved to be received with serious attention and without prejudice, notwithstanding the novel symbolism and nomenclature used. Laurent had a definite contribution to make to chemistry. His rejection by the Paris clique had the result of increasing the contrast between his thought and language and that of his contemporaries.

The establishment in Paris which controlled French science in the mid-nineteenth century can be seen at its worst in the cases of Gerhardt and Laurent. The rejection of *les deux* was tempered by several acts of kindness and the definite patronage of two men: Gerhardt owed a debt to Thenard and Laurent to Biot. Unfortunately neither Thenard nor Biot was adroit in academic politics and their support was not sufficient to tip the balance in favour of the younger men. What is significant here, therefore, is intention rather than accomplishment. The two greybeards, who had been active in the Arcueil group some forty years previously, did their best to acquit themselves of their debt to the previous generation.

Pasteur and Biot

One of the great names of nineteenth-century science, a man whose work defies restriction to any one branch of science, was Louis Pasteur. He acquired fame by the application of physical methods to the study of chemistry but went on to win an even greater renown in his studies in the biological field. Yet what connection can this great man of science, who was born on 27 December 1822, barely one month after the death of Berthollet, have with the men who had once assembled at Arcueil? The connection is through Biot, who figures prominently in the early scientific life of Pasteur.

Pasteur's brilliant work on the optically different kinds of tartaric acid and the relation between the form of the crystal and the effect of the solution on polarized light was arrived at by combining studies of crystallography and polarography to chemistry. Pasteur's principal precursors in each of these fields were Haüy and Biot respectively, and he was also encouraged by the successful application in chemistry of Mitscherlich's law of isomorphism. But whilst Biot's work on the applications of polarized light to chemical problems, to be seen in its full context in relation to Pasteur, must be put alongside previous work on crystal structure, Pasteur's debt to Biot was far greater than to anyone else, since it was not merely a case of drawing on the record of Biot's published work. The personal help and encouragement which Biot gave to this young man from the provinces serves to correct the picture of Biot as a tireless worker untouched by personal affection. By helping Pasteur, Biot was able in some small measure to repay the benefits he had received through the patronage of Laplace. Pasteur for his own part felt that Biot's work on the rotation of the plane of polarized light of liquids had been unjustly neglected by chemists.[1] We must now, therefore, turn back to examine Biot's earlier work.

In a memoir which he read to the *Académie des Sciences* in 1818,[2] Biot drew attention to the desirability of studying the individual properties of the constituent parts of bodies. This would be helpful in the study of states of aggregation and the 'energy' associated with each, crystallization, capillary attraction and chemical affinity. (One notes in Biot's approach the union of chemistry and physics.) Yet in practice, what one usually encountered experimentally was not the property of an individual particle but of an aggregate of particles. Biot then claimed that he had found a property of substances, which depended entirely on the nature of the substance and not on the quantity present or the state of aggregation, nor even on the state of chemical combination. It must therefore be a property of the individual particles. Biot and Arago had previously discovered that certain crystals rotated the plane of polarized light. Biot's important discovery was that a similar effect took place in a *liquid* such as turpentine. This was therefore a property dependent on the individual molecules and not on their arrangement. Biot discovered a similar effect with certain solutions such as that of camphor in alcohol. The latter solution and the turpentine had the effect of rotating the plane of polarization of light in opposite directions and Biot found that by mixing them in suitable proportions the effect on polarized light cancelled out. Biot used the term 'compensated' (*compensé*) to express this effect. He did some preliminary experiments on a solution of cane sugar and beet sugar to demonstrate their identity.

In another memoir, which Biot read to the *Académie des Sciences* in 1832, he went further with his comparative investigations of sugars in collaboration with Persoz, a younger colleague at the *Collège de France*.[3] They tried the effect of sulphuric acid on an aqueous solution of cane sugar and noted that it made the product have the same effect on polarized light as

---

[1] Pasteur in his doctoral thesis said that he was 'guidé par les travaux nombreux et importants de M. Biot sur la polarisation rotatoire des liquides, travaux trop negligés des chimistes . . .', Pasteur, *Oeuvres*, Paris, 1922, vol. i, p. 20.

[2] *Mém. Acad. Sc. Inst.*, ii (1817), 41–136.

[3] *Ibid.*, xiii (1835), 39–175, especially 160–75.

grape sugar—an effect which Biot in an additional note of 1833 described as 'inversion'. Biot concluded his memoir by expressing the hope that further use of polarized light would help to resolve many of the current difficulties of organic chemistry. In another long memoir, read in 1836, Biot paid particular attention to tartaric acid,[1] and his memoir of the following year is quoted by Pasteur.[2] We might mention as a further connection with the Arcueil group that it was Gay-Lussac who gave the name 'racemic acid' to a second form of tartaric acid and demonstrated that it had an identical chemical composition.[3] The true relation between racemic acid and tartaric acid was to be discovered by Pasteur.

In 1848 Pasteur discovered that there were different types of tartaric acid, distinguished by the ability of their solutions to rotate the plane of polarized light either to the right or to the left, and these could be separated by hand by an examination of their crystalline forms which were related as mirror images. He found, moreover, that when equal quantities of the two forms of tartaric acid were mixed together, their opposite effects on polarized light cancelled out.

Balard, who was Pasteur's teacher at the *École Normale*, and who had been elected to the *Académie des Sciences* on the strength of his discovery of bromine, did not hesitate to tell his colleagues at the *Académie* of his pupil's discovery. Biot was sceptical that a young man who had just obtained his doctorate could have made such a fundamental discovery. Rather than reject it out of hand, however, he decided to try it out in his laboratory.

In the course of two lectures which he delivered to the Chemical Society of Paris in 1860, lectures dedicated to Biot, Pasteur told the story of his first association with Biot. He described in detail how Biot was won over from scepticism to enthusiasm. It is best to let Pasteur himself speak:

The announcement of the above facts naturally placed me in communication with Biot, who was not without doubts regarding their accuracy. Being charged with giving an account of them to the Academy, he made me come to him and repeat before his

[1] *Ibid.*, xv (1838), 93–279.
[2] *Ibid.*, xvi (1838), 229–396; Pasteur, *Oeuvres*, vol. i, p. 105.
[3] *Cours de chimie*, Brussels, 1828, vol. ii, Leçon 24, p. 23.

eyes the decisive experiment. He handed over to me some para-tartaric [i.e. racemic] acid which he had himself previously studied with particular care, and which he had found to be per-fectly indifferent to polarized light. I prepared the double salt in his presence, with soda and ammonia, which he had likewise desired to provide.

The liquid was set aside for slow evaporation in one of his rooms. When it had furnished about 30 to 40 grams of crystals, he asked me to call at the *Collège de France* in order to collect them and isolate before him, by recognition of their crystallographic character, the right and the left crystals, requesting me to state once more whether I really affirmed that the crystals which I should place at his right would deviate to the right, and the others to the left. This done, he told me that he would undertake the rest. He prepared the solutions with carefully measured quan-tities, and when ready to examine them in the polarizing appara-tus, he once more invited me to come into his room.

He first placed in the apparatus the more interesting solution, that which ought to deviate to the left. Without even making a measurement, he saw by the appearance of the tints of the two images, ordinary and extraordinary, in the analyser, that there was a strong deviation to the left. Then, very visibly affected, the illustrious old man took me by the arm and said:

'*My dear child, I have loved science so much throughout my life that this makes my heart throb.*'[1]

Pasteur went on to explain that here

the emotion of the scientific man was mingled with the personal pleasure of seeing his conjectures realized. For more than thirty years Biot had striven in vain to induce chemists to share his con-viction that the study of rotatory polarization offered one of the surest means of gaining knowledge of the molecular constitution of substances.

For anyone who has looked through Biot's extensive memoirs on polarization and realizes the tremendous labour which he had lavished on this subject, his emotion at Pasteur's discovery is understandable.

In 1849 Pasteur took up a teaching appointment in Stras-bourg which enabled him to make one prolonged visit to Paris every summer. He tended to organize his work in a yearly cycle, ending with a memoir read to the *Académie* in the early

[1] Pasteur, *Researches on Molecular Assymetry*, A.C.R. No. 14, pp. 20–1.

autumn. During his 'pilgrimage' from Strasbourg to Paris in the summer of 1852, Biot introduced the young Pasteur to Mitscherlich and Gustav Rose, who were then on a short stay in Paris. In a letter to his father, Pasteur described a dinner to which he was invited by Thenard and at which the other guests included such men as Dumas, Chevreul, Regnault, as well as Mitscherlich and Rose.

As Pasteur's biographer, Vallery-Radot, remarks, as Biot got older, instead of living in his memories and contemplating his own contribution to science, he kept his mind active and he was happy to look forwards through his association with Pasteur. Pasteur, in his letters to his father, speaks of Biot's kindness and constant encouragement. Biot, for example, compared the field opened up by Pasteur's work to the discovery of the potential riches of California. When Pasteur's father came to Paris on a visit, he was cordially received by Biot, who told him how much he admired the talent, enthusiasm and capacity for work of his son. Pasteur's introduction to the distinguished physicist had come about through his development of the latter's earlier work, but Biot's attachment to Pasteur was due to the young man's sincerity and, not least, a trait they shared, an enthusiasm for work. In a letter to Pasteur's father in 1851 Biot remarked:

> It is the greatest pleasure that I can experience in my old age, to see young men of talent working industriously and trying to progress in a scientific career by means of a steady and persevering labour, and not by wretched intriguing. That is what has made your son dear to me . . .

Biot advised the man nearly fifty years younger than himself not only on the details of his research but on the kind of research he should undertake and the advancement of his scientific career. When Pasteur had the idea of exploring the effect of magnetism on vegetation, it was Biot who advised him against it, but we must also record that Biot advised him against undertaking his research on spontaneous generation, a piece of advice that Pasteur did not heed and which Biot lived to recognize as mistaken. Biot supported Pasteur in his candidature for the *Académie des Sciences*. He was unsuccessful in 1857, when a vacancy occurred in the section of mineralogy. No other vacancy even vaguely related to Pasteur's qualifications occurred until 1861. There was then a vacancy in the botany section. Biot, determined at all costs to get his protégé into the *Académie,* supported him for election with the claim that of the 21 memoirs published by Pasteur, 10 were related to 'vegetable physiology'. This attempt to paint Pasteur as a botanist was doomed to failure and it is sad to record that Biot died in February 1862 without having achieved one of his dearest ambitions. It was only in December 1862 that Pasteur entered the *Académie* in the section of mineralogy.

It is no exaggeration to say that Biot was a second father to Pasteur. When a photograph was taken of Biot in the last years of his life (Plate 206), he presented a copy to Pasteur with the words:

> If you place this portrait beside the portrait of your father, you will be able to see together the faces of two persons who have loved you more or less in the same way.

Patronage by Arago

Arago's patronage of young men and new causes in the 1830's and 1840's was no less than that of Biot; in many ways it was more successful. Arago's official position as Secretary of the *Académie des Sciences* and later, Director of the Observatory, gave him ample opportunity of sponsoring research and encouraging particular projects. Among these were the early photographic process developed by Daguerre, the early astronomical work of Leverrier, and his ideas on determining the velocity of light, which was put into practice by Foucault. In none of these developments does Arago appear as the only sponsor. It is pleasing to find also other former members of the Arcueil circle contributing indirectly to scientific advance.

In about 1826 Joseph Nicephore Niepce succeeded in obtaining a permanent image on a plate of an outdoor scene.[1] The following year he came to England in the hope of finding a patron for his secret process but he was unsuccessful in interesting the Royal Society, King George IV or the Royal Society of Arts, whom he approached in turn. In 1837 a quicker process

---

[1] The following account is based almost entirely on Gernsheim's *History of Photography.* It is interesting that this lays emphasis on the patronage of Arago.

for fixing the image was discovered by Louis Daguerre. Daguerre had found that mercury vapour could be used to fix the image formed on a film of the light-sensitive silver iodide. He approached Niepce with the suggestion of a partnership. They hoped to obtain support for the development of 'heliography' and 'daguerreotype' by public subscription, but by the end of 1838 they had been unable to raise the necessary funds. Daguerre then approached several leading scientists in Paris including Biot, Humboldt, Arago and Dumas in the hope of using their support to interest the government.

Daguerre was fortunate in finding an influential patron in Arago, since Arago not only held a pre-eminent place in the scientific life of Paris but was also a member of the Chamber of Deputies. It was at a meeting of the *Académie des Sciences* on 7 January 1839 that Arago made the first official announcement of Daguerre's discovery. He wrote a letter in the strongest terms to the Minister of the Interior, urging that Daguerre should receive suitable financial recognition for his discovery. Arago stated that other countries were interested in the process and it was the duty of the French government to take the initiative. Daguerre could hardly have had a more energetic sponsor. Thanks to Arago's intervention he was awarded an annual pension of 6,000 francs and a pension of 4,000 francs was given to the family of Niepce.

Arago was enthusiastic about the process of Daguerre:

> The daguerreotype does not demand a single manipulation which is not perfectly easy to every person. It requires no knowledge of drawing, and does not depend upon any manual dexterity. By observing a few very simple directions, anyone may succeed with the same certainty and perform as well as the author of the invention.

While Arago was praising the daguerreotype in the lower house, Gay-Lussac, as spokesman of a special committee appointed by the Chamber of Peers to examine the subject, presented it in a most favourable light to the Upper Chamber. He said that the process

> is the origin of a new art in the midst of an old civilization; an art which will constitute an era, and be preserved as a title of glory . . . Let it stand forth as a splendid evidence of the protection

which the Chambers, indeed the whole country, afford to great inventions.

The Bill granting pensions in recognition of this process was passed enthusiastically by both Chambers. The time had now come to make the process public. This was done on 19 August 1839 at a joint meeting of the *Académie des Sciences* and the *Académie des Beaux Arts*. It was appropriate that, when Daguerre through shyness declined to address the meeting, the announcement should have been made by the man who had fought so hard for official recognition of daguerreotype, Arago.[1] Arago identified himself completely with the advancement of daguerreotype, so passionately in fact that he probably did less than justice to one or two other men who developed other ideas of photography about the same time.

Arago's interest in photography was not confined to the popular field. As an astronomer, he saw immediately some of the possibilities of its application to astronomy.[2] Arago also made important contributions to photometry, developing, for example, an instrument which made it easy to compare the relative light intensities of two stars in close proximity. His study of the light from the sun was the subject of a generous tribute by Sir David Brewster in 1850, who referred to

the remarkable discovery . . . made by M. Arago, by means of a silver plate, that the rays that proceed from the central parts of the sun's disc have a higher photogenic action than those which issue from its margin. This interesting discovery of M. Arago is one of a series on photometry which that distinguished philosopher is now occupied in publishing. Threatened with a calamity which the civilized world will deplore—the loss of that sight which has detected so many brilliant phenomena, and penetrated so deeply the mysteries of the material world—he is now completing, with the aid of other eyes than his own, those splendid researches which will immortalize his own name and add to the scientific glory of his country.[3]

---

[1] *Comptes Rendus*, ix (1839), 250–67.
[2] Report to the Chamber of Deputies in 1839. Arago, *Oeuvres, Notices scientifiques*, vol. iv, pp. 498 ff.
[3] Address to the British Association. *Report of Twentieth Meeting of the British Association for the Advancement of Science*, Edinburgh, 1850, p. xxxvii.

In Arago's later years the guidance he gave to others became more important than his own contributions and this is well illustrated by the case of Leverrier. Urbain Jean Joseph Leverrier in 1846 discovered by calculation the existence of a new planet, Neptune. His early scientific career brought him into contact with several of the men who had once been associates at Arcueil. Leverrier, born in 1811, entered the *École Polytechnique* in 1831. He graduated with distinction and with several choices of a career in the public service, he chose to work under Gay-Lussac at the headquarters of the tobacco administration. Leverrier was very interested in chemistry and managed to carry out some research. He published two memoirs on phosphorus which attracted the attention of Dulong. According to one biographer (Aoust), Dulong at this period visited him nearly every day and spoke in the highest terms of his chemical ability.

When the post of *répétiteur* in chemistry at the *École Polytechnique* fell vacant in 1837 the choice of nominating a suitable chemist lay with Gay-Lussac. He was in a difficult position, not knowing which of two former students to recommend, Regnault or Leverrier. The dilemma was resolved by the occurrence of a further vacancy, that of *répétiteur* in astronomy. Knowing that Leverrier was interested in mathematics, Gay-Lussac set him on his astronomical career by recommending him for the second post.

The mathematical ability of Leverrier attracted the attention of Arago, who was the director of the Paris Observatory and at this time the most influential figure in French astronomy. It was due to the suggestion of Arago that he should investigate an anomaly in the orbit of the planet Uranus that Leverrier was led to make his discovery of Neptune. It was in the year 1845 that Arago urged Leverrier to undertake the solution of this problem and Arago confided to him the unpublished observations made at the Paris Observatory during the previous ten years. On 31 August 1846 Leverrier was able to publish the conclusion of his research. The value of the French work is hardly lessened by the fact that Adams in England was at this time in the process of solving the problem independently.

This brief description of the rise to fame of Leverrier cannot end without a reference to Biot. In 1843 Biot resigned his chair of astronomy at the *Collège de France* in favour of Leverrier and in 1849 when the existence of the new planet, the position of which had been calculated by Leverrier, was challenged in the *Académie des Sciences*, the record shows that Biot as one of the senior Academicians rose to support the younger man. Thus Leverrier, whose astronomical work was in a sense based on the *Mécanique céleste* of Laplace, came to be helped successively in his career by Gay-Lussac, Dulong, Biot and Arago. It was fitting that on Arago's death the man appointed to succeed him as director of the Observatory should be Leverrier.

Finally we must mention Arago's contribution to Foucault's work on the determination of the velocity of light. In the seventeenth century Roemer's observations of the eclipses of the satellites of Jupiter had established that light had a finite but very great velocity. Little further progress was made in the determination of the velocity of light till the nineteenth century. It was Arago who, at a meeting of the *Académie des Sciences* in December 1838, made a step in this direction by proposing that the velocities with which light moves in air or in a liquid such as water or carbon disulphide should be compared. The object of the experiment was to decide finally between the corpuscular theory of light and the wave theory. According to the former theory, light was propagated more swiftly in water than in air and according to the wave theory the reverse was true. It is interesting to recall that Arago had himself first undertaken a study of the velocity of light at the instigation of Laplace.[1]

Arago, developing the idea of Wheatstone (who was concerned with the velocity of electricity) suggested that two parallel beams of light should be allowed to travel at the same instant through a tube filled with water and through air. The light would impinge on a rotating mirror and from the position of the images formed of the two point sources of light, it could be inferred which had reached the mirror first. Arago entered into all the details of the proposed experiment, including the speed of rotation of the mirror. He ended by suggesting that this method might be applied to the determination of the absolute velocity of light. In 1850 he returned to the subject and suggested that the practical problem of obtaining a mirror capable of rotating a thousand times a second could be sur-

[1] Arago, *Oeuvres, Tables*, p. cxiv.

mounted by using several rotating mirrors. By now Fizeau[1] and Foucault had both shown an interest in performing Arago's proposed experiment but as they considered that he had a proprietary right to this, they first obtained his formal permission. Arago willingly lent Fizeau one of his mirrors and approved of Foucault developing a modification of his apparatus, saying,

> I can only, in the present condition of my sight, accompany with my good wishes, the experimenters who desire to follow my ideas.

At the meeting of the *Académie des Sciences* on 6 May 1850, a week after Arago had made this statement, Foucault was able to report that with his modification of Arago's apparatus he had been entirely successful in comparing the velocities of light in two media. This, however, was only an interim report to establish priority. Foucault continued:

> If physicists receive favourably the fruit of my first efforts, all the honour should go to M. Arago, who, by a bold and imaginative idea, has shown that questions about the speed of light could be transferred from the realm of astronomy to that of physics. Arago, by generously standing down, has allowed young scientists to launch out with enthusiasm along the path which he has shown them.

The main modification which Foucault made to Arago's apparatus had the effect of ensuring that the light reflected from the revolving mirror all went in a particular direction so that it could be observed, instead of leaving this to chance. Foucault did this simply by using a continuous source of light instead of an intermittent one. Foucault also arranged for the rotating mirror to be moved directly by steam pressure instead of by a falling weight operating a complicated system of gears. Six weeks after Foucault, Fizeau was also successful in the experimental determination of the relative velocities of light.

To determine the absolute velocity of light Foucault made ingenious use of a toothed wheel. His experiment of 1862 is described in text-books of physics. Before leaving Foucault, however, mention should be made of his other claim to fame —the pendulum experiment which is named after him. In his description of this, Foucault refers to a memoir by Poisson on

[1] Fizeau in 1849 published a quite different method of determining the velocity of light.

projectiles and it was by comparing the movement of the pendulum to a projectile that Foucault was able to demonstrate the rotation of the earth.[1] He had the brilliant inspiration that, whereas the effect of the earth's motion on a projectile would be too small to be observed, on a pendulum the effect would be cumulative and therefore this effect, first pointed out by Poisson, would pass from the realm of theoretical interest to practical observation.

The personality of Dulong was completely different from that of Arago. He was never influential in academic politics and his heart was not in his teaching. Yet as a man who lived for research he was able to stimulate some further research from others.[2] Among these we may number Hess, whose law of thermochemistry made a fundamental contribution to physical chemistry in the nineteenth century. Hess (1802–50) was professor of chemistry at the University of St Petersburg. In the summer of 1837 he visited Paris and made contact with Dulong. Dulong had been working on heats of reaction but, being dissatisfied with some of the data he had obtained, had not published his research. He entrusted some of his results to Hess on the understanding that the latter would not make use of them in any publication until his own work appeared in print in the immediate future. Dulong, however, died in July 1838.

Hearing of Dulong's death, Hess, now back in Russia, wrote immediately to Arago as permanent secretary of the *Académie des Sciences*, urging him to publish Dulong's important work.[3] In his letter Hess observed that Dulong was mainly concerned with quantitative values of heats of formation of compounds. The very evening after his discussion with Dulong, he had made notes which include the following generalizations:

> The quantities of heat evolved are approximately the same for the same substances, combining at different temperatures.

---

[1] *Recueil des Travaux Scientifiques de Léon Foucault*, 1878, p. 382.

[2] Dulong's rôle as patron of the philosopher Auguste Comte may also be mentioned. In 1837 Dulong took advantage of his position as Director of Studies at the *École Polytechnique* to secure the appointment of Comte as entrance examiner, despite his lack of formal qualifications in mathematics. For many years Comte's livelihood depended entirely on his mathematics teaching. Comte, however, blamed Arago for blocking his advance.

[3] *Comptes Rendus*, vii (1838), 871–2.

Equal volumes of all gases in combining with oxygen give out the same quantity of heat.

The interesting thing here is Hess's concern with generalizing about heats of reaction.

Hess's next communication to Arago came eighteen months later.[1] He thanked Arago for having recovered Dulong's papers and publishing them. He was now free to publish the research which had originated from his discussion with Dulong. He then stated the fundamental law which bears his name:

In any chemical reaction the heat evolved is constant, whether combination takes place directly or indirectly in several stages.

He provided data on which this law was based and was at pains to point out that it also agreed with the data left by Dulong.

The Role of Former Members of the Society of Arcueil in the Affairs of the 'Académie des Sciences'

One might well ask what was the position in French science in the second quarter of the nineteenth century of the men who had once been the centre of activity of the Arcueil group: Gay-Lussac and Thenard, Arago and Biot. In his later years Gay-Lussac was mainly concerned with industrial chemistry. Thenard was more concerned with education and spent a considerable time on administration. He attended regularly the meetings of the *Académie des Sciences* and was the senior member of the chemistry section from 1837 to his death in 1857. Neither Gay-Lussac nor Thenard figures prominently in the affairs of the *Académie* although each had the honour of being successively vice-president and president.[2] Neither did Biot find the politics of the *Académie* to his taste. This role was reserved for Arago.

Berthollet had not been the only distinguished man of science to die in 1822. A few months earlier the *Académie des Sciences* had been deprived of Delambre, one of its two permanent secretaries. The post involved responsibility for mathematics and all the physical sciences. There were three candidates for the

[1] *Ibid.*, x (1840), 759–63.
[2] Gay-Lussac was vice-president in 1821 and 1833 and president in 1822 and 1834. Thenard succeeded Gay-Lussac as vice-president in 1822 and became president in 1823.

H H

election: Biot, Arago and Fourier. Arago declared that he already held all the official appointments he could manage reasonably and he declared that Biot was in a similar position. He therefore supported the election of Fourier. It seems that with two powerful adversaries, neither of whom would accept with good grace the victory of the other, Fourier achieved his success as a compromise candidate. Fourier was therefore secretary from 1822 until his death in 1830. When a ballot was held for Fourier's successor, Arago received 39 votes out of the 44 cast and he was permanent secretary of the *Académie des Sciences* over the period 1830 to 1853. During this time he occupied a dominant position in French science. Arago could never be considered in a dehumanized way as someone who produced scientific work. He had considerable personal qualities and the influence which he exerted depended as much on this as upon the quality of his scientific work. Arago made an excellent secretary by virtue of his wide grasp of science and his ability to handle men.

In the conduct of the affairs of the *Académie des Sciences* a fundamental principle separated Biot and Arago. Arago had been responsible for the introduction of the *Comptes Rendus Hebdomadaires* in 1835, a weekly bulletin summarizing the work of the *Académie*. A means had thus been found of circumventing the long delays in publication of the work of the official body of French science, which earlier in the century had amounted to a scandal. This would seem to have been a most desirable move. To understand Biot's objections and his strong feelings on the privileges of the *Académie*, it is necessary to go back to see the connection between admitting the public to meetings of the *Académie* and the later publication of the *Comptes Rendus*. As regards the admission of the public, Biot and many other Academicians felt that this had the effect of lowering the standard of work presented, since speakers would tend to avoid technicalities and aim at generalizations which could be more readily understood. The speaker would try to justify himself to the public as much as to his colleagues. The public included newspaper reporters and in 1825 one of the Paris newspapers, *Le Globe*, had begun to give a regular column to the proceedings of the *Académie des Sciences*, and other newspapers soon adopted a similar practice. Certain technical difficulties in accurate reporting immediately arose. In addition to factual reporting there were press comments, not all favourable to the *Académie*, an institution which by its very exclusiveness was almost bound to foster hostile criticism. The *Comptes Rendus* therefore came into existence as a measure of self defence. It was distributed to each resident member of the *Académie* as well as to correspondents and foreign scientific societies and libraries. It had been the intention at first to give only the briefest summary of papers read to the *Académie*, but in practice this would have made the publication of very little value. On the other hand, if a substantial part of the original paper was published in the *Comptes Rendus*, this resulted in an overlap with the *Mémoires*.

The frequency and regularity of publication of the *Comptes Rendus* as well as its wide distribution made a significant contribution to science in the nineteenth century. Biot's suggestion that the rapidity of publication would produce contributions of less permanent value than would be possible in the *Mémoires* was hardly justified. The *Comptes Rendus* in many ways came to eclipse the *Mémoires* in the valuable contribution it made to scientific literature and much of the credit for this must go to Arago.

Arago also possessed to a high degree the powers of analysis of the scientific work of his colleagues over a wide range of subject matter. He quickly grasped the essentials of a memoir and with his powers of expression he was able to hold the attention of his colleagues and even their admiration. One of the tasks of the two secretaries of the *Académie des Sciences* was to compose a biography of the most distinguished of their colleagues who had recently died and this *éloge* was read at the annual public meeting. It was appropriate that Arago's first *éloge* should be of his friend and protégé, Fresnel, and he read it at a meeting of the *Académie* on 26 July 1830, only seven weeks after his appointment as secretary. This was followed in later years by biographies of other distinguished members of the *Académie*, both foreign members, such as Volta and Watt and resident members, such as Carnot and Ampère. The last three biographies he composed were those of Poisson, Gay-Lussac and Malus. It is fitting that it should be their former colleague of Arcueil, who had known them so well, who should be their official biographer for the *Académie des Sciences*.

In the late 1840's Arago's sight was becoming feebler and he eventually became blind. His intellectual powers, however, remained and he was able to carry out his duties at the *Académie des Sciences* with the help of an amanuensis. In 1833 Arago had been appointed 'director of observations' at the Paris Observatory. In theory, the administration of the Observatory was the responsibility of the *Bureau des Longitudes*, but in practice Arago became the effective director. Thus the domination of Laplace in the affairs of the *Bureau des Longitudes* and the Observatory in the first quarter of the nineteenth century was replaced by the control of another member of the Arcueil circle in the second quarter.

Immediately after Biot's defeat in 1822 for the post of secretary of the *Académie des Sciences*, he tended to withdraw from active participation in the work of the *Académie*, spending nearly all his time on research and teaching. Nor did the election of Arago to the post of secretary in 1830 do anything to bring Biot closer to the *Académie*. In the 1840's, however, he again began to take an interest in its affairs. The session of 18 April 1853 was marked by the congratulations extended to Biot upon the occasion of his academic jubilee. Thenard observed that it was sufficient tribute to Biot to say simply 'that it was fortunate for science that Biot had been a member of the *Académie des Sciences* for fifty years'.

As the senior member of the *Académie*, this institution came to occupy a major part of Biot's life. At times he almost looked upon himself as a personification of the *Académie*. He was always sensitive to its privileges and felt, for example, that in the publication of the *Comptes Rendus*, the *Académie*, in wishing to be known to the multitude, had lost much of its independence. When he died at the age of 87 he was indisputably the grand old man of French science. He had retained the full exercise of his intellectual powers to the end. One of his compatriots wrote:

> Biot's death is a sad loss to our scientific world. He was the only member of the Institute who belonged to the Consular period . . . A whole age, a whole scientific world has been borne with Biot to the tomb.

In the conviction that Biot was the most illustrious embodiment of the *Académie des Sciences*, it was felt desirable that his place in the section of mathematics should remain vacant for one year as a mark of respect.

Influence through Publications

When Arago was organizing the *Comptes Rendus* of the *Académie des Sciences*, Biot was responsible for the editing of scientific articles in the *Journal des Savans*. The most important editorial post in French science, however, was probably that of the *Annales de chimie et de physique*, of which the editors were Gay-Lussac for chemistry and Arago for physics. Sir John Herschel[1] singled out the *Annales* for special praise as a journal conducted on efficient lines with contributions of a consistently high quality unlike, he said, the 'crude and undigested scientific matter' to be found in British scientific journals of the time. Gay-Lussac and Arago continued as sole joint editors of the *Annales* until 1840, when the editorial board was expanded to include leading representatives of the next generation of French scientists: Chevreul, Savary, Dumas, Pelouze, Boussingault and Regnault. Gay-Lussac continued on the editorial board until his death in 1850 and Arago until his death in 1853. Even Bérard in Montpellier did not escape editorial responsibility. He joined forces with a small group of chemists and manufacturers to produce the *Annales de l'industrie française et étrangère*.[2]

The books written by members of the Arcueil circle continued to influence certain aspects of science after the deaths of their authors. The primary concern of this chapter has been with people, but it might be appropriate to mention also the influence of a few selected publications. The range of publications by members of the Arcueil circle has been discussed earlier; here we are concerned primarily with influence.

In the course of this book there have been frequent references to Laplace's *Mécanique céleste*. This book was one of the really great scientific works of the early nineteenth century. Among many who studied it we may mention the Belgian statistician Quetelet, who had come under the influence of Laplace when he visited Paris in 1822 (or 1823).[3] Quetelet later wrote of the

---

[1] Article: 'Sound', *Encyclopaedia Metropolitana*, 1817–45, vol. iv, p. 810n.

[2] Six volumes, 1828–30.

[3] J. Lottin, *Quetelet, Statisticien et Sociologue*, Louvain and Paris, 1912, pp. 16, 19–20, 26n.

'lessons' he had received from Laplace, Bouvard, Poisson and others—presumably referring to his debt in conversation and discussion rather than the attendance at any formal course. The *Mécanique céleste* was, however, an exceedingly difficult book even for mathematicians such as Quetelet.

In the popular imagination it was in connection with the nebular hypothesis on the origin of the solar system that the name of Laplace lived on in the nineteenth century. The publication of this hypothesis in Laplace's *Exposition du Système du monde* in 1796 obviously belongs to an earlier period than the association with Arcueil, yet in its influence it dominated cosmogony in the nineteenth century. In the words of the editors of the *Source Book in Astronomy*,[1] Laplace's nebular hypothesis 'was a valuable and powerful stimulant to scientific thought throughout the nineteenth century'. When Thenard was championing the cause of a state sponsored edition of the works of Laplace, we must remember that this included the *Système du monde* as much as work more closely related to that of the Arcueil group.

In the field of chemistry one of the main contributions to development in the nineteenth century was Gay-Lussac's memoir on the combining volumes of gases. It had an immediate influence on Avogadro, whose hypothesis provided a key to one of the crucial problems of chemistry in the nineteenth century, the problem of atomic weights. Avogadro[2] took Gay-Lussac's work as his starting point and mentions the name of the French chemist twenty times in less than that number of pages. It was one of the misfortunes of the time that, for half a century after Avogadro enunciated his principle in 1811, it was ignored. Gay-Lussac, therefore, had a more immediate influence on nineteenth-century chemistry through Berzelius and Liebig.

The major chemical work in the Arcueil tradition was Berthollet's *Essai de statique chimique*. Of the influence of this book, we may say that it would have been more widely read and understood, if it had been written more clearly. Yet it is undoubtedly one of the early classics of physical chemistry. Its

[1] H. Shapley and H. E. Howarth, *op. cit.*, New York, 1929, p. 155.
[2] *Journal de physique*, lxxiii (1811), 58–76. *Foundations of the Molecular Theory*, A.C.R. No. 4, pp. 28–51.

ideas on reversible reactions and the influence of mass were explored by chemists for many years before they received a triumphant vindication and extension in the statement of the Law of Mass Action by Guldberg and Waage in 1867.

Even an elementary text-book could make a powerful impact on persons who had no personal contact with the author. The second edition of Biot's *Traité élémentaire d'astronomie physique* (1810–11), for example, had a considerable influence on the next generation of astronomers and this influence was not confined to France. The British Astronomer Royal, Sir George Airy (1801–92), said that it was from this book that he had acquired a taste for astronomy and it was here that he had learned the principles of the subject.

The Contributions of the Younger Members of the Arcueil Group to Nineteenth-century Science

The work of the Arcueil group has an important place in the history of the physical sciences in the nineteenth century. In the study of light Malus' discovery of polarization was the starting point of a whole train of investigation. Arago and Biot were among the first to appreciate the significance of Malus' work and to carry his research further. Brewster in Britain was not far behind. Recognition in Britain of the value of Malus' achievement came with the award to him of the Rumford medal by the Royal Society. Biot's interest in the relation of polarized light to chemical constitution was scarcely less vital than the discovery of Malus. We have seen how Biot became the patron of Pasteur. Biot's work on the inversion of cane sugar was carried further by Emil Fischer, one of the great German chemists of the second half of the nineteenth century.

Electrical research figures less prominently in the work of the Arcueil group than optical research. The contributions of Gay-Lussac and Thenard were useful, but they fail to strike the imagination in the same way as Davy's work. Arago's work on electromagnetism, following the discovery of Oersted of the effect of an electric current on a magnetic needle, does not rank as highly as the work of Ampère or Faraday, but this is no reason why it should be overlooked.

It was Arago who brought the news of Oersted's discovery to

The Society of Arcueil

Paris. The news had first reached Geneva, and Arago, who was there on a visit, had repeated Oersted's experiments in the presence of de la Rive, Prevost, Pictet, de Saussure, Marcet and Candolle. At the first meeting of the *Académie des Sciences* after his return from Geneva, that is on 4 September 1820, Arago had described Oersted's experiments for the benefit of the Paris scientists, and at the following meeting on 11 September he gave a practical demonstration. A week later Ampère announced his great discovery of the mutual attraction/repulsion of two parallel wires carrying an electric current. When Ampère developed a theory of electrodynamics in September 1820, his first concern was to explain it to Humboldt and then to visit Laplace to obtain his comments and possible support.[1]

Even though the major immediate consequence of Oersted's discovery was developed by Ampère, the members of the Arcueil circle were not idle. Within two months of the announcement by Arago of Oersted's discovery, two further important contributions to electro-magnetism had been presented to the *Académie des Sciences*. The *Annales de chimie et de physique* had the distinction of publishing all three memoirs in the same volume. On 25 September Arago announced to the *Académie* that he had discovered that an electric current can magnetize iron filings.[2] He showed that the effect of a current on soft iron was to induce temporary magnetism, but if steel were used the effect was permanent. He continued further experiments on electromagnetism in collaboration with Ampère.

Biot had been out of Paris when Arago arrived with the news of Oersted's discovery. On his return to the capital he was said to be working day and night to make up for lost time in exploring this new field.[3] Biot and Savart presented the result of their joint research to the *Académie* on 30 October 1820. During the eighteenth century scientists, working in a Newtonian framework, had compared the strength of magnets by measuring the *force* they would exert on another magnet. This was done simply by timing the oscillations of the magnet. Biot and Savart

[1] Ampère, *Correspondance*, p. 562.
[2] *Ann. chim. phys.*, xv (1820), 93–100. A similar discovery was made independently about the same time by Davy and by Seebeck.
[3] Letter from Dulong to Berzelius, 2 October 1820, Berzelius, *Bref*, vol. 2, part iv, p. 19.

extended this method of investigation to electromagnetism. They measured the rate of oscillation of a suspended magnet placed at various distances from a conductor carrying a current. They were thus able to show that the magnetic force acts at right angles to the perpendicular joining the point considered to the conductor and that its intensity was inversely proportional to the distance ('Biot and Savart's Law').[1]

On 7 March 1825 Arago announced to the *Académie* his discovery that if a plate of copper is rotated close to a magnetic needle or a magnet suspended in such a way that the latter is able to rotate in a plane parallel to the former, the magnet tends to follow the motion of the plate; similarly if a magnet is rotated, the plate tends to follow.[2] The name 'Arago's disc' commemorates the discoverer of this curious phenomenon. For Arago's discovery that non-ferrous metals could exhibit magnetic properties he was awarded the Copley Medal by the Royal Society in 1825. Although the medal had been available for annual award since the previous century, this was the first time that it had gone to a Frenchman. Arago was now given an award which had been considered appropriate for such eighteenth-century figures as Stephen Hales, John Harrison, Benjamin Franklin and Joseph Priestley. More recently Davy and Oersted had been similarly honoured. It is interesting to find Arago's Copley Medal followed in 1832 by a similar award to Poisson for his work on capillarity. Poisson was also responsible for a theory of magnetism and a powerful theory of electric potential.

Other members of the Arcueil group made contributions to science which were taken as the starting point by various workers later in the century. The influence of the work of Humboldt on terrestrial magnetism should not be overlooked, nor his fundamental studies of climate. Arago too made important contributions in these fields. The study of plant geography virtually began with the work of Humboldt and Candolle. Both Gay-Lussac and Arago did important work on thermometry, as did Dulong and Petit.

One of the great achievements of nineteenth-century physics was the principle of conservation of energy. If Gay-Lussac's

[1] *Ann. chim. phys.*, xv (1820), 222–3.
[2] Arago, *Oeuvres, Notices scientifiques*, vol. i, pp. 424 ff.

memoir of 1807, which gave vital information about the internal energy of a gas, remained unknown to Joule, the fault lies with, as much as anyone, the editors of the British journals for neglecting to provide a translation into English, as had been done in German. Julius Robert Mayer, however, has at least as strong a claim as Joule to the discovery of the principle of conservation of energy. Mayer was quite aware of Gay-Lussac's work and used his results.[1] He also made considerable use of data obtained by Dulong. Mayer calculated the mechanical equivalent of heat from the specific heat of air at constant pressure and at constant volume. For the former he used the value given by Delaroche and Bérard and for the latter he used the value published by Dulong. Once more, therefore, in the work of Mayer we see the relevance of the work of the men who had once met at Arcueil to the main stream of nineteenth-century physical science.

Turning to chemistry, any detailed assessment of the influence of the work of the Arcueil chemists would require considerable space and to try to give a summary would result in a list involving repetition of much that has already been described. To show the Arcueil tradition at its best we may perhaps single out Gay-Lussac as a man who made important contributions to most branches of chemistry: physical, inorganic, organic, analytical and industrial. His physical approach to chemistry in the Lavoisier tradition did not prevent him from drastically modifying Lavoisier's oxygen theory of acids by introducing the theory of hydracids. Gay-Lussac was responsible for one of the standard methods of determining vapour densities,[2] although it is usually known as Hofmann's method after the man who improved upon it half a century later. Gay-Lussac's discovery of the cyanogen radical provided the first example of an organic radical, although the significance of this discovery was not fully appreciated at the time. The statement by Gay-Lussac and Thenard of a 'law' relating the proportions of hydrogen and oxygen in certain organic compounds led to the appreciation of the class of carbohydrates. As early as 1828 Gay-Lussac pointed out that when chlorine

---

[1] Mayer, *Die Mechanik der Wärme* (1842, 45), Ostwald's Klassiker No. 180, Leipzig, 1911; see especially pp. 16, 18–19, 28, 38, 40.
[2] *Ann. chim.*, lxxx (1811), 218.

combines with oils, hydrochloric acid is formed together with another substance in which 'part of the chlorine . . . takes the place of the hydrogen which has been removed'.[1] It was a further ten years before the principle of substitutions in organic chemistry was developed by Dumas. Gay-Lussac's contributions to volumetric analysis have already been mentioned, as have his ideas on the precipitation of metallic sulphides, the basis of the group separation of metals. The Gay-Lussac tower is an example of a lasting contribution by him to chemical industry.

Nor should Gay-Lussac's work as joint editor of the *Annales de chimie et de physique* be forgotten. It was he, for example, who in 1824[2] drew attention to the similarity in the results of Wöhler's analysis of silver cyanide and Liebig's analysis of silver fulminate, and before long Berzelius had to coin the word 'isomerism' to describe such phenomena.

The importance of the Arcueil group to the development of chemistry in the first half of the nineteenth century does not lie in the work of one man, however brilliant. It was the privilege of the Arcueil group to hand on the torch of Lavoisier to the nineteenth century.[3] If we consider who were the three great names in chemistry in the 1830's and 1840's, we must recognize that Berzelius, Liebig and Dumas, however differing in their ideas, had a common bond in their contact with Berthollet and his followers.

State Support for Technology and Science (1830–50)

We have seen how the young men of Arcueil in the period of the First Empire became the elder statesmen of science under Louis-Philippe. Their activities extended beyond their lecture rooms and laboratories. Arago, Gay-Lussac and Thenard all took some part in politics and were able to exert some influence on the attitude of the French government to science and technology.

In the Chamber of Deputies Arago in the period 1834–44 spoke repeatedly on the necessity of government financial

[1] Gay-Lussac, *Cours de Chimie*, Brussels, 1829, vol. ii, Leçon 28 (16 juillet 1828), p. 12.   [2] *Ann. chim. phys.*, xxvii (1824), 200n.
[3] See Crosland, 'Lavoisier and Arcueil', *Actes du XIᵉ Congrès de l'Histoire des Sciences*, Warsaw, 1965 (in press).

support for technology and in particular the construction of steam engines.[1] During his parliamentary career Arago also embraced the cause of the development of railways.[2] In the 1840's Arago firmly supported the newly invented electric telegraph and insisted that its use should not be allowed to become a government monopoly.[3] The claim to national recognition by the award of a generous pension to Vicat, who had made a cement which set under water, was also given firm support by Arago. In his exposition of the history of this development, he did not neglect to mention a contribution made by his former colleague, Descotils.[4] Arago also concerned himself with the improvement of waterways and lighthouses, fortifications and water supply,[5] a fairly comprehensive contribution to the development of the national economy. With his expert knowledge he was able to urge the expansion of the *Conservatoire des Arts et Métiers*, to criticize the physics laboratory that had been built at the *Collège de France* and to justify further public expenditure on his own Observatory.[6] He suggested the establishment of a patent law that would act as a stimulus to inventors without prejudicing further development.[7]

In the period 1831–9 Gay-Lussac, as a member of the Chamber of Deputies, had several occasions to use his scientific knowledge to influence government decisions, whether to obtain greater financial support for the *Muséum d'Histoire Naturelle* or to rationalize weights and measures. In 1839 he was made a peer of the realm by Louis-Philippe. Peers could only be chosen from such classes as senior ranks of the army or senior civil servants. Gay-Lussac was doubly eligible as a member of the *Académie des Sciences* and a deputy of several years' standing. In the upper house Gay-Lussac spoke on industrial patents, conditions in factories, the adulteration of wine and the salt tax, among other issues.

Thenard was also a deputy for several years. In 1832 he was nominated a peer, occupying a vacancy in the Upper House caused by the death of Cuvier. In the Chamber of Peers, like Gay-Lussac, he contributed to the discussion of several scientific

---

[1] Arago, *Oeuvres, Notices scientifiques*, vol. ii, pp. 181–232.
[2] *Ibid.*, pp. 233–466; vol. *Tables*, pp. lxxxiv–lxxxvi.
[3] *Ibid.*, pp. 467–89.   [4] *Ibid.*, p. 497.   [5] *Ibid.*, vols. ii and iii.
[6] *Ibid.*, vol. iii, pp. 545, 601, 564.   [7] *Ibid.*, pp. 677–98.

questions, including railways, coinage and education. In a long-drawn-out battle over state support of beet sugar, he strongly and effectively supported the home producers of sugar. He must have derived considerable personal satisfaction from his successful advocacy in the Chamber of a law authorizing the republication at the expense of the state of the complete works of Laplace. The man who piloted this measure through the Lower House in 1842 was Arago, thus providing a reminder of former loyalties at Arcueil.

Thenard's elevation to the peerage was probably the immediate cause of a long outburst in print by Liebig, criticizing the organization of French science in the 1830's. We shall quote only one remark:

> The era has passed when Berthollet was able to gather about him at Arcueil a circle of eminent young talent. These men have now grown old and have attained high office in the State and that has perforce robbed them of the leisure and the inclination for scientific work.[1]

*   *   *

Later in the nineteenth century France was too often content to live on the memory of the scientific achievements of earlier generations. Yet if French science was to become something more than the exposition of past achievements, if France was to continue to make important contributions on the frontiers of knowledge, some major source of patronage was needed. Hence the complaint in 1868 of Pasteur, who pointed to the almost total lack of laboratories provided by the State.[2] There had been a long tradition of private laboratories—Lavoisier at the Arsenal and Berthollet at Arcueil were followed by Dumas, whose experimental work was carried out in a laboratory set up at his own expense. The decline of science in France relative to Britain and Germany is a complex phenomenon involving many factors. Apart from the provision of laboratory facilities, we must take into account less tangible factors such as the influence of Romanticism and even the triumph of positivism.[3] We cannot ignore political considerations, since not only

[1] *Annales der Pharmacie*, ii (1832), 20.
[2] *Le budget de la science*, 1868.
[3] J. Herivel, ' Aspects of French theoretical physics in the nineteenth century', *British Journal for the History of Science*, No. 10 (Dec. 1966).

national politics but also the nastier aspects of academic politics had so profound an effect on the careers of so many French men of science.

In the course of this book Arcueil has come to mean something more than the hospitality of Berthollet's country house and laboratories. Arcueil has a connotation of patronage extending to the support of one's own candidate to the exclusion of all outsiders. As Molière puts it in *Les Femmes Savantes*: 'Nul n'aura de l'esprit, hors nous et nos amis.' However great French science was at the beginning of the nineteenth century, this attitude has persisted and has been a weakening factor ever since.

Select Bibliography of Printed Sources

WHERE FRENCH books were published in Paris or English books in London the place of publication has been omitted. For convenience all biographies other than those of members of the Society of Arcueil are placed together in the first section under 'General'.

GENERAL

AMPÈRE, A. M., *Correspondance du grand Ampère*, 3 parts, 1936, 43.
ANNALES DE CHIMIE, 96 vols., 1789–1815.
continued as: ANNALES DE CHIMIE ET DE PHYSIQUE, vol. i, 1816, etc.
ARAGO, D. F. J., *Oeuvres*, 17 vols., 1854–62:
vol. i–vol. iii, *Notices biographiques*.
vol. iv–vol. viii, *Notices scientifiques*.
vol. ix, *Instructions, rapports et notices sur les questions à résoudre pendant les voyages scientifiques*.
vol. x–vol. xi, *Mémoires scientifiques*.
vol. xii, *Mélanges*.
vol. xiii–vol. xvi, *Astronomie populaire*.
vol. xvii, *Tables*.
Biographies of distinguished scientific men, trans. W. H. Smyth, Baden Powell and R. Grant, 1857.
AULARD, F. V. A., *Paris sous le Consulat*, 4 vols., 1903–9.
Paris sous le premier Empire, 2 vols., 1912.
BALTEAU, J. (ed.), *Dictionnaire de biographie française*, 1933–61 (in progress).
Bibliographie Annuelle de l'Histoire de France, 1953–4(1964)–1964 (1965).
Biographie des Hommes vivants ou historiques par ordre alphabétique de tous les hommes qui se sont fait remarquer par leurs actions ou leurs écrits.
Biographie Moderne ou Galérie historique, 2nd edn., 3 vols., 1816.
BIOT, J. B., *Essai sur l'histoire générale des sciences pendant la révolution française*, 1803.
Mélanges scientifiques et littéraires, 3 vols., 1858.
CARON, P., *Manuel pratique pour l'étude de la révolution française*, 1912.
COBBAN, A., *A history of modern France*, 2 vols., 1957, 61.

475

CRAWLEY, C. W. (ed.), The New Cambridge Modern History, vol. ix, *War and Peace in an Age of Upheaval, 1793–1830*, Cambridge, 1965.

CUVIER, J. L. N. F., *Rapport historique sur les progrès des sciences*, 1810.

DAVY, H., *Collected works*, 9 vols., 1839–40.

FRANCE: *Almanach Impérial* (published annually under the Empire). Convention Nationale: *Procès-verbaux du comité d'instruction publique de la Convention Nationale*, ed. J. Guillaume, 7 vols., 1891–1957.

HOEFER, F. (ed.), *Nouvelle biographie générale*, 46 vols., 1855–76.

JONES, B., *The Royal Institution*, 1871.

LACROIX, A., 'La vie et l'oeuvre de l'abbé Haüy', *Bulletin de la Société Française de Minéralogie*, lxvii (1944), nos. 1–6.

LAPLACE, P.-S., *Oeuvres complètes*, 14 vols., 1878–1904.

LAUNAY, L. DE, *Le Grand Ampère*, 1925.

Les Brongniart, 1940.

Un grand Français. Monge, fondateur de l'École Polytechnique, 1933.

MASCART, J., *La vie et les travaux du chevalier Jean-Charles de Borda (1733–99)*, Université de Lyon: *Annales*. Nouvelle Serie II, droit, lettres, fasc. 33, 1919.

MERZ, J. T., *A history of European thought in the nineteenth century*, 4 vols., 1896–1914.

MICHAUD, L. G. (ed.) *Biographie universelle*, 55 vols., 1811–33. *Supplément*, vols. 56–86, 1834–62.

LE MONITEUR.

OLMSTED, J. M. D., *François Magendie*, New York, 1944.

PARIS, J. A., *The life of Sir Humphry Davy*, 2 vols., 1831.

ROYAL SOCIETY, *Catalogue of scientific papers (1800–1863)*, 6 vols., 1867–72. *Philosophical Transactions*.

SMEATON, W. A., *Fourcroy, chemist and revolutionary (1755–1809)*, 1962.

THOMSON, T., *History of chemistry*, 2 vols., 1830, 31.

TOURNEUX, M., *Bibliographie de l'histoire de Paris pendant la révolution française*, 5 vols., 1890–1913.

VALSON, C. A., *La vie et les travaux du Baron Cauchy*, 2 vols., 1868.

VILLAT, L., *La révolution et l'Empire*, vol. ii, *Napoléon (1799–1815)*, 1947.

WARD, A. W., PROTHERO, G. W. & LEATHES, S., Cambridge Modern History, vol. ix, *Napoleon*, Cambridge, 1907.

WILLIAMS, L. P., 'The physical sciences in the first half of the nineteenth century: Problems and sources', *History of Science*, i (1962), 1–15.

CHAPTER ONE

AULARD, F. V. A., 'Napoléon et l'athée Lalande', *Études et leçons sur la révolution française*, Série 4, no. x, 1904.

BALLOT, C., *L'introduction du machinisme dans l'industrie française*, Lille and Paris, 1923. (Comité des travaux historiques et scientifiques. Notes, Inventaires et Documents, no. 9.)

BARRAL, G., *Histoire des sciences sous Napoléon Bonaparte*, 1889.

BONNEVILLE DE MARSAGNY, *La Légion d'Honneur, 1802–1900*, 1900.

BOURRIENNE, L. A. FAUVELET DE, *Mémoires de M. de Bourrienne, Ministre d'État sous Napoléon*, 10 vols., 1831.

CHAPTAL, J. A., *Mes souvenirs sur Napoléon*, 1893.

CHLADNI, E. E. F., *Traité d'acoustique*, 1809.

CLOUZOT, H., *Histoire de la manufacture de Jouy et de la toile imprimée en France*, 2 vols., 1928.

DE BEER, SIR GAVIN, *The sciences were never at war*, 1960.

DICKINSON, H. W., *Robert Fulton, engineer and artist. His life and works*, 1913.

DUGUIT, L., MONNIER, H. & BONNARD, R., *Les constitutions et les principales lois politiques de la France depuis 1789*, 7th edn., 1952.

FAGES, U., 'Industriels et inventeurs: Christophe Oberkampf', *Revue des Deux Mondes*, xxix (1860), 594–626.

FISHER, H. A. L., 'The Napoleonic state' in: *Bonapartism*, Oxford, 1908.

FRANCE: *Rapports et discussions de toutes les classes de l'Institut de France sur les ouvrages admis au concours pour les prix décennaux*, 1810.
Seconde Exposition publique des produits de l'industrie française. Procès verbal des opérations du jury, Vendémiaire an 10.

FURBER, H., 'Fulton and Napoleon in 1800: New light on the submarine Nautilus', *American Historical Review*, xxxix (1934), 489–494.

GEOFFROY SAINT-HILAIRE, E., *Lettres écrites d'Égypte*, ed. E. T. Hamy, 1901.

GOURGAUD, G., BARON, *The St Helena journal of general Baron Gourgaud*, trans., 1932.

HEALEY, F. G., *The literary culture of Napoleon*, Geneva, 1959.

HUDSON, D. & LUCKHURST, K. W., *The Royal Society of Arts, 1754–1954*, 1954.

LABOUCHÈRE, A., *Oberkamf*, 1866.

LACOUR-GAYET, G., *Bonaparte, membre de l'Institut*, 1921.

LANZAC DE LABORIE, L. DE, *Paris sous Napoléon*, 8 vols., 1905–1913.

LAS CASES, COUNT, *Journal of the private life and conversations of the Emperor Napoleon at Saint Helena*, trans., 4 vols., 1824.

LEVASSEUR, E., *Histoire des classes ouvrières et de l'industrie en France de 1789 à 1870*, 2nd edn., 1903, vol. i.

MADELIN, L., *Histoire du Consulat et de l'Empire*, 16 vols., 1949–54.

MAINDRON, E., *Les fondations de prix de l'Académie des Sciences*, 1881.

MARGAGGI, J. B., *La genèse de Napoléon. Sa formation intellectuelle et morale jusqu'au siège de Toulon*, 1902.

MARKHAM, F. M. H., *Napoleon*, 1963.

MONTET, A. DE, *Dictionnaire biographique des Genevois*, 2 vols., Lausanne, 1877, 78.

NAPOLEON I, *Correspondance de Napoléon I*, 32 vols., 1858–69.
Lettres inédits de Napoléon, ed. Lecestre, 2 vols., 1897.
Napoleon's letters, selected, translated and edited by J. M. Thomson, Everyman edn., 1954.
Catalogue of the library of the late Emperor Napoleon removed from the island of St Helena, sold at Sotheby, 23 July 1823.

PARISET, G., *Histoire de France contemporaine*, vol. iii, *Le Consulat et l'Empire (1799–1815)*, 1921.

PICARD, A., *Paris—Exposition universelle internationale de 1889, Rapport général*, vol. i, *Historique des expositions universelles*, 1891.

REMACLE, L., *Bonaparte et les Bourbons*, 1899.

REMUSAT, C., *Mémoires*, 3 vols., 1905, 1906.

REVUE DES ÉTUDES NAPOLÉONIENNES, 1912, etc.

ROSE, J. H., *The life of Napoleon*, 1904.

STENDAHL [BEYLE], *Vie de Napoléon*, ed. L. Royer, 1929.

VANDAL, *L'Avènement de Bonaparte*, 6th edn., 2 vols., 1903.

VIENNET, O., *Napoléon et l'industrie française. La crise de 1810–1811*, 1947.

VOLTA, Z., *Alessandro Volta a Parigi*, Milan, 1879.

WILLIAMS, L. P., 'Science, education and Napoleon I', *Isis*, xlvii (1956), 369–82.

CHAPTER TWO

BROTONNE, L. DE, *Les Sénateurs du Consulat et de l'Empire*, 1895.

CHARLES-ROUX, F., *Bonaparte, gouverneur d'Égypte*, 1935.

DESLANDRES, M., *Histoire constitutionelle de la France de 1789 à 1870*, vol. i, 1932.

DUVEEN, D. I. & HAHN, R., 'Laplace's succession to Bézout's post of *examinateur des élèves de l'artillérie*. A case history in the "lobbying" for scientific appointments during the period preceding the French revolution', *Isis*, xlviii (1957), 416–27.

EGYPT: *A bibliographical account and collation of 'La Description de l'Égypte' presented to the library of the Royal Institution*, 1839.

FISCHER, E. G., *Physique mécanique*, 1813.

FOURIER, J. J., 'Préface historique' to: *Description de l'Égypte, Antiquités*, Planches, vol. i, 1809.

FRANCE: Ministère de l'Intérieur: *Recueil des lettres, instructions, arrêtés et discours publics émanés des Cns. Quinette, Laplace, Lucien Bonaparte et Chaptal, Ministres de l'Intérieur*, 4 vols., 1799, 1802.

GOUHIER, H., *La jeunesse d'Auguste Comte et la fondation du positivisme*, vol. ii, *Saint-Simon jusqu'à la restauration*, 1936.

GUÉMARD, G., *Bibliographie critique de la commission des sciences et arts de l'Institut d'Égypte*, Cairo, 1936.

HAHN, R., 'Laplace's religious views', *Archives internationales d'histoire des sciences*, 8e année (1955), 38–40.

HAYEK, F. A. V., ' The Counter-Revolution of Science', *Economica*, New series, viii (1941), 9–36, 119–50, 281–320.

HEROLD, J. C., *Bonaparte in Egypt*, 1962.

INSTITUT D'ÉGYPTE: *Mémoires sur l'Égypte*, 4 vols., années VIII–XI.

LAGRANGE, L. J., *Correspondance, Oeuvres*, vols. 13 & 14, 1882–92.

MALUS, E. L., *L'agenda de Malus*, 1892.

MARMOTTAN, P. (ed.), *Lettres de Madame de Laplace à Elisa Napoléon*, 1897.

PELSENEER, J., 'La religion de Laplace', *Isis*, xxxvi (1945), 158–60.

PICTET, M. A., 'Journal d'un Genevois à Paris sous le Consulat', *Mémoires et documents publiés par la société d'histoire et d'archéologie de Genève*, 2e série, v (1893–1901), 98–133.

ROTOURS, J. A. DES, 'Les Sénatoreries', *Le Correspondant*, ccxxix (1907), 336–57.

SAVANT, J., *Les ministres de Napoléon*, 1959.

SCHLABRENDORF, G. VON, *Bonaparte and the French people under his consulate*, 2nd edn., 1804.

THIRY, J., *Le Sénat de Napoléon (1800–1814)*, 1932.

BIOGRAPHIES OF INDIVIDUAL MEMBERS OF THE SOCIETY OF ARCUEIL

ARAGO

ARAGO, D. F. J., 'Histoire de ma jeunesse', *Oeuvres, Notices biographiques*, vol. i, 1854, pp. 1–102.

'The history of my youth', *Biographies of distinguished scientific men*, trans., 1857, pp. 1–59.

BARRAL, J. A., 'Notice chronologique sur les oeuvres d'Arago', Arago, *Oeuvres, Tables*, 1862.

BERTRAND, J., *Arago et sa vie scientifique*, 1865.

CHAUVET, H., *François Arago et son temps*, Perpignan, 1954.

DAUMAS, M., *Arago*, 1943.

BÉRARD

BÉCHAMP, 'Discours de M. Béchamp. Prononcé à l'Hôpital Générale sur la tombe de M. Bérard', *L'Union Nationale*, Montpellier, dimanche 13 juin 1869.

C. L. BERTHOLLET

AUGER, 'Notice nécrologique sur M. Berthollet', *Annales de la littérature étrangère*, ix (1822), 290–9.

CHAPTAL, J. A., 'Discours prononcé par M. le comte Chaptal à l'occasion de la mort de M. le comte Berthollet': Chambre des Pairs de France, Session de 1823, Séance du mardi 19 février 1823. *Chambres des Pairs. Impressions diverses*, vol. i (1823).

COLQUHOUN, H., 'On the life and writings of Claude Louis Berthollet', *Annals of Philosophy*, [2], ix (1825), 1–18, 81–96, 161–85.

CUVIER, J. L. N. F., 'Éloge historique de M. le Comte Berthollet', lu le 7 juin 1824, *Recueil des éloges historiques*, vol. iii, 1827, pp. 179–227.

FÄRBER, E., (biography in:) G. BUGGE, (ed.), *Das Buch der grossen Chemiker*, Berlin, 1929, 30, vol. i, pp. 342–9.

JOMARD, E. M., *Notice sur la vie et les ouvrages de C. L. Berthollet*, Annecy, 1844.

LEMAY, P. & OESPER, R. E., 'Claude Louis Berthollet (1748–1822)', *Journal of Chemical Education*, xxiii (1946), 158–65; 230–6.

PARISET, E., 'Éloge de M. le Comte Berthollet' (1826), *Histoire des membres de l'Académie Royale de Médecine*, vol. i, 1850, pp. 164–208.

PATTERSON, T. S., 'Claude Louis Berthollet', *Chemistry and Industry*, lxiii (1944), 99–102.

TAPPONNIER, P., 'Le chimiste Claude Louis Berthollet', *Annales Savoisiennes*, i (1949), 47–9.

A. B. BERTHOLLET

QUÉRARD, J. M., ref.: 'Berthollet (Amédée)' in: *La France littéraire*, 1827–39.

THOMSON, T., *History of chemistry*, vol. ii, p. 151.

BIOT

LEFORT, F., 'Un savant Chrétien, J. B. Biot', *Le Correspondant*, Nouvelle Série, xxxvi (1867), 955–95.

PICARD, E., *La vie et l'oeuvre de J. B. Biot*, 1927.

CANDOLLE

CANDOLLE, A. P. DE, *Mémoires et souvenirs de Augustin Pyramus de Candolle écrits par lui-même et publiés par son fils*, Geneva and Paris, 1862.

FLOURENS, 'Éloge historique de Pyramus de Candolle' lu à la séance publique du 19 décembre 1842, *Mém. Acad. Sc. Inst.*, xix (1845), i–xlviii.

LA RIVE, A. DE, *A. P. de Candolle, sa vie et ses travaux*, 1851.

CHAPTAL

CHAPTAL, J. A., *La vie et l'oeuvre de Chaptal. Mémoires personnels rédigés par lui-même de 1756 à 1804. Continués, d'après ses notes, par son arrière-petit-fils jusqu'en 1832*, 1893.

FLOURENS, P., 'Éloge historique de Jean Antoine Chaptal' lu à la séance publique de 28 decembre 1835, *Mém. Acad. Sc. Inst.*, xv (1838), i–xxxix.

GERANDO, J. M. DE, BARON, *Notice sur Chaptal*, Lue à la séance générale de la Société d'Encouragement, le 22 août 1832.

PIGEIRE, J., *La vie et l'oeuvre de Chaptal (1756–1832)*, 1932.

DESCOTILS

ANON., Notice nécrologique, *Annales des mines*, i (1816), 496–7.

GAY-LUSSAC, L. J., 'Notice sur Hippolyte-Victor Collet-Descotils', *Ann. chim. phys.*, iv (1817), 213–220. trans. T. Thomson, *Annals of Philosophy*, ix (1817), 417–21.

DULONG

ACADÉMIE ROYALE DES SCIENCES: *Funerailles de M. Dulong* (Speeches by Arago, Chevreul and Thenard), 1838.

GIRARDIN, J., *Dulong de Rouen. Sa vie et ses ouvrages*, Rouen, 1854.

LEMAY, P. & OESPER, R. E., 'Pierre Louis Dulong, his life and work', *Chymia*, i (1948), 171–90.

LEMOINE, G., 'Dulong', *Livre du centenaire de l'École Polytechnique*, 1895, vol. i, 269–78.

GAY-LUSSAC

ARAGO, D. F. J., 'Biographie lue en séance de l'Académie des Sciences le 20 Decembre 1852', *Oeuvres, Notices biographiques*, vol. iii, pp. 1–112.

BIOT, J. B., 'Notice sur Gay-Lussac' (Read at Royal Society of London, 30 November 1850, published in: *Journal des Savans*, December 1850), *Mélanges scientifiques et littéraires*, 1858, vol. iii, pp. 125–42.

BLANC, E. & DELHOUME, L., *La vie émouvante et noble de Gay-Lussac*, 1950.

BLOCH, M., (biography in:) G. BUGGE, *Das Buch der grossen Chemiker*, Berlin, 1929, 30, vol. i, pp. 386–404.

DAUMAS, M., 'Gay-Lussac', *Revue d'histoire des sciences*, iii (1950), 335–42.

JOLIBOIS, P., 'Centenaire de la mort de Gay-Lussac', *Bulletin de la Société chimique de France*, 1950, 992–5.

LECOMTE, J., 'Quelques documents inédits sur Gay-Lussac. Remarques sur son oeuvre scientifique', *87e Congrès des Sociétés Savantes*, 1962, 123–48.

HUMBOLDT

BRUHNS, K., *Life of Alexander von Humboldt*, trans., 1873, 2 vols.

DEUTSCHE AKADEMIE DER WISSENSCHAFTEN ZU BERLIN, Humboldt Kommission: *Alexander von Humboldt . . . Gedenkschrift zur 100 Wiederkehr seines Todestages*, 1959.

Gespräche Alexander von Humboldts, 1959.

KELLNER, L., *Alexander von Humboldt*, 1963.

[LETTERS:] HAMY, E. T., (ed.), *Lettres americaines d'Alexandre de Humboldt*, 1905.

Correspondance d'Alexandre de Humboldt avec François Arago (1809–1853), 1908.

'Lettres d'Alexandre de Humboldt à Marc-Auguste Pictet (1795–1824)', *Mémoires de la Société de Géographie de Genève*, vii (1868), 127–204.

LAPLACE

ANDOYER, H., *L'oeuvre scientifique de Laplace*, 1922.

ARAGO, D. F. J., (Report to *Chambre des députés* on behalf of commission given the task in 1842 of examining a proposal by the minister of education that the works of Laplace should be published at the expense of the state), *Oeuvres, Notices biographiques*, vol. iii, pp. 456–515.

Ibid., trans., *Biographies of distinguished scientific men*, 1857, 196–241.

BIOT, J. B., 'Une anecdote relatif à Laplace', *Mélanges scientifiques et littéraires*, 1858, vol. i, pp. 1–10.

COURNOT, A. A., *Souvenirs (1760–1860)*, 1913.

FOURIER, J. J., 'Éloge historique sur M. le marquis de Laplace, prononcé dans la séance publique de l'Académie des Sciences le 15 juin 1829', *Mém. Acad. Sc. Inst.*, x (1831), lxxxi–cii. trans., *Phil. Mag.*, [2], vi, 370–81.

PASTORET, 'Éloge de Laplace' (1827), Laplace, *Oeuvres complètes*, vol. xiv (1912), 388–92.

PEARSON, K., 'Laplace, being extracts from lectures delivered by Karl Pearson', *Biometrika*, xxi (1929), 202–16.

SIMON, ABBÉ G. A., 'Les origines de Laplace: Son genéalogie, ses études.' *Biometrika*, xxi (1929), 217–30.

MALUS

ARAGO, D. F. J., 'Biographie préparée pour la séance publique de l'Académie des Sciences de l'année 1854', *Oeuvres, Notices biographiques*, vol. iii, pp. 113–55. trans., *Biographies of distinguished scientific men*, 1857, 362–98.

DELAMBRE, J. B. J., 'Notice sur la vie et les ouvrages de M. Malus', lue le 3 janvier 1814, *Mém. Inst.*, 1812, Pt. 2, *Histoire*, xxviii–xxxiii.

POISSON

ARAGO, D. F. J., 'Poisson'. Biographie lue par extraits en séance publique de l'Académie des Sciences, le 16 décembre 1850, *Oeuvres, Notices biographiques*, vol. ii, pp. 593–671.

ROYAL SOCIETY: Obituary notices of deceased Fellows: (Poisson), *Phil. Mag.*, [2], xviii (1841), 74–7.

THENARD

DUBOIS, F., *Éloge de M. Thenard*, prononcé dans la séance publique annuelle de l'Académie Impériale de Médecine du 9 Décembre 1862, 1863.

FLOURENS, P., 'Éloge historique de Louis-Jacques Thenard', *Éloges historiques*, 3me série, 1862, pp. 201–48.

LE CANU, L. R., *Souvenirs de M. Thenard*, 1857.

THENARD, P., *Un grand Français. Le chimiste Thenard, 1777–1857*, par son fils; avec introduction et notes de Georges Bouchard, Dijon, 1950.

CHAPTER THREE

GENERAL

Annuaire de l'Instruction publique pour l'an IX de l'ère française et l'année 1801 de l'ère chrétienne.

Annuaire des Sociétés savantes de la France et l'Étranger, Première Année, 1846.

PARIS: *La décade philosophique*, 1794–1804. Continued as: *La revue philosophique*, 1804–1807.

Mémoires des sociétés savantes, an IX–X, 3 parts.

THE INSTITUTE

AUCOC, L., *L'Institut de France. Lois, Status et règlements concernant les anciennes Académies et l'Institut de 1635 à 1889*, 1889.

BOUILLIER, F., *L'Institut et les Académies de province*, 1879.

GAUJA, P., *L'Académie des Sciences de l'Institut de France*, 1934.

INSTITUT DE FRANCE: *Index biographique des membres et correspondants de l'Académie des Sciences*, 1954.

Procès-verbaux des séances de l'Académie des Sciences, tenues depuis la fondation de l'Institut jusqu'au mois d'août 1835, publiés conformément à une décision de L'Académie par MM. les Secrétaires perpétuels, 10 vols., Hendaye, 1910–22.

MAINDRON, E., *L'Académie des Sciences*, 1888.

MAURY, L. F. A., *Les Académies d'autrefois: L'Ancienne Académie des Sciences*, 1864.

POTIQUET, A., *L'Institut national de France, ses diverses organisations, ses membres*, etc., 1871.

SIMON, J., *Une Académie sous le Directoire*, 1885.

THE PHILOMATIC SOCIETY

BERTHELOT, M., 'Sur les publications de la Société Philomatique et sur ses origines', *Journal des Savans*, Août 1888, 477–93.

Bulletin des Sciences par la Société Philomathique, no. 1, Germinal an V (April 1797)—no. 96, Ventose an XIII (March 1805), 3 vols. Continued as: *Nouveau Bulletin des Sciences par la Société Philomathique de Paris*, 3 vols., 1807–13.

DUVEEN, D. I., 'Augustin François Silvestre and the Société Philomathique', *Annals of Science*, x (1954), 339–41.

Rapports généraux des travaux de la Société Philomathique de Paris, depuis son installation au 10 décembre 1788 jusqu'au premier janvier 1792. Par les citoyens Riche et Silvestre, secrétaires de cette société, vol. i, 1792, vol. ii, 1798, vol. iii, 1800, vol. iv, 1801.

OTHER SOCIETIES

Annuaire de l'Athénée des Arts pour l'an 1805.

CHARMES, X., (ed.), 'Bibliographie des sociétés savantes de la France', *Collection de Documents inédits sur l'histoire de France*, vol. ii, 1886, pp. 475–586.

DEPPING, 'Notice sur les premiers temps de la Société Philotechnique', *Annuaire de la Société Philotechnique*, i (1840), 5–32; ii (1841), 1–13.

Journal du galvanisme, de vaccine, etc. Par une société de physiciens, de chimistes et de médecins. Rédigé par J. Nauche, 2 vols., 1803.

Mémoires des sociétés savantes et littéraires de la République française, recueillis et rédigés par les citoyens Prony, Parmentier, Duhamel, Garnier, Lausel, Marchis, Doussin-Dubreuil, Tourlet, nos. 1–13, ans IX–X (1801–3).

SCHELER, L., *Lavoisier et la Révolution Française. I. Le Lycée des Arts*, 1957.

SMEATON, W. A., 'The early years of the Lycée and the Lycée des Arts. A chapter in the lives of A. L. Lavoisier and A. F. de Fourcroy', *Annals of Science*, xi (1944), 257–67; 309–19.

SOCIÉTÉ D'ENCOURAGEMENT POUR L'INDUSTRIE NATIONALE, *Bulletin*, An X (1802), etc.

Histoire de la fondation de la société d'encouragement pour l'industrie nationale, 1850.

SOCIÉTÉ DES AMATEURS DES SCIENCES PHYSIQUES ET NATURELLES, *Notice des travaux de la société* . . . Année 1, 2, 2 parts, 1807, 1808.

SOCIÉTÉ DES SCIENCES, LETTRES ET ARTS DE PARIS, *Programme des lectures qui auront lieu à la séance publique du 9 Nivôse an VIII, etc.*

Règlement, An V (1797), An VII (1799).

CHAPTER FOUR

ÉCOLE NORMALE

Séances des Écoles Normales, recueillis par des sténographes et revues par les professeurs, 2nd edn., 10 vols., 1800, 1801.

ÉCOLE NORMALE SUPÉRIEUR, *Notice historique*, 1884.

ÉCOLE POLYTECHNIQUE

ÉCOLE POLYTECHNIQUE, *Livre du centenaire, 1794–1894*, vol. i, *L'École et la Science*, 1895.

FOURCY, A., *Histoire de l'École Polytechnique*, 1828.

HACHETTE, J. N. P. (ed.), *Correspondance sur l'École Polytechnique*, vol. i (1804–8), 2nd edn., 1813; vol. ii (1809–13), 1813; vol. iii (1814–16), 1816.

Journal de l'École Polytechnique, cahiers 1–64, 1795–1894.

MARIELLE, C. P., *Répertoire de l'École Impériale Polytechnique*, 1855.

PINET, G., *Histoire de l'École Polytechnique*, 1887.

BUREAU DES LONGITUDES

BIGOURDAN, M. G., 'Le Bureau des Longitudes. Son histoire et ses travaux de l'origine (1795) à ce jour', *Annuaire du Bureau des Longitudes*, 1928, A1–A72; 1929, C1–C92; 1930, A1–A110; 1931, A1–A145; 1932, A1–A117.

Connaissance des Temps . . . publie pas le Bureau des Longitudes, 1806, etc.

COLLÈGE DE FRANCE

Le Collège de France (1530–1930), *Livre Jubilaire*, 1932.

LEFRANC, A., *Histoire du Collège de France*, 1893.

ÉCOLE DES MINES

AGUILLON, L., 'L'École des mines de Paris. Notice historique', *Annales des mines*, 8e série, *Mémoires*, xv (1889), 433–686.

THE FACULTY OF SCIENCE

AULARD, F. V. A., *Napoléon Ier et le monopole universitaire*, 1911.

IRSAY, S. D', *Histoire des universités françaises et étrangères*, 2 vols., 1933, 35.

RENDU, A., (ed.), *Code universitaire ou lois, statuts et règlements de l'université de France*, 2nd edn., 1835.

ÉCOLE VÉTÉRINAIRE D'ALFORT

RAILLET, A. & MOULÉ, L., *Histoire de l'École d'Alfort*, 1908.

Muséum d'histoire Naturelle

cap, p. a., *Le Muséum d'Histoire Naturelle*, vol. i, 1854, Introduction.
deleuze, j. p. f., *Histoire et description du Muséum*, 1823.

CHAPTERS FIVE TO EIGHT

The Society of Arcueil

The following articles of a few pages each deal with the Society of Arcueil either directly or indirectly.[1] They are included for the sake of completeness but the only one that can be reasonably recommended as an introduction is the lecture delivered by M. Maurice Daumas. M. Daumas was kind enough to send me a copy of this.

blanc, e. & delhoume, l., 'Les amitiés d'Arcueil', Chapter 4 (pp. 53–69) of *La vie émouvante et noble de Gay-Lussac*, 1950. This includes a large proportion of quotations *in extenso* from Arago. It does, however, also contain two letters of eulogy and reminiscence by Mme. Gay-Lussac and mentions the destruction of relevant letters by Gay-Lussac himself.

daumas, m., *Les savants d'Arcueil et la science du XIXe siècle*, Les Conférences du Palais de la Découverte, Série D, no. 30, 1954.

jolibois, p., 'Les continuateurs immédiats de Lavoisier, La Société d'Arcueil', *Commemoration du bicentenaire de la naissance de Lavoisier*, 1944, pp. 17–19.

lemay, p., 'Berthollet et la Société d'Arcueil', *Courrier Médicale*, 1934, 59–60.

thenard, p., 'Laplace et la Société d'Arcueil', Chapter 5 (pp. 94–7) of *Un grand français. Le chimiste Thenard*, Dijon, 1950.

*   *   *

arcueil, *Mémoires de physique et de chimie de la Société d'Arcueil* vol. i, 1807; vol. ii, 1809; vol. iii, 1817.
Écoles Albert le Grand et Laplace (1894?). (Prospectus).
berthollet, c. l., *Essai de statique chimique*, 2 vols., 1803.
Trans., *Essay on chemical statics*, 2 vols., 1804.
berzelius, j. j., *Bref*, ed H. G. Söderbaum, 15 parts, Uppsala, 1912–25.
Autobiographical notes, published by the Royal Swedish Academy of Sciences through H. G. Söderbaum, trans. O. Larsell, Baltimore, 1934.

[1] See also: Crosland, 'The origins of Gay-Lussac's law', etc.' listed below.

488 *The Society of Arcueil*

BLAGDEN, C., 'A preliminary note on the Blagden Manuscripts' by H. W. Robinson, *Notes and Records of the Royal Society*, v (1947–8), 137–9.

BUCKLEY, H., *A short history of physics*, 1927.

BURY, J. P. T., 'The end of the Napoleonic Senate', *Cambridge Historical Journal*, ix (1947–9), 165–89.

CAJORI, F., *A history of physics*, New York, 1917.

CARR, SIR J., *Les Anglais en France après la paix d'Amiens*, Étude, traduction et notes par Albert Babeau, 1898.

CROSLAND, M. P., *Historical studies in the language of chemistry*, 1962. 'The origins of Gay-Lussac's law of combining volumes of gases', *Annals of Science*, xvii (1961), 1–26.

DALTON, J., *A new system of chemical philosophy*, vol. i, part 1, Manchester, 1808; vol. ii, part 2, Manchester, 1810; vol. ii, part 1, London, 1827.

DARU, P., *Notice statistique sur la libraire*, 1827.

DELALAIN, P. A., *L'imprimerie à Paris de 1798 à 1813*, 1899.

DUMAS, J. B., *Leçons sur la philosophie chimique*, 1837.

DUVEEN, D. I. & KLICKSTEIN, H. S., *Bibliography of the Works of A. L. Lavoisier*, 1954.

DUVEEN, D. I., [*Ibid.*], *Supplement*, 1965.

EYMERY, A., *Dictionnaire des girouettes*, 1815.

FINN, B. S., 'Laplace and the speed of sound', *Isis*, lv (1964), 7–19.

FRESNEL, A., *Oeuvres complètes*, publiés par MM. Henri de Senarmont, Émile Verdet et Léonor Fresnel, 3 vols., 1866–70.

GAY-LUSSAC, L. J., 'Memoir on the combination of gaseous substances with each other', trans., A.C.R. No. 4, Reissue, Edinburgh, 1950.

GAY-LUSSAC, L. J. & THENARD, L. J., *Recherches physico-chimiques*, 1811.

GRIMAUX, E., *Lavoisier, 1743–1794*, 1888.

GUARESCHI, I., 'Sulla legge della dilatazione dei gas di Volta. Notizie storiche', *Archiv für die Geschichte der Naturwissenschaften und der Technik*, v (1915), 142–53, 209–25.

HAHN, R. & DUVEEN, D. I., 'Deux lettres de Laplace à Lavoisier', *Revue d'Histoire des Sciences*, xi (1958), 337–42.

HARTSHORNE, R., *The nature of geography*, Lancaster, Pennsylvania, 1939.

HENRY, W. C., *Memoirs of the life and scientific researches of John Dalton*, 1854.

HERSCHEL, W., *The scientific papers of Sir William Herschel*, 2 vols., London, 1912.

HOPPE, E., *Geschichte der Physik*, Brunswick, 1926.

INSTITUT DE FRANCE, ACADÉMIE DES SCIENCES, *Funerailles de*

M. le Comte Berthollet (Speeches by Chaptal, Thenard, Gay-Lussac and Jomard), 1822.

JAMIN, J., 'Études sur la chaleur statique: Dulong et Petit', *Revue des Deux Mondes*, xi (1855), 375–412.

JUNOT, DUCHESSE D'ABRANTES, *Histoire des salons de Paris*, 4 vols., 1893.

LAVOISIER, A. L., *Oeuvres*, 6 vols., 1862–93.
Elements of chemistry, trans. J. Kerr, Edinburgh, 1790.

MACH, E., *The principles of physical optics. An historical and philosophical treatment*, trans. 1926, Dover Books, Constable, London.

MAGIE, W. F., *A source book in physics*, Cambridge, Mass., 1935, reprinted 1963.

MCKIE, D., *Antoine Lavoisier, scientist, economist, social reformer*, 1952.

NASH, L. K., 'The atomic-molecular theory', Case 4 in: *Harvard case histories in experimental science*, ed. J. B. Conant, vol. i, Cambridge, Mass., 1957.

NEWTON, I., *Opticks*, 4th edn., 1730. Facsimile reprint, Dover Books, Constable, London, 1952.

OERSTED, H. C., *Breve fra og til Hans Christian Ørsted udgivne af Mathilde Ørsted*, 2 parts, Copenhagen, 1870.
Correspondance de H. C. Örsted avec divers savants, 2 vols., 1920.
Scientific papers, Introduction by Kirstine Meyer, vol. i, Copenhagen, 1920.

PARTINGTON, J. R., *History of chemistry*, vol. iii, 1963, vol. iv, 1964.

ROSCOE, H. E. & HARDEN, A., *A new view of the origin of Dalton's atomic theory*, 1896.

SACHS, J. VON, *History of botany (1530–1860)*, trans. H. E. F. Garney, revised I. B. Balfour, Oxford, 1890.

SEINE, Department, *État des Communes. Arcueil-Cachan. Notice historique et renseignements administratifs*, Montévrain, 1901.

SIEGFRIED, R., 'The discovery of potassium and sodium and the problem of the chemical elements', *Isis*, liv (1963), 247–54.

THOMSON, T., *Système de chimie*, traduit de l'anglais sur la dernière édition de 1807 par Jean Riffault, précédé d'une introduction de C. L. Berthollet, 9 vols., 1809.

VEYSSIÈRE, L. L., *Arcueil et Cachan*, 1947.

VOLTA, A., *Epistolario di Alessandro Volta*, edizione nazionale, vol. iv, (1800–5), Bologna, 1953.

WATT, J., *The origins and progress of the mechanical inventions of James Watt* by J. P. Muirhead, 3 vols., 1854. [Vol. ii ('Extracts from correspondence') includes several letters to and from Berthollet.]

WEEKS, M. E., *Discovery of the elements*, 5th edn., Easton, Pennsylvania, 1948.

WHITTAKER, E., *A history of the theories of aether and electricity*, vol. i, *The classical theories*, 1951.
WILSON, W., *A hundred years of physics*, 1950.

CHAPTER NINE

BOUSSINGAULT, J. B., *Mémoires*, 5 vols., 1892–1903.
CHRISTISON, R., *The life of Sir Robert Christison, Bart.* . . . edited by his sons, 2 vols., 1885, 86.
DARWIN, C., *Life and letters of Charles Darwin*, 3 vols., 1887.
DAUMAS, M., 'L'École des chimistes français vers 1840', *Chymia*, i (1948), 55–65.
DELAUNAY, 'Essay on the velocity of light', *Annual report of the Board of Regents of the Smithsonian Institution*, 1864, 135–65.
DUMAS, J. B., (A. W. von Hofmann), 'Zur Erinnerung an Jean-Baptiste-André Dumas', *Zur Erinnerung an vorangegangene Freunde*, Brunswick, 1888, vol. ii, pp. 207–397. Trans. 'Scientific worthies XIV: Jean Baptiste André Dumas', *Nature*, xxi (1880), Extra No., 6 February 1880, i–xl.
(Obituary notice by W. Perkin), *J. Chem. Soc., Transactions*, xlvii (1885), 310–23.
FOUCAULT, J. B. L., *Recueil des travaux scientifiques*, ed. C. M. Gariel, Introduction by J. Bertrand, 1878.
GERHARDT, C. F.
   E. Grimaux & C. F. Gerhardt, *Charles Gerhardt. Sa vie, son oeuvre, sa correspondance*, 1900.
   M. Tiffenau (ed.), *Correspondance de Charles Gerhardt*, vol. i, 1918.
GERNSHEIM, H. & A., *The history of photography*, 1955.
HUMBOLDT, F. H. A., *Kosmos. Entwurf einer physischen Weltbeschreibung*, 5 vols., Stuttgart and Tübingen, 1845–1862.
LAURENT, A., *Chemical method, notation, classification and nomenclature*, trans., W. Odling, 1855.
LIEBIG, J. VON, 'Autobiographical sketch', trans. J. C. Brown, *Chemical News*, lxiii (1891), 265–7, 276–8.
   A. W. von Hofmann, 'The life work of Liebig' (The Faraday lecture for 1875), *Zur Erinnerung an vorangegangene Freunde*, Brunswick, 1888, vol. i, pp. 195–305.
   E. von Meyer, 'Aus Justus Liebig's Lehr- und Wanderjahren', *Journal für Praktische Chemie*, N.F., lxvii (1903), 433–44.
MAGNUS, H. G., 'Life and labours of Henry Gustav Magnus' (from *Archives des sciences physiques et naturelles*, Geneva), *Annual Report of the Board of Regents of the Smithsonian Institution*, 1870, 223–30.
'Extrait du mémoire de M. Magnus sur la dilatation des gaz' (lu

à l'Académie de Berlin 25 November 1841), *Comptes Rendus*, xiv (1842), 165–70.

MOTTELAY, P. F., *Bibliographical history of electricity and magnetism*, 1922.

PASTEUR, L., *Oeuvres*, ed. Vallery-Radot, vol. i, *Dissymétrie moléculaire*, 1922.

Le budget de la science, 1868.

R. Vallery-Radot, *The life of Pasteur*, trans., Dover Publications, New York, 1960.

SHAPLEY, H. & HOWARTH, H. E., *Source book in astronomy*, New York, 1929.

TODHUNTER, I., *A history of the mathematical theory of probability from the time of Pascal to that of Laplace*, Cambridge and London, 1865.

A history of the theories of attraction and the figure of the earth from the time of Newton to that of Laplace, 2 vols., 1873.

TODHUNTER, I. & PEARSON, K., *A history of the elasticity and strength of materials*, Cambridge, 1886.

Name Index

Subject Index